Conic Sections

Circle:

$(x - h)^2 + (y - k)^2 = r^2$

Ellipse:

$$\frac{(x - h)^2}{a^2} + \frac{(y - k)^2}{b^2} = 1$$

Hyperbola:

$$\frac{(x - h)^2}{a^2} - \frac{(y - k)^2}{b^2} = 1$$

Hyperbola:

$$\frac{(y - k)^2}{a^2} - \frac{(x - h)^2}{b^2} = 1$$

Parabola:

$y - k = a(x - h)^2$

Parabola:

$x - h = a(y - k)^2$

Sequences and Series

Arithmetic Sequence: $\quad a_n = a_1 + (n - 1)d$

$$S_n = \frac{n}{2}(a_1 + a_n) = \frac{n}{2}[2a_1 + (n - 1)d]$$

Geometric Sequence: $\quad a_n = a_1 r^{n-1}$

$$S_n = \frac{a_1(1 - r^n)}{1 - r} \quad \text{if } r \neq 1$$

$$= na_1 \qquad \text{if } r = 1$$

Infinite Geometric Series: $\quad S = \dfrac{a_1}{1 - r}, \quad |r| < 1$

College Algebra and Trigonometry

3rd Edition

College Algebra and Trigonometry

3rd Edition

LEONARD I. HOLDER

Gettysburg College

Wadsworth Publishing Company
Belmont, California
A Division of Wadsworth, Inc.

Mathematics Editor: Rich Jones
Production: Mary Forkner, Publication Alternatives
Cover Designer: Gary Head
Cover Art: *Folded Diamond Phase #48*, reproduced from
            an original painting by Guy John Cavalli
Copy Editor: Don Yoder
Technical Illustrator: Carl Brown, Georg Klatt
Typesetter: Syntax International

Portions of this material have appeared under the title *A Primer for Calculus* by Leonard I. Holder.

Printed in the United States of America
1 2 3 4 5 6 7 8 9 10—88 87 86 85 84

Library of Congress Cataloging in Publication Data

Holder, Leonard Irvin, 1923–
   College algebra and trigonometry.

   Includes index.
   1. Algebra. 2. Trigonometry. I. Title.
QA154.2.H632   1983   512′.13   83-12414

ISBN 0-534-02917-5

Contents

The Use of Calculators

The scientific hand calculator has made the use of tables virtually obsolete. Both in terms of accuracy and speed the calculator has a great advantage. In various places throughout this book a calculator would be useful, especially in parts of Chapters 6, 7, and 8.

Scientific calculators include keys for the following functions: exponential, e^x; logarithmic, $\boxed{\ln x}$ and $\boxed{\log x}$; trigonometric, $\boxed{\sin x}$, $\boxed{\cos x}$, and $\boxed{\tan x}$; and inverse functions, $\boxed{\text{inv}}$ or $\boxed{\text{arc}}$. They include other functions as well, but these are the ones that distinguish the scientific calculator from the simple "four-function" and business-type calculators. For this and other courses in mathematics, science, and engineering, the scientific calculator is the appropriate one to purchase.

A great variety of makes and models of scientific calculators exist, many of which are not very expensive. Most employ either what is called an algebraic operating system (AOS) or reverse Polish notation (RPN). It is a matter of individual preference as to which type is the more convenient to use. In either case you will need to study the instructions to learn how to use your calculator correctly and effectively.

In a few selected examples in Chapters 6, 7, and 8 we have shown sequences of calculator operations, called "keystroke" displays, for a calculator with an algebraic operating system. You may need to modify these for your own calculator.

TI-55-II   Courtesy of Texas Instruments

HP-11C   Courtesy of Hewlett-Packard

Preface

This edition of *College Algebra and Trigonometry* retains the original objectives of presenting the material in an informal yet mathematically sound style that is readable by students. Besides adding topics suggested by users of the second edition, many changes have been made in exposition, in examples, and in the exercises, with the view of making the material easier for students to understand. Certain organizational changes are aimed toward making the flow and pacing of topics better from the instructor's viewpoint.

A major strength cited by users of the second edition was the breadth and variety of the exercise sets. These features have been retained in the present edition. Some 400 new problems have been added, mostly in the A exercises, to provide more practice and help fix concepts and techniques in the student's mind. The number of problems now exceeds 4,800, allowing for considerable flexibility in making assignments. The chapter review exercises, along with the cumulative reviews, not only give the student ample review material but also provide many good test questions.

Major Changes

1. New units have been added: partial fractions, Descartes' rule of signs, vectors, polar coordinates, and inverses of matrices.
2. Explanations have been simplified in a number of places. In particular, the material in Chapter 2 on the binomial theorem and in Chapter 3 on inequalities has been rewritten. Moreover, the treatment of linear and quadratic equations has been divided into two sections.
3. The material in Chapter 4 on functions has been reorganized. Graphing of functions now precedes one-to-one functions.
4. The distance formula has been moved to Chapter 5, and the midpoint formula has been added to this new section.
5. A number of A exercises have been added for additional drill, especially in the early chapters.
6. The material on trigonometric identities in Chapter 9 has been reorganized. Problems involving basic identities now precede those involving multiple angle identities.

Calculators Versus Tables

My conviction has been strengthened since writing the earlier editions that scientific hand calculators have made use of tables virtually obsolete. Accordingly, I have mentioned tables of trigonometric functions only briefly and have entirely omitted discussion of computation with common logarithms. I have, however, included standard tables in the back so that instructors may supplement the book with discussion of their use. While I assume that most problems involving numerical computation will be done with a hand calculator, I do not give any instructions on their use in view of the variation among different models and makes.

Finally, I wish to express my appreciation to Lowanda Bowers for her masterful job of interpreting and typing my handwritten manuscript and to Richard Jones, managing editor of Wadsworth, for his help and encouragement.

Leonard I. Holder

Books that are effective teaching tools (for us) and learning tools (for our students) are not so much *written* as they are *developed* out of our classroom experience. The more experiences of colleagues an author is exposed to, the more the text is thoroughly developed into a reliable teaching tool. I am indebted to many users of the second edition of this book for their helpful suggestions. In particular, I wish to thank the following colleagues:

**Reviewers of
the Second
Edition**

E. Ray Bobo
Georgetown University

Otha Britton
University of Tennessee, Martin

Anand M. Chak
University of West Virginia

James F. Chew
North Carolina A&T University

Romae Cormier
Northern Illinois University

Edwin Creasy
State University of New York
A&T, Canton

Robert Dahlin
University of Wisconsin, Superior

Robert Dean
Central Washington University

Marvin Eargle
Appalachian State University

Richard Fast
Mesa College

Karl Ray Gentry
University of North Carolina,
Greensboro

James E. Hall
University of Wisconsin, Madison

Ferdinand Haring
North Dakota State University

David Hoak
University of California,
Los Angeles

Louis Hoelzle
Bucks County Community College

Paul Hutchens
St. Louis Community College

Gail Jones
Delgado Junior College

William Jones
Xavier University

Charles Kinzek
Los Angeles Valley College

James McKim
University of Central Arkansas

Jerold C. Mathews
Iowa State University

Jane Morrison
Thornton Community College

Gary R. Penner
Richland College

John Petro
Western Michigan University

Edward Pettit
Augusta College

Glenn Prigge
University of North Dakota

Venice Scheurich
Del Mar College

Edwin Schulz
Elgin Community College

Donald Smith
Louisiana State University,
Shreveport

E. Genevieve Stanton
Portland State University

Bruno Wichnoski
University of North Carolina,
Charlotte

Reviewers of the Third Edition

James Arnold
University of Wisconsin, Milwaukee

Edward S. Boylan
Rutgers University

Roger L. Creech
East Carolina University

Felix A. Defino
Morris College

John Hornsby
University of New Orleans

Robert Morrow
Central Piedmont Community College

K. L. Nielsen
Butler University

Elaine Rhoades
Illinois State University, Normal

John Spellman
Southwest Texas State University

Johnny S. Smith
Jacksonville State University

Lettie Stallings
Gordon Junior College

Jan Vandever
South Dakota State University

John L. Whitcomb
University of North Dakota

1

The Real Number System

1 Introduction

Most of the so-called rules of algebra, so mysterious to many students on first exposure, have their justification in the fundamental properties of what is known as the **real number system.** We could start with a basic set of assumptions (or axioms) about real numbers, together with certain definitions, and from these we could derive other properties of real numbers. Then we could prove the rules of algebra from these properties. We will not do this, since to do so would almost be a course in itself. However, in the next two sections, we will list these assumptions and definitions, and we will indicate how certain further properties can then be derived.

The simplest real numbers are the **natural numbers,** which are just the ordinary counting numbers 1, 2, 3, ... Natural numbers are also called **positive integers,** and they, together with 0, and their negatives (the **negative integers** −1, −2, −3, . . .), comprise the **integers.** The **rational numbers** are numbers that can be expressed as the ratio of two integers, that is, in the form m/n, where m and n are integers and n is not equal to 0. Rational numbers include ordinary fractions, such as $\frac{3}{4}$, but they also include the integers themselves, since any integer m can be written as $m/1$. Real numbers that are not rational are called **irrational.** These include such numbers as $\sqrt{2}$, π, and $\sqrt[3]{7}$.* Rational numbers and irrational numbers together form the set of real numbers.

One convenient way to visualize the real numbers is by way of a **number line,** as shown in Figure 1. After selecting a point as the **origin** to correspond to 0 and another point to correspond to 1, both a scale and a direction are determined. Points corresponding to both positive and negative integers can be determined. At least theoretically, we can see how to locate points corresponding to any rational number. For example, if we wanted to locate $\frac{13}{25}$, the unit interval from 0 to 1 could be divided into 25 equal intervals; then the right

Figure 1

---

* Exponents and radicals will be studied in Sections 5 and 6, but some familiarity with these concepts is assumed.

1

end point of the thirteenth interval starting from 0 would be the desired point. It is more difficult to locate irrational numbers, but they are there (in abundance!). Irrationals are rather elusive, but they can always be approximated to any desired degree of accuracy by rationals. For example, the well-known number we designate by π is typically approximated by the rational number 3.1416 ($\frac{31,416}{10,000}$), and $\sqrt{2}$ is approximately 1.414. It should be kept in mind that these are approximations only; in fact, we can never write down in decimal form the exact value of any irrational number.

A significant feature of the real numbers is that they occupy *every* position on the number line. There are no gaps. This would not be true if we limited consideration to the rationals only, for while the rationals are infinite in number and are dense on the line (that is, between any two points, however close together, there are rationals), they do not occupy all of the line. In fact, the gaps (that is, the irrationals) are more numerous than the rational points.

The rational numbers have two forms when expressed as decimal expansions: (1) terminating, such as 1.25, or (2) repeating, such as 0.666 . . . . All other decimal expansions are irrational numbers. The real numbers, then, can be characterized as being the **set** of all decimal expansions.

We will frequently have occasion to refer to a **set** of things, by which we mean a *collection*. Sets are usually designated by using braces, { }, and inside the braces either listing the **members** of the set or giving a rule that describes the set. The members of a set are also called its **elements,** and we use a symbol such as $a \in A$ to indicate that a is an element of the set A. If every element of a set B is also an element of the set A, then B is said to be a **subset** of A, designated $B \subseteq A$. It is also convenient to be able to speak of a set that has no elements, and we call this the **empty set** and designate it by the symbol $\varnothing$. All other sets are said to be **nonempty.** The sets we will be primarily concerned with in this chapter are the set R of real numbers and its most important **subsets,** namely the set Q of rational numbers, the set I of irrational numbers, the set J of integers, and the set N of natural numbers. In Chapter 3 we will introduce the set C of complex numbers.

EXERCISE SET 1

A   In Problems 1 and 2 express the numbers as repeating or terminating decimals.

1. a. $\frac{2}{3}$ **b.** $\frac{5}{8}$ **c.** $\frac{2}{11}$ **d.** $-\frac{8}{5}$ **e.** $\frac{10}{27}$

2. a. $\frac{15}{16}$ **b.** $-\frac{75}{8}$ **c.** $\frac{4}{9}$ **d.** $\frac{10}{7}$ **e.** $\frac{9}{37}$

3. The number π is sometimes approximated by the rational number $\frac{22}{7}$. How good is this approximation? (The value of π correct to ten decimal places is 3.1415926536.)

4. The decimal expansion of a certain number is 1.01001000100001 . . . , with the pattern continuing in the obvious way. Is this number rational or irrational? Give your reason.

5. State which of the following are rational and which are irrational:

   a. $\dfrac{\sqrt{81}}{4}$ **b.** -2 **c.** $\sqrt{5}$ **d.** $\sqrt[3]{-8}$ **e.** $\frac{1}{2} + \frac{2}{3}$

6. What can you conclude about $x + y$ if:
   a. x and y are rational?   **b.** x and y are irrational?
   c. x is rational and y is irrational?

7. Answer parts a, b, and c of Problem 6 for the product $x \cdot y$.

8. Determine the number $x = 1.242424\ldots$ in the form m/n, where m and n are integers, by considering $100x - x$.

In Problems 9–11 show that each number is rational by expressing it in the form m/n, where m and n are integers. Use the idea of Problem 8.

9. **a.** $0.666\ldots$ **b.** $3.111\ldots$
10. **a.** $0.272727\ldots$ **b.** $0.0121212\ldots$
11. **a.** $0.243243243\ldots$ **b.** $5.132132132\ldots$

B 12. Without doing the division, state the maximum number of digits there can be in one cycle of the decimal expansion of $\frac{53}{137}$. Explain in general how you can be sure that m/n will always result in a repeating or terminating decimal.

13. The point corresponding to $\sqrt{2}$ on the number line can be located geometrically by constructing a square on the unit interval from 0 to 1 and, with a compass, describing an arc of a circle with center at 0 and with radius equal to the diagonal of the square. The point at which the arc crosses the number line is the desired point.
   a. Explain the basis for this procedure.
   b. How can $\sqrt{5}$ be located in a similar way?
   Hint. For this problem you will need the Pythagorean theorem, which says that in a right triangle with legs a and b and hypotenuse c, $a^2 + b^2 = c^2$.

14. Carry out the details outlined here to show that $\sqrt{2}$ is irrational. Begin by *assuming* $\sqrt{2}$ is rational. Then we can write $\sqrt{2} = m/n$ where m and n have no common factor other than 1. Square both sides of this equation and solve for m^2. Observe that m^2 is an even number, and explain why it follows that m itself must be even. From this conclude that n^2 is even, and also therefore that n is even. Why is this a contradiction? What do you conclude about the original assumption?

2 Basic Properties

In this section we list the basic properties (or axioms) of the real number system, R. From these, all other properties of real numbers can be derived. Since the concept of equality is fundamental to everything that follows, we will begin by stating the properties that provide the basis for working with all equalities. In mathematics the symbol $A = B$ means A and B are two names for the same thing. Thus, we may replace B by A or A by B in any expression involving either symbol. So equality means "is identical to." Following are the fundamental properties, where the letters a, b, and c stand for real numbers:*

---

* They may also stand for complex numbers, and when we study complex numbers in Chapter 3, we will use these properties without further discussion.

> **Properties of Equality**
>
> 1. $a = a$ Reflexive property
> 2. If $a = b$, then $b = a$. Symmetric property
> 3. If $a = b$ and $b = c$, then $a = c$. Transitive property
> 4. If $a = b$, then $a + c = b + c$ and $ac = bc$.
> 5. If $ac = bc$ and $c \neq 0$, then $a = b$.

Property 4 is sometimes read "equals may be added to, or multiplied by, equals."

The basic properties of the set of real numbers R can now be given:

1. The set R is **closed** with respect to addition and multiplication. That is, **both $a + b$ and $a \cdot b$ are in R.**

Here, the word *closed* means that any number that results from the addition or multiplication of members of R must also be a member of R.

2. Addition and multiplication in R are **commutative.** That is, $a + b = b + a$ **and** $a \cdot b = b \cdot a$.

Thus, the order of adding or multiplying two real numbers is immaterial.

3. Addition and multiplication in R are **associative.** That is, $a + (b + c) = (a + b) + c$ **and** $a \cdot (b \cdot c) = (a \cdot b) \cdot c$.

Without this property we would not know, for example, how to interpret $2 + 3 + 4$. The associative property asserts that we may add like this: $2 + (3 + 4) = 2 + 7 = 9$; or like this: $(2 + 3) + 4 = 5 + 4 = 9$. Similar comments apply to multiplication.

4. Multiplication is **distributive** over addition. That is, $a(b + c) = ab + ac$.

For example, we may evaluate $13(12 + 8)$ either this way: $13(12 + 8) = 13(20) = 260$; or by distributing the multiplication: $13(12 + 8) = 13(12) + 13(8) = 156 + 104 = 260$.

5. The number **0 is the additive identity** in R, and the number **1 is the multiplicative identity** in R. That is, $a + 0 = a$ **and** $a \cdot 1 = a$.

In simpler terms, when 0 is added to any number, this leaves the number unchanged, and when a number is multiplied by 1, the number is unchanged.

6. For each element a in R there is a unique **additive inverse** in R, designated by $-a$, and for each $a \neq 0$, there is a unique **multiplicative inverse** in R, designated by a^{-1}. Thus, $a + (-a) = 0$ **and** $a \cdot a^{-1} = 1$.

So the additive inverse of a number is that number which must be added to it to give 0, and the multiplicative inverse of a number is that number by which it must be multiplied to give 1. For example, the additive inverse of 2 is -2, and the additive inverse of $-\frac{2}{3}$ is $\frac{2}{3}$; that is, $2 + (-2) = 0$ and $-\frac{2}{3} + \frac{2}{3} = 0$.

The multiplicative inverse of 2 is $\frac{1}{2}$, and the multiplicative inverse of $\frac{2}{3}$ is $\frac{3}{2}$; that is, $2 \cdot 2^{-1} = 2 \cdot \frac{1}{2} = 1$ and $\frac{2}{3} \cdot (\frac{2}{3})^{-1} = \frac{2}{3} \cdot \frac{3}{2} = 1$. It is important to note that 0 has no multiplicative inverse. (Why?)

7. The **positive real numbers,** designated by R^+, constitute a subset of R with the following properties:

   a. **If a and b are in R^+, so are $a + b$ and $a \cdot b$.** That is, R^+ is closed with respect to addition and multiplication.

   b. Every real number falls into exactly one of three distinct categories: **It is in R^+, it is zero, or its additive inverse is in R^+.**

Property 7a says that if you add or multiply two positive real numbers, the result is positive. Property 7b divides R into three disjoint classes: (1) the positive real numbers, (2) zero, and (3) the negative real numbers (that is, numbers with additive inverses that are positive).

Before stating the final basic property, it is necessary to give some definitions. You may have wondered why the properties stated so far do not mention subtraction or division. This is because these operations are defined in terms of addition and multiplication.

DEFINITION 1   The **difference** between a and b is defined by

$$a - b = a + (-b)$$

This explains the origin of the rule: "To subtract, change the sign of the subtrahend and add."

DEFINITION 2   If $b \neq 0$, the **quotient** of a by b is defined by

$$\frac{a}{b} = a \cdot b^{-1}$$

The notation $a \div b$ is also used for the quotient of a by b. Note that $a/0$ is not defined, since 0 has no multiplicative inverse. This should be stressed. **The denominator of a fraction cannot be 0; that is, you cannot divide by 0.**

DEFINITION 3   The number a is said to be **less than b,** written $a < b$, provided $b - a$ is positive. Alternately, we may say b is **greater than a,** and write $b > a$. If a is **either less than or equal to b,** we write $a \leq b$. Alternately, we say b is **greater than or equal to a,** and write $b \geq a$.

DEFINITION 4   A subset S of R is said to be **bounded above** if there is a real number k such that every number in S is less than or equal to k. Such a number k is called an **upper bound** for S. If no upper bound of S is less than k, then k is said to be the **least upper bound** of S.

EXAMPLE 1   The set $\{1, 1\frac{1}{2}, 1\frac{3}{4}, 1\frac{7}{8}, 1\frac{15}{16}, \ldots\}$ is bounded above by 4, 5, 100, and many other numbers. But 2 is the least upper bound.

We can now state the final basic property of the real numbers:

8. The set R is **complete** in the sense that every nonempty subset of R that is bounded above has a least upper bound in R.

This property is admittedly rather difficult to understand, and in this course it will not be necessary to explore its meaning in depth. But you should be aware that this property guarantees that every point on the number line corresponds to some real number and also that every infinite decimal represents a real number.

A host of properties can be derived from the basic ones. We list some of these below for reference.

Further Properties of Real Numbers

1. The right-hand distributive property: $(a + b)c = ac + bc$.

2. The extended associative properties: The result is the same regardless of the order of adding or of multiplying any finite collection of real numbers. For example, consider

$$2 + 3 + 4 + 5$$

We may perform this addition in any of the following ways:

$$(2 + 3) + (4 + 5) = 5 + 9 = 14$$
$$[2 + (3 + 4)] + 5 = [2 + 7] + 5 = 9 + 5 = 14$$
$$2 + [3 + (4 + 5)] = 2 + [3 + 9] = 2 + 12 = 14$$

and so on.

3. When 0 is multiplied by any number, the result is 0, that is: $a \cdot 0 = 0$.

4. $-a = (-1)a$

5. $(-a)(b) = -(ab)$

6. $(-a)(-b) = ab$

7. If $ab = 0$,   then either $a = 0$ or $b = 0$.

More properties will be given after introducing more definitions.

EXAMPLE 2   Show that $(-a)(b) = -(ab)$.

Note.   The instruction "show that" is equivalent to "prove that."

Solution   In the proof we will indicate the justification for each step to the right of the step.

$$a + (-a) = 0 \qquad \text{Definition of additive inverse}$$
$$[a + (-a)] \cdot b = 0 \cdot b \qquad \text{Equality property 4}$$
$$ab + (-a)(b) = 0 \cdot b \qquad \text{Right-hand distributive property}$$
$$ab + (-a)(b) = 0 \qquad \text{Property of 0 (see Problem 10, Exercise Set 2)}$$

The last equation says that $(-a)(b)$ is a number which when added to ab gives 0, and since additive inverses are unique (see Problem 11, Exercise Set 2), it follows that $(-a)(b)$ is the additive inverse of ab, that is,

$$(-a)(b) = -(ab)$$

EXERCISE SET 2

A   **1.**   State the basic property of R used in each of the following:
a. $2(3 + 4) = 2 \cdot 3 + 2 \cdot 4$ **b.** $4 + (-4) = 0$
c. $(3 \cdot 3^{-1}) \cdot 6 = 1 \cdot 6$ **d.** $1 + 0 = 1$
e. $1 \cdot 0 = 0$ **f.** $(-2 + 3) + 5 = -2 + (3 + 5)$
g. $2 \cdot (3 \cdot 4) = (2 \cdot 3) \cdot 4$ **h.** $(3 + 2) \cdot 5 = (2 + 3) \cdot 5$
i. $(5 + 7) \cdot 6 = 6 \cdot (5 + 7)$ **j.** $(2 + 0) \cdot 7 = 2 \cdot 7$

2.   **a.**   Give the additive inverse of each of the following: 2,   8, -2, $\frac{3}{4}$, $-\frac{5}{2}$.
b.   Give the multiplicative inverse of each of the following: 5, -3,   2, $\frac{2}{5}$, $-\frac{7}{3}$.

3.   Evaluate each of the following:
a. $2(-3)$ **b.** $(-3)(-5)$ **c.** $-(-2)$ **d.** 3^{-1} **e.** $3 + [4 + (5 + 7)]$

4.   Evaluate each of the following:
a. $a - 0$ **b.** $0 - a$ **c.** $\frac{0}{1}$ **d.** $(-3)^{-1}$ **e.** $(\frac{3}{4})^{-1}$

5.   **a.**   What is the additive inverse of 0?
b.   What is the multiplicative inverse of 1?
c.   What is the multiplicative inverse of -1?
d.   Are there any other "self-inverses"?

6.   Does the commutative property hold for:
a.   Subtraction? **b.**   Division?
Justify your answers.

7.   Does the associative property hold for:
a.   Subtraction? **b.**   Division?
Justify your answers.

8.   Is addition distributive over multiplication? Justify your answer.

9.   Determine the least upper bound of each of the following sets:
a. $\{1, 2, 5, 3, -2\}$ **b.** $\{1, \frac{3}{2}, \frac{7}{4}, \frac{15}{8}, \frac{31}{16}, \frac{63}{32}, \ldots\}$
c. $\{-1, -\frac{1}{2}, -\frac{1}{3}, -\frac{1}{4}, -\frac{1}{5}, \ldots\}$
d. $\{x \in R: \quad x < 5\}$
Note.   This is read "the set of all x in R such that x is less than 5."
e. $\left\{ 3 - \frac{1}{n}: \quad n \in N \right\}$

10. State the basic property of R employed in each step of the following proof that $a \cdot 0 = 0$:

$$a \cdot (0 + 0) = a \cdot 0$$
$$a \cdot 0 + a \cdot 0 = a \cdot 0$$
$$-(a \cdot 0) + (a \cdot 0 + a \cdot 0) = -(a \cdot 0) + a \cdot 0 \qquad \text{Property of equality}$$
$$-(a \cdot 0) + (a \cdot 0 + a \cdot 0) = 0$$
$$[-(a \cdot 0) + a \cdot 0] + a \cdot 0 = 0$$
$$0 + a \cdot 0 = 0$$
$$a \cdot 0 = 0$$

11. The following proof shows that there can be only one additive inverse of a given real number, that is, additive inverses are unique. State the basic property of R used in each step of the proof.*

Let $a \in R$. By basic property 6 we know there is an additive inverse of a, which we designate by $-a$. Suppose b is also an additive inverse of a, so that

$$a + b = 0$$

We add $-a$ to both sides and proceed as shown.

$$-a + (a + b) = -a + 0$$
$$-a + (a + b) = -a$$
$$(-a + a) + b = -a$$
$$0 + b = -a$$
$$b = -a$$

So b is the same as $-a$, which shows there is only one additive inverse of a.

12. Use basic properties of R to prove the right-hand distributive law:

$$(a + b)c = ac + bc$$

B 13. Follow a procedure similar to that used in Problem 11 to prove that the multiplicative inverse of a nonzero real number a is unique.

14. Show that R is closed with respect to subtraction. Is R closed with respect to division? Show why or why not.

15. Show that $a(b - c) = ab - ac$.

16. Show that $-(a + b) = -a - b$.

17. Show that if $b \neq 0$, then $1/b = b^{-1}$.

18. Show that if $b \neq 0$, then $0/b = 0$.

19. Show that if $a \neq 0$ and $b \neq 0$, then $(ab)^{-1} = a^{-1}b^{-1}$.

20. A **lower bound** of a set S of real numbers is a number that is less than or equal to every element of S, and the **greatest lower bound** of S is a lower bound of S that is greater than or equal to all other lower bounds of S. Show that the number m is the greatest lower bound of a set S of real numbers provided the following two conditions are satisfied: (1) $x \geq m$ for all $x \in S$ and (2) if $x \geq k$ for all $x \in S$, then $k \leq m$.

21. Find the greatest lower bound of each of the following sets (see Problem 20):

a. $\{3, -1, 2, 4, 0\}$ b. $\{1, \frac{1}{2}, \frac{1}{3}, \frac{1}{4}, \frac{1}{5}, \ldots\}$ c. $\left\{ \dfrac{n+1}{n} : \ n \in N \right\}$

d. $\{x \in R: \ x > 5\}$ e. $\{y \in R: \ y > -2\}$

---

*We included uniqueness in the statement of the basic property on additive inverses. This problem shows that uniqueness need not be assumed but is a consequence of the other properties.

3 Order Properties and Absolute Value

The following properties of **inequality** can be deduced as consequences of the properties of R given in Section 2.

1. $a > 0$ **if and only if a is positive.**

So, henceforth, the statements "a is positive" and "a is greater than 0" may be used interchangeably.

2. **If** $a \neq 0$, **then** $a^2 > 0$.

In particular, $1 > 0$, since $1^2 = 1$.

3. **If** $a < b$, **then** $a + c < b + c$.

This says that the same number may be added to both sides of an inequality without changing the sense of the inequality (that is, the symbol $<$ is unchanged in direction).

4. **If** $a < b$, **then** $\begin{cases} ac < bc & \text{if} \quad c > 0 \\ ac > bc & \text{if} \quad c < 0 \end{cases}$

The situation in multiplication is more complicated. Multiplying by a positive number leaves the sense of an inequality unchanged, but multiplying by a negative number reverses the sense.

5. **If a is any real number, then precisely one of the following is true: $a > 0$, $a = 0$, $a < 0$.**

This is the property of **trichotomy.**

6. **If** $a < b$ **and** $b < c$, **then** $a < c$.

This is the property of **transitivity.**

7. **If** $a < b$ **and** $c < d$, **then** $a + c < b + d$.

Note the distinction between this and property 3. It says that as long as both inequalities are of the same type (both "less than" as shown), we may add the respective sides and retain the same sense of inequality.

8. **If** $a < b$ **and** $a \cdot b > 0$, **then** $1/a > 1/b$.

Thus, taking reciprocals reverses the sense of the inequality *provided* both numbers are positive or both numbers are negative.

These properties provide the basis for working with more complicated inequalities in algebra, as we will see in Chapter 3. There are times when it is useful to write a combined inequality of the form

$$a < b < c$$

This means that both $a < b$ *and $b < c$*. It is convenient sometimes to read from the middle and say "b is less than c and greater than a."

We next introduce the concept of the **absolute value** of a number, which is, roughly speaking, the magnitude of the number without regard to sign. The precise definition follows.

DEFINITION 5   The **absolute value** of a real number a is equal to a itself if $a \geq 0$ and is equal to $-a$ if $a < 0$. The absolute value of a is designated by $|a|$.

From this we see that $|a|$ is always nonnegative. For example, $|2| = 2$ and $|-3| = -(-3) = 3$. Note that when a is negative, $|a| = -a$, and since a itself is negative, $-a$ is positive (despite appearances).

Geometrically, the absolute value of a number a can be interpreted as the distance between a and 0 on a number line, as illustrated in Figure 2.

Figure 2

Absolute values and inequalities are often used in combination. For example, consider the set*

$$S = \{x:\ |x| < 1\}$$

The set S consists of all real numbers whose distance from 0 is less than 1, namely the numbers between -1 and 1. So another way of writing S is

$$S = \{x:\ -1 < x < 1\}$$

This can be shown on a number line, as in Figure 3. The parentheses at -1 and 1 indicate that these points are not included. If the end points are to be included, we use square brackets, as in Figure 4, which depicts the set $\{x:\ |x| \leq 1\}$.

Figure 3

Figure 4

More generally, we can say that the numbers x that satisfy the inequality

$$|x| < a$$

are the same as those that satisfy

$$-a < x < a$$

Similarly, the inequality

$$|x| > a$$

---

* In descriptions of sets such as this we will understand x to be real unless otherwise specified.

is satisfied by those numbers x whose distance from 0 is greater than a. When x is positive, this means that x is to the right of a, that is, $x > a$. When x is negative, x is to the left of $-a$, that is, $x < -a$. So

$$\textbf{either} \quad x > a \quad \textbf{or} \quad x < -a$$

For example, consider the set

$$T = \{x: \ |x| > 2\}$$

We can write this as

$$T = \{x: \ x > 2 \ \text{or} \ x < -2\}$$

It is convenient here to use the idea of **the union of two sets, which is defined as the set of all elements in either, or both, of the two given sets.** The union of two sets A and B is designated by $A \cup B$. We can therefore write the set T above as

$$T = \{x: \ x > 2\} \cup \{x: \ x < -2\}$$

Figure 5 shows how this can be indicated on a number line.

Figure 5

EXERCISE SET 3

A In Problems 1 and 2 replace each question mark by the appropriate inequality sign.

1. **a.** $-10 \ ? \ 2$ **b.** $-7 \ ? \ -9$ **c.** $0 \ ? \ 4$ **d.** $0 \ ? \ -1$ **e.** $-100 \ ? \ 1$
2. **a.** $\frac{2}{3} \ ? \ \frac{5}{9}$ **b.** $-\frac{1}{2} \ ? \ -\frac{1}{3}$ **c.** $\sqrt{5} \ ? \ 2.4$
   d. $3.6 \ ? \ \frac{15}{4}$ **e.** $-5 \ ? \ -\sqrt{17}$

3. Use Definition 3 to show that each of the following is true:
   a. $3 < 7$ **b.** $-2 < 4$ **c.** $-4 < -1$ **d.** $5 > 2$ **e.** $-3 > -5$

In Problems 4 and 5 write each statement using inequality symbols.

4. **a.** x is greater than 5 **b.** x is less than or equal to 2
   c. x is nonnegative **d.** x is negative
   e. x is not positive
5. **a.** x is less than 5 and greater than 2
   b. x is less than or equal to 0 and greater than -1
   c. x is greater than or equal to 0 and less than 2
   d. x is nonnegative and less than or equal to 6
   e. x is greater than 3 but does not exceed 4

In Problems 6 and 7 show each set on a number line.

6. **a.** $\{x: \ x < 2\}$ **b.** $\{x: \ x \geq 3\}$
   c. $\{x: \ 2 < x < 4\}$ **d.** $\{x: \ x < 0\} \cup \{x: \ x > 3\}$
   e. $\{x \in R^+: \ x < 5\}$
7. **a.** $\{x: \ x < 3\} \cup \{x: \ x \geq 5\}$ **b.** $\{x: \ x \leq 0\} \cup \{x: \ x > 2\}$
   c. $\{x: \ -1 \leq x < 2\}$ **d.** $\{x: \ 2 < x \leq 6\}$
   e. $\{x: \ x < 0\} \cup \{x: \ x > 0\}$

8. Give the value of each of the following:
   a. $|-6|$ **b.** $|\pi|$ **c.** $|-1.5|$ **d.** $|0|$ **e.** $|a|$, where $a \in R$
9. Write the following inequalities in equivalent ways without absolute value signs:
   a. $|x| < 2$ **b.** $|y| > 1$ **c.** $|t| \le 3$ **d.** $|w| \ge 2$
10. Give an equivalent representation of each of the following sets that does not use absolute value signs, and show each set on a number line:
    a. $\{x: \; |x| < 3\}$ **b.** $\{x: \; |x| > 2\}$
    c. $\{x: \; |x| \le 1\}$ **d.** $\{x: \; |x| \ge 3\}$
11. Give an equivalent representation of each of the following sets that makes use of absolute value signs:
    a. $\{x: \; -5 < x < 5\}$ **b.** $\{x: \; x > 6\} \cup \{x: \; x < -6\}$
    c. $\{x: \; -4 \le x \le 4\}$ **d.** $\{x: \; x \le -8\} \cup \{x: \; x \ge 8\}$

B   Problems 12–17 refer to the properties of inequalities given at the beginning of this section.

12. Prove property 1.   13. Prove property 2.
14. Prove property 3.   15. Prove property 4.
16. Prove property 6.   17. Prove property 7.
                            Hint.   Use properties 3 and 6

18. Prove that if $a > 0$, then $a^{-1} > 0$.
    Hint.   Consider the product of a and a^{-1} and suppose a^{-1} is not positive.
19. Use the result of Problem 18 to give a rule for dividing both sides of an inequality by the same nonzero number, and justify your result.
20. Prove inequality property 8.
    Hint.   Multiply both sides of $a < b$ by $a^{-1}b^{-1}$ and explain why this is valid based on Problem 18.
21. Prove or disprove: If $a < b$ and $c < d$, then $a - c < b - d$.
22. If A and B are sets, **the intersection of A and B, designated $A \cap B$, is defined to be the set of all elements in both A and B.** Write each of the following in an equivalent form as the intersection of two sets:
    a. $\{x: \; -3 < x < 2\}$ **b.** $\{x: \; 2 < x \le 6\}$
    c. $\{x: \; a < x < b\}$ **d.** $\{x: \; |x| < a\}$

4   The Arithmetic of Rational Numbers

Our primary goal in this section is to derive the rules for adding and multiplying rational numbers. Subtraction and division can then be accomplished by making use of Definitions 1 and 2. Since rational numbers are ratios of integers, we begin by stating rules for adding and multiplying integers.

The arithmetic of the natural numbers (or positive integers) will be taken as given. Let m and n designate arbitrary positive integers. Then $-m$ and $-n$ are negative integers, and the rules listed below apply. These can be proved on the basis of the properties of R given in Section 3.

1. $m + (-n) = \begin{cases} +(m-n) & \text{if } m \ge n \\ -(n-m) & \text{if } n > m \end{cases}$

2. $(-m) + (-n) = -(m+n)$
3. $m(-n) = -(mn)$
4. $(-m)(-n) = mn$

By rule 1, when we add integers of unlike sign, we actually subtract the smaller absolute value from the larger and give the result the sign of the larger. (When writing positive integers the plus sign is usually omitted.) Adding numbers of unlike sign can be thought of as finding the net value.

EXAMPLE 3   Find the indicated sums and products.

  a. $5 + (-2)$ **b.** $2 + (-5)$ **c.** $(-2) + (-5)$
  d. $3(-4)$ **e.** $(-3)(-4)$

Solution   **a.** By rule 1, $5 + (-2) = 5 - 2 = 3.$
    b. By rule 1, $2 + (-5) = -(5 - 2) = -3.$
    c. By rule 2, $(-2) + (-5) = -(2 + 5) = -7.$
    d. By rule 3, $3(-4) = -(3 \cdot 4) = -12.$
    e. By rule 4, $(-3)(-4) = 3 \cdot 4 = 12.$

Subtraction is accomplished by using Definition 1. That is, $a - b = a + (-b)$. Here it should be emphasized that the additive inverse of a negative integer is the corresponding positive integer. This says that $-(-m) = m$. Thus, for example,

$$3 - (-5) = \mathbf{3 + [-(-5)]} = 3 + 5 = 8$$

In the future, we will omit the second step in discussions of this type of problem.

EXAMPLE 4   Evaluate:

  a. $4 - 7$ **b.** $3 - (-4)$ **c.** $-2 - 7$ **d.** $-2 - (-7)$

Solution   **a.** $4 - 7 = 4 + (-7) = -3$ **b.** $3 - (-4) = 3 + 4 = 7$
    c. $-2 - 7 = -2 + (-7) = -9$ **d.** $-2 - (-7) = -2 + 7 = 5$

Now let a, b, c, and d denote arbitrary integers, with c and d not equal to 0. Then a/b and c/d are rational numbers. Their product is found as follows:

$$\frac{a}{b} \cdot \frac{c}{d} = (a \cdot b^{-1}) \cdot (c \cdot d^{-1}) = (a \cdot c)(b^{-1} \cdot d^{-1})$$

$$= (ac)(bd)^{-1} = \frac{ac}{bd}$$

You will be asked to supply the reasons for these steps in Problem 26, Exercise Set 4. The result,

$$\frac{a}{b} \cdot \frac{c}{d} = \frac{ac}{bd}$$

says that "the product of two fractions is the product of their numerators over the product of their denominators."

Before giving the rule for addition, we observe that for any number $c \neq 0$,

$$\frac{a}{b} = \frac{a}{b} \cdot 1 = \frac{a}{b} \cdot (cc^{-1}) = \frac{a}{b} \cdot \frac{c}{c} = \frac{ac}{bc}$$

or, stated in reverse,

$$\frac{ac}{bc} = \frac{a}{b}$$

This is sometimes referred to as the **fundamental property of fractions** and is the basis for such simplifications as $\frac{6}{8} = \frac{3}{4}$.

A Word of Caution.   The fundamental property of fractions applies only when *products* are involved in the numerator and denominator. It is not true for sums. For example, in general

$$\frac{a + c}{b + c} \neq \frac{a}{b}$$

For addition, we have

$$\frac{a}{b} + \frac{c}{d} = \frac{ad}{bd} + \frac{bc}{bd} = (ad)(bd)^{-1} + (bc)(bd)^{-1}$$

$$= (ad + bc)(bd)^{-1}$$

$$= \frac{ad + bc}{bd}$$

Thus,

$$\frac{a}{b} + \frac{c}{d} = \frac{ad + bc}{bd}$$

While this formula always leads to the correct result, it is not always the most efficient way of arriving at the simplest form of the answer. Suppose the two fractions have the same denominator, say, $a/c + b/c$. Then an application of the above formula, together with the fundamental property, gives

$$\frac{a}{c} + \frac{b}{c} = \frac{ac + bc}{cc} = \frac{(a + b)c}{c \cdot c} = \frac{a + b}{c}$$

Thus,

$$\frac{a}{c} + \frac{b}{c} = \frac{a + b}{c}$$

This says: "To add two fractions with the same denominator, add the numerators and write the sum over the common denominator."

When the fractions have different denominators, the trick is to express each fraction with the smallest possible **common denominator,** called the **lowest common denominator (LCD).** With relatively small denominators this can usually be done mentally. For example, consider $\frac{3}{4} + \frac{5}{6}$. It is easy to see that

12 is the smallest natural number that is a multiple of both 4 and 6. So we write

$$\frac{3}{4} + \frac{5}{6} = \frac{3 \cdot 3}{4 \cdot 3} + \frac{5 \cdot 2}{6 \cdot 2} = \frac{9}{12} + \frac{10}{12} = \frac{19}{12}$$

For larger denominators it may be useful to write each denominator as a product of **primes.** You may recall that **a prime number is a natural number other than 1 that cannot be written as a product of natural numbers other than itself and 1.** Examples of primes are 2, 3, 5, 7, 11, 13, ... All other natural numbers except 1 are called **composite,** and they can be expressed as products of primes.

EXAMPLE 5   Find the following sums:

   a. $\frac{3}{4} + \frac{-7}{6}$ **b.** $\frac{-5}{16} + \frac{3}{28}$ **c.** $\frac{7}{780} + \frac{11}{504}$

Solution   **a.** $\dfrac{3}{4} + \dfrac{-7}{6} = \dfrac{9}{12} + \dfrac{-14}{12} = \dfrac{9 + (-14)}{12} = \dfrac{-5}{12}$

   b. To find the LCD of 16 and 28 we note that $16 = 4 \cdot 4$ and $28 = 4 \cdot 7$. So the LCD $= 4 \cdot 4 \cdot 7$, since this is the smallest number that both $4 \cdot 4$ and $4 \cdot 7$ will divide evenly.

   $$\frac{-5}{16} + \frac{3}{28} = \frac{-5}{4 \cdot 4} \cdot \frac{7}{7} + \frac{3}{4 \cdot 7} \cdot \frac{4}{4} = \frac{-35 + 12}{4 \cdot 4 \cdot 7} = \frac{-23}{112}$$

   c. This time we write each denominator as a product of primes.

2	780
2	390
3	195
5	65
	13

So $780 = 2^2 \cdot 3 \cdot 5 \cdot 13$

2	504
2	252
2	126
3	63
3	21
	7

So $504 = 2^3 \cdot 3^2 \cdot 7$

Thus, the LCD $= 2^3 \cdot 3^2 \cdot 5 \cdot 7 \cdot 13$. Notice that the LCD contains each prime number occurring in either number to the *highest* power to which it appears. So we multiply the numerator and denominator of each fraction by the primes that do not appear in its denominator to make both denominators equal to the LCD:

$$\frac{7}{780} + \frac{11}{504} = \frac{7}{780} \cdot \frac{2 \cdot 3 \cdot 7}{2 \cdot 3 \cdot 7} + \frac{11}{504} \cdot \frac{5 \cdot 13}{5 \cdot 13} = \frac{294 + 715}{32,760}$$

$$= \frac{1,009}{32,760}$$

The handling of signs is made easier by the following considerations. Since

$$\frac{a}{b} + \frac{(-a)}{b} = \frac{a + (-a)}{b} = \frac{0}{b} = 0$$

it follows that $-a/b$ is the additive inverse of a/b; that is,

$$\frac{-a}{b} = -\frac{a}{b}$$

Also,

$$\frac{a}{-b} = \frac{a}{-b} \cdot \frac{-1}{-1} = \frac{-(a \cdot 1)}{b \cdot 1} = \frac{-a}{b}$$

We also have that

$$\frac{-a}{-b} = \frac{a(-1)}{b(-1)} = \frac{a}{b}$$

Combining these results, we obtain

$$\frac{-a}{b} = \frac{a}{-b} = -\frac{a}{b} = -\frac{-a}{-b}$$

We can often save some steps in handling products of fractions by anticipating an application of the fundamental property. Since

$$\frac{a}{b} \cdot \frac{c}{a} = \frac{ac}{ba} = \frac{ca}{ba} = \frac{c}{b}$$

we can skip the middle step by "dividing out" the a before multiplication, as follows:

$$\frac{\cancel{a}}{b} \cdot \frac{c}{\cancel{a}} = \frac{c}{b}$$

More generally, whenever two or more fractions are to be multiplied, any number that occurs as a **factor** in one of the numerators and also as a factor in one of the denominators can (and should) be divided out before multiplication. For example,

$$\frac{\overset{2}{\cancel{4}} \cdot 7}{9 \ \underset{5}{\cancel{10}}} = \frac{14}{45}$$

A Word of Caution. The key word in the above discussion is *factor*. **A factor is one member of a product.** What we have said about dividing out a **common factor,** then, does not apply to sums and differences. For example, it would be *incorrect* to "divide out" the 2 as shown in

$$\frac{\cancel{2}}{3} + \frac{5}{\cancel{2}}$$

A fraction is said to be in **lowest terms** if the numerator and denominator have no integer factor in common other than 1 or -1. A fraction may be reduced to lowest terms by using the fundamental property.

EXAMPLE 6   Perform the indicated operations and reduce answers to **lowest terms.**

a. $\frac{-3}{5} - \frac{1}{2} - \frac{-7}{-4}$ b. $\frac{2}{3}(\frac{3}{5} - \frac{1}{2})$

Solution

a. $\dfrac{-3}{5} - \dfrac{1}{2} - \dfrac{-7}{-4} = \dfrac{-3}{5} + \dfrac{-1}{2} + \dfrac{-7}{4} = \dfrac{-12}{20} + \dfrac{-10}{20} + \dfrac{-35}{20} = \dfrac{-57}{20}$

b. $\dfrac{2}{3}\left(\dfrac{3}{5} - \dfrac{1}{2}\right) = \dfrac{2}{3}\left(\dfrac{6}{10} + \dfrac{-5}{10}\right) = \dfrac{2}{3}\left(\dfrac{1}{10}\right) = \dfrac{2}{30} = \dfrac{1}{15}$

Following is a summary of the rules for the arithmetic of rational numbers:

$$\frac{a}{b} + \frac{c}{d} = \frac{ad + bc}{bd} \tag{1}$$

$$\frac{a}{c} + \frac{b}{c} = \frac{a + b}{c} \tag{2}$$

$$\frac{a}{b} \cdot \frac{c}{d} = \frac{ac}{bd} \tag{3}$$

$$\frac{ac}{bc} = \frac{a}{b} \tag{4}$$

$$-\frac{a}{b} = \frac{-a}{b} = \frac{a}{-b} = -\frac{-a}{-b} \tag{5}$$

EXERCISE SET 4

A   Perform the indicated operations in Problems 1–18.

1. a. $-5 + 7$ b. $3 + (-6)$ c. $-2 + (-4)$
    d. $6 - 8$ e. $5 - (-3)$

2. a. $3 + (-4)$ b. $-4 + (-7)$ c. $-3 - (-5)$
    d. $10 - (-4)$ e. $-8 - (-2)$

3. a. $2(-3)$ b. $(-4)(5)$ c. $(-5)(-6)$
    d. $3 - 2(4)$ e. $5 + 2(-3)$

4. a. $(-3)(-4)$ b. $(-5)(9)$ c. $-2 + [(-7) + (-9)]$
    d. $(-3)[(-2) + (-5)]$ e. $(-5)(-2 + 8)$

5. a. $|-3 + 7|$ b. $|8 - 15|$ c. $|-3(-5)|$
    d. $|-6 - 9|$ e. $|2(-6)|$

6. a. $|2 - (-3)(4)|$ b. $|5(-7) + (-2)(-6)|$
    c. $|8(-2) - (-3)(4)|$ d. $|3(-2) - (-4)(-5) + (-7)(-6)|$

7. a. $\frac{5}{6} + \frac{3}{4}$ b. $\frac{7}{8} - \frac{5}{12}$

8. a. $\frac{2}{3} - \frac{1}{2}$ b. $\frac{3}{8} + \frac{7}{10}$

9. a. $\frac{1}{2} - \frac{2}{3} + \frac{5}{4}$ b. $\frac{3}{4} + \frac{5}{6} - \frac{7}{12}$

10. a. $\frac{7}{10} + \frac{-2}{15}$ b. $\frac{-7}{24} + \frac{11}{18}$

11. a. $2 - \frac{-3}{5}$ b. $\frac{5}{-6} - 1$

12. a. $-\frac{3}{4} - \frac{-1}{2} + 2$ b. $\frac{2}{3} - 1 - \frac{7}{-4}$

13. a. $\frac{2}{3}(\frac{-6}{7})$ b. $(\frac{-5}{2})(\frac{-9}{10})$

14. **a.** $3(\frac{5}{12})$ **b.** $(-\frac{9}{16})(-2)$

15. **a.** $\frac{11}{36} - \frac{19}{54}$ **b.** $\frac{7}{126} + \frac{5}{84} - \frac{17}{210}$

16. **a.** $\frac{3}{140} + \frac{5}{126}$ **b.** $\frac{7}{540} - \frac{17}{324}$

17. **a.** $-\frac{3}{4}(\frac{2}{3} - \frac{4}{5})$ **b.** $\frac{5}{6}\left(\frac{3}{4} - \frac{-4}{15}\right)$

18. **a.** $\frac{2}{5}(\frac{5}{8} - \frac{3}{4})$ **b.** $\frac{3}{11}\left(-\frac{5}{6} - \frac{-3}{8}\right)$

19. If a, b, and c are natural numbers such that $a = bc$, then both b and c are said to be **divisors** of a. The **greatest common divisor (GCD)** of two natural numbers is the largest natural number that is a divisor of both numbers. Find the GCD of each of the following pairs:
  a. 32, 48   **b.** 26, 78   **c.** 84, 56   **d.** 128, 320   **e.** 540, 315

B **20.** A definition of subtraction that is valid for the natural numbers N is as follows: "If a and b are natural numbers, then $a - b$ equals that natural number c, if it exists, which when added to b gives a." Show that when a, b, and c are elements of R, this definition is equivalent to Definition 1.

21. A definition of division applicable to the integers J is as follows: "If a and b are integers with $b \neq 0$, then $a \div b$ equals that integer c, if it exists, which when multiplied by b gives a." Show that when a, b, and c are elements of R, this definition is equivalent to Definition 2.

22. Prove each of the following:
  a. The set N is not closed with respect to subtraction, but J is.
  b. The set J is not closed with respect to division by numbers other than 0, but Q is.

In Problems 23–25 perform the indicated operations.

23. **a.** $3(-\frac{2}{5})(-\frac{1}{4}) + \frac{5}{8}(-\frac{2}{3} + 6)$ **b.** $-(-\frac{2}{3})(-\frac{7}{8}) - 2(\frac{5}{-6} + \frac{-3}{8}) - 1$

24. **a.** $\frac{5}{32} - \frac{3}{5}(\frac{7}{-8}) + \frac{2}{3}(3 - \frac{8}{5})$ **b.** $1 - \frac{9}{14} + \frac{2}{3}(\frac{-5}{7}) - (-\frac{2}{7})(\frac{5}{12})$

25. **a.** $-\frac{5}{16} - \frac{3}{4}(\frac{2}{3} - \frac{5}{6}) + \frac{5}{2}(-\frac{3}{8})$ **b.** $(-\frac{3}{5})(\frac{-7}{8} - \frac{5}{6}) - 2 + \frac{7}{12}(-\frac{4}{5} + \frac{3}{2})$

26. Justify each step of the derivation of the rule for the product of two rational numbers found on page 13.

---

5 Complex Fractions

Rules (1)–(5) in Section 4 are not limited to rational numbers of the form a/b, in which a and b are integers ($b \neq 0$). In fact, an examination of their derivation will show that, as long as the denominators involved are not 0, these rules hold for all real numbers. In particular, the numerators and denominators themselves may contain fractions, giving rise to **complex fractions.**

The first such situation to consider is the quotient of two fractions:*

$$\frac{\dfrac{a}{b}}{\dfrac{c}{d}}$$

---

* Note that for this to be defined we must not only have $b \neq 0$ and $d \neq 0$, but also $c \neq 0$, so that $c/d \neq 0$.

The definition of division requires that we have

$$\frac{\dfrac{a}{b}}{\dfrac{c}{d}} = \frac{a}{b} \cdot \left(\frac{c}{d}\right)^{-1}$$

But what is $(c/d)^{-1}$? Since $(c/d) \cdot (d/c) = (cd/dc) = 1$, and multiplicative inverses are unique, we see that

$$\left(\frac{c}{d}\right)^{-1} = \frac{d}{c}$$

$$\frac{\dfrac{a}{b}}{\dfrac{c}{d}} = \frac{a}{b} \cdot \frac{d}{c} = \frac{ad}{bc} \tag{6}$$

This is the familiar rule: "To divide fractions, invert the denominator and multiply."

The following examples illustrate how to handle more complicated complex fractions.

EXAMPLE 7   Simplify: $\dfrac{\frac{2}{3} + \frac{3}{4}}{\frac{5}{6} + \frac{1}{2}}$

Solution   In general, the best approach to this sort of problem is first to multiply the numerator and denominator of the main fraction by the LCD of all **minor denominators.** This is justified by rule (4). In this case, the LCD is 12. So we have

$$\frac{(\frac{2}{3} + \frac{3}{4})}{(\frac{5}{6} + \frac{1}{2})} \cdot \frac{12}{12} = \frac{8 + 9}{10 + 6} = \frac{17}{16}$$

The omitted steps can be done mentally. It is important to note that when multiplying the numerator and denominator by 12, *every* term must be multiplied. Notice, too, that in multiplying we have divided out common factors *before* multiplication. For example, the operations done mentally on the numerator are shown in more detail as

$$\left(\frac{2}{3} + \frac{3}{4}\right)12 = \frac{2}{3} \cdot 12 + \frac{3}{4} \cdot 12 = \frac{2}{\overset{}{\underset{1}{3}}} \cdot \frac{\overset{4}{12}}{1} + \frac{3}{\overset{}{\underset{1}{4}}} \cdot \frac{\overset{3}{12}}{1} = 8 + 9$$

As an alternative way of doing this problem, we could perform the additions on the numerator and denominator separately and then use rule (6). Doing it this way we get

$$\frac{\frac{2}{3} + \frac{3}{4}}{\frac{5}{6} + \frac{1}{2}} = \frac{\frac{8}{12} + \frac{9}{12}}{\frac{5}{6} + \frac{3}{6}} = \frac{\frac{17}{12}}{\frac{8}{6}} = \frac{17}{\underset{2}{12}} \cdot \frac{\overset{1}{6}}{8} = \frac{17}{16}$$

The first method is usually easier, but there are exceptions.

EXAMPLE 8   Simplify: $\dfrac{\frac{2}{3} - \frac{1}{4}(\frac{5}{6})}{\frac{5}{12} - \frac{-3}{2}}$

Solution   Here we must be careful to note that $(\frac{1}{4})(\frac{5}{6}) = \frac{5}{24}$, so that the desired LCD is 24.

$$\frac{\frac{2}{3} - \frac{1}{4}(\frac{5}{6})}{\frac{5}{12} - \frac{-3}{2}} \cdot \frac{24}{24} = \frac{16 - 5}{10 + 36} = \frac{11}{46}$$

EXAMPLE 9   Simplify: $\dfrac{2}{1 - \dfrac{1}{2 - \frac{3}{4}}}$

Solution   We do this in stages, beginning with the complex fraction in the denominator.

$$\frac{2}{1 - \dfrac{1}{2 - \frac{3}{4}}} = \frac{2}{1 - \dfrac{1}{2 - \frac{3}{4}} \cdot \frac{4}{4}} = \frac{2}{1 - \dfrac{4}{8 - 3}}$$

$$= \frac{2}{1 - \frac{4}{5}} \cdot \frac{5}{5} = \frac{10}{5 - 4} = \frac{10}{1} = 10$$

EXERCISE SET 5

Express each complex fraction as a simple fraction in lowest terms.

A   1. $\dfrac{\frac{1}{2} - \frac{1}{3}}{\frac{3}{4} + \frac{1}{6}}$ 　　　　2. $\dfrac{\frac{2}{3} - \frac{3}{5}}{1 - \frac{1}{5}}$

3. $\dfrac{\frac{3}{8} + \frac{5}{6}}{\frac{5}{12} - \frac{3}{4}}$ 　　　　4. $\dfrac{2 + \frac{3}{8}}{\frac{1}{4} - \frac{1}{6}}$

5. $\dfrac{3 - (-\frac{1}{2})}{-2 - \frac{3}{4}}$ 　　　　6. $\dfrac{\frac{-3}{2} - \frac{-4}{3}}{\frac{3}{4} - \frac{5}{6}}$

7. $\dfrac{\frac{5}{8} - 2}{\frac{2}{3} + 1}$ 　　　　8. $\dfrac{\frac{4}{15} - \frac{3}{5}}{1 - \frac{7}{3}}$

9. $\dfrac{\frac{3}{2} - \frac{4}{3}}{-\frac{5}{6} - 1}$ 　　　　10. $\dfrac{\frac{3}{5} - \frac{9}{4}}{\frac{-7}{2} + \frac{6}{5}}$

11. $\dfrac{\frac{3}{4} + \frac{1}{2}}{1 - (\frac{3}{4})(\frac{1}{2})}$ 　　　　12. $\dfrac{\frac{1}{4} + \frac{1}{2}(\frac{2}{3})}{1 - (\frac{3}{4})(\frac{2}{3})}$

13. $\dfrac{\frac{5}{12} - \frac{3}{4}}{1 + (\frac{3}{4})(\frac{5}{12})}$ 　　　　14. $\dfrac{\frac{1}{3} - \frac{5}{6}}{\frac{2}{7} - \frac{3}{14}}$

15. $1 - \dfrac{1}{2 - \frac{1}{2}}$ 　　　　16. $\dfrac{1}{\dfrac{1}{1 - \frac{2}{3}} - \frac{1}{2}}$

B 17. $1 - \dfrac{1}{1 - \dfrac{3}{1 - \frac{2}{3}}}$

18. $\dfrac{\dfrac{2}{3} - \dfrac{1 + \frac{4}{9}}{2 \cdot \frac{2}{3}}}{\frac{4}{9}}$

19. $\dfrac{\dfrac{10}{9}\left(\dfrac{1}{3}\right) - \dfrac{\frac{25}{81}}{4\left(\frac{1}{3}\right)}}{2 \cdot \frac{5}{9} - 1}$

20. $\dfrac{-\dfrac{3}{2} - \left(\dfrac{-27}{8} - 1\right) \cdot \dfrac{1}{3 \cdot \frac{9}{4}}}{\frac{9}{4}}$

---

6 Integral Exponents

Exponents originated as a shorthand for repeated multiplication of a number by itself. For example, $2^3 = 2 \cdot 2 \cdot 2$. In general, if a is any real number and n is a positive integer, then

$$a^n = \underbrace{a \cdot a \cdot a \cdot \cdots \cdot a}_{n \text{ factors}}$$

In particular, $a^1 = a$. The familiar rules for multiplication and division are immediate:

$$a^m \cdot a^n = (\overbrace{a \cdot a \cdot \cdots \cdot a}^{m \text{ factors}})(\overbrace{a \cdot a \cdot \cdots \cdot a}^{n \text{ factors}})$$

$$= \overbrace{a \cdot a \cdot a \cdot a \cdot \cdots \cdot a}^{m + n \text{ factors}} = a^{m+n}$$

If $m > n$, then

$$\frac{a^m}{a^n} = \frac{a \cdot a \cdot \cdots \cdot a \cdot \overbrace{a \cdot a \cdot \cdots \cdot a}^{m - n \text{ factors}}}{a \cdot a \cdot \cdots \cdot a} = a^{m-n} \qquad (a \neq 0)$$

If $m = n$, then

$$\frac{a^m}{a^n} = 1 \qquad (a \neq 0)$$

Whereas if $n > m$, then

$$\frac{a^m}{a^n} = \frac{a \cdot a \cdot \cdots \cdot a}{a \cdot a \cdot \cdots \cdot a \cdot \underbrace{a \cdot a \cdot \cdots \cdot a}_{n - m \text{ factors}}} = \frac{1}{a^{n-m}} \qquad (a \neq 0)$$

These relationships are summarized as follows:

$$a^m \cdot a^n = a^{m+n} \qquad\qquad (7)$$

$$\frac{a^m}{a^n} = \begin{cases} a^{m-n} & \text{if } m > n \\ 1 & \text{if } m = n \qquad (a \neq 0) \\ \dfrac{1}{a^{n-m}} & \text{if } n > m \end{cases} \qquad (8)$$

For example,

$$2^3 \cdot 2^5 = 2^8 \qquad \frac{2^5}{2^3} = 2^2 \qquad \frac{2^3}{2^5} = \frac{1}{2^2}$$

Rule (7) can be used to obtain the formula $(a^m)^n = a^{mn}$. To illustrate, consider $(2^3)^4$. We have, by definition of the outer exponent,

$$(2^3)^4 = 2^3 \cdot 2^3 \cdot 2^3 \cdot 2^3$$

and by extending rule (7),

$$2^3 \cdot 2^3 \cdot 2^3 \cdot 2^3 = 2^{12}$$

So, $(2^3)^4 = 2^{12}$. More generally,

$$(a^m)^n = \overbrace{a^m \cdot a^m \cdot \ \cdots \ \cdot a^m}^{n \text{ factors}} = a^{mn} \qquad (9)$$

since the sum of n m's is $nm = mn$.

One additional property of exponents should be noted, namely, that $(a \cdot b)^n = a^n b^n$. This follows from the definition and from commutativity and associativity:

$$(ab)^n = (ab)(ab)(ab) \cdots (ab)$$
$$= (a \cdot a \cdot a \cdot \ \cdots \ \cdot a)(b \cdot b \cdot b \cdot \ \cdots \ \cdot b) = a^n b^n \qquad (10)$$

This would be about all we could say concerning exponents if consideration were limited to exponents that are positive integers. Their usefulness is greatly extended, however, by giving meaning to negative and zero exponents, and even more by permitting rational and finally irrational exponents.

To arrive at a definition of negative integral exponents, we define a^{-1} for $a \neq 0$ as the unique multiplicative inverse of a. (This is not new, but the symbol a^{-1} as used previously was not thought of as "a raised to the power negative one.") Since

$$u \cdot \frac{1}{a} = \frac{a}{1} \cdot \frac{1}{a} = \frac{a}{a} = 1$$

it follows that $1/a$ is the multiplicative inverse of a. So $a^{-1} = 1/a$. For consistency with rule (9), we then have

$$a^{-n} = a^{(-1)n} = (a^{-1})^n = \left(\frac{1}{a}\right)^n = \underbrace{\frac{1}{a} \cdot \frac{1}{a} \cdot \ \cdots \ \cdot \frac{1}{a}}_{n \text{ factors}} = \frac{1}{a^n}$$

Here, again, it is essential that $a \neq 0$.

To see how we might reasonably define a^0, consider a^m/a^m with $a \neq 0$. This clearly equals 1 (by the definition of division). However, if we extend the first part of rule (8) to $m = n$, we obtain $a^m/a^m = a^{m-m} = a^0$. So we are led to the definition $a^0 = 1$.

It can now be shown that rules (7)–(10) remain true with m and n positive, negative, or zero integral exponents, but we will omit the details. The important definitions and results are summarized in the box.

Laws of Exponents

1. $a^0 = 1$

2. $a^{-n} = \dfrac{1}{a^n}$

3. $a^m \cdot a^n = a^{m+n}$

4. $\dfrac{a^m}{a^n} = a^{m-n} = \dfrac{1}{a^{n-m}}$

5. $(a^m)^n = a^{mn}$

6. $(ab)^n = a^n b^n$

The proviso that $a \neq 0$ must be inserted whenever zero or negative exponents are involved. Note that because zero and negative exponents are permitted, it is not necessary to give any conditions on m and n in the three forms of the quotient rule (8).

A special case involving a negative power should be mentioned. Consider $(a/b)^{-n}$. Since $(a/b)(b/a) = ab/ab = 1$, it follows that $(a/b)^{-1} = b/a$. Thus,

$$\left(\frac{a}{b}\right)^{-n} = \left[\left(\frac{a}{b}\right)^{-1}\right]^n = \left(\frac{b}{a}\right)^n$$

This result is easy to remember and should be used whenever a fraction is raised to a negative power. So rather than writing, for example,

$$\left(\frac{2}{3}\right)^{-2} = \frac{1}{(\frac{2}{3})^2} = \frac{1}{\frac{4}{9}} = \frac{9}{4}$$

we write immediately

$$\left(\frac{2}{3}\right)^{-2} = \left(\frac{3}{2}\right)^2 = \frac{9}{4}$$

The following examples illustrate how the laws of exponents can be used to simplify certain complex expressions. In all cases answers are written with positive exponents only.

EXAMPLE 10   Simplify:

a. $(3)^{-2}$ **b.** $\left(\dfrac{2}{3}\right)^0$ **c.** $\left(\dfrac{1}{2}\right)^{-3} \cdot 4^{-2}$ **d.** $\dfrac{2^4 \cdot 3^{-2}}{2^2 \cdot 3^{-5}}$

Solution   **a.** $\dfrac{1}{3^2} = \dfrac{1}{9}$ **b.** 1 **c.** $2^3 \cdot \dfrac{1}{4^2} = \dfrac{8}{16} = \dfrac{1}{2}$ **d.** $2^2 \cdot 3^3 = 4 \cdot 27 = 108$

EXAMPLE 11 Simplify: $\dfrac{2^0 \cdot a^2 \cdot b^{-3} \cdot c^7}{3^2 \cdot a^5 \cdot b \cdot c^{-2}}$

Solution

$$\frac{2^0 \cdot a^2 \cdot b^{-3} \cdot c^7}{3^2 \cdot a^5 \cdot b \cdot c^{-2}} = \frac{c^9}{9a^3b^4}$$

Note that the form of the quotient rule to be used is determined by which produces a final answer with positive exponents, since this is preferred to an answer with negative exponents. Thus, in solving the problem we wrote

$$\frac{a^2}{a^5} = \frac{1}{a^3} \qquad \frac{b^{-3}}{b} = \frac{1}{b^{1-(-3)}} = \frac{1}{b^4} \qquad \frac{c^7}{c^{-2}} = c^{7-(-2)} = c^9$$

EXAMPLE 12 Simplify: $\dfrac{x^{-2} \cdot y^{-3} \cdot z^4 \cdot x^5}{y^{-2} \cdot z^{-3} \cdot x^8}$

Solution

$$\frac{x^{-2} \cdot y^{-3} \cdot z^4 \cdot x^5}{y^{-2} \cdot z^{-3} \cdot x^8} = \frac{x^3 y^{-3} z^4}{y^{-2} z^{-3} x^8} = \frac{z^7}{x^5 y}$$

In dealing with very large or very small numbers it is often convenient to use what is called **scientific notation.** A number is expressed in scientific notation when it is written as a product of a number between 1 and 10, multiplied by a power of 10. For example,

$$2{,}500{,}000{,}000 = 2.5 \times 10^9$$

(It is customary to use "$\times$" as the multiplication symbol in scientific notation.) The exponent of 10, when it is positive, indicates how many places to the *right* the decimal should go. A negative exponent indicates how many places to the *left* the decimal should go:

$$0.00000000003 = 3 \times 10^{-11}$$

Scientific notation, combined with the laws of exponents, can often greatly simplify complicated arithmetic problems. The next example illustrates this.

EXAMPLE 13 Evaluate: $\dfrac{(72{,}000{,}000)(0.0000000036)}{(0.12)(27{,}000)}$

Solution

$$\frac{(72{,}000{,}000)(0.0000000036)}{(0.12)(27{,}000)} = \frac{(7.2 \times 10^7)(3.6 \times 10^{-9})}{(1.2 \times 10^{-1})(2.7 \times 10^4)}$$

$$= \frac{(7.2)(3.6)}{(1.2)(2.7)} \times \frac{10^{-2}}{10^3} = 8.0 \times 10^{-5}$$

$$= 0.000080$$

When numbers are expressed in scientific notation, they can be added or subtracted provided they involve the same power of 10. For example,

$$2.3 \times 10^{-5} + 5.8 \times 10^{-5} = 8.1 \times 10^{-5}$$

If they do not involve the same power of 10, then we can alter the form of one of them to make them agree. For example, consider

$$3 \times 10^2 + 5 \times 10^3$$

We can multiply and divide the first number by 10 to get

$$3 \times 10^2 = 3 \times 10^2 \times \tfrac{10}{10} = \tfrac{3}{10} \times 10^3 = 0.3 \times 10^3$$

Note that we can go immediately from the first step to the last by observing that dividing by 10 is equivalent to moving the decimal one place to the left. So we can now do the problem as follows:

$$3 \times 10^2 + 5 \times 10^3 = 0.3 \times 10^3 + 5 \times 10^3 = 5.3 \times 10^3$$

Many hand calculators have scientific notation capability which is automatically employed when the size of the number would otherwise exceed the capacity of the calculator. For example, if you enter the number 23,200 and then multiply by 4,500,000, the answer shown would be

$$1.044 \qquad 11$$

which is to be interpreted as 1.044×10^{11}. Numbers can also be entered in scientific notation on such calculators.

Remarks on Accuracy in Computations. When calculations are made with numbers that are approximations to true values, it is important to realize that **the answer can be no more accurate than the least accurate of the numbers involved.** It is necessary, therefore, in many instances to **round off the answer** to make it conform to this restriction. A number is rounded up or down according to whether the amount dropped is greater than or less than one-half unit in the last place retained. When it is exactly one-half, we will follow the convention of rounding so that the last digit retained is even. Here are some examples, then, of numbers rounded to two decimal places:

Number	Rounded number	
32.576	32.58	
5.2349	5.23	
163.045	163.04	**We rounded to the**
77.875	77.88	*even* **number**
2.045001	2.05	

In addition and subtraction it is the number of decimal places that is important, whereas in multiplication and division it is the number of **significant digits** that controls the accuracy. All digits other than 0 are always significant. The digit 0 is significant except when it is used solely to place the decimal, as in 0.0021. To avoid ambiguity about the significance of the zeros in whole numbers ending in 0, we can use scientific notation. For example, if by 1,200 we mean only two significant digits (accuracy to the nearest hundred), we can write 1.2×10^3. On the other hand, if we mean three, or four, digits to be significant, we can write 1.20×10^3, or 1.200×10^3, respectively. Here are some more examples:

Number	Number of significant digits
237	3
1.02	3
0.045	2
0.0450	3
2,001	4
1.234×10^{12}	4
3.00×10^{-5}	3

Before stating the rules for computation, we introduce the concept of the comparative **precision** of two numbers. A number A is more precise than a number B if the last significant digit of A occurs in a position to the right of the last significant digit of B. For example, 0.0032 is more precise than 2.753 (even though the latter has more significant digits).

Rule for Addition and Subtraction of Approximate Data.   Carry out the computations with the data given and round the answer back so that its precision is that of the least precise of the data. The more precise data may first be rounded to *one place greater* precision than will be retained in the final answer, but they should not be rounded all the way back to that of the least precise data until the calculations have been performed. (An exception is when only two numbers are being added or subtracted.)

Rule for Multiplication and Division of Approximate Data.   Carry out the computations with the given data and round off the answer so that it has the same number of significant digits as the number in the data with the least number of significant digits. Again, it is permissible to round the more accurate data initially to *one more* significant digit than will be retained ultimately.

In computations involving powers and roots, the rule for multiplication and division should be used.

The subject of errors in computed results is a deep one, requiring far more analysis than we can go into here, but the rules stated provide reasonable results. It should be noted, however, that even when these rules are followed, there can be some doubt about the reliability of the answer, especially in the last digit. It is especially important to be aware of the limitations on accuracy when using a hand calculator, since it is easy to have delusions of accuracy. For example, to find the area of a circle with radius that has been measured to be 4.53 cm, on a calculator (using $A = \pi r^2$) we could get $A = 64.46830869 \text{ cm}^2$, which is an absurd answer. Our best approximation to the answer would be 64.5 cm^2.

EXERCISE SET 6

A   In Problems 1–13 simplify each of the expressions and give answers with positive exponents only. (All letters represent real numbers that are understood to be nonzero whenever they occur in a denominator or to a negative or zero power.)

1. a. 3^4 **b.** 4^{-1} **c.** $(-2)^3$
   d. $(15)^0$ **e.** $(\frac{1}{2})^{-2}$

2. a. $2^7 \cdot 2^3$ **b.** $\dfrac{3^8}{3^5}$ **c.** $\dfrac{5^4}{5^6}$

   d. $\dfrac{3^2}{3^{-4}}$ **e.** $\dfrac{4^{-2}}{4^{-3}}$

3. a. 2^{-4} **b.** $(\frac{3}{2})^{-1}$ **c.** $5^0 \cdot (-3)^3$

   d. $\dfrac{3^3 \cdot 5^{-2}}{3^{-2} \cdot 5^{-1}}$ **e.** $(\frac{3}{4})^{-2} \cdot 2^{-3}$

4. a. $2^0 \cdot 3^{-1}$ **b.** $3^{-2}(-2)^3$ **c.** $(\frac{3}{2})^{-1}(\frac{2}{3})^2$

   d. $\dfrac{2^{-3} \cdot 3^2 \cdot 5^{-1}}{2^2 \cdot 3^{-4} \cdot 5^{-2}}$ **e.** $\dfrac{4^3 \cdot 3^{-4} \cdot 7^2}{2^4 \cdot 3^{-2} \cdot 7^3}$

5. a. $x^5 \cdot x^2$ **b.** $\dfrac{x^7}{x^3}$ **c.** $(x^3)^4$

   d. $(x^2 y^3)^2$ **e.** $(2x^3)^0$

6. a. $(2x^2)^3$ **b.** $(2x^4)(3x^5)$ **c.** $(5^0 x^{-2})(x^4)$

   d. $\left(\dfrac{2}{3x}\right)^{-3}$ **e.** $\dfrac{x^{-2}}{x^5}$

7. a. $(-3a^2)^3$ **b.** $(4a^{-3})(2a^{-2})$ **c.** $(2^3 a^{-2})(2^{-5} a^6)$

   d. $\left(\dfrac{3a^{-1}}{2b^2}\right)^{-2}$ **e.** $\dfrac{12a^3}{16a^{-2}}$

8. a. $\dfrac{a^2 b^{-4}}{a^{-3} b}$ **b.** $\dfrac{a^{-2} b^4 c^0}{a^{-5} b^{-2} c^3}$ **c.** $\dfrac{6s^{-2} t^{-3}}{9s^4 t^{-7}}$

9. a. $\dfrac{x^{-3} y^2}{x^2 y^{-4}}$ **b.** $\dfrac{r^{-1} s^{-2} t^3}{r^{-3} s t^0}$ **c.** $\dfrac{8a^{-5} b^2}{12a^{-2} b^{-4}}$

10. a. $\dfrac{4a^3 b^{-4}}{6a^{-5} b^{-7}}$ **b.** $\dfrac{(-3)^2 x^{-3} y^{-1}}{6x^2 y^{-3}}$ **c.** $\dfrac{2^{-3} a^2 b^{-4}}{2^{-1} a^{-5} b^{-3}}$

11. a. $\dfrac{3^{-2} x^4 y^{-2} z^3}{3x^0 y^{-5} z^4}$ **b.** $\dfrac{2^2 x^{-2} y^{-1}}{-8x^{-3} y^2 z^{-4}}$

12. a. $\dfrac{2^3 a^2 b^{-3} c^0}{2^{-5} a^4 b^{-7}}$ **b.** $\dfrac{(-2)^3 a^{-1} b^2 c^{-3}}{4^2 a^{-2} b^{-3} c^4}$

13. a. $\left(\dfrac{a}{b^2}\right)^{-3} \cdot \left(\dfrac{c^3}{d^{-2}}\right)^{-2}$ **b.** $\dfrac{\left(\dfrac{x^2}{y^3}\right)^4}{\left(\dfrac{x}{y^2}\right)^{-2}}$

14. Substitute $x = 3$, $y = 2$ in the following expression and simplify the result:
$$\frac{2x^{-1} - 3y^{-1}}{x^{-2} - y^{-2}}$$

15. Substitute $a = 2$, $b = 3$ in the following expression and simplify the result:
$$\frac{a^2b^{-1} - a^{-2}b}{2a^{-1} - 3b^{-2}}$$

16. Substitute $x = \frac{1}{2}$, $y = \frac{3}{4}$ in the following expression and simplify the result:
$$\frac{x^{-1}y - 2x^{-2}y^{-1}}{3xy^{-2} - (2y)^{-1}}$$

17. Express in scientific notation:
   a. 2,000,000,000,000   b. 0.000007   c. 3,100,000
   d. 0.13   e. 254,000,000

In Problems 18–20 perform the indicated calculations using scientific notation.

18. a. $(3.2 \times 10^4)(2 \times 10^{-2})$ b. $\dfrac{5.6 \times 10^7}{7 \times 10^2}$

19. a. $6.2 \times 10^4 + 3.8 \times 10^3$ b. $5 \times 10^2 - 3 \times 10^3$
20. a. $8 \times 10^6 + 4 \times 10^4$ b. $2.7 \times 10^{-3} - 5.2 \times 10^{-2}$

21. Use scientific notation to calculate
$$\frac{(0.0015)(25,000,000)}{(300,000,000)(0.00005)}$$

22. The nearest star is approximately 4 light-years away. Light travels at approximately 186,000 miles per second. Taking 365 as the number of days in a year, find the distance in miles to the nearest star. Use scientific notation.

23. a. The mass of a hydrogen atom is approximately 0.00000000000000000000000001673 gram. Express this number in scientific notation.
   b. There are approximately 6.023×10^{23} atoms in a mole (a unit of measure used in chemistry). Express this number as an integer.

B   In Problems 24 and 25 m and n are integers.

24. Prove that the formula $a^m \cdot a^n = a^{m+n}$ holds true:
   a. When m is positive and n is negative
   b. When both m and n are negative
   c. When $n = 0$
   Hint. For part a let $n = -p$, where p is positive.

25. Prove that $(a^m)^n = a^{mn}$ under the following conditions:
   a. m is positive and n is negative
   b. m is negative and n is positive
   c. m and n are both negative
   d. $n = 0$

26. Use scientific notation to calculate
$$\frac{(120,000)^2\sqrt{0.0000000009}}{50,000,000}$$

27. Calculate the following using scientific notation and a hand calculator:
$$\frac{(129,000,000)^2\sqrt{0.0005873}}{(0.0002597)^2\sqrt[3]{32,460}}$$

7 Radicals and Fractional Exponents

For $a \geq 0$, the symbol $\sqrt{a}$ means the nonnegative real number whose square is a. This is called the principal square root of a. It is also true that $-\sqrt{a}$ is a square root of a. It is a common mistake to suppose that $\sqrt{a}$ means both the principal square root and its negative, but this would lead to ambiguity and confusion. Thus, $\sqrt{4} = 2$, whereas $\sqrt{4} \neq -2$. The symbol $\sqrt{}$ is called a **radical sign.**

The fact that square roots of all nonnegative numbers exist can be proved using the basic properties of R, but the proof is beyond the level of this course. If $a < 0$, then $\sqrt{a}$ does not exist in R (however, it does exist in the complex number system, which we will discuss briefly in Chapter 3).

In a similar way, $\sqrt[n]{a}$, where n is any natural number greater than 1 and $a \geq 0$, is defined to mean the (unique) nonnegative real number whose nth power is a. If $a < 0$ and n is an odd natural number greater than 1, then $\sqrt[n]{a}$ is the negative real number whose nth power is a. For example, $\sqrt[3]{-8}, = -2$, since $(-2)^3 = (-2)(-2)(-2) = -8$. If n is even and $a < 0$, then $\sqrt[n]{a}$ does not exist in R. The number designated by $\sqrt[n]{a}$ is called the **principal nth root of a.**

From the laws of exponents in Section 6 we see that if $a \geq 0$ and $b \geq 0$, then

$$(\sqrt[n]{a}\,\sqrt[n]{b})^n = (\sqrt[n]{a})^n(\sqrt[n]{b})^n = ab$$

It follows that

$$\sqrt[n]{ab} = \sqrt[n]{a}\,\sqrt[n]{b} \tag{11}$$

This can be extended to arbitrary finite products.

By using equation (11) we can often simplify expressions involving radicals. The object is to write the quantity under the radical (called the **radicand**) as a product of the largest possible perfect nth power, times whatever is left. The nth root of the perfect nth power can be written without the radical sign. This is what we will mean by the instruction "simplify" in connection with problems involving radicals.

EXAMPLE 14 Simplify:

a. $\sqrt{50}$ b. $\sqrt{45}$ c. $\sqrt{32} - \sqrt{18}$ d. $\sqrt[3]{81} + \sqrt[3]{24} + \sqrt[3]{192}$

Solution a. $\sqrt{50} = \sqrt{25 \cdot 2} = \sqrt{25}\,\sqrt{2} = 5\sqrt{2}$

b. $\sqrt{45} = \sqrt{9 \cdot 5} = \sqrt{9}\,\sqrt{5} = 3\sqrt{5}$

c. $\sqrt{32} - \sqrt{18} = \sqrt{16 \cdot 2} - \sqrt{9 \cdot 2} = 4\sqrt{2} - 3\sqrt{2} = \sqrt{2}$

d. $\sqrt[3]{81} + \sqrt[3]{24} + \sqrt[3]{192} = \sqrt[3]{27 \cdot 3} + \sqrt[3]{8 \cdot 3} + \sqrt[3]{64 \cdot 3}$

$$= 3\sqrt[3]{3} + 2\sqrt[3]{3} + 4\sqrt[3]{3}$$
$$= 9\sqrt[3]{3}$$

EXAMPLE 15 Simplify the following, where $x \geq 0$ and $y \geq 0$:

a. $\sqrt{112x^3y^6}$ b. $\sqrt{6xy^3}\,\sqrt{2xy}$

Solution a. $\sqrt{112x^3y^6} = \sqrt{16 \cdot 7x^2 \cdot x(y^3)^2} = 4xy^3\sqrt{7x}$

b. $\sqrt{6xy^3}\,\sqrt{2xy} = \sqrt{12x^2y^4} = \sqrt{3 \cdot 4x^2y^4} = 2xy^2\sqrt{3}$

If $b \neq 0$ and $\sqrt[n]{a}$ and $\sqrt[n]{b}$ exist, then the following formula for division, analogous to rule (11), holds true:

$$\sqrt[n]{\frac{a}{b}} = \frac{\sqrt[n]{a}}{\sqrt[n]{b}} \qquad (12)$$

You will be asked to prove this in Problem 28, Exercise Set 7. We can use this to remove the radical sign from the denominator, as we show in the next example. This process is called **rationalizing the denominator.**

EXAMPLE 16   Rationalize the denominators in each of the following:

a. $\sqrt{\dfrac{1}{2}}$ **b.** $\sqrt{\dfrac{5}{18}}$ **c.** $\dfrac{3}{\sqrt{5}}$ **d.** $\sqrt[3]{\dfrac{2}{9}}$ **e.** $\sqrt[4]{\dfrac{x^5}{y}}\ (x \geq 0, y > 0)$

Solution   We can make each denominator a perfect power by multiplying the numerator and denominator by an appropriate number. Then rule (12) can be applied.

a. $\sqrt{\dfrac{1}{2}} = \sqrt{\dfrac{1}{2} \cdot \dfrac{2}{2}} = \sqrt{\dfrac{2}{4}} = \dfrac{\sqrt{2}}{\sqrt{4}} = \dfrac{\sqrt{2}}{2}$

b. $\sqrt{\dfrac{5}{18}} = \sqrt{\dfrac{5}{18} \cdot \dfrac{2}{2}} = \sqrt{\dfrac{10}{36}} = \dfrac{\sqrt{10}}{\sqrt{36}} = \dfrac{\sqrt{10}}{6}$

c. $\dfrac{3}{\sqrt{5}} = \dfrac{3}{\sqrt{5}} \cdot \dfrac{\sqrt{5}}{\sqrt{5}} = \dfrac{3\sqrt{5}}{5}$

d. $\sqrt[3]{\dfrac{2}{9}} = \sqrt[3]{\dfrac{2}{9} \cdot \dfrac{3}{3}} = \sqrt[3]{\dfrac{6}{27}} = \dfrac{\sqrt[3]{6}}{\sqrt[3]{27}} = \dfrac{\sqrt[3]{6}}{3}$

e. $\sqrt[4]{\dfrac{x^5}{y}} = \sqrt[4]{\dfrac{x^5}{y} \cdot \dfrac{y^3}{y^3}} = \sqrt[4]{\dfrac{xx^4 y^3}{y^4}} = \dfrac{x}{y}\sqrt[4]{xy^3}$

We are now in a position to give a reasonable definition of fractional exponents. First consider $a^{1/n}$, where n is a natural number. In order to be consistent with the laws of exponents in Section 5, we must have

$$(a^{1/n})^n = a^{(1/n)n} = a^1 = a$$

So, we are led to the definition

$$a^{1/n} = \sqrt[n]{a}$$

The restriction that $a \geq 0$ when n is even must be observed. Also, for any integer m,

$$a^{m/n} = a^{(1/n)m} = (a^{1/n})^m = (\sqrt[n]{a})^m \qquad (13)$$

Alternately, we can write

$$a^{m/n} = a^{m(1/n)} = (a^m)^{1/n} = \sqrt[n]{a^m} \qquad (14)$$

Again, if n is even, we must have $a \geq 0$. In words, the fractional (rational) exponent m/n means: "Take the nth root and raise to the mth power, in either order." Taking the root first, as in (13), is more desirable than raising to the power first, as in (14), whenever a is a perfect nth power. For example, using (13), we have

$$(27)^{4/3} = (\sqrt[3]{27})^4 = 3^4 = 81$$

whereas using (14),

$$(27)^{4/3} = \sqrt[3]{(27)^4} = \sqrt[3]{531,441}$$

This again yields the answer 81, but it is obviously much more difficult to calculate.

All the laws of exponents in Section 6 continue to hold true for rational exponents, but the details of showing this are tedious and will be omitted here.

EXAMPLE 17   Give an equivalent expression that does not involve radicals, and simplify.

a. $\sqrt[4]{4x^6y^3}$ $(x, y \geq 0)$ **b.** $\sqrt[6]{(8a^4b^3)^2}$ $(a, b \geq 0)$

Solution   **a.** $\sqrt[4]{4x^6y^3} = (2^2x^6y^3)^{1/4} = 2^{2/4}x^{6/4}y^{3/4} = 2^{1/2}x^{3/2}y^{3/4}$

b. $\sqrt[6]{(8a^4b^3)^2} = (2^3a^4b^3)^{2/6} = (2^3a^4b^3)^{1/3} = 2a^{4/3}b$

EXERCISE SET 7

In the problems that follow we will understand that all letters represent nonnegative numbers when even roots are involved and are not equal to zero when in the denominator or raised to a nonpositive power.

A In Problems 1–16 simplify each expression.

1. a. $\sqrt{125}$ **b.** $\sqrt[3]{40}$

2. a. $\sqrt{147}$ **b.** $\sqrt[3]{-250}$

3. a. $\sqrt{45} + \sqrt{80}$ **b.** $2\sqrt{50} - 3\sqrt{162}$

4. a. $\sqrt[3]{-108} + 3\sqrt[3]{32}$ **b.** $4\sqrt{75} - 3\sqrt{48} - \sqrt{108}$

5. $\sqrt{50x^4y^7}$ **6.** $\sqrt{75a^3b^{-4}}$

7. $\sqrt{18x^3y^0z^5}$ **8.** $\sqrt{72a^5b^4c^{-2}}$

9. $\sqrt{\dfrac{300a^3b^{-1}c^6}{ab^5c^2}}$ **10.** $\sqrt{\dfrac{128x^{-3}y^9z^{-7}}{x^5y^{-3}z^{-13}}}$

11. $\sqrt[3]{\dfrac{500a^{-7}b^{12}c^5}{4a^2b^0c^{-10}}}$ **12.** $\sqrt[3]{-54x^6y^7z^5}$

13. $\sqrt{3xy^3}\sqrt{6x^5y}$ **14.** $\sqrt[3]{4a^2b^4}\sqrt[3]{144ab}$

15. $\sqrt[3]{-81a^5b^6c^0}$ **16.** $\sqrt{15s^{-3}t}\sqrt{30s^6t^5}$

In Problems 17–20 rationalize the denominator and simplify.

17. a. $\sqrt{\dfrac{2}{3}}$ **b.** $\sqrt{\dfrac{8}{5}}$ **c.** $\dfrac{2}{\sqrt{7}}$ **d.** $\sqrt[3]{\dfrac{1}{4}}$ **e.** $\sqrt{\dfrac{27}{50}}$

18. a. $\sqrt{\dfrac{2}{7}}$ **b.** $\sqrt{\dfrac{3}{8}}$ **c.** $\sqrt{\dfrac{5}{28}}$ **d.** $\dfrac{1}{\sqrt{50}}$ **e.** $\sqrt[3]{\dfrac{7}{18}}$

19. a. $\sqrt{\dfrac{a^3}{b}}$ b. $\sqrt{\dfrac{a}{3b^3}}$

20. a. $\sqrt{\dfrac{x}{2y^2z}}$ b. $\sqrt[3]{\dfrac{3a}{4b^2c}}$

21. $\sqrt{\dfrac{32x^{-5}y^3}{3xy^{-7}}}$

22. $\sqrt{\dfrac{5x^{-3}yz^3}{18x^{-2}y^{-3}z^{-1}}}$

In Problems 23–37 simplify the expressions. Write answers without using negative exponents.

23. a. $(2)^{1/3} \cdot (2)^{3/4}$ b. $(3)^{-1/2} \cdot (3)^{2/3}$ c. $(8)^{-2/3} \cdot (\tfrac{9}{16})^{-1/2}$
     d. $(32)^{-2/5} \cdot (8)^{2/3}$

24. a. $(-8)^{5/3}(4)^{-3/2}$ b. $(16)^{-1/2}(4^0)$ c. $(-3)^{-2}(\tfrac{4}{9})^{-1/2}$
     d. $[3^2 \cdot (2^0) + (\tfrac{1}{32})^{-4/5}]^{-1/2}$

25. a. $(2x^{1/3})(3x^{1/2})$ b. $\dfrac{x^{3/4}y^{1/2}}{x^{2/3}y^{1/3}}$ c. $(8x)^{1/3}(4x)^{1/2}$

26. a. $(x^{2/3})^{3/4}$ b. $(x^{-3/2})^{-4/3}$ c. $(4x^{4/3}y^{8/9})^{3/2}$
27. a. $(a^{3/2})^{4/3}$ b. $(4a^{-2/3})^{3/2}$ c. $(-8a^{3/2}b^{-6})^{2/3}$
28. a. $(4x^{-2})^{3/2}$ b. $(-27x^{-3}y^{3/4})^{2/3}$ c. $(16a^{-4/3}b^{8/3})^{-3/4}$
29. a. $(8x^6)^{1/3}$ b. $(16a^4b^{-2})^{1/2}$ c. $(-125x^{-9}y^{12})^{1/3}$
30. a. $(27a^3b^6)^{2/3}$ b. $(16x^4y^6)^{3/2}$ c. $(-8a^{-3}b^6)^{5/3}$
31. a. $(64a^6b^9)^{4/3}$ b. $(-8a^3b^{-6})^{7/3}$ c. $(36a^2b^4c^0)^{3/2}$
32. a. $(8x^{3/4}y^{-9/2})^{-2/3}$ b. $(16a^{4/3}b^{-2/3}c^{4/9})^{-3/2}$
33. a. $(32x^{-5/4}y^{10/3})^{-2/5}$ b. $(27a^{3/4}b^{-3/2}c^{-9/8})^{-4/3}$

34. a. $\left(\dfrac{81x^{-2}y^6}{16x^6y^{-10}}\right)^{3/4}$ b. $\left(\dfrac{49x^2y^{-6}}{25x^{-4}y^{-2}}\right)^{3/2}$

35. a. $\left(\dfrac{8a^{-2}b^{-5}c^0}{27a^{-5}b}\right)^{-2/3}$ b. $\left(\dfrac{-32a^3b^{-2}}{243a^{-7}b^3}\right)^{3/5}$

36. a. $\left(\dfrac{9x^{4/3}}{4y^{-2/3}}\right)^{3\,2}$ b. $\left(\dfrac{-27a^{9/2}b^{-3/4}}{8c^6}\right)^{-4/3}$

37. a. $\left(\dfrac{16a^{5/3}b^{-5/6}}{81a^{-1}b^{1/2}}\right)^{-3/4}$ h. $\left(\dfrac{32x^{3/4}y}{-243x^{-3}y^{7/2}}\right)^{-2/5}$

In Problems 38–39 give an equivalent expression that does not involve radicals.

38. a. $\sqrt[3]{8a^4b^2}$ b. $(\sqrt{2a^3b^5})^3$ c. $\sqrt[3]{(5x^2y^4)^4}$
39. a. $\sqrt{4x^5y^3}$ b. $\sqrt{(2a^4b)^3}$ c. $(\sqrt[3]{4x^5y^2})^2$

B 40. Prove rule (12).
41. Prove that for any natural number k, $\sqrt[kn]{a^{km}} = \sqrt[n]{a^m}$, where $a \ge 0$, and m and n are natural numbers greater than or equal to 2.
42. Use the result of Problem 41 to simplify each of the following:
     a. $\sqrt[4]{4}$ b. $\sqrt[6]{8x^9}$ c. $\sqrt[8]{9x^6y^{12}}$ d. $\sqrt[4]{64a^{10}b^8c^2}$
43. Prove that $\sqrt[m]{\sqrt[n]{a}} = \sqrt[mn]{a}$, where $a \ge 0$ and m and n are natural numbers greater than or equal to 2.
     Hint. Use fractional exponents.

44. Using the results of Problems 41 and 43, write each of the following with only one radical sign, and simplify the result:
    a. $\sqrt{\sqrt{32}}$ **b.** $\sqrt[3]{\sqrt{64x^9}}$ **c.** $\sqrt{8\sqrt[3]{16a^4b^6}}$ **d.** $\sqrt[3]{27\sqrt{8x^6y^{10}}}$

45. Prove that

$$\left(\frac{a}{b}\right)^{-m/n} = \left(\frac{b}{a}\right)^{m/n}$$

46. Using the result of Problem 45, simplify the following:
    a. $\left(\dfrac{27a^9b^6}{343c^{12}}\right)^{-2/3}$ **b.** $\left(\dfrac{256x^{12}}{81y^8z^4}\right)^{-3/4}$

Simplify each of the expressions in Problems 47–51. Express answers without negative exponents and without radical signs in the denominator or fractions under radical signs.

47. $\dfrac{2\sqrt{72}}{3} - \dfrac{3\sqrt{128}}{4} + 5\sqrt{\dfrac{1}{2}}$

48. $\dfrac{1}{2}\sqrt{\dfrac{4}{3}} - \dfrac{3}{4}\sqrt{\dfrac{1}{12}} + \dfrac{\sqrt{75}}{2}$

49. $\sqrt[3]{32} - \sqrt[3]{\dfrac{27}{2}} + \dfrac{1}{3}\sqrt[3]{256}$

50. $\sqrt{\dfrac{125x^4y^{-2}z^5}{72x^{-2}y^{-7}z}}$

51. $\sqrt[3]{\dfrac{729a^0b^7c^{-4}}{128a^{-6}b^{-2}c}}$

52. Express in scientific notation and simplify:

$$\frac{(0.003)^2\sqrt{0.005}\sqrt{5,000}}{\sqrt[3]{0.000000000027}}$$

Review Exercise Set

A   **1.** Express as a repeating or terminating decimal.
    a. $\frac{11}{16}$ **b.** $\frac{25}{8}$ **c.** $\frac{3}{7}$ **d.** $\frac{5}{27}$ **e.** $-\frac{13}{6}$

  2. Express in the form m/n, where m and n are integers.
    a. $0.111\ldots$ **b.** $0.242424\ldots$ **c.** $1.0363636\ldots$ **d.** $0.216216216\ldots$

  3. Identify which numbers are rational and which are irrational.
    a. $-\sqrt[3]{27}$ **b.** $\dfrac{5}{\sqrt{121}}$ **c.** $\dfrac{1}{\sqrt{2}}$ **d.** $\sqrt[3]{-125}$ **e.** $(\sqrt{3})^6$

    f. $\sqrt{3} + 2$ **g.** $\dfrac{0}{\sqrt{7}}$ **h.** $\left(\dfrac{2}{3}\right)^{-1}$ **i.** π^2 **j.** $\sqrt{32}$

  4. Evaluate each of the following:
    a. $(-3)(-4)(-2)$ **b.** $(-2) - (-6)$
    c. $-3 + (-2)[(-4) - (-7)]$ **d.** $[5 + (-2)](-6)$

  5. Evaluate:
    a. $|-3 - (-6)|$ **b.** $|4 + (-9)|$ **c.** $|-10 + (-2)|$
    d. $|(-2)(-7) + 3(-4)|$ **e.** $|-(-6)(-8) - (5)(-7)|$

  6. Write an equivalent expression without using absolute value signs.
    a. $|x| < 7$ **b.** $|x| \le 4$ **c.** $|x| > 8$ **d.** $|x| \ge 3$

  7. Show each of the following sets on a number line:
    a. $\{x:\ x > -1\}$ **b.** $\{x:\ 0 < x \le 2\}$ **c.** $\{x:\ |x| < 3\}$
    d. $\{x:\ |x| \ge 2\}$ **e.** $\{x:\ x < -2\} \cup \{x:\ x \ge 1\}$

In Problems 8–13 perform the indicated operations. Reduce final answers to lowest terms.

8. **a.** $\frac{3}{7} + \frac{5}{9}$ **b.** $\frac{2}{3} - \frac{3}{4} + \frac{5}{6}$

9. **a.** $\frac{8}{9} + \frac{-5}{6}$ **b.** $\frac{5}{24} - \frac{11}{-18}$

10. **a.** $\frac{11}{180} - \frac{5}{168}$ **b.** $\frac{1}{792} + \frac{1}{1134}$

11. **a.** $\frac{5}{96} - \frac{7}{160} + \frac{3}{112}$ **b.** $(-\frac{15}{16})(-\frac{7}{10} + \frac{3}{2})$

12. **a.** $\dfrac{\frac{2}{3} - \frac{1}{2}}{\frac{5}{6} + \frac{3}{2}}$ **b.** $\dfrac{1 - \frac{3}{4}}{\frac{1}{3} - \frac{1}{2}}$

13. **a.** $\dfrac{-2 + \frac{3}{8}}{\frac{3}{4} - \frac{5}{6}}$ **b.** $\dfrac{\frac{2}{3} - \frac{1}{4}}{1 + (\frac{2}{3})(\frac{1}{4})}$

14. Write in scientific notation:
     a. 132,000,000   **b.** 0.00023   **c.** 207,000   **d.** 0.00000035

15. Evaluate using scientific notation:
     a. $3.7 \times 10^5 + 2.4 \times 10^4$ **b.** $1.5 \times 10^{-7} - 3.6 \times 10^{-5}$

     c. $\dfrac{(260,000)(0.0003)}{(0.013)(12,000,000)}$

In Problems 16–20 simplify the expressions, writing answers without using negative exponents.

16. **a.** $(3x^4y^2)(4x^3y^5)$ **b.** $(5x^3y^{-2}z^0)(2x^{-1}y^5)$

17. **a.** $\dfrac{3^2x^4y^{-8}z^0}{3^{-4}x^6y^{-5}z^{-2}}$ **b.** $\dfrac{2^{-3}a^{-2}b^5}{2^{-5}a^{-4}b^3}$

18. **a.** $\dfrac{24x^5y^{-2}z^{-4}}{64x^{-3}y^{-8}z^2}$ **b.** $\dfrac{42a^{-3}b^4c^0}{24a^{-5}b^{-2}}$

19. **a.** $(3x^{-2}y^3z)^3$ **b.** $\left(\dfrac{x^2y^{-1}}{2x^{-3}y^2}\right)^2$

20. **a.** $(81x^{-12}y^4z^{-8})^{3/4}$ **b.** $\left(\dfrac{-8a^2b^{-5}}{27a^{-1}b}\right)^{-2/3}$

Simplify the expressions in Problems 21–23.

21. **a.** $\sqrt{50x^3y^4z^0}$ **b.** $\sqrt[3]{-32a^6b^{-3}}$

22. **a.** $\sqrt{6xy^3}\sqrt{12x^3y^5}$ **b.** $\sqrt{\dfrac{98x^{-3}y^5}{125x^{-1}y^{-3}}}$

23. **a.** $\sqrt{\dfrac{2}{3}}$ **b.** $\dfrac{2}{\sqrt{5}}$ **c.** $\sqrt[3]{\dfrac{16}{9}}$ **d.** $\sqrt{\dfrac{3x}{8y}}$

B   **24.** By using the meaning of the additive inverse of a number, together with its uniqueness, show that $-(-a) = a$.

25. Prove that if a, b, and c are real numbers, with $a > b$, then $a - c > b - c$.

26. Sometimes the definition for $a < b$ is given as follows: "$a < b$ means there is a positive real number c such that $b = a + c$." Show that this is equivalent to Definition 3.

27. Show that if $a \cdot b = 0$, then either $a = 0$ or $b = 0$.
     Hint. Suppose $a \neq 0$, so that a^{-1} exists. Multiply both sides by a^{-1}.

28. Simplify:

    a. $\sqrt{18} - \dfrac{2\sqrt{200}}{3} + \sqrt{\dfrac{81}{2}}$ **b.** $\sqrt{\dfrac{2}{3}} - \dfrac{\sqrt{24}}{5} + \sqrt{\dfrac{27}{2}}$

Simplify the expressions in Problems 29 and 30.

29.

$$\dfrac{\dfrac{5}{6}\left(2 + \dfrac{\frac{4}{3} + \frac{3}{4}}{\frac{5}{6}}\right) - \dfrac{25}{12}\left(2 \cdot \dfrac{\frac{25}{12}}{\frac{3}{2} - \frac{2}{3}} - 1\right)}{\left(\dfrac{3}{2} - \dfrac{2}{3}\right)^2}$$

30.   **a.** $(9x^{-2/3}y^{4/9}z^{-1/3})^{-3/2}$ **b.** $\sqrt{\dfrac{576x^{-5}y^{-2}z^3}{343x^3y^{-7}z^0}}$

In Problems 31–32 evaluate using scientific notation.

31. $\dfrac{(320{,}000)(0.000025)^{1/2}}{(0.00008)(5{,}000{,}000)}$ **32.** $\dfrac{\sqrt[5]{243{,}000{,}000{,}000{,}000{,}000}}{\sqrt[3]{0.0002}\,\sqrt[3]{40{,}000}}$

33. Use a hand calculator to evaluate:

$$\dfrac{(2{,}637{,}000)^3\sqrt{0.0000000003514}}{(734{,}000{,}000)^{3/2}}$$

2 Basic Algebraic Concepts

In the applications of mathematics to virtually any field the simplification of algebraic expressions is needed time and again. One such simplification is illustrated in the following derivation from an economics textbook.* **You are not expected to understand the meanings of the terms employed but are just asked to observe the use of algebra.**

If the income elasticity of a commodity is greater than one, then a consumer will increase the *fraction* of his income on that good when money income increases (prices remaining unchanged). Suppose at income M the individual consumes x and suppose that his consumption changes by dx when M increases by dM. Before the income change the fraction of income spent on x is $p_x x/M$ and after income changes this fraction is $p_x(x + dx)/(M + dM)$. The ratio of these fractions is

$$\frac{\dfrac{p_x(x + dx)}{M + dM}}{\dfrac{p_x x}{M}} = \left(\frac{x + dx}{x}\right)\left(\frac{M}{M + dM}\right) = \frac{1 + \dfrac{dx}{x}}{1 + \dfrac{dM}{M}} = \frac{\dfrac{M}{dM} + \dfrac{dx}{dM}\dfrac{M}{x}}{\dfrac{M}{dM} + 1}$$

and this last expression is greater than 1 if

$$y_m = \frac{dx}{dM}\frac{M}{x}$$

is greater than 1.

This illustrates the rule for division of fractions as well as repeated use of the fundamental principle of fractions. In this chapter we will study the simplification of such complex fractions as this as well as other basic algebraic operations.

---

* C. E. Ferguson and J. P. Gould, *Microeconomic Theory, Fourth Edition* (Homewood, Ill.: Richard D. Irwin, 1975), pp. 43–44. © 1975 by Richard D. Irwin, Inc.

1 Introduction

One of the distinctive features of algebra is the use of letters to represent numbers. Among other things, this permits us to state general rules about numbers in a clear and concise way, as we saw in Chapter 1. Also, letters are used to represent unknown quantities in equations and inequalities, the object being to find the correct value or values that make the relation true. The point to be emphasized is that whenever letters are used in elementary algebra, they are used to represent numbers—usually real numbers. This fact enables us to use all the properties of real numbers given in Chapter 1 in algebra problems. In the discussion that follows, unless specifically stated otherwise, all letters used will be understood to represent real numbers. When a letter is used in this way, it is called a **variable. A variable is a letter that may be assigned any value from a given set of numbers.** Letters may also be used to designate fixed, but unspecified, numbers, and in this case they are called **constants.** Specific numbers also are called constants. Thus, in the expressions $2x + 3$ and $ax + b$, the specific numbers 2 and 3 are constants, and the letters a and b represent constants, even though they are unspecified. The letter x is a variable. Usually, the context will make clear whether a letter represents a constant or a variable. Frequently, letters from the latter part of the alphabet, such as x, y, or z, are used for variables, and letters such as a, b, c, from the first part are used for constants.

We use the term **algebraic expression** to mean any combination of variables and constants that is formed using a finite number of the operations of addition, subtraction, multiplication, division, raising to a power, or taking roots. Thus,

$$ax^3 \qquad \frac{x^{-1} - y^{-1}}{x^{-2} - y^{-2}} \qquad \frac{-10\sqrt{x-y}}{(u+v)^8}$$

are examples of algebraic expressions.

Of particular interest in this chapter will be algebraic expressions called **polynomials.** Examples of polynomials are

$$2x^3 - 3x^2 + 5x - 8 \qquad x^{10} - y^{10} \qquad 4x^2y^3z - 3xyz^3 + 5x^3yz^5$$

A **term** of a polynomial consists of a constant, called the **coefficient,** multiplied by one or more variables each raised to a nonnegative integral power. So a term of a polynomial in one variable has the form ax^m, and in two variables, ax^my^n, and so on. A polynomial consists of the sum of finitely many such terms. This includes differences since we may write, for example,

$$2x^3 - 3x^2 + 5x - 8 = 2x^3 + (-3)x^2 + 5x + (-8)$$

The **degree of a term** of a polynomial is the sum of the exponents on the variables in that term. For example, the degree of $2x^3$ is 3, whereas the degree of $4x^2y^3z$ is $2 + 3 + 1 = 6$ (remember that $z = z^1$). The **degree of a polynomial** is the largest of the degrees of its terms. A polynomial of degree n in one variable x can always be written in the form

$$a_nx^n + a_{n-1}x^{n-1} + \cdots + a_1x + a_0 \qquad (a_n \neq 0)$$

If $n = 0$ and $a_0 \neq 0$, the polynomial is a **constant polynomial** and has degree 0. The constant 0 has no degree. A polynomial having only one term is called a **monomial,** one with two terms is a **binomial,** and one with three terms is a **trinomial.**

2 The Arithmetic of Polynomials

In this section we show how to add, subtract, multiply, and divide polynomials.

ADDITION   Consider the sum
$$(2x^2 + 3x + 5) + (3x^2 - x + 7)$$

The addition is carried out term-by-term, where **like terms** are added, that is, terms involving the same variable (or variables) raised to the same power are added. Therefore, the sum is $5x^2 + 2x + 12$. This is justified by use of the commutative, associative, and distributive properties, as can be seen by the following calculations:

$$(2x^2 + 3x + 5) + (3x^2 - x + 7) = (2x^2 + 3x^2) + (3x - x) + (5 + 7)$$
$$= (2 + 3)x^2 + (3 - 1)x + (5 + 7)$$
$$= 5x^2 + 2x + 12$$

SUBTRACTION   Subtraction is also carried out term-by-term. For example,
$$(2x^2 + 3x + 5) - (3x^2 - x + 7) = -x^2 + 4x - 2$$

MULTIPLICATION   Multiplication of polynomials is carried out by repeated use of the distributive property of real numbers. Consider a product of the form
$$(a + b)(c + d)$$

We first treat $(a + b)$ as a single term and distribute the multiplication of it over the sum $(c + d)$:
$$(a + b)(c + d) = (a + b)c + (a + b)d$$

Now we can apply the right-hand distributive law to each of the products on the right to obtain
$$(a + b)(c + d) = ac + bc + ad + bd$$

Observe that **the result is the sum of all possible products involving one term from the first factor and one term from the second.** This result holds true in general. For example,
$$(a + b)(c + d + e) = ac + ad + ae + bc + bd + be$$

and similarly for any number of terms in either of the factors.

If we apply this result to two binomials in x, say, $(2x + 3)(4x + 5)$, we have
$$(2x + 3)(4x + 5) = 8x^2 + 12x + 10x + 15 = 8x^2 + 22x + 15$$

In this case the combining of like terms is possible, and this situation is typical. This combining of terms can be anticipated when multiplying two *like* binomials, for example, both binomials in x or in x and y. The result is generalized by the following:

$$(ax + b)(cx + d) = acx^2 + (ad + bc)x + bd \qquad (1)$$

This should not be memorized as a formula, but the process of arriving at the answer is important. The diagram below illustrates how each term on the right is obtained.

First term: $(ax + b)(cx + d)$

First times First $= acx^2$

First times Last $= adx$

Middle term: $(ax + b)(cx + d)$ Combine: $adx + bcx = (ad + bc)x$

Last times First $= bcx$

Last term: $(ax + b)(cx + d)$

Last times Last $= bd$

All this can be done mentally in some problems. For example,

$$(2x + 3)(4x + 5) = 8x^2 + 22x + 15$$

Here are some other examples:

$$(3x + 2)(5x - 4) = 15x^2 - 2x - 8$$

(Notice that the middle term is the sum of $-12x$ and $10x$.)

$$(2 + 3t)(4 + t) = 8 + 14t + 3t^2$$
$$(x - 2y)(x + 3y) = x^2 + xy - 6y^2$$

Two special cases of products that should be memorized are:

DIFF PERF^2 $(a + b)(a - b) = a^2 - b^2$ \qquad (2)

and

SUM PERF^2 $(a + b)^2 = a^2 + 2ab + b^2$ \qquad (3)

The first of these is immediately seen to be true, since the middle term drops out $(-ab + ba = 0)$. The second, called a **perfect square,** is verified by writing

$$(a + b)^2 = (a + b)(a + b) = a^2 + (ab + ba) + b^2 = a^2 + 2ab + b^2$$

Similarly, we have

$$(a - b)^2 = a^2 - 2ab + b^2 \qquad (4)$$

It is useful to express these formulas in words. We can express equation (2) by saying: "The sum of two numbers times their difference is the difference of their squares." For the perfect square we can say: "The square of the sum (difference) of two numbers is the square of the first, plus (minus) twice the product of the two, plus the square of the last."

These results are illustrated by the following examples:

Product of sum and difference of two terms:

$$(x + 2)(x - 2) = x^2 - 4$$
$$(2x - 3)(2x + 3) = 4x^2 - 9$$
$$(4s + 5t)(4s - 5t) = 16s^2 - 25t^2$$

Perfect square:

$$(x + 5)^2 = x^2 + 10x + 25$$
$$(2x - 3)^2 = 4x^2 - 12x + 9$$
$$(3x^2 - 8y)^2 = 9x^4 - 48x^2y + 64y^2$$

DIVISION

Division of polynomials is carried out in much the same way as long division in arithmetic. For example, consider the problem $(2x^4 - 3x^3 + 5x^2 - 4) \div (x^2 - 3x + 4)$.

Divisor / Dividend / Quotient / Remainder

$$2x^2 + 3x + 4 \quad \text{Quotient}$$

division work: $x^2 - 3x + 4 \overline{)2x^4 - 3x^3 + 5x^2 \quad\quad - 4}$

$2x^4 + 6x^3 + 8x^2$

$3x^3 - 5x^2$

$3x^3 - 9x^2 + 12x$

$4x^2 - 12x - 4$

$4x^2 - 12x + 16$

$-20 \leftarrow$ Remainder

Note that a space is left for the missing power of x in the dividend. The successive terms of the quotient are obtained by dividing the leading term of the divisor (x^2) into the terms that are circled. Each time we get a term of the quotient it is multiplied by the divisor to get the next line of work, which is then subtracted from the previous line. We may write the answer as

$$2x^2 + 3x + 4, \quad \text{Remainder} -20$$

Note. For this procedure to work, it is essential that both divisor and dividend be written in descending powers of x.

EXERCISE SET 2

A Perform the indicated operations.

1. $(2x^2 + 3x + 5) + (3x^2 + 7x + 8)$
2. $(3x^2 - 2x + 10) + (5x^2 + x - 6)$
3. $(5y^3 - 2y^2 + 3y - 4) + (3y^3 + 4y^2 - y - 7)$
4. $(x^3 - 3x^2 + 5) + (2x^3 + 9x - 8)$
5. $(3t^2 - 6t + 10) - (2t^2 - 3t - 4)$
6. $(x^2 + 2x - 1) - (4x^2 - 7x + 2)$
7. $(2x^2 - 3xy + 4y^2) + (5x^2 + 7xy - 2y^2)$
8. $(8u^2 + 2uv - 3v^2) - (6u^2 - 3uv + 4v^2)$
9. $(x^2 - 2x + 4) + (3x^2 + 2x - 7) - (2x^2 - x - 6)$
10. $(5x^2 - 3x + 4) - (2x^2 - 7) + (6x^2 - x + 3)$
11. $(x + 3)(x + 4)$
12. $(x - 1)(x - 2)$

13. $(x - 3)(x + 4)$
14. $(x + 3)(x - 5)$
15. $(x + y)(x + 2y)$
16. $(x + 3y)(x - 2y)$
17. $(1 - x)(2 + x)$
18. $(x + 2)(3x + 4)$
19. $(2x + 1)(3x + 7)$
20. $(4x - 2)(x + 3)$
21. $(2t - 3)(4t + 2)$
22. $(3x - 2y)(4x + 3y)$
23. $(5y - 4)(2y - 3)$
24. $(x^2 - 2y)(3x^2 + 5y)$
25. $(2 - 3x)(4 - x)$
26. $(x - 1)(x + 1)$
27. $(x + 4)(x - 4)$
28. $(t - 3)(t + 3)$
29. $(2x - 1)(2x + 1)$
30. $(x - 3y)(x + 3y)$
31. $(a - 2b)(a + 2b)$
32. $(5x + 4)(5x - 4)$
33. $(3a - 7bc)(3a + 7bc)$
34. $(x + 7)^2$
35. $(x - 2)^2$
36. $(3x + 1)^2$
37. $(x - 2y)^2$
38. $(1 - 2t)^2$
39. $(2x - 3)^2$
40. $(5x + 2y)^2$
41. $(a^2 - 3b^2)^2$
42. $(x^2 - 2x + 7) \div (x - 3)$
43. $(2x^3 + 3x^2 - 4) \div (x + 4)$
44. $(x^3 - 2x^2 + 4x - 5) \div (x^2 + 2x - 2)$
45. $(4x^4 - 3x^2 + 2x + 8) \div (x^2 - 3x + 1)$

B
46. $(x + 1)(x^2 + x + 2)$
47. $(x - 2)(x^2 + 2x - 1)$
48. $(2x - 1)(3x^2 - 2x + 4)$
49. $(x^2 - 3x + 4)(x^2 - x + 2)$
50. $(2a^2 - a - 1)(3a^2 + 2a - 4)$
51. $[(x + y) + 2][(x + y) - 2]$
52. $(3x - 2y + 4)(3x - 2y - 4)$
53. $[x + (y - 1)][x - (y - 1)]$
54. $(x + 2y + 3)(x - 2y - 3)$
55. $(4 - x + y)(4 + x - y)$
56. $(a + b + c)^2$
57. $(2x - 3y + 4)^2$
58. $(a - 2b + 4c)^2$
59. $(2x^5 - 3x^3 + 5x^2 - 8) \div (3x^2 + 4)$

3 The Binomial Theorem

The formula for $(a + b)^2$ is often used in applications. Other powers, such as $(a + b)^3$ and $(a + b)^4$, are used less often but nevertheless are important to know. One by one these powers can be obtained through multiplication, but the process rapidly becomes tedious, as the following calculations show:

$$(a + b)^3 = (a + b)(a + b)^2 = (a + b)(a^2 + 2ab + b^2)$$
$$= a^3 + 2a^2b + ab^2 + ba^2 + 2ab^2 + b^3$$
$$= a^3 + 3a^2b + 3ab^2 + b^3$$

$$(a + b)^4 = (a + b)(a + b)^3 = (a + b)(a^3 + 3a^2b + 3ab^2 + b^3)$$
$$= a^4 + 3a^3b + 3a^2b^2 + ab^3 + ba^3 + 3a^2b^2 + 3ab^3 + b^4$$
$$= a^4 + 4a^3b + 6a^2b^2 + 4ab^3 + b^4$$

We might hope for a pattern to emerge that permits the result to be written down at once for any power. And it turns out that the powers of a and b in the successive terms on the right *can* easily be anticipated. For example, we would expect that in the expansion of $(a + b)^5$ the respective terms on the right would be of the form

$$a^5, \quad a^4b, \quad a^3b^2, \quad a^2b^3, \quad ab^4, \quad b^5$$

But what are the coefficients? If you do not already know the answer, you may wish to carry out a few more multiplications and try to conjecture the general pattern.

The brilliant French mathematician Blaise Pascal (1623–1662) discovered the following scheme for the coefficients in the expansion of $(a + b)^n$. This is known as **Pascal's triangle.**

Coefficients

$n = 0$ 1
$n = 1$ 1   1
$n = 2$ 1   2   1
$n = 3$ 1   3   3   1
$n = 4$ 1   4   6   4   1
$n = 5$ 1   5   10   10   5   1
$n = 6$ 1   6   15   20   15   6   1

Do you see how to get the next row? Think about it before you read on. Each time the leading 1 is written one space farther to the left. Then, each succeeding coefficient through the next-to-last one is obtained by adding the two above. For example, we get the coefficients for $n = 7$ from those for $n = 6$ as shown:

$n = 6$ 1   6   15   20   15   6   1

$n = 7$ 1   7   21   35   35   21   7   1

Using Pascal's triangle, we get, for example,

$$(a + b)^5 = a^5 + 5a^4b + 10a^3b^2 + 10a^2b^3 + 5ab^4 + b^5$$

Pascal's triangle is interesting and useful, but it does have its limitations. If we wanted a large power, say $(a + b)^{20}$ (which admittedly is not very likely), we would need to construct a rather large triangle. Moreover, there are times when we need a formula for the coefficients for an *arbitrary* value of n. The answer is provided in the **binomial theorem,** which is stated below. We defer the proof until a later chapter. Do not be intimidated by the formula. We will explain it.

BINOMIAL THEOREM

For any positive integer n,

$$(a + b)^n = a^n + na^{n-1}b + \frac{n(n-1)}{1 \cdot 2}a^{n-2}b^2 + \frac{n(n-1)(n-2)}{1 \cdot 2 \cdot 3}a^{n-3}b^3$$
$$+ \cdots + nab^{n-1} + b^n \tag{5}$$

We make the following observations:

1. In the expansion of $(a + b)^n$ there are $n + 1$ terms.
2. Beginning with a^n in the first term, the powers of a diminish by consecutive integers in each succeeding term, reaching the first power in the next-to-last term. In the second term, b is to the first power, and the powers of b

increase by consecutive integers in each succeeding term, reaching b^n in the last term.

3. In each term, the sum of the exponents on a and b is n.

4. The coefficient of the second term is n, so the first two terms are easy to remember. For example, the sum of the first two terms in the expansion of $(a + b)^{10}$ is $a^{10} + 10a^9b$.

5. Succeeding coefficients can be obtained as follows: Multiply the coefficient of the *preceding* term by the exponent of a in that term and then divide by one more than the exponent of b in that term. For example, having found $a^{10} + 10a^9b$ as the sum of the first two terms of $(a + b)^{10}$, we calculate the next coefficient as

$$\frac{10 \cdot 9}{2} = 45$$

So the first three terms are

$$a^{10} + 10a^9b + 45a^8b^2$$

(Now calculate the next coefficient. You should get 120.)

6. For any integer k where $1 \le k < n$, the **(k + 1)st** term in the expansion of $(a + b)^n$ is given by the formula

$$\frac{n(n - 1)(n - 2) \cdots (n - k + 1)}{1 \cdot 2 \cdot 3 \cdots k} a^{n-k}b^k \tag{6}$$

Note that the numerator of the coefficient has k factors starting with n and decreasing by 1 in each succeeding factor, whereas the denominator has k factors starting with 1 and increasing by 1 in each succeeding factor. For example, we can use formula (6) to get the fourth term of $(a + b)^{10}$. We put $k + 1 = 4$ and get $k = 3$. So the answer is

$$\frac{10 \cdot 9 \cdot 8}{1 \cdot 2 \cdot 3} a^{10-3}b^3 = 120a^7b^3$$

EXAMPLE 1   Use equation (5) to expand $(a + b)^4$.

Solution
$$(a + b)^4 = a^4 + 4a^3b + \frac{4 \cdot 3}{1 \cdot 2}a^2b^2 + \frac{4 \cdot 3 \cdot 2}{1 \cdot 2 \cdot 3}ab^3 + \frac{4 \cdot 3 \cdot 2 \cdot 1}{1 \cdot 2 \cdot 3 \cdot 4}b^4$$
$$= a^4 + 4a^3b + 6a^2b^2 + 4ab^3 + b^4$$

EXAMPLE 2   Expand $(a + b)^5$, using item 5 above to calculate the coefficients.

Solution   We know that the sum of the first two terms is $a^5 + 5a^4b$. To get the third coefficient we multiply 5 by 4 and divide by $1 + 1 = 2$. The result is $20 \div 2 = 10$. Up to this point we have

$$(a + b)^5 = a^5 + 5a^4b + 10a^3b^2 + \cdots$$

The next coefficient is $10 \cdot 3 \div 3 = 10$. Continuing in this way we get the complete expansion:

$$(a + b)^5 = a^5 + 5a^4b + 10a^3b^2 + 10a^2b^3 + 5ab^4 + b^5$$

EXAMPLE 3   Expand $(x + 2y)^3$.

Solution   Using item 5 above, we get

$$(x + 2y)^3 = x^3 + 3x^2(2y) + 3x(2y)^2 + (2y)^3$$
$$= x^3 + 6x^2y + 12xy^2 + 8y^3$$

EXAMPLE 4   Expand $(3x - y)^5$.

Solution $$(3x - y)^5 = [3x + (-y)]^5 = (3x)^5 + 5(3x)^4(-y) + 10(3x)^3(-y)^2$$
$$+ 10(3x)^2(-y)^3 + 5(3x)(-y)^4 + (-y)^5$$
$$= 243x^5 - 405x^4y + 270x^3y^2 - 90x^2y^3 + 15xy^4 - y^5$$

EXAMPLE 5   Find the eighth term of the expansion of $(a + b)^{12}$.

Solution   We let $k + 1 = 8$ in formula (6). So $k = 7$. Thus, the eighth term is

$$\frac{12 \cdot 11 \cdot 10 \cdot 9 \cdot 8 \cdot 7 \cdot 6}{1 \cdot 2 \cdot 3 \cdot 4 \cdot 5 \cdot 6 \cdot 7} a^{12-7}b^7 = 792a^5b^7$$

EXAMPLE 6   Find the sixth term in the expansion of $(x - 2y)^{10}$.

Solution   We write this first as $[x + (-2y)]^{10}$. We let $k + 1 = 6$, so that $k = 5$, and by formula (6) we obtain

$$\frac{10 \cdot 9 \cdot 8 \cdot 7 \cdot 6}{1 \cdot 2 \cdot 3 \cdot 4 \cdot 5} x^{10-5}(-2y)^5 = 252x^5(-32y^5)$$

$$= -8,064x^5y^5$$

EXERCISE SET 3

A   In Problems 1–5 use equation (5) to expand, and simplify the results.

1. $(a + b)^7$ 2. $(x + y)^8$ 3. $(a - b)^6$
4. $(x - y)^5$ 5. $(1 + x)^6$

In Problems 6–15 expand using rule 5 to calculate the coefficients, and simplify the results.

6. $(x + y)^5$ 7. $(2x + y)^4$ 8. $(x - 3y)^3$

9. $(2x + 3y)^4$ **10.** $(3x - 2y)^4$ **11.** $(5x - y^2)^3$

12. $(3 - t)^6$ **13.** $\left(\dfrac{2}{s} - 3\right)^5$ **14.** $(1 + \sqrt{x})^8$

15. $(x^2 - 2y)^5$

In Problems 16–20 find the indicated term of the expansion, using formula (6).

16. Fifth term of $(x + y)^{12}$ **17.** Eighth term of $(a - b)^{10}$
18. Sixth term of $(2x + y)^9$ **19.** Fourth term of $(2x - 3y)^8$
20. Seventh term of $(x^2 - 2)^{11}$

B **21.** Show that the signs in the expansion of $(a - b)^n$ alternate between plus and minus.
   22. The symbol $n!$ is read *n factorial* and means $1 \cdot 2 \cdot 3 \cdots n$. For example, $4! = 1 \cdot 2 \cdot 3 \cdot 4 = 24$. We define $0! = 1$. Show that formula (6) can be put in the form

$$\frac{n!}{k!(n - k)!} a^{n-k} b^k$$

Hint.   In formula (6) multiply the numerator and denominator by $(n - k)!$
   23. Use the formula given in Problem 22 to find:
   a.   The eighth term in the expansion of $(2x^2 - y)^{12}$
   b.   The seventh term in the expansion of $(\sqrt{x} - 3)^9$
   24. Find the term in the expansion of

$$\left(2x - \frac{1}{3x}\right)^{12}$$

   that does not involve x.
   25. Find the term in the expansion of $(4a^2 + b^3)^8$ that involves b^{12}.
   26. Find the term involving y^4 in the expansion of $(xy - 2y^{-1})^{10}$.
   27. Find the first four terms in the expansion of $(2a^2 - 3b^{-2})^{15}$.
   28. Find the first four terms in the expansion of $(3a^{-1} + 4\sqrt{b})^{20}$.

4 Factoring

To factor an algebraic expression means to write it as a product. So, factoring is just the reverse of multiplication. One might reasonably ask why it is important to factor anything. Some of the reasons are: (1) to simplify a fraction by dividing out common factors, (2) to help recognize the lowest common denominator in adding fractions, (3) to facilitate the solution of equations and inequalities, and (4) to help analyze the sign of an algebraic expression.
   The most common factoring problems fall into one of the categories described below.

Common Factors.   The distributive law provides justification for an important factoring technique. When read from right to left, this law says,

$$ab + ac = a(b + c)$$

Since a appears as a factor of each term on the left, it is referred to as a **common factor.** Applying the distributive law to obtain the right-hand side is referred to as "factoring out the common factor." This technique is illustrated in the following examples.

EXAMPLE 7
$$4xy^2 + 6x^3y = 2xy(2y + 3x^2)$$

EXAMPLE 8
$$3a^2b^3 - 6a^4b^2c + 9a^3b^4c^2 = 3a^2b^2(b - 2a^2c + 3ab^2c^2)$$

EXAMPLE 9
$$2x^{3/2} - 4x^{1/2} = 2x^{1/2}(x - 2)$$

It is almost always desirable to factor out *all* common factors, that is, to take out the greatest common factor.

In Examples 7 and 8 the common factors were monomials. The expression in Example 9 is not a polynomial, since the exponents are not integers, but we still factored out a single term. It often happens that common factors consist of more than one term. Common binomial factors occur in the next three examples.

EXAMPLE 10
$$(a + 2)b + (a + 2)c = (a + 2)(b + c)$$

The common factor is the binomial $(a + 2)$. It is treated as a unit and factored out just as if it were a single term.

EXAMPLE 11
$$2x^2 + 4xy + xy^2 + 2y^3 = (2x^2 + 4xy) + (xy^2 + 2y^3)$$
$$= 2x(x + 2y) + y^2(x + 2y) = (2x + y^2)(x + 2y)$$

The initial step here is called **grouping.** We grouped the first two terms together and the last two together. After factoring out the common factor $2x$ from the first group and y^2 from the second, we recognize the binomial factor $(x + 2y)$ as being common to the two groups.

EXAMPLE 12
$$ax + 9by - 3ay - 3bx = ax - 3ay - 3bx + 9by$$
$$= a(x - 3y) - 3b(x - 3y)$$
$$= (a - 3b)(x - 3y)$$

Here it was necessary to group the first and third terms together and the second and fourth together. A common error occurs in problems such as this because of the negative signs. The troublesome step is

$$-3bx + 9by = -3b(x - 3y)$$

The point to remember is that when a negative term is factored out, the signs inside the parentheses must be changed.

The Perfect Square and the General Trinomial. Equations (3) and (4) of Section 2 provide useful formulas for factoring. Written in reverse order, these become

$$a^2 + 2ab + b^2 = (a + b)^2$$
$$a^2 - 2ab + b^2 = (a - b)^2$$

Consider, for example, the problem of factoring $4x^2 + 20x + 25$. This might be a perfect square, with $a = 2x$ and $b = 5$. We check the middle term and find that the trinomial is a perfect square. So

$$4x^2 + 20x + 25 = (2x + 5)^2$$

Here are some other examples.

EXAMPLE 13 $4x^2 + 4x + 1 = (2x)^2 + 2(2x) \cdot 1 + 1^2 = (2x + 1)^2$

EXAMPLE 14 $9x^2 - 12xy + 4y^2 = (3x)^2 - 2(3x)(2y) + (2y)^2 = (3x - 2y)^2$

EXAMPLE 15 $a^4 + 8a^2 + 16 = (a^2)^2 + 2(a^2) \cdot 4 + 4^2 = (a^2 + 4)^2$

EXAMPLE 16
$$\begin{aligned}18x^3y - 60x^2y^2 + 50xy^3 &= 2xy(9x^2 - 30xy + 25y^2) \\ &= 2xy[(3x)^2 - 2(3x)(5y) + (5y)^2] \\ &= 2xy(3x - 5y)^2\end{aligned}$$

Here we first factored out the common factor $2xy$ and then recognized the other factor as a perfect square. Any existing common factor should always be factored out first.

A trinomial that is a perfect square of a binomial is, of course, a special situation. Certain trinomials that are not perfect squares can also be factored. We rely here on the multiplication formula (1):

$$(ax + b)(cx + d) = acx^2 + (ad + bc)x + bd$$

To illustrate, consider $6x^2 + 17x + 12$. To put this into the form $(ax+b)(cx+d)$, there are various possibilities to consider. The product of a and c must be 6, and b times d must be 12. The key is the middle term. In this case, we find (after several attempts) that the correct combination is $(2x + 3)(3x + 4)$. This is a trial-and-error procedure, but the number of trials is finite. Often, trials can be made mentally.

EXAMPLE 17 $x^2 - 2x - 8 = (x - 4)(x + 2)$

EXAMPLE 18 $4x^2 + 5x - 6 = (4x - 3)(x + 2)$

EXAMPLE 19 $2x^2 + xy - 15y^2 = (2x - 5y)(x + 3y)$

EXAMPLE 20 $10x^4 - 11x^2 - 6 = (5x^2 + 2)(2x^2 - 3)$

Difference of Squares and Sum and Difference of Cubes.   Equation (2) in reverse order reads

$$a^2 - b^2 = (a + b)(a - b)$$

and this is an important factoring formula called the **difference of squares.** The examples below illustrate its use.

EXAMPLE 21   Factor each of the following:

a. $x^2 - 4$ b. $4x^2 - 9y^2$ c. $m^2 - 4k^2$
d. $a^4 - b^4$ e. $3y^2 - 5$ (Factor over the reals.)

Solution   a. $x^2 - 4 = (x - 2)(x + 2)$ b. $4x^2 - 9y^2 = (2x - 3y)(2x + 3y)$
c. $m^2 - 4k^2 = (m - 2k)(m + 2k)$ d. $a^4 - b^4 = (a^2 - b^2)(a^2 + b^2)$
e. $3y^2 - 5 = (\sqrt{3}y + \sqrt{5})(\sqrt{3}y - \sqrt{5})$ $= (a - b)(a + b)(a^2 + b^2)$

Note.   A polynomial that cannot be written as a product of two other polynomials of positive degree is said to be **irreducible.** Part e of Example 21 is therefore irreducible over the rationals but is reducible over the reals.

EXAMPLE 22   Factor:
a. $x^2 - 4x + 4 - y^2$ b. $a^2 - b^2 + 2b - 1$

Solution In both of these it is necessary to group the terms first.

a. $x^2 - 4x + 4 - y^2 = (x^2 - 4x + 4) - y^2$
$$= (x - 2)^2 - y^2$$
$$= [(x - 2) - y][(x - 2) + y]$$
$$= (x - y - 2)(x + y - 2)$$

b. $a^2 - b^2 + 2b - 1 = a^2 - (b^2 - 2b + 1)$
$$= a^2 - (b - 1)^2$$
$$= [a - (b - 1)][a + (b - 1)]$$
$$= (a - b + 1)(a + b - 1)$$

Since the difference of two squares factors in such a nice way, we might be led to consider the difference of two cubes, $a^3 - b^3$. A reasonable guess is that one of the factors is $a - b$. This is, in fact, correct, and the complete factorization is given by

$$a^3 - b^3 = (a - b)(a^2 + ab + b^2)$$

You can verify this by multiplying the factors on the right.
There is a similar result for the sum of cubes:

$$a^3 + b^3 = (a + b)(a^2 - ab + b^2)$$

So while the sum of squares, $a^2 + b^2$, is irreducible, the sum of cubes can be factored.

EXAMPLE 23 Factor:
a. $x^3 - 8$ b. $a^3 + 27$ c. $8x^3 - 125y^3$ d. $x^6 - 1$ e. $x^6 + 1$

Solution a. $x^3 - 8 = (x - 2)(x^2 + 2x + 4)$
b. $a^3 + 27 = (a + 3)(a^2 - 3a + 9)$
c. $8x^3 - 125y^3 = (2x)^3 - (5y)^3 = (2x - 5y)(4x^2 + 10xy + 25y^2)$
d. This problem is best handled by first factoring $x^6 - 1$ as the difference of squares, resulting in the difference and sum of cubes:

$$x^6 - 1 = (x^3 - 1)(x^3 + 1) = (x - 1)(x^2 + x + 1)(x + 1)(x^2 - x + 1)$$

e. We treat this as $(x^2)^3 + 1$ to get

$$x^6 + 1 = (x^2 + 1)(x^4 - x^2 + 1)$$

Use of the Binomial Theorem. There are occasions when a polynomial can be recognized as being a perfect nth power of a binomial. For example, we saw in Section 3 that

$$a^3 + 3a^2b + 3ab^2 + b^3 = (a + b)^3$$

and that

$$a^4 + 4a^3b + 6a^2b^2 + 4ab^3 + b^4 = (a + b)^4$$

The best approach here is to be alert to the possibility that a polynomial might be a perfect nth power by observation of the exponents; then check by means of the binomial theorem to see if this is indeed the case.

Caution. Do not confuse $(a + b)^3$ with $a^3 + b^3$, or $(a - b)^3$ with $a^3 - b^3$.

EXAMPLE 24   Factor: $x^3 + 6x^2y + 12xy^2 + 8y^3$

Solution   By observing the pattern of the exponents, we see that this has a chance of being the expansion of $(x + 2y)^3$, and upon checking we find that this is correct. So the answer is $(x + 2y)^3$.

EXAMPLE 25   Factor: $x^5 - 5x^4 + 10x^3 - 10x^2 + 5x - 1$

Solution   A possibility is $(x - 1)^5$, and this does work.

EXERCISE SET 4

Factor all problems completely with rational coefficients unless otherwise specified.

A   Problems 1–10 involve common factors.

1. a. $2a^2b - 4ab^2$ b. $6a^3b^4c + 9a^2b^3c^2$
2. a. $4a^2b^3 - 10a^4b^4$ b. $36x^5y^4z - 42x^4y^3$
3. a. $24x^3y^2 - 40x^5y^3z + 48x^2y^4z^2$ b. $156a^4b - 260a^3b^2$
4. a. $3\sqrt{x} - 6x$ b. $10x^{3/2} + 15x^{5/2}$
5. a. $2x^{4/3} - 4x^{1/3}$ b. $12\sqrt[3]{x} + 18x^{4/3}$
6. a. $x(y - 2) + 3(y - 2)$ b. $(2a + 3)b - (2a + 3)c$
7. a. $(x + 2)y + (x + 2)$ b. $(b - 1) - a(b - 1)$
8. a. $xy - x + 2y - 2$ b. $ab - ac + bd - cd$
9. a. $x^2 - x + xy - y$ b. $x^2y - xy + x - 1$
10. a. $a^2b + 2ab^2 - 2ac - 4bc$ b. $x^3 - x^2y - y^3 + xy^2$

Problems 11–20 involve perfect squares and general trinomials.

11. a. $x^2 - 4x + 4$ b. $a^2 + 8a + 16$
12. a. $t^2 - 12t + 36$ b. $9m^2 + 6m + 1$
13. a. $9x^2 - 30x + 25$ b. $49a^2 + 28ab + 4b^2$
14. a. $4x^2 - 12xy + 9y^2$ b. $16t^2 - 72st + 81s^2$
15. a. $x^2 - 4x + 3$ b. $a^2 + 7a + 12$
16. a. $x^2 + 3x + 2$ b. $x^2 - x - 2$
17. a. $t^2 - t - 12$ b. $x^2 - 3x - 10$
18. a. $y^2 + 5y - 14$ b. $a^2 + 5a - 24$

19.   **a.** $2x^2 + 7x + 3$ **b.** $3x^2 + 11x + 6$
20.   **a.** $6x^2 - 5x - 6$ **b.** $8x^2 + 6xy - 9y^2$

Problems 21–30 involve difference of squares and sum and difference of cubes.

21.   **a.** $4x^2 - 9$ **b.** $16m^2 - 25n^2$
22.   **a.** $x^4 - 16$ **b.** $b^3 - a^2b$
23.   **a.** $a^8 - 1$ **b.** $x^2y^4 - y^2$
24.   **a.** $81x^4 - 256y^4$ **b.** $121 - 49t^2$
25.   **a.** $(x - 2)^2 - y^2$ **b.** $x^2 - (y - 2)^2$
26.   **a.** $x^2 - 2x + 1 - 4y^2$ **b.** $4x^2 + 4x + 1 - y^2$
27.   **a.** $x^2 - y^2 + 4x + 4$ **b.** $16a^2 - 25b^2 - 40a + 25$
28.   **a.** $x^2 - 16 - y^2 - 8y$ **b.** $a^2 - 4b - 1 - 4b^2$
29.   **a.** $x^3 - 64$ **b.** $27a^3 + 8$
30.   **a.** $1 - 8x^3$ **b.** $27x^3 + 125y^3$

Problems 31–36 involve use of the binomial theorem.

31. $x^3 + 3x^2y + 3xy^2 + y^3$ **32.** $8x^3 - 12x^2y + 6xy^2 - y^3$
33. $a^4 - 4a^3b + 6a^2b^2 - 4ab^3 + b^4$ **34.** $x^4 - 8x^3 + 24x^2 - 32x + 16$
35. $x^3 + 9x^2 + 27x + 27$
36. $a^5 - 5a^4b + 10a^3b^2 - 10a^2b^3 + 5ab^4 - b^5$

In Problems 37–82 factor in whatever way is appropriate.

37. $12x^2 + 14x - 40$ **38.** $9x^3 - 25x$
39. $x^4 - 5x^2 + 4$ **40.** $6x^3 - 20x^2 + 6x$
41. $a^3 + a^2b + ab^2 + b^3$ **42.** $x^4 - 8x^2 + 16$
43. $x^2 - 2xy + y^2 - 4$ **44.** $64x^3 + 125$
45. $48a^2 + 37ab - 36b^2$ **46.** $x^2 - y^2 - 2x + 1$
47. $x^3 + x^2 - 4x - 4$ **48.** $8t^3 - 28t^2 + 24t$
49. $x^6 - 64$ **50.** $27a^3 + 64b^3$
51. $a^2 - b^2 - 2ab^2 + 2b^3$ **52.** $2a^3b + 6a^2b^2 - 8a^2b$
53. $18a^2 + 37ab - 20b^2$ **54.** $xy - x - y + 1$
55. $2m^2 + 3n - mn - 6m$ **56.** $2x^4 + 9x^2 + 4$
57. $10 + x - 2x^2$ **58.** $12 + xy - 4x - 3y$
59. $t^3 - 12t^2 + 48t - 64$ **60.** $64t^4 + 8t$
61. $8u^3 - 27v^3$ **62.** $8x^3 + 36x^2y^2 + 54xy^4 + 27y^6$
63. $18x^2 - 84xy + 98y^2$

B   **64.** $75x^3y^2 + 60x^2y^3 - 36xy^4$ **65.** $32a^3b + 144a^2b^2 + 162ab^3$
66. $48x^2yz - 30y^3z - 36xy^2z$ **67.** $40x^2 + 18x - 63$
68. $a^2 + b^2 + c^2 + 2ab + 2ac + 2bc$ **69.** $x^2 + 4y^2 + 1 - 4xy + 2x - 4y$
70. $4x^4 - 9$ (Factor over the reals.)   **71.**   **a.** $x^6 - 64$ **b.** $x^6 + 64$
72. $x^2 + 2xy + y^2 - a^2 - 2ab - b^2$
  Hint.   Use groups of three.
73. $x^2 - z^2 + y^2 - 2xy - 4 + 4z$
  Hint.   Rearrange and use groups of three.

74. $x^8 - y^8$ 75. $a^{12} - b^{12}$
76. $8x^3 + 36x^2y + 54xy^2 + 27y^3$
77. $x^5 - 15x^4 + 90x^3 - 270x^2 + 405x - 243$
78. $27a^3 - 54a^2 + 36a - 8$ 79. $a^3 - b^3 + a - b$
80. $x^8 - 256$ 81. $x^2 - 2xy + y^2 - 4x + 4y$
82. $a^6 + 7a^3b^3 - 8b^6$

5 Rational Fractions

Fractions that are quotients of polynomials are called **rational.** Examples are

$$\frac{x + 3}{x^2 - 2x + 5} \qquad \frac{1}{x + 2} \qquad \frac{x^6 - y^6}{x^2 + 2xy + y^2}$$

The arithmetic associated with these is governed by rules already established in Sections 4 and 5 of Chapter 1. Factoring plays a key role in carrying out the steps involved. When a common factor appears in the numerator and denominator, we make use of the fundamental property of fractions to reduce the fraction to lowest terms. To "simplify" an expression involving rational fractions means to perform the indicated operations and express the result as a simple fraction in which no common factor (other than 1) exists in the numerator and denominator.

The examples below illustrate the most important techniques.

EXAMPLE 26   Perform the indicated operations and simplify.

a. $\dfrac{x^2 - x - 6}{x^2 - 6x + 9}$ b. $\dfrac{x^2 + 4x + 4}{x^2 - 3x - 4} \cdot \dfrac{2x^2 + x - 1}{x^2 - 3x - 10}$

c. $\dfrac{2x^2 - 6x}{2x^2 - x - 10} \div \dfrac{x^2 - 5x + 6}{x^2 - 4}$

Solution   a. $\dfrac{x^2 - x - 6}{x^2 - 6x + 9} = \dfrac{\overset{1}{\cancel{(x - 3)}}(x + 2)}{(x - 3)^{\cancel{2}^1}} = \dfrac{x + 2}{x - 3}$

b. $\dfrac{x^2 + 4x + 4}{x^2 - 3x - 4} \cdot \dfrac{2x^2 + x - 1}{x^2 - 3x - 10} = \dfrac{(x + 2)^{\overset{1}{\cancel{2}}}}{(x - 4)\cancel{(x + 1)}} \cdot \dfrac{(2x - 1)\overset{1}{\cancel{(x + 1)}}}{(x - 5)\cancel{(x + 2)}}$

$= \dfrac{(x + 2)(2x - 1)}{(x - 4)(x - 5)} = \dfrac{2x^2 + 3x - 2}{x^2 - 9x + 20}$

c. From Section 4 of Chapter 1 we know that to divide, we invert the denominator and multiply:

$$\frac{2x^2 - 6x}{2x^2 - x - 10} \div \frac{x^2 - 5x + 6}{x^2 - 4} = \frac{2x^2 - 6x}{2x^2 - x - 10} \cdot \frac{x^2 - 4}{x^2 - 5x + 6}$$

$$= \frac{2x\cancel{(x-3)}}{(2x-5)\cancel{(x+2)}} \cdot \frac{\cancel{(x+2)}\cancel{(x-2)}}{\cancel{(x-3)}\cancel{(x-2)}} = \frac{2x}{2x-5}$$

The basic procedure used in adding and subtracting rational expressions is to write each fraction with the same denominator (the LCD) and then to use the result from Chapter 1 that $a/c + b/c = (a + b)/c$. The next three examples illustrate this procedure.

EXAMPLE 27   Perform the indicated operations.

a. $\dfrac{1}{x - 1} + \dfrac{3}{x + 2}$ **b.** $\dfrac{x}{2x - 1} - \dfrac{3}{x + 2}$

Solution   **a.**   The LCD is the product $(x - 1)(x + 2)$. We change each fraction to one having this expression as its denominator as follows:

$$\frac{1}{x - 1} + \frac{3}{x + 2} = \frac{1}{x - 1} \cdot \frac{x + 2}{x + 2} + \frac{3}{x + 2} \cdot \frac{x - 1}{x - 1}$$

$$= \frac{x + 2}{(x - 1)(x + 2)} + \frac{3(x - 1)}{(x + 2)(x - 1)}$$

Now the fractions can be added to give

$$\frac{x + 2 + 3x - 3}{(x - 1)(x + 2)} = \frac{4x - 1}{(x - 1)(x + 2)}$$

With a little practice the work can be shortened as follows:

$$\frac{1}{x - 1} + \frac{3}{x + 2} = \frac{(x + 2) + 3(x - 1)}{(x - 1)(x + 2)} = \frac{x + 2 + 3x - 3}{(x - 1)(x + 2)} = \frac{4x - 1}{(x - 1)(x + 2)}$$

b.   The basic idea is the same as in part a.

$$\frac{x}{2x - 1} - \frac{3}{x + 2} = \frac{x}{2x - 1} \cdot \frac{x + 2}{x + 2} - \frac{3}{x + 2} \cdot \frac{2x - 1}{2x - 1}$$

Be careful here.

$$- \frac{x^2 + 2x - 6x + 3}{(2x - 1)(x + 2)}$$

$$= \frac{x^2 - 4x + 3}{(2x - 1)(x + 2)}$$

$$= \frac{(x - 3)(x - 1)}{(2x - 1)(x + 2)}$$

Note. We factored the numerator to see if it had a factor in common with the denominator. In this case it did not, but it is good practice to see if the fraction can be reduced by writing both numerator and denominator in factored form.

EXAMPLE 28   Combine and simplify: $\dfrac{2}{x+y} - \dfrac{x-y}{x^2 + 3xy + 2y^2} + \dfrac{3}{x+2y}$

Solution   By factoring the denominator of the second fraction we recognize the LCD as $(x+y)(x+2y)$. To obtain equivalent fractions having this LCD as the denominator, the numerator of the first fraction must be multiplied by $(x+2y)$ and the numerator of the third fraction must be multiplied by $(x+y)$. This gives

$$\frac{2}{x+y} - \frac{x-y}{(x+2y)(x+y)} + \frac{3}{x+2y} = \frac{2(x+2y) - (x-y) + 3(x+y)}{(x+y)(x+2y)}$$

$$= \frac{2x+4y - x + y + 3x + 3y}{(x+y)(x+2y)}$$

$$= \frac{4x+8y}{(x+y)(x+2y)}$$

$$= \frac{\overset{1}{4(x+2y)}}{(x+y)\underset{1}{(x+2y)}}$$

$$= \frac{4}{x+y}$$

EXAMPLE 29   Combine and simplify: $\dfrac{1}{2x+4} - \dfrac{2}{2-x} + \dfrac{4}{3x-6}$

Solution   The first thing to observe is that the denominator of the second fraction would be easier to deal with if it were $x-2$ instead of $2-x$. Since these factors are negatives of each other, this change can be accomplished using the fact that $a/(-b) = -a/b$. Thus,

$$\frac{2}{2-x} = -\frac{2}{x-2}$$

so that the problem becomes

$$\frac{1}{2(x+2)} + \frac{2}{x-2} + \frac{4}{3(x-2)} = \frac{3(x-2) + 12(x+2) + 8(x+2)}{6(x+2)(x-2)}$$

$$= \frac{3x - 6 + 12x + 24 + 8x + 16}{6(x+2)(x-2)}$$

$$= \frac{23x + 34}{6(x^2 - 4)}$$

The next three examples involve complex fractions. They are handled just as in Section 5 of Chapter 1.

EXAMPLE 30   Simplify:
$$\dfrac{\dfrac{1}{a^2} - \dfrac{2}{ab}}{\dfrac{3}{b^2} + \dfrac{1}{2ab}}$$

Solution   Just as in Section 5 of Chapter 1, we multiply the numerator and denominator of the main fraction by the LCD of all minor denominators—in this case $2a^2b^2$.

$$\dfrac{\dfrac{1}{a^2} - \dfrac{2}{ab}}{\dfrac{3}{b^2} + \dfrac{1}{2ab}} \cdot \dfrac{\dfrac{2a^2b^2}{1}}{\dfrac{2a^2b^2}{1}} = \dfrac{2b^2 - 4ab}{6a^2 + ab} = \dfrac{2b(b - 2a)}{a(6a + b)}$$

EXAMPLE 31   Simplify:
$$\dfrac{\dfrac{1}{x - 1} + \dfrac{1}{x^2 - 1}}{x - \dfrac{2}{x + 1}}$$

Solution   Here the LCD of the minor denominators is $(x + 1)(x - 1) = x^2 - 1$. Proceeding as above, we obtain

$$\dfrac{\dfrac{1}{x - 1} + \dfrac{1}{x^2 - 1}}{x - \dfrac{2}{x + 1}} \cdot \dfrac{\dfrac{(x + 1)(x - 1)}{1}}{\dfrac{(x + 1)(x - 1)}{1}} = \dfrac{x + 1 + 1}{x(x + 1)(x - 1) - 2(x - 1)}$$

$$= \dfrac{x + 2}{(x - 1)(x^2 + x - 2)}$$

$$= \dfrac{\overset{1}{\cancel{x + 2}}}{(x - 1)\underset{1}{\cancel{(x + 2)}}(x - 1)}$$

$$= \dfrac{1}{(x - 1)^2}$$

Note that in the second step the factors appearing in the terms of the denominator were not multiplied out. This enabled us to recognize the common factor $(x - 1)$. Had the multiplication been done, the result would have been $x^3 - 3x + 2$, and factoring this would have been far more difficult. (Try it!)

EXAMPLE 32   Simplify:
$$\frac{\dfrac{x}{x-1}-2}{x-2}$$

Solution
$$\frac{\dfrac{x}{x-1}-2}{x-2}\cdot\frac{\dfrac{x-1}{1}}{\dfrac{x-1}{1}}=\frac{x-2(x-1)}{(x-2)(x-1)}$$

$$=\frac{x-2x+2}{(x-2)(x-1)}$$

$$=\frac{-x+2}{(x-2)(x-1)}$$

$$=-\frac{\overset{1}{\cancel{x-2}}}{\underset{1}{\cancel{(x-2)}}(x-1)}$$

$$=-\frac{1}{x-1}$$

Note carefully the handling of signs in this problem.

EXERCISE SET 5

A Perform the indicated operations. Reduce final answers to simplest form.

1. **a.** $\dfrac{x^2-1}{x^2+3x+2}$ **b.** $\dfrac{2x^2+x-6}{x^2+4x+4}$

2. **a.** $\dfrac{t^2-4}{t^3+4t^2+4t}$ **b.** $\dfrac{6x^2+5x-4}{2x^2-9x+4}$

3. $\dfrac{x^2-2x-8}{x^2-1}\cdot\dfrac{2x^2-x-3}{x^2-8x+16}$

4. $\dfrac{2x^2+4x}{3x^2+2x-1}\cdot\dfrac{3x^2-10x+3}{x^3-x^2-6x}$

5. $\dfrac{x^3-1}{x^2-5x-6}\cdot\dfrac{x^2+3x+2}{x^2+x-2}$

6. $\dfrac{6x^2+xy-12y^2}{2x^2+xy-3y^2}\div\dfrac{3x^2-xy-4y^2}{x^2-2xy+y^2}$

7. $\dfrac{2x^2+x-1}{x^2-1}\div\dfrac{x^2+6x+9}{x^2+2x-3}$

8. $\dfrac{3x^2+2x-8}{2x^2-x-6}\div\dfrac{x^2-4}{2x^2+3x}$

9. $\dfrac{3}{x+4}+\dfrac{1}{x-2}$

10. $\dfrac{x}{x-3}-\dfrac{1}{x+1}$

11. $\dfrac{1}{x-1}+\dfrac{2}{x+1}$

12. $\dfrac{3}{x+2}+\dfrac{2}{x-1}$

13. $\dfrac{1}{x-4}-\dfrac{1}{x+3}$

14. $\dfrac{2}{x-3}-\dfrac{1}{x+2}$

15. $\dfrac{3}{x+2}-\dfrac{2}{x-2}+\dfrac{8}{x^2-4}$

16. $\dfrac{5}{2x-1}-\dfrac{2}{x+2}-\dfrac{10}{2x^2+3x-2}$

17. $\dfrac{2}{x-1}+\dfrac{3}{x+1}-\dfrac{x-5}{x^2-1}$

18. $\dfrac{3}{a+2}-\dfrac{2a-1}{a^2-a-6}+\dfrac{1}{a-3}$

19. $1 - \dfrac{2}{x} - \dfrac{3}{x-2}$

20. $\dfrac{x-3}{x^2+3x+2} + \dfrac{2x-5}{x^2+x-2} - \dfrac{x-3}{x^2-1}$

21. $\dfrac{x^2-10}{x+4} - x + 7$

22. $\dfrac{x^2+1}{x-2} - x + 3$

23. $\dfrac{1}{x-2} - \dfrac{3}{2-x} + 1$

24. $\dfrac{a}{x+a} - \dfrac{x}{x-a} - \dfrac{2x^2}{a^2-x^2}$

25. $\dfrac{3}{x^2-x-2} + \dfrac{5}{2+3x-2x^2}$

26. $\dfrac{\dfrac{a}{b} - \dfrac{b}{a}}{\dfrac{1}{b^2} - \dfrac{1}{a^2}}$

27. $\dfrac{\dfrac{1}{x^2} - \dfrac{1}{4}}{x-2}$

28. $\dfrac{\dfrac{1}{x-1} - \dfrac{8}{x^2-1}}{\dfrac{2}{x+1} - \dfrac{1}{x-1}}$

29. $\dfrac{\dfrac{x}{x-2} - 2}{x-4}$

30. $\dfrac{\dfrac{y}{x-1} - \dfrac{y}{x+1}}{1 + \dfrac{y^2}{x^2-1}}$

31. $\dfrac{\dfrac{x^2}{y} - \dfrac{y^2}{x}}{\dfrac{x}{y} + \dfrac{y}{x} + 1}$

32. $\dfrac{y+3 - \dfrac{16}{y+3}}{y-6 + \dfrac{20}{y+3}}$

33. $\dfrac{\dfrac{2}{a+h} - \dfrac{2}{a}}{h}$

34. $\dfrac{\dfrac{2+h}{1+h} - 2}{h}$

35. $\dfrac{\dfrac{1}{z} + 2}{5 + 2\left(z + \dfrac{1}{z}\right)}$

36. $\dfrac{\dfrac{x-1}{x+1} - \dfrac{1}{3}}{x-2}$

37. $\dfrac{\dfrac{x^2}{x+2} - \dfrac{a^2}{a+2}}{x-a}$

38. $\dfrac{\dfrac{2x+3}{x^2} - 1}{x+1}$

39. $\dfrac{\dfrac{2}{(x+h)^2} - \dfrac{2}{x^2}}{h}$

B **40.** $\dfrac{x-3}{2x^2-x-3} + \dfrac{x+2}{2x^2-7x+6} - \dfrac{x-1}{x^2-x-2}$

41. $\dfrac{1}{x^2-1} - \dfrac{x^2+3}{x^4+x}$

42. $\dfrac{2(x-2)^3(x+1) - 3(x+1)^2(x-2)^2}{(x-2)^6}$

43. $\dfrac{3(2x-3)^2(x+4)^2 - 4(x+4)^3(2x-3)}{(2x-3)^4}$

44. $\dfrac{\dfrac{x+h-2}{x+h+3} - \dfrac{x-2}{x+3}}{h}$

45. $\dfrac{\dfrac{x^2}{1-2x}-\dfrac{a^2}{1-2a}}{x-a}$

46. $\dfrac{1-x^3}{1+\dfrac{x}{1-\dfrac{x}{1+x}}}$

47. $\dfrac{3x^2+10x-8}{2-\dfrac{3}{1-\dfrac{x}{x-2}}}$

Hint. First work with complex fractions in the denominator.

---

6 Other Fractional Expressions

All the rules for working with rational fractions continue to hold for fractions involving negative and fractional exponents or radicals. To simplify such expressions means to perform indicated operations, to divide out common factors, and to write the answer with positive exponents.

EXAMPLE 33 Simplify: $\dfrac{x^{-1}-y^{-1}}{x^{-2}-y^{-2}}$

Solution We replace each term by its equivalent expressed with a positive exponent and then proceed as in Section 5.

$$\frac{x^{-1}-y^{-1}}{x^{-2}-y^{-2}}=\frac{\dfrac{1}{x}-\dfrac{1}{y}}{\dfrac{1}{x^2}-\dfrac{1}{y^2}}\cdot\frac{\dfrac{x^2y^2}{1}}{\dfrac{x^2y^2}{1}}=\frac{xy^2-x^2y}{y^2-x^2}=\frac{xy(\overset{1}{\cancel{y-x}})}{(y+x)(\underset{1}{\cancel{y-x}})}=\frac{xy}{y+x}$$

EXAMPLE 34 Simplify: $x(1-x)^{-3}+(1-x)^{-2}$

Solution There are two ways to proceed.
a. Write with positive exponents first.

$$x(1-x)^{-3}+(1-x)^{-2}=\frac{x}{(1-x)^3}+\frac{1}{(1-x)^2}$$

$$=\frac{x+(1-x)}{(1-x)^3}=\frac{1}{(1-x)^3}$$

b. Factor out the common factor $(1-x)^{-3}$. It is important to take out the factor with the negative exponent which is largest in absolute value, so that the remaining factor will have positive exponents only.

$$x(1-x)^{-3}+(1-x)^{-2}=(1-x)^{-3}(x+1-x)=\frac{1}{(1-x)^3}$$

EXAMPLE 35   Simplify: $\dfrac{(x^2 - 1)^{1/2} - x^2(x^2 - 1)^{-1/2}}{x^2 - 1}$

Solution   Just as with a complex fraction, we multiply the numerator and denominator by the same quantity. This time we choose the factor that will eliminate all negative powers, namely, $(x^2 - 1)^{1/2}$:

$$\frac{(x^2 - 1)^{1/2} - x^2(x^2 - 1)^{-1/2}}{x^2 - 1} \cdot \frac{(x^2 - 1)^{1/2}}{(x^2 - 1)^{1/2}} = \frac{x^2 - 1 - x^2}{(x^2 - 1)^{3/2}} = \frac{-1}{(x^2 - 1)^{3/2}}$$

EXAMPLE 36   Simplify: $\dfrac{\dfrac{x^2}{\sqrt{x^2 - 1}} - \sqrt{x^2 - 1}}{x^2}$

Solution   We multiply the numerator and denominator by $\sqrt{x^2 - 1}$ to obtain

$$\frac{\dfrac{x^2}{\sqrt{x^2 - 1}} - \sqrt{x^2 - 1}}{x^2} \cdot \frac{\dfrac{\sqrt{x^2 - 1}}{1}}{\dfrac{\sqrt{x^2 - 1}}{1}} = \frac{x^2 - (x^2 - 1)}{x^2\sqrt{x^2 - 1}} = \frac{1}{x^2\sqrt{x^2 - 1}}$$

EXAMPLE 37   Rationalize the denominator.

$$\frac{1}{\sqrt{a} - \sqrt{b}}$$

Solution   To *rationalize* means to make the expression rational—that is, to get rid of radicals. We can accomplish this by multiplying numerator and denominator by $\sqrt{a} + \sqrt{b}$.

$$\frac{1}{\sqrt{a} - \sqrt{b}} = \frac{1}{\sqrt{a} - \sqrt{b}} \cdot \frac{\sqrt{a} + \sqrt{b}}{\sqrt{a} + \sqrt{b}} = \frac{\sqrt{a} + \sqrt{b}}{a - b}$$

Note that we used the fact that the difference of two numbers times their sum equals the difference of their squares.

EXAMPLE 38   Rationalize the numerator: $\dfrac{\sqrt{x + 2} - 2}{x - 2}$

Solution   This type of problem frequently occurs early in the study of calculus. We make the numerator rational by multiplying the numerator and denominator by $\sqrt{x + 2} + 2$:

$$\frac{\sqrt{x+2}-2}{x-2} \cdot \frac{\sqrt{x+2}+2}{\sqrt{x+2}+2} = \frac{(x+2)-4}{(x-2)(\sqrt{x+2}+2)}$$

$$= \frac{\overset{1}{\cancel{x-2}}}{\underset{1}{\cancel{(x-2)}}(\sqrt{x+2}+2)} = \frac{1}{\sqrt{x+2}+2}$$

EXERCISE SET 6

A   Simplify the expressions in Problems 1–20. Express answers with positive exponents only.

1. $x^{-1} - y^{-1}$

2. $\dfrac{x^{-1}+y^{-1}}{x^{-2}-y^{-2}}$

3. $\dfrac{a^{-2}-b^{-2}}{a^{-1}+b^{-1}}$

4. $x^{-1} - x^{-2}(1+x)$

5. $x^{-2} - 2(x+2)x^{-3}$

6. $2x(x-2)^{-1} - x^2(x-2)^{-2}$

7. $2(x+1)(x-1)^{-1} - (x+1)^2(x-1)^{-2}$

8. $\dfrac{2x^{-1}-y^{-1}}{4x^{-2}-4x^{-1}y^{-1}+y^{-2}}$

9. $\dfrac{2x^{-2}-3x^{-1}+1}{1-x^{-2}}$

10. $\dfrac{x}{\sqrt{1+x}} + 2\sqrt{1+x}$

11. $\dfrac{1+x}{2\sqrt{x}} - \sqrt{x}$

12. $\dfrac{2x^2}{\sqrt{x^2+1}} + \sqrt{x^2+1}$

13. $\sqrt{1-2x} + \dfrac{x}{\sqrt{1-2x}}$

14. $\dfrac{\sqrt{1-x} + \dfrac{x}{2\sqrt{1-x}}}{1-x}$

15. $\dfrac{\sqrt{x^2+4} - \dfrac{5}{\sqrt{x^2+4}}}{x+1}$

16. $\dfrac{(x-1)^{1/2} - 2x(x-1)^{-1/2}}{x+1}$

17. $\dfrac{\sqrt{4-x^2} + x^2(4-x^2)^{-1/2}}{4-x^2}$

18. $(x-1)^{-1/2}(x+1)^{1/2} - (x+1)^{-1/2}(x-1)^{1/2}$

19. $\dfrac{2y(1-y^2)^{1/2} + \dfrac{y^3}{\sqrt{1-y^2}}}{1-y^2}$

20. $\dfrac{\dfrac{1+x^2}{2\sqrt{x}} - 2x\sqrt{x}}{(1+x^2)^2}$

In Problems 21–26 rationalize the denominator.

21. $\dfrac{1}{\sqrt{3}-\sqrt{2}}$

22. $\dfrac{1}{\sqrt{5}+2}$

23. $\dfrac{6}{3\sqrt{2}-4}$

24. $\dfrac{1}{\sqrt{x}-\sqrt{a}}$

25. $\dfrac{1}{\sqrt{x+1}-\sqrt{x+2}}$

26. $\dfrac{1}{x+\sqrt{x-1}}$

In Problems 27–32 rationalize the numerator.

27. $\dfrac{\sqrt{x}-1}{x-1}$

28. $\dfrac{\sqrt{1+h}-1}{h}$

29. $\dfrac{\sqrt{x+1}-1}{x}$

30. $\dfrac{\sqrt{x-3}-1}{x-4}$

31. $\dfrac{\sqrt{2(x+h)+1}-\sqrt{2x+1}}{h}$

32. $\dfrac{\sqrt{2x+3}-3}{x-3}$

B Simplify the expressions completely. Express answers with positive exponents only.

33. $-\dfrac{8x^2}{9}(x^2 - 1)^{-4/3} + \tfrac{4}{3}(x^2 - 1)^{-1/3}$

34. $\dfrac{(3 - x)^{1/2}(2 + x)^{-1/2} + (3 - x)^{-1/2}(2 + x)^{1/2}}{2(3 - x)}$

35. $\dfrac{(1 - 2x)^{3/2} \cdot 2x - x^2 \cdot \tfrac{3}{2}(-2)(1 - 2x)^{1/2}}{(1 - 2x)^3}$

36. $\dfrac{x^{-3} + y^{-3}}{xy^{-1} + x^{-1}y - 1}$

37. $\dfrac{\dfrac{1}{\sqrt{x + h}} - \dfrac{1}{\sqrt{x}}}{h}$

38. $\dfrac{\sqrt[3]{x} - \sqrt[3]{a}}{x - a}$

Hint. Multiply the numerator and denominator by a factor that will rationalize the numerator.

39. $\dfrac{\sqrt[3]{x^2 - 1} - x^2 \cdot \tfrac{2}{3}(x^2 - 1)^{-2/3}}{(x^2 - 1)^{2/3}}$

40. $\dfrac{\tfrac{1}{3}(2x + 3)^{1/4}(x + 1)^{-2/3} - (x + 1)^{1/3} \cdot \tfrac{1}{2}(2x + 3)^{-3/4}}{\sqrt{2x + 3}}$

41. $\dfrac{(x^2 - 4)^{1/2} \cdot \tfrac{1}{3}(x^2 - 1)^{-2/3}(2x) - (x^2 - 1)^{1/3} \cdot \tfrac{1}{2}(x^2 - 4)^{-1/2}(2x)}{(x^2 - 4)}$

Review Exercise Set

A In Problems 1–5 perform the indicated operations.

1. **a.** $(2x^2 - 3x - 4) + (3x^2 + 7x - 5)$
   b. $(7x^2 - 2xy - 3y^2) - (5x^2 - 2xy - y^2)$
2. **a.** $(2x^3 - 3x^2 + 4x - 8) + (x^3 - 5x + 7)$
   b. $(3t^2 - 4t + 6) - (t^2 - 3t + 2)$
3. **a.** $(2x - 3y)(5x + 4y)$ **b.** $(x + 2y)(x - 2y)$
4. **a.** $(3x - 5)^2$ **b.** $(x - 1)(x^3 + 2x^2 - 3x + 4)$
5. **a.** $(x^3 - 3x^2 + 4x - 5) \div (x - 3)$ **b.** $(2x^4 - 5x^2 - 2x + 7) \div (x^2 + 3x - 2)$
6. Expand: 7. Expand:
   a. $(x + 2y)^5$ **b.** $(3a - 2b)^4$ **a.** $(3a + 4b)^3$ **b.** $(x^2 - 3)^6$
8. Expand:
   a. $(1 - 2\sqrt{x})^4$ **b.** $\left(2t + \dfrac{3}{t}\right)^5$

Find the indicated term of the expansion in Problems 9 and 10.

9. **a.** Sixth term of $(3a - b^2)^{11}$ **b.** Fifth term of $(2\sqrt{x} + 3)^{20}$

10. **a.** Eighth term of $(t^{-1} - 3t)^{12}$ **b.** Seventh term of $\left(1 - \dfrac{2}{x}\right)^{15}$

In Problems 11–23 factor completely with rational coefficients.

11. **a.** $3x^2 - 5x - 2$ **b.** $x^3y - 12x^2y^2 + 36xy^3$

12. **a.** $18x^2 + 33x - 40$ **b.** $a^3 - a^2b - ab^2 + b^3$

13. **a.** $2x^4 - 5x^2 - 12$ **b.** $x^2 - y^2 + 4x + 4$

14. **a.** $x^2 - 4y^2 - 2x + 4y$ **b.** $a^3 + 27$

15. **a.** $24x^3 - 23x^2y - 12xy^2$ **b.** $a^3 + 3a^2 - 9a - 27$

16. **a.** $2x^5y^3 - 16x^2$ **b.** $a^4 - 256$

17. **a.** $4 - x^2 - y^2 + 2xy$ **b.** $6x^4 - 5x^2y - 6y^2$

18. **a.** $a^2b - 4b - a^2 + 4$ **b.** $x^2 - x - y^2 + y$

19. **a.** $x^6 - \dfrac{y^3}{8}$ **b.** $x^8 - 1$

20. **a.** $15x^2 - xy - 28y^2$ **b.** $16a^4 + 32a^3b^2 + 24a^2b^4 + 8ab^6 + b^8$

21. **a.** $12a^2 - 36ab + 27b^2$ **b.** $s^3 + 64t^6$

22. **a.** $2x^{7/2} + 16x^{1/2}$ **b.** $3x^2(x^2 - 4)^{3/2} + (x^2 - 4)^{5/2}$

23. **a.** $3x^2(x^2 - 1)^{1/2} + 2x(x^2 - 1)^{3/2}$ **b.** $6x(1 - 2x)^{4/3} - 8x^2 \sqrt[3]{1 - 2x}$

In Problems 24–33 perform the indicated operations and simplify the result. Express all answers with positive exponents only.

24. **a.** $\dfrac{2x^2 + 5x - 12}{x^2 - 25} \cdot \dfrac{3x^2 + 13x - 10}{6x^2 - 13x + 6}$ **b.** $\dfrac{3x^2 - 7x - 20}{x^2 - 8x + 16} \div \dfrac{3x^2 + 14x + 15}{2x^2 - 9x + 4}$

25. $\dfrac{1}{x + 2} + \dfrac{3}{2 - x} + \dfrac{4}{x^2 - 4}$ 26. $\dfrac{4x + 5}{2x - 3} - \dfrac{x + 7}{x + 4} - \dfrac{25x + 23}{2x^2 + 5x - 12}$

27. $\dfrac{\dfrac{2x}{x - 3} + 4}{x - 2}$ 28. $\dfrac{\dfrac{1}{x - 2} - \dfrac{3}{x + 2}}{\dfrac{3x}{x^2 - 4} - \dfrac{2}{x - 2}}$

29. $\dfrac{2\sqrt{x^2 - 4} - \dfrac{x(2x + 3)}{\sqrt{x^2 - 4}}}{x^2 - 4}$ 30. $3x^2(1 - 2x)^{-2} + 4x^3(1 - 2x)^{-3}$

31. $\dfrac{\sqrt{1 - x^2} + \dfrac{x^2}{\sqrt{1 - x^2}}}{1 - x^2}$ 32. $-(x^{-2} + x^{-1})^{-2}(-2x^{-3} - x^{-2})$

33. $\dfrac{2}{3}\left(\dfrac{x^2 + 1}{x^2 - 1}\right)^{-1/3} \cdot \dfrac{(x^2 - 1)2x - (x^2 + 1)2x}{(x^2 - 1)^2}$

34. Rationalize the numerator:

      a. $\dfrac{\sqrt{2x - 3} - 1}{x - 2}$ **b.** $\dfrac{\sqrt{x + h - 2} - \sqrt{x - 2}}{h}$

35. Rationalize the denominator:

      a. $\dfrac{1}{\sqrt{x + 3} - 2}$ **b.** $\dfrac{\sqrt{a + 4} - \sqrt{a - 4}}{\sqrt{a + 4} + \sqrt{a - 4}}$

B 36. Multiply:

      a. $(x^2 - 2x + 3)(2x^2 - 5x - 4)$ **b.** $(x - 2y + 5)^2$

In Problems 37–39 factor completely with rational coefficients.

37. **a.** $x^2 - 4 + 4y^2 - 4xy$ **b.** $x^4 - 2x^3 - x + 2$

38. **a.** $4x^2 - 3xy - 10y^2 - 3x + 6y$ **b.** $8x^3 - 60x^2y + 150xy^2 - 125y^3$

39. $4x^2 + 9y^2 - z^2 - 12xy - 6z - 9$

In Problems 40–44 perform the indicated operations and simplify the result. Express answers with positive exponents only.

40. $\dfrac{2x - 1}{x^2 + x - 2} - \dfrac{x + 5}{x^2 - 1} - \dfrac{x + 3}{x^2 + 3x + 2}$

41. $\dfrac{9(2x - 5)^2(3x + 2)^2 - 4(3x + 2)^3(2x - 5)}{(2x - 5)^3}$

42. $\dfrac{2x\sqrt[3]{1 - x^2} + \frac{2}{3}x^3(1 - x^2)^{-2/3}}{(1 - x^2)^{2/3}}$

43. $\dfrac{\sqrt[3]{3x - 1} \cdot \dfrac{1}{2\sqrt{x + 1}} - \sqrt{x + 1} \cdot (3x - 1)^{-2/3}}{(3x - 1)^{2/3}}$

44. $\dfrac{(x + 1)\left[\dfrac{-x^2}{\sqrt{1 - x^2}} + \sqrt{1 - x^2}\right] - x\sqrt{1 - x^2}}{(x + 1)^2}$

3

Equations and Inequalities of the First and Second Degree

Equations occur wherever mathematics is applied. An application from an introductory chemistry textbook* is given below.

Substituting into the expression for K_c, we obtain

$$\frac{(0.22 + 2x)^2}{(1.00 - x)(0.70 - x)} = 0.10$$

This time, we cannot solve for x as simply . . . , since the denominator of the left-hand side is not a perfect square. Instead, we use the general method of solving a quadratic equation, which involves rearranging to the form

$$ax^2 + bx + c = 0$$

and applying the "quadratic formula"

$$x = \frac{-b \pm \sqrt{b^2 - 4ac}}{2a}$$

To convert the equilibrium equation to the desired form, we proceed as follows:

$$(0.22 + 2x)^2 = 0.10(1.00 - x)(0.70 - x)$$

$$0.0484 + 0.88x + 4x^2 = 0.10(0.70 - 1.70x + x^2) = 0.0700 - 0.17x + 0.10x^2$$

Bringing all terms to the left-hand side, we obtain

$$3.90x^2 + 1.05x - 0.0216 = 0$$

so $a = 3.90$, $b = 1.05$, $c = -0.0216$, and

$$x = \frac{-1.05 \pm \sqrt{(1.05)^2 + 4(3.90)(0.0216)}}{7.80} = \frac{-1.05 \pm \sqrt{1.44}}{7.80}$$

$$= \frac{-1.05 \pm 1.20}{7.80} = \frac{0.15}{7.80} \quad \text{or} \quad \frac{-2.25}{7.80} \text{ (i.e. } 0.02 \quad \text{or} \quad -0.29)$$

Of the two answers, only 0.02 is plausible. A value of -0.29 would imply that the reaction proceeds in the opposite direction and that the concentration of NO at equilibrium is negative!

The importance of the quadratic formula cannot be overemphasized. We will derive the formula in this chapter. We will also see a variety of applications of both linear (first-degree) and quadratic (second-degree) equations.

---

* William L. Masterton and Emil J. Slowinski, *Chemical Principles*, 4th ed. (Philadelphia: W. B. Saunders Company, 1977), p. 366. Reprinted by permission.

1 Introduction

The solution of equations lies at the very heart of algebra and its applications. Much of what we have done up to this point has provided tools for solving equations. The importance of equations stems from the fact that they provide a means by which many complicated relationships in real-world problems can be written down in a concise and precise form. In the terminology used by mathematicians (and others), equations often provide **mathematical models** of real-world problems.

Equations that arise as mathematical models often involve more than algebraic concepts. Some involve trigonometry, and many involve calculus. Even in these more complicated equations, however, a knowledge of the techniques of algebra is essential. In this chapter we consider algebraic equations involving only one unknown. Equations with more than one unknown will be discussed later, when we consider systems of several equations.

Equations of special importance are **polynomial equations in one unknown.** Some examples are

$$2x - 3 = 7$$
$$x^2 - 3x + 2 = 0$$
$$x^3 - 2x^2 - 3 = 0$$

In general, if n is a positive integer, a polynomial equation of the nth degree in the variable x is an equation that can be written in the form

$$a_n x^n + a_{n-1} x^{n-1} + \cdots + a_1 x + a_0 = 0$$

where $a_0, a_1, \ldots, a_n$ are constants, with $a_n \neq 0$. If $n = 1$, the equation is called **linear or first degree,** and for $n = 2$, it is called **quadratic or second degree.** Higher-degree equations are sometimes given names (for example cubic, quartic, and quintic for $n = 3$, 4, and 5, respectively), but we usually treat these as a group. In this chapter we consider the two simplest cases—linear and quadratic equations. A distinction should be made between a polynomial in x and a polynomial equation in x. For example, consider the polynomial

$$2x^2 - 3x - 5$$

and the polynomial equation

$$2x^2 - 3x - 5 = 0$$

In the first case, no restriction is placed on the variable x, and in fact, x is simply left unspecified unless further instructions are given. In the polynomial equation, however, we are seeking the specific values of x that make the equation true. For this reason, we often refer to the variable in such an equation as an **unknown**; it is something with a value that is yet to be determined.

By a **solution** to an equation we mean a number which when substituted for the unknown makes the equation a true statement. A solution is also referred to as a **root** of the equation. For example, the number 2 is a solution, or root, of $x^2 - 4 = 0$, since when 2 is substituted for x we get $4 - 4 = 0$, which is true. The set of all solutions to an equation is called its **solution set.** Since $(-2)^2 = 4$, we see that -2 is also a solution to the equation $x^2 - 4 = 0$, and we will soon see that 2 and -2 are the only solutions. So we can say that the solution set of this equation is $\{2, -2\}$. Two equations are said to be **equivalent** if they have exactly the same solution set. To **solve** an equation means to find its solution set.

2 Linear Equations

By definition, **a linear equation is of the form**

$$ax + b = 0 \qquad (a \neq 0)$$

and by adding $-b$ to both sides and dividing by a we obtain

$$x = -\frac{b}{a}$$

Thus, the only possible solution is $x = -b/a$. We can verify that this is the solution by substitution:

$$a\left(-\frac{b}{a}\right) + b = -b + b = 0$$

We could say that the solution set is $\{-b/a\}$.

There is no point, of course, in memorizing the result just obtained. It is simple enough in each situation to carry out the steps leading to the answer.

EXAMPLE 1   Solve the equation: $3x - 4 = x + 7$

Solution
$$3x - 4 = x + 7 \qquad \text{Add } -x + 4 \text{ to both sides}$$
$$2x = 11 \qquad \text{Divide both sides by 2}$$
$$x = \tfrac{11}{2}$$

EXAMPLE 2   Solve the equation: $2(x - 3) = 5x - 8$

Solution
$$2(x - 3) = 5x - 8 \qquad \text{Perform multiplication on left}$$
$$2x - 6 = 5x - 8 \qquad \text{Add } -2x + 8 \text{ to both sides}$$
$$2 = 3x \qquad \text{Divide by 3 and interchange right and left sides}$$
$$x = \tfrac{2}{3}$$

In solving equations we make repeated use of the properties of equality given in Section 2 of Chapter 1. In particular, we may interchange the two sides of an equation as in Example 2, using the reflexive property. We may add the same quantity to both sides (this includes subtraction, since this is the same as adding a negative quantity), and we may multiply by the same *nonzero* quantity.

EXAMPLE 3   Solve the equation: $\dfrac{2x}{3} - \dfrac{5}{4} = \dfrac{1}{2}\left(\dfrac{x}{4} + 1\right)$

Solution   When an equation involves fractions, it is best to clear it of fractions by multiplying both sides by the LCD. In this problem we need first to multiply out the right-hand side in order to recognize the LCD. This gives

$$\frac{2x}{3} - \frac{5}{4} = \frac{x}{8} + \frac{1}{2}$$

Now we see that the LCD is 24. It is essential that we multiply *every* term on both sides by this LCD. We show the details as follows.

$$24\left(\frac{2x}{3} - \frac{5}{4}\right) = 24\left(\frac{x}{8} + \frac{1}{2}\right)$$

$$\overset{8}{\frac{\cancel{24}}{1}} \cdot \frac{2x}{\cancel{3}} - \overset{6}{\frac{\cancel{24}}{1}} \cdot \frac{5}{\cancel{4}} = \overset{3}{\frac{\cancel{24}}{1}} \cdot \frac{x}{\cancel{8}} + \overset{12}{\frac{\cancel{24}}{1}} \cdot \frac{1}{\cancel{2}}$$

$$16x - 30 = 3x + 12$$

$$13x = 42$$

$$x = \tfrac{42}{13}$$

With care, the second step can be done mentally.

EXAMPLE 4   Solve for t: $at + d = b - ct$

Solution
$$at + d = b - ct$$
$$at + ct = b - d$$
$$(a + c)t = b - d$$
$$t = \frac{b - d}{a + c} \qquad (c \neq -a)$$

EXERCISE SET 2

A   Find the complete solution for each of the following equations:

1. $2x - 3 = 5$
2. $3x + 4 = 10$
3. $2x - 3 = 8 + 3x$
4. $3x + 7 = 8 - 2x$
5. $2 - x = 6 + x$
6. $4 - 2x = x + 7$
7. $2(x - 1) = 3x + 4$
8. $3 - 4x = 5(3x + 2)$
9. $4(x - 2) = 6$
10. $3(2 - x) = 2x + 1$
11. $\dfrac{x}{2} + \dfrac{1}{3} = 1$
12. $\dfrac{2x}{3} - \dfrac{1}{4} = \dfrac{x}{2}$
13. $\dfrac{x}{3} - \dfrac{1}{2} = \dfrac{3}{4}$
14. $\dfrac{3x + 4}{2} = 1 - \dfrac{x}{3}$

15. $\dfrac{3}{5} - \dfrac{7x}{10} = \dfrac{1}{2}$

16. $2 - \dfrac{3x}{8} = \dfrac{5x}{2} + \dfrac{3}{4}$

17. $\dfrac{2x-1}{3} = \dfrac{4x+2}{5}$

18. $\dfrac{1-3t}{4} - \dfrac{1}{2} = \dfrac{t+6}{3}$

19. $\dfrac{5s+1}{6} - \dfrac{2-3s}{8} = 1$

20. $\dfrac{3}{4}\left(\dfrac{m}{2} - \dfrac{1}{3}\right) = \dfrac{2-m}{6}$

21. $\dfrac{2}{3}\left(\dfrac{x}{4} - 1\right) = \dfrac{3x}{4} - \dfrac{1}{2}$

22. $\dfrac{3}{5}\left(\dfrac{1}{2} - \dfrac{s}{3}\right) = \dfrac{5s}{6} + \dfrac{7}{15}$

23. $\dfrac{1}{2}\left(t - \dfrac{1}{3}\right) = \dfrac{3}{4} - \dfrac{t}{6}$

24. $\dfrac{2y-3}{15} - 1 = \dfrac{1}{3} - y$

25. $\dfrac{4}{3}\left(\dfrac{2x-5}{3}\right) - \dfrac{5}{6} = \dfrac{5x}{2} - \dfrac{4}{3}$

26. $\dfrac{3}{2}\left(\dfrac{1}{4} - \dfrac{3x}{8}\right) = \dfrac{x-5}{12} + \dfrac{3}{16}$

B Solve for the unknown indicated in Problems 27–30.

27. x: $ax - b = cx + d$

28. s: $rs - at = bt - s$

29. x: $\dfrac{3xy - 4}{2y + 3} = 1 - x$

30. n: $\dfrac{2mn - 3}{1 + m} = 4 - n$

31. Find k so that $x = 2$ is a solution of

$$\frac{5x}{3} - \frac{3k}{2} = \frac{3}{2}\left(\frac{k}{4} + \frac{5x}{6}\right)$$

32. Find k so that $x = -3$ is a solution of

$$\frac{2x + 3k}{5} = \frac{2}{3}\left(k - \frac{x}{2}\right)$$

---

3 Quadratic Equations

There are three principal techniques for solving quadratic equations: (1) by factoring, (2) by completing the square, and (3) by the quadratic formula. In this section we consider the solution by factoring, and in Section 4 we will study the other two methods.

Of fundamental importance in the solution by factoring is the fact that if a and b are real numbers, then $a \cdot b = 0$ if and only if $a = 0$ or $b = 0$. We will prove this important result. Suppose that $a \cdot b = 0$. If $a \neq 0$, we may multiply both sides by a^{-1} to obtain

$$a^{-1}(ab) = a^{-1} \cdot 0$$
$$(a^{-1}a)b = 0$$
$$1 \cdot b = 0$$
$$b = 0$$

So if $a \neq 0$, then b must be 0. On the other hand, if either $a = 0$ or $b = 0$, then the equation $ab = 0$ is satisfied. So the proof is complete.

A Word of Caution. The reasoning used in the above argument is not valid if the right-hand side is any number other than 0. For example, consider the following *fallacious argument*:

$$x^2 - 2x = 4$$
$$x(x - 2) = 4$$
$$x = 4 \quad \text{or} \quad x - 2 = 4, \quad \text{so that} \quad x = 6$$

A check of these results reveals that they are wrong. The trouble lies in the fact that if $ab = 4$, we cannot infer anything about the values of a and b.

The next three examples illustrate how to solve a quadratic equation by factoring.

EXAMPLE 5   Solve the equation: $x^2 - x - 2 = 0$

Solution
$$x^2 - x - 2 = 0$$
$$(x - 2)(x + 1) = 0$$

Now, from what we have just shown we know that the product $(x - 2)(x + 1)$ will be 0 if and only if either $x - 2 = 0$ or $x + 1 = 0$, that is, if $x = 2$ or $x = -1$. So these two numbers are solutions, and they are the only solutions. Therefore, the solution set is $\{2, -1\}$.

EXAMPLE 6   Solve: $\dfrac{2x^2}{3} - x - \dfrac{5}{3} = 0$

Solution   We first clear of fractions by multiplying both sides by 3.

$$2x^2 - 3x - 5 = 0$$
$$(2x - 5)(x + 1) = 0$$

$$\begin{array}{c|c} 2x - 5 = 0 & x + 1 = 0 \\ x = \frac{5}{2} & x = -1 \end{array}$$

So the solution set is $\{\frac{5}{2}, -1\}$. Again, either of these numbers satisfies the original equation, but no other numbers do so.

EXAMPLE 7   Solve: $x(x - 3) = 4$

Solution   As we have seen, it is essential for one side of the equation to be 0. So we add -4 to both sides. This gives

$$x(x - 3) - 4 = 0$$
$$x^2 - 3x - 4 = 0$$
$$(x - 4)(x + 1) = 0$$

$$\begin{array}{c|c} x - 4 = 0 & x + 1 = 0 \\ x = 4 & x = -1 \end{array}$$

So the solution set is $\{4, -1\}$.

EXERCISE SET 3

A Find the complete solution set.

1. $x^2 - 3x + 2 = 0$
2. $y^2 + 5y - 6 = 0$
3. $t^2 + 5t + 6 = 0$
4. $2t^2 - 3t - 2 = 0$

5. $3x^2 - 13x + 4 = 0$
6. $2t^2 + \dfrac{t}{3} = \dfrac{2}{3}$

7. $\frac{3}{5}x^2 + 2x - \frac{8}{5} = 0$
8. $4x^2 - 3x = 0$
9. $4m^2 - 5m = 6$
10. $12v^2 + 11v - 15 = 0$
11. $4r^2 - 9 = 0$
12. $4r^2 - 9r = 0$
13. $15y^2 + 8 = 26y$
14. $16t^2 - 8t + 1 = 0$
15. $2x^2 = x + 3$
16. $3t^2 - t = 10$
17. $24x^2 + 16x - 30 = 0$
18. $25 - 16s^2 = 0$
19. $t(2t + 1) = 1$
20. $24 + 28x - 12x^2 = 0$
21. $x^2 - 3x = 10$
22. $t(t + 1) = 6$
23. $2x^2 = 1 + x$
24. $x(6x + 1) = 35$
25. $11x - 4 = 6x^2$
26. $x(2 - x) = 3(x - 4)$
27. $(x - 1)(2x + 3) = 3$
28. $t(5t + 2) = 2t(1 - t) + 7$
29. $3x(x + 1) = 2(x + 2)$
30. $2a(a + 3) = a(1 - a) + 2$

B Solve for the unknown indicated in Problems 31–34.

31. x: $8a^2x^2 - 2abx - 15b^2 = 0$
32. r: $2s^2t^2 - 5rst - 3r^2 = 0$
33. n: $n(6n - m) = m^2$
34. t: $3(k^2t^2 - 5s^2) = 4kst$

35. Find k so that $x = 2$ is a solution of $2(k - 3) + 3kx - 2k^2 = 0$.
36. Find k so that $x = \frac{3}{2}$ is a solution of $2k^2x^2 + (3k - 4)x + 12k = 0$.

4 Completing the Square and the Quadratic Formula

The technique of factoring a quadratic polynomial to solve an equation is applicable only when the factors can be readily determined. There is a more general technique by which *all* quadratic equations can be solved, which leads to the **quadratic formula.** This is the technique known as **completing the square.** In order to illustrate it, we need to recall the form of the square of a binomial $(x + a)$. This is

$$(x + a)^2 = x^2 + 2ax + a^2$$

Now, suppose we are confronted with an expression such as

$$x^2 + 6x$$

and we wish to determine what should be added to this to make it a perfect square. We see that $2a = 6$, so that $a = 3$. Therefore, $a^2 = 9$, which is the correct term to add, yielding

$$x^2 + 6x + 9 = (x + 3)^2$$

More generally, since the coefficient of x in the expansion of $(x + a)^2$ is $2a$, it follows that **the correct constant term to add is the square of one-half of the coefficient of x.** Here are some examples.

EXAMPLE 8   Determine what number should be added to each of the following to make it a perfect square:

    a. $x^2 + 4x$ **b.** $x^2 + 12x$ **c.** $x^2 + 3x$ **d.** $x^2 - 8x$

    e. $x^2 - 5x$ **f.** $x^2 + \frac{3}{4}x$ **g.** $x^2 - \frac{5}{3}x$

Solution   **a.** $\left(\frac{1}{2} \cdot 4\right)^2 = 2^2 = 4$ **b.** $\left(\frac{1}{2} \cdot 12\right)^2 = 6^2 = 36$

             c. $\left(\frac{1}{2} \cdot 3\right)^2 = \frac{9}{4}$ **d.** $\left[\frac{1}{2} \cdot (-8)\right]^2 = (-4)^2 = 16$

             e. $\left[\frac{1}{2} \cdot (-5)\right]^2 = \frac{25}{4}$ **f.** $\left(\frac{1}{2} \cdot \frac{3}{4}\right)^2 = \left(\frac{3}{8}\right)^2 = \frac{9}{64}$

             g. $\left[\frac{1}{2} \cdot \left(-\frac{5}{3}\right)\right]^2 = \left(\frac{-5}{6}\right)^2 = \frac{25}{36}$

One additional fact is needed before proceeding to the solution of equations by this method. This is that $a^2 = b^2$ if and only if $a = b$ or $a = -b$ (or, more briefly, $a = \pm b$). If either $a = b$ or $a = -b$, then squaring both sides shows that $a^2 = b^2$. On the other hand, if $a^2 = b^2$, we have

$$a^2 - b^2 = 0$$
$$(a - b)(a + b) = 0$$

$$a - b = 0 \quad \bigg| \quad a + b = 0$$
$$a = b \quad \bigg| \quad a = -b$$

The next two examples illustrate the technique of solution by completing the square.

EXAMPLE 9   Solve: $x^2 + 3x - 2 = 0$

Solution   We determine that there are no rational factors and proceed as follows: Add 2 to both sides:

$$x^2 + 3x = 2$$

Complete the square on the left and add the same number on the right:

$$x^2 + 3x + \tfrac{9}{4} = 2 + \tfrac{9}{4}$$

Factor the left side and simplify the right:

$$\left(x + \frac{3}{2}\right)^2 = \frac{17}{4}$$

Use fact that $a^2 = b^2$ if and only if $a = \pm b$:

$$x + \frac{3}{2} = \pm \frac{\sqrt{17}}{2}$$

Solve for x:

$$x = -\frac{3}{2} \pm \frac{\sqrt{17}}{2} = \frac{-3 \pm \sqrt{17}}{2}$$

EXAMPLE 10 Solve: $2x^2 - 8x + 3 = 0$

Solution We will carry out steps similar to those in Example 9 but will omit the explanation. The fact that the coefficient of x^2 is not 1 is a slight complication, but this is handled by dividing both sides of the equation by 2. In solving a quadratic equation by completing the square, this step of dividing both sides of the equation by the coefficient of x^2, if it is not 1 to begin with, should always be done first.

$$2x^2 - 8x + 3 = 0$$
$$x^2 - 4x + \tfrac{3}{2} = 0$$
$$x^2 - 4x = -\tfrac{3}{2}$$
$$x^2 - 4x + 4 = -\tfrac{3}{2} + 4$$
$$(x - 2)^2 = \tfrac{5}{2}$$
$$x - 2 = \pm \sqrt{\tfrac{5}{2}}$$
$$x = 2 \pm \sqrt{\frac{5}{2} \cdot \frac{2}{2}} = 2 \pm \frac{\sqrt{10}}{2} = \frac{4 \pm \sqrt{10}}{2}$$

We now apply this technique to a general quadratic equation, that is, one in which we do not specify the coefficients. Such an equation may be written in the form

$$ax^2 + bx + c = 0 \qquad (a \neq 0) \tag{1}$$

Remark. In defining a polynomial equation of degree n we used a_0, a_1, $a_2, \ldots, a_n$ for the coefficients because to use different letters of the alphabet would be complicated by not knowing how many letters are needed. But in the present case we know we need three coefficients, so we choose to use a, b, and c rather than a_0, a_1, and a_2.

We proceed as in Example 9:

$$ax^2 + bx + c = 0$$

Divide both sides by a:

$$x^2 + \frac{b}{a}x + \frac{c}{a} = 0$$

Add $(-c)/a$ to both sides:

$$x^2 + \frac{b}{a}x = -\frac{c}{a}$$

Complete the square by adding $[\frac{1}{2} \cdot (b/a)]^2 = b^2/(4a^2)$ to both sides:

$$x^2 + \frac{b}{a}x + \frac{b^2}{4a^2} = -\frac{c}{a} + \frac{b^2}{4a^2}$$

Factor the left side and collect terms on the right:

$$\left(x + \frac{b}{2a}\right)^2 = \frac{b^2 - 4ac}{4a^2}$$

Take square roots:

$$x + \frac{b}{2a} = \frac{\pm\sqrt{b^2 - 4ac}}{2a}$$

Finally, solve for x, thus obtaining the **quadratic formula:**

$$x = \frac{-b \pm \sqrt{b^2 - 4ac}}{2a}$$

By committing this formula to memory, you can write down at once the solutions to any quadratic equation. It should be emphasized, however, that factoring is usually easier when the factors can be readily found.

It is essential before attempting to apply the quadratic formula that the equation be written precisely in the form given in equation (1) so that the correct values of a, b, and c can be determined. We call this the **standard form.**

EXAMPLE 11   Solve the equation $2x^2 - 3x - 7 = 0$ by the quadratic formula.

Solution   We think of the equation in the equivalent form $2x^2 + (-3)x + (-7)$, so that $a = 2$, $b = -3$, and $c = -7$. So

$$x = \frac{-(-3) \pm \sqrt{(-3)^2 - 4(2)(-7)}}{2 \cdot 2} = \frac{3 \pm \sqrt{9 + 56}}{4}$$

$$= \frac{3 \pm \sqrt{65}}{4}$$

There is a difficulty that an alert reader might have noticed. The quantity $(b^2 - 4ac)$ appearing under the radical in the quadratic formula could be negative, in which case there is no solution in the set of real numbers. As we have seen, if a is any nonzero real number, then $a^2 > 0$, so that there is no square root of a negative number in R. To overcome this difficulty, it is necessary to consider a wider class of numbers called the **complex numbers.** These will be discussed in the next section.

EXERCISE SET 4

A   Solve Problems 1–16 by completing the square.

1. $x^2 + 4x - 12 = 0$
2. $x^2 - 6x + 8 = 0$
3. $3 + 2x - x^2 = 0$
4. $7 - 6x - x^2 = 0$
5. $y^2 + 3y - 10 = 0$
6. $x^2 - 7x + 6 = 0$
7. $t^2 - 5t = 24$
8. $2x^2 - 7x + 6 = 0$
9. $t^2 - 4t + 2 = 0$
10. $4 + 8x - x^2 = 0$
11. $32 + 4x - 3x^2 = 0$
12. $t^2 + 2t - 4 = 0$
13. $m^2 - 5m = 3$
14. $n^2 + 2 = 3n$
15. $2x^2 = 3(x + 3)$
16. $2x(x - 2) = 3$

Solve Problems 17–32 by the quadratic formula.

17. $x^2 - 2x - 2 = 0$
18. $x^2 - 3x - 6 = 0$
19. $t^2 + 5t = 9$
20. $x^2 + x = 1$
21. $2x^2 - x = 5$
22. $2x^2 - 3x - 5 = 0$
23. $3x^2 = 2x + 2$
24. $3x^2 + 10x + 2 = 0$
25. $5y^2 - y = 3$
26. $5t^2 + 10t + 4 = 0$
27. $2x + 3 = 4x^2$
28. $6x = 4x^2 - 1$
29. $x(2x - 3) = 4$
30. $3x(x - 2) = 4(x + 1)$
31. $(t - 2)(2t + 1) = 1$
32. $3t^2 = 2(2 - t)$

B   Solve Problems 33–39 for the unknown indicated.

33. t: $\frac{1}{2}gt^2 - v_0 t - s_0 = 0$
34. x: $x^2 + 2t(x + 1) = 1$
35. R: $w = \dfrac{mgR^2}{(x + R)^2}$ $(R > 0, x > 0)$
36. r: $S = \pi r^2 + 2\pi r l$
37. s: $2s^2 - \sqrt{3}ks - 9k^2 = 0$ $(k > 0)$
38. r: $Lr^2 + Rr + \dfrac{1}{C} = 0$
39. x: $2x^2 + 3kx - (3k + 2) = 0$ $(k > 0)$

In Problems 40 and 41 solve for x with the aid of a hand calculator.

40. $2.38x^2 - 5.47x + 1.32 = 0$
41. $32.43 + 2.054x - 0.03172x^2 = 0$

5 Complex Numbers

We have already noted that certain quadratic equations cannot be solved in the domain of real numbers. Even the simple equation $x^2 + 1 = 0$ falls in this category. If x is any real number, its square is nonnegative, so adding it to the positive integer 1 results in a positive number, which is therefore greater than zero. This difficulty persists in higher-degree equations. The resolution of the problem lies in expanding our number system.

Number systems have evolved over thousands of years, and each step has met with resistance from segments of the intellectual community. The introduction of negative and irrational numbers were certainly two of the most controversial stages. As a matter of fact, all numbers are creations of the human mind (even the integers, Kronecker notwithstanding*). Numbers do not exist in nature, waiting to be discovered. They exist only in the realm of ideas. We are free, then, to invent new numbers if a need exists. To make them useful, additions should be consistent with our known number systems and should, in some sense, include these as subsystems. The real numbers, for example, include the rational numbers as a subsystem, which include the integers, which in turn include the natural numbers.

The **complex numbers** provide just such an extension of the reals. **They consist of elements of the form $a + bi$, where a and b are arbitrary real numbers, and i is the "imaginary unit" defined by $i^2 = -1$.** These complex numbers exist just as surely as any numbers do; there is nothing imaginary about them. It is an unfortunate fact of history that the terms *real* and *imaginary* are used, because of their connotations. One might better refer to real numbers as one-dimensional numbers and complex numbers as two-dimensional numbers. This terminology reflects the fact that real numbers can be associated with points on a line, whereas complex numbers can be made to correspond to points in a plane.

The real numbers are included among the complex numbers, since a real number a may be thought of as being of the form $a + 0i$. If $b \neq 0$, the complex number $a + bi$ is called an **imaginary number.** Complex numbers of the form $0 + bi = bi$ with $b \neq 0$ are called **pure imaginary numbers.**

Two complex numbers $a + bi$ and $c + di$ are equal if and only if $a = c$ and $b = d$. Addition is defined by

$$(a + bi) + (c + di) = (a + c) + (b + d)i$$

and multiplication by

$$(a + bi)(c + di) = (ac - bd) + (ad + bc)i$$

The latter formula is the result of multiplying as with two real binomials and

---

* Leopold Kronecker (1823–1891) said that "God made the integers, and all the rest is the work of man."

then substituting $i^2 = -1$:

$$(a + bi)(c + di) = ac + bic + adi + bdi^2 = ac + i(bc + ad) + bd(-1)$$
$$= (ac - bd) + (ad + bc)i$$

Multiplication is usually carried out in this way rather than by simply memorizing the definition. For example,

$$(2 + 3i)(4 - 7i) = 8 - 2i - 21i^2 = 8 - 2i + 21 = 29 - 2i$$

The identity elements are $0 = 0 + 0i$ and $1 = 1 + 0i$. The additive inverse of $a + bi$ is seen to be $(-a) + (-b)i$. When a and b are not both equal to 0 (that is, when $a + bi \neq 0$), we can show that the number $a + bi$ has a multiplicative inverse within the complex number system. To do this we must show that $(a + bi)^{-1}$ is a number of the form $A + Bi$, where A and B are real. The following calculations show that this is the case, with $A = a/(a^2 + b^2)$ and $B = -b/(a^2 + b^2)$:

$$(a + bi)^{-1} = \frac{1}{a + bi} = \frac{1}{a + bi} \cdot \frac{a - bi}{a - bi} = \frac{a - bi}{a^2 - b^2 i^2} = \frac{a - bi}{a^2 + b^2}$$

$$= \frac{a}{a^2 + b^2} + \frac{-b}{a^2 + b^2} i$$

Rather than learning this result, it is better to learn the procedure. For example,

$$\frac{1}{2 + 3i} = \frac{1}{2 + 3i} \cdot \frac{2 - 3i}{2 - 3i} = \frac{2 - 3i}{4 - 9i^2} = \frac{2 - 3i}{4 + 9} = \frac{2}{13} + \frac{-3}{13} i$$

We define the conjugate of a complex number $a + bi$ to be the number $a - bi$. So to find the inverse of a complex number, we write its reciprocal and then multiply the numerator and denominator by its conjugate.

Division is accomplished in a similar way. For example:

$$\frac{3 + 2i}{5 - 4i} = \frac{3 + 2i}{5 - 4i} \cdot \frac{5 + 4i}{5 + 4i} = \frac{15 + 22i + 8i^2}{25 - 16i^2} = \frac{15 + 22i - 8}{25 + 16} = \frac{7}{41} + \frac{22}{41} i$$

More generally,

$$\frac{a + bi}{c + di} = \frac{a + bi}{c + di} \cdot \frac{c - di}{c - di} = \frac{(ac + bd) + (bc - ad)i}{c^2 + d^2} = \frac{ac + bd}{c^2 + d^2} + \frac{bc - ad}{c^2 + d^2} i$$

To indicate the operation of taking the conjugate, a bar is used above the number:

$$\overline{a + bi} = a - bi$$

For example:

$$\overline{2 + 3i} = 2 - 3i$$
$$\overline{5 - 4i} = 5 + 4i$$
$$\overline{-7i} = \overline{0 - 7i} = 7i$$
$$\overline{-2} = \overline{-2 + 0i} = -2 - 0i = -2$$

Often the letter z is used to designate a complex number. Then $\bar{z}$ indicates its conjugate. The following facts about conjugates can be shown:

---

1. $\overline{z_1 + z_2} = \bar{z}_1 + \bar{z}_2$ Conjugate of a sum = Sum of conjugates

2. $\overline{z_1 \cdot z_2} = \bar{z}_1 \cdot \bar{z}_2$ Conjugate of a product = Product of conjugates

3. $\overline{\left(\dfrac{z_1}{z_2}\right)} = \dfrac{\bar{z}_1}{\bar{z}_2}$ Conjugate of a quotient = Quotient of conjugates

4. $z\bar{z}$ is real

5. If z is real, then $\bar{z} = z$.

Facts 4 and 5 result from the following reasoning: Suppose $z = a + bi$. Then $z\bar{z} = (a + bi)(a - bi) = a^2 - b^2i^2 = a^2 + b^2$, which is real. If $z = a$, where a is real, we have $\bar{z} = \bar{a} = \overline{a + 0i} = a - 0i = a = z$.

It is useful to know the various powers of i:

$$i = \sqrt{-1}$$
$$i^2 = -1$$
$$i^3 = i^2 \cdot i = (-1)i = -i$$
$$i^4 = i^2 \cdot i^2 = (-1)(-1) = 1$$

Now, higher powers can be readily calculated. For example, $i^{22} = i^{20} \cdot i^2 = (i^4)^5 \cdot i^2 = (1)^5 \cdot i^2 = i^2 = -1$. Also, $i^{35} = i^{32} \cdot i^3 = (i^4)^8 \cdot i^3 = (1)^8 \cdot i^3 = i^3 = -i$. The object is to factor out the highest power of i^4, which is 1, and the remaining factor can be evaluated using the results just obtained, that is, $i^1 = i$, $i^2 = -1$, $i^3 = -i$, $i^4 = 1$. More generally, if $n > 4$, and we write $n = 4k + r$, where $0 \le r \le 3$, then $i^n = i^{4k+r} = (i^{4k}) \cdot i^r = (i^4)^k \cdot i^r = 1^k \cdot i^r = i^r$.

In applications of the quadratic formula, and elsewhere, we sometimes encounter expressions of the form $\sqrt{-p}$, where p is a positive real number. We define this as follows:

$$\sqrt{-p} - \sqrt{(-1)p} = \sqrt{-1}\,\sqrt{p} = i\sqrt{p}$$

Whenever such an expression occurs, it is important to change it immediately to the form $i\sqrt{p}$. To see why, consider $\sqrt{-2} \cdot \sqrt{-5}$. If we carelessly applied formula (11) from Chapter 1, we would get

$$\sqrt{-2} \cdot \sqrt{-5} = \sqrt{(-2)(-5)} = \sqrt{10}$$

This is incorrect. Instead, we should do as follows:

$$\sqrt{-2} \cdot \sqrt{-5} = (i\sqrt{2})(i\sqrt{5}) = i^2(\sqrt{2} \cdot \sqrt{5}) = -\sqrt{10}$$

Let us return now to the solution of quadratic equations. Recall that by the quadratic formula, the solutions of

$$ax^2 + bx + c = 0 \qquad (a \ne 0)$$

are given by

$$\frac{-b + \sqrt{b^2 - 4ac}}{2a} \qquad \text{and} \qquad \frac{-b - \sqrt{b^2 - 4ac}}{2a}$$

Although the quadratic formula holds true even when a, b, and c are complex, for the present we assume them to be real. The nature of these two solutions depends on the number under the radical. This number, $b^2 - 4ac$, is called the **discriminant of the quadratic equation.** When the discriminant is positive, the square root is a positive real number, so the solutions are real and distinct. When the discriminant is 0, the square root is 0, so the solutions are real and equal. (There is only one solution in this case.) Finally, when the discriminant is negative, the square root is imaginary, so the solutions are imaginary; they are, in fact, conjugates of each other. We summarize these results in the box.

$$\text{If} \quad b^2 - 4ac \begin{cases} >0 \\ =0 \quad \text{the solutions are} \\ <0 \end{cases} \begin{cases} \text{real and unequal} \\ \text{real and equal} \\ \text{imaginary} \end{cases}$$

EXAMPLE 12 Without solving, determine the nature of the solutions of each of the following.
   a. $2x^2 - 3x - 4 = 0$ **b.** $9x^2 - 24x + 16 = 0$ **c.** $3x^2 - 2x + 4 = 0$

Solution **a.** $b^2 - 4ac = (-3)^2 - 4(2)(-4) = 9 + 32 = 41 > 0$. So the solutions are real and unequal.
   b. $b^2 - 4ac = (-24)^2 - 4(9)(16) = 576 - 576 = 0$. So the solutions are real and equal.
   c. $b^2 - 4ac = (-2)^2 - 4(3)(4) = 4 - 48 = -44 < 0$. So the solutions are imaginary.

EXAMPLE 13 Solve: $x^2 - 6x + 10 = 0$

Solution By the quadratic formula we obtain

$$x = \frac{6 \pm \sqrt{36 - 40}}{2} = \frac{6 \pm \sqrt{-4}}{2} = \frac{6 \pm i\sqrt{4}}{2}$$

$$= \frac{6 \pm 2i}{2} = 3 \pm i$$

EXERCISE SET 5

A In Problems 1–8 perform the indicated operations. Express answers in the form $a + bi$.

   1. **a.** $(2 - 5i) + (7 + 3i)$ **b.** $(3 + 2i) + (-5 - 7i)$
       c. $(5 + 8i) - (6 - i)$ **d.** $(3 - i) - (2i - 3)$
   2. **a.** $(3 + 7i) + (2 + 3i)$ **b.** $(5 - 3i) + (2 + i)$
       c. $(6 - 2i) - (3 + 4i)$ **d.** $(4i + 2) - (3 - 8i)$

3. **a.** $(4 + 3i)(3 - 2i)$ **b.** $(2 - i)(2 + i)$
   c. $(5i - 9)(4i + 7)$ **d.** $(i + 3)(4 - 3i)$
4. **a.** $(5 + 4i)(6 + 7i)$ **b.** $(2 - 5i)(3 + i)$
   c. $(3 + 4i)(3 - 4i)$ **d.** $(2i - 3)(4 + 5i)$

5. **a.** $\dfrac{1}{1 + i}$ **b.** $(3 - 2i)^{-1}$ **c.** $\dfrac{1}{i}$ **d.** $\dfrac{1}{7 + 8i}$

6. **a.** $\dfrac{1}{2 + 3i}$ **b.** $(4 - i)^{-1}$ **c.** $\dfrac{1}{i - 1}$ **d.** $(5 - 4i)^{-1}$

7. **a.** $\dfrac{2 + 3i}{3 - 2i}$ **b.** $\dfrac{1 - i}{1 + i}$ **c.** $\dfrac{3 + 4i}{5 - 3i}$ **d.** $\dfrac{3i - 1}{6 + 5i}$

8. **a.** $\dfrac{3 - i}{2 + 3i}$ **b.** $\dfrac{4 + 3i}{4 - 3i}$ **c.** $\dfrac{i}{i + 1}$ **d.** $\dfrac{2i - 3}{5 - 2i}$

In Problems 9–12 simplify the expressions by using properties of i.

9. **a.** $\sqrt{-4}$ **b.** $\sqrt{-162}$ **c.** $\sqrt{-40}$
   d. $\sqrt{-4}\sqrt{-9}$ **e.** $\sqrt{-2}\sqrt{-8}$

10. **a.** $\sqrt{-75}$ **b.** $\dfrac{1}{\sqrt{-12}}$ **c.** $\sqrt{-3}\sqrt{-6}$

   d. $\dfrac{\sqrt{20}}{\sqrt{-5}}$ **e.** $\sqrt{-8}\sqrt{2}$

11. **a.** i^7 **b.** i^9 **c.** i^{12} **d.** i^{25} **e.** i^{18}

12. **a.** $\dfrac{1}{i^2}$ **b.** $\dfrac{1}{i^3}$ **c.** $\dfrac{1}{i^9}$ **d.** i^{-5} **e.** i^{-10}

In Problems 13–20 solve the quadratic equations.

13. **a.** $x^2 + 4 = 0$ **b.** $x^2 - x + 2 = 0$
14. **a.** $x^2 = -9$ **b.** $4x^2 + 25 = 0$
15. **a.** $x^2 + 3x + 3 = 0$ **b.** $2x^2 + 5 = 6x$
16. **a.** $x^2 - 2x + 6 = 0$ **b.** $t^2 + 3t = -4$
17. **a.** $3m^2 - 4m + 6 = 0$ **b.** $5t^2 + 2 = 4t$
18. **a.** $2s^2 - 5s + 6 = 0$ **b.** $3s^2 + 2s + 1 = 0$
19. **a.** $2t^2 = 6t - 7$ **b.** $t(5t + 6) + 4 = 0$
20. **a.** $5 + 7x^2 = 8x$ **b.** $x(8 - 5x) = 4$

In Problems 21–23 determine whether the solutions are real and unequal, real and equal, or imaginary by using the discriminant. Do not solve.

21. **a.** $3x^2 - 9x + 5 = 0$ **b.** $7x^2 + 6x + 3 = 0$
22. **a.** $2t^2 - 8 = 3t$ **b.** $9m^2 = 5(6m - 5)$
23. **a.** $y(4y - 7) + 3 = 0$ **b.** $8 + 6s^2 = 13s$

B In Problems 24 and 25 expand and simplify.

24. **a.** $(2 + 3i)^3$ **b.** $(1 + i)^5$
25. **a.** $(2 - i)^4$ **b.** $(3 - 4i)^3$

26. Evaluate the polynomial $x^3 - 5x^2 + 17x - 13$ when $x = 2 - 3i$.
27. Evaluate the polynomial $2x^3 - 7x^2 - 10x - 6$ when $x = 1 - i$.
28. Solve the following quadratic equations:
    a. $3x^2 - 8ix - 4 = 0$ b. $x^2 - x + 1 + i = 0$
29. Prove the following, where $z_1 = a + bi$ and $z_2 = c + di$.

    a. $\overline{z_1 z_2} = \overline{z_1} \cdot \overline{z_2}$ b. $\overline{\left(\dfrac{z_1}{z_2}\right)} = \dfrac{\overline{z_1}}{\overline{z_2}}$

30. For what values of k will the equation $k^2 x^2 + (k-1)x + 4 =$ have equal solutions?

---

6   Equations That Are Convertible to Linear or Quadratic Forms

Some equations, although they are not linear or quadratic, can nevertheless be solved using techniques developed in this chapter. We consider first equations that are **quadratic in form.** These are equations that can be written in the form

$$a(\ \ )^2 + b(\ \ ) + c = 0$$

where the same expression appears in each set of parentheses. For example,

$$x^4 - 5x^2 + 4 = 0$$

is quadratic in form, since it can be written

$$(x^2)^2 - 5(x^2) + 4 = 0$$

We could say it is quadratic in the unknown x^2. Another example is

$$3x^{-2} - 4x^{-1} + 1 = 0$$

which can be written

$$3(x^{-1})^2 - 4(x^{-1}) + 1 = 0$$

In the next example we solve these two equations.

EXAMPLE 14   Solve the equations:
a. $x^4 - 5x^2 + 4 = 0$ b. $3x^{-2} - 4x^{-1} + 1 = 0$

Solution   a.   We solve by factoring, first treating x^2 as the unknown.

$$x^4 - 5x^2 + 4 = 0$$
$$(x^2 - 1)(x^2 - 4) = 0$$

$$\begin{array}{c|c} x^2 - 1 = 0 & x^2 - 4 = 0 \\ x^2 = 1 & x^2 = 4 \\ x = \pm 1 & x = \pm 2 \end{array}$$

So the solution set is $\{\pm 1, \pm 2\}$.

b.
$$3x^{-2} - 4x^{-1} + 1 = 0$$
$$(3x^{-1} - 1)(x^{-1} - 1) = 0$$

$3x^{-1} - 1 = 0$	$x^{-1} - 1 = 0$
$3x^{-1} = 1$	$x^{-1} = 1$
$\dfrac{3}{x} = 1$	$\dfrac{1}{x} = 1$
$x = 3$	$x = 1$

So the solution set is $\{3, 1\}$.

As an alternate procedure we may make an appropriate substitution so that the equation becomes quadratic. In part a, for example, we could let $t = x^2$. Then the equation becomes

$$t^2 - 5t + 4 = 0$$

Solving for t yields $t = 1$ or $t = 4$. Finally, we replace t by x^2 in each case and solve for x:

$t = x^2 = 1$	$t = x^2 = 4$
$x = \pm 1$	$x = \pm 2$

Similarly in part b, we could let $t = x^{-1}$. The equation would become

$$3t^2 - 4t + 1 = 0$$

yielding $t = \frac{1}{3}$ or $t = 1$, from which we would get

$x^{-1} = \frac{1}{3}$	$x^{-1} = 1$
$\dfrac{1}{x} = \dfrac{1}{3}$	$\dfrac{1}{x} = 1$
$x = 3$	$x = 1$

The next type of equation we consider is one involving fractions, where the unknown appears in a denominator. Our procedure will be to clear of fractions by multiplying both sides by the LCD. Now we know that multiplying an equation by a nonzero number results in an equivalent equation. But if the LCD involves the unknown, then we do not know in advance if the number we are multiplying by is nonzero. The way out of this dilemma is to proceed with the clearing of fractions and solve the resulting equation but then to check the answer. A complete check is to substitute each value found for x into the *original* equation to see if the equation is satisfied. This complete check is recommended, but sometimes it can be quite tedious. A *minimum requirement* is to check each value of x obtained by substituting it in the LCD to see that the LCD $\neq 0$. If the LCD $= 0$ for a value of x, this value must be discarded. It should be noted that simply showing that the LCD $\neq 0$ for a value of x which has been found as a possible solution shows that our procedure was justified for that value of x, but it does not guarantee that the solution is correct (an arithmetic error may have been made).

EXAMPLE 15   Solve for x: $\dfrac{1}{x-2} - \dfrac{2}{x+1} = \dfrac{7}{x^2 - x - 2}$

Solution   The procedure is to multiply both sides of the equation by the LCD, which in this case is $(x-2)(x+1)$. It is essential to multiply every term on both sides of the equation. In so doing, all denominators cancel.

$$\left(\frac{1}{x-2} - \frac{2}{x+1}\right)\frac{(x-2)(x+1)}{1} = \frac{7}{x^2-x-2}\frac{(x-2)(x+1)}{1}$$

$$x + 1 - 2(x-2) = 7$$

$$x + 1 - 2x + 4 = 7$$

$$-x = 2$$

$$x = -2$$

We check $x = -2$ in the LCD and see that it is not 0. So (assuming no arithmetic error) the solution is $x = -2$.

EXAMPLE 16   Solve for x: $\dfrac{3}{x-3} - \dfrac{2}{x-2} = \dfrac{3}{x^2 - 5x + 6}$

Solution   The LCD is $(x-3)(x-2)$. Multiplying both sides by this yields

$$3(x-2) - 2(x-3) = 3$$

$$3x - 6 - 2x + 6 = 3$$

$$x = 3$$

Checking the LCD, we find that it is 0 for this value of x. Since this is the only possible solution and it is not admissible, we conclude that the equation has **no solution.** The solution set is therefore the empty set.

EXAMPLE 17   Solve for x: $\dfrac{1}{x-1} + \dfrac{3}{x+3} = 1$

Solution   We multiply both sides by the LCD, $(x-1)(x+3)$, to obtain

$$x + 3 + 3(x-1) = (x-1)(x+3)$$

$$x + 3 + 3x - 3 = x^2 + 2x - 3$$

$$0 = x^2 - 2x - 3$$

$$(x-3)(x+1) = 0$$

$$x = 3 \quad | \quad x = -1$$

Since the LCD is nonzero for each of these, the solution set is $\{-1, 3\}$.

EXAMPLE 18   Solve for y and check the results: $\dfrac{2}{3y} + \dfrac{1}{y-1} = \dfrac{1}{2}$

Solution   The LCD is $6y(y-1)$. Multiplying by this yields

$$4(y-1) + 6y = 3y(y-1)$$
$$4y - 4 + 6y = 3y^2 - 3y$$
$$3y^2 - 13y + 4 = 0$$
$$(3y - 1)(y - 4) = 0$$

$3y - 1 = 0$	$y - 4 = 0$
$3y = 1$	$y = 4$
$y = \frac{1}{3}$	

The LCD is nonzero, so we know the equation obtained after multiplication is equivalent to the original. To verify that these actually are solutions, we substitute in the original equation.

Check. $y = \frac{1}{3}$

$$\frac{2}{3 \cdot \frac{1}{3}} + \frac{1}{\frac{1}{3} - 1} = \frac{2}{1} + \frac{3}{1 - 3} = 2 + \frac{3}{-2} = 2 - \frac{3}{2} = \frac{4}{2} - \frac{3}{2} = \frac{1}{2}$$

So $y = \frac{1}{3}$ is a solution.

Check. $y = 4$

$$\frac{2}{3 \cdot 4} + \frac{1}{4 - 1} = \frac{2}{12} + \frac{1}{3} = \frac{1}{6} + \frac{1}{3} = \frac{1}{6} + \frac{2}{6} = \frac{3}{6} = \frac{1}{2}$$

So $y = 4$ is also a solution. The solution set is therefore $\{\frac{1}{3}, 4\}$.

Remark.   Multiplying both sides of an equation by an expression involving the unknown may introduce extraneous roots (as in Example 16). On the other hand, dividing both sides by such an expression may result in the loss of solutions. To illustrate the latter, if in the equation $x^2 = 4x$, we divide both sides by x, getting $x = 4$, we lose the solution $x = 0$.

The next three examples involve squaring both sides of an equation. This may or may not lead to an equivalent equation, as the following considerations show: If $a = b$, then clearly $a^2 = b^2$. But conversely, if $a^2 = b^2$, then we have either $a = b$ or $a = -b$. So squaring both sides of an equation results in the possibility of additional solutions not contained in the original (namely, those contained in $a = -b$). So, when squaring is desirable, the appropriate way to proceed is to square both sides, solve the resulting problem, and check all answers in the original equation. The squared equation contains all solutions of the original, but it may contain additional solutions that are not valid.

EXAMPLE 19   Solve for x: $\sqrt{x-1}=2$

Solution   On squaring, we obtain

$$x - 1 = 4$$
$$x = 5$$

Check. $\sqrt{5-1}=\sqrt{4}=2$
So the answer is 5.

EXAMPLE 20   Solve for x: $\sqrt{2x-3}+x=3$

Solution   Before squaring we wish to isolate the radical in order to eliminate it after squaring. So, we first add $-x$ to both sides:

$$\sqrt{2x-3} = 3 - x$$
$$2x - 3 = 9 - 6x + x^2$$
$$x^2 - 8x + 12 = 0$$
$$(x - 2)(x - 6) = 0$$
$$x = 2 \quad | \quad x = 6$$

Check. $x = 2$

$$\sqrt{2\cdot 2 - 3} + 2 = \sqrt{1} + 2 = 1 + 2 = 3$$

So $x = 2$ is a solution.

Check. $x = 6$

$$\sqrt{2\cdot 6 - 3} + 6 = \sqrt{9} + 6 = 3 + 6 = 9 \neq 3$$

So $x = 6$ is not a solution.

EXAMPLE 21   Solve for x: $\sqrt{2x+3}-\sqrt{x+1}=1$

Solution   In a situation such as this it is usually best to isolate the more complicated radical, square once, isolate the remaining radical, and square again.

$$\sqrt{2x+3} = 1 + \sqrt{x+1}$$
$$(\sqrt{2x+3})^2 = (1 + \sqrt{x+1})^2$$
$$2x + 3 = 1 + 2\sqrt{x+1} + x + 1$$
$$x + 1 = 2\sqrt{x+1}$$
$$x^2 + 2x + 1 = 4(x+1)$$
$$x^2 - 2x - 3 = 0$$
$$(x - 3)(x + 1) = 0$$
$$x = 3 \quad | \quad x = -1$$

Check. $x = 3$

$$\sqrt{2 \cdot 3 + 3} - \sqrt{3 + 1} = \sqrt{9} - \sqrt{4} = 3 - 2 = 1$$

So $x = 3$ checks.

Check. $x = -1$

$$\sqrt{2(-1) + 3} - \sqrt{-1 + 1} = \sqrt{-2 + 3} - 0 = \sqrt{1} = 1$$

So $x = -1$ also checks. The complete solution set is therefore $\{-1, 3\}$.

EXERCISE SET 6

A   Solve the equations.

1. $4x^4 - 13x^2 + 9 = 0$

2. $x^4 - 13x^2 + 36 = 0$

3. $x^{-2} - x^{-1} - 6 = 0$

4. $2x^{-2} - 3x^{-1} - 5 = 0$

5. $x^4 + 3x^2 - 4 = 0$

6. $4x^{-4} - 13x^{-2} + 9 = 0$

7. $4x^4 - 25x^2 + 36 = 0$

8. $3x^{-2} - 10x^{-1} + 8 = 0$

9. $x^{2/3} - 2x^{1/3} - 3 = 0$

10. $6x^{-2/3} + 7x^{-1/3} - 3 = 0$

11. $\dfrac{1}{x - 1} = \dfrac{2}{x + 3}$

12. $\dfrac{3}{x} - \dfrac{4}{x - 2} = 0$

13. $\dfrac{3}{x} + \dfrac{1}{2} = \dfrac{x}{x + 4}$

14. $\dfrac{4}{2x - 3} = \dfrac{5}{3x - 4}$

(Check your answer to see that it works.)

15. $\dfrac{1}{x + 2} - \dfrac{2}{x - 1} = \dfrac{3}{x^2 + x - 2}$

16. $\dfrac{2}{x + 2} - \dfrac{3}{x} = \dfrac{1}{x^2 + 2x}$

17. $\dfrac{1}{x} - \dfrac{1}{x - 3} = \dfrac{2}{x^2}$

18. $\dfrac{1}{x + 1} - \dfrac{2}{2x - 3} = \dfrac{4x + 5}{2x^2 - x - 3}$

(Check your answer to see that it works.)

19. $\dfrac{3}{2x} - \dfrac{1}{x - 5} = 1$

20. $\dfrac{2}{x - 1} + \dfrac{3}{x + 1} = 3$

21. $\dfrac{1}{x - 3} + \dfrac{6}{x + 2} = 2$

22. $\dfrac{5}{2x + 1} - \dfrac{x - 4}{x + 2} = 0$

23. $\dfrac{4}{2x + 3} + \dfrac{2}{x - 6} = 1$

24. $\dfrac{3x + 2}{x - 1} + \dfrac{7}{2x} = 0$

25. $\dfrac{x}{x - 2} + \dfrac{3}{x} = \dfrac{4}{x^2 - 2x}$

26. $\sqrt{2x - 5} = 1$

27. $\sqrt{x + 3} = -1$

28. $\sqrt{2x - 1} = 1$

29. $\sqrt{x + 2} = x$

30. $\sqrt{2x + 5} - 1 = x$

31. $2\sqrt{x + 4} = \sqrt{1 - x}$

32. $\sqrt{x + 5} = 1 + \sqrt{x}$

33. $\sqrt{2x - 1} + 2 = x$

B 34. $\dfrac{2x + 1}{x - 1} - \dfrac{x}{x + 3} = 3$

35. $\dfrac{x}{x + 2} - \dfrac{x - 1}{2x + 5} + 1 = 0$

36. $\dfrac{2x + 3}{x + 2} - \dfrac{x - 2}{x - 1} = \dfrac{2x + 7}{x^2 + x - 2}$

37. $\dfrac{x + 3}{2x - 3} - \dfrac{2x - 5}{x - 2} = 1$

38. $\dfrac{2x}{x-3} + \dfrac{3}{1-x} = \dfrac{2x+4}{x^2-4x+3}$

39. $\dfrac{x}{2x+5} - \dfrac{4x-1}{1-x} = \dfrac{2x+1}{2x^2+3x-5}$

40. $\sqrt{x+4} = \sqrt{1-x} - 1$

41. $\sqrt{x+1} = 2 - \sqrt{3-x}$

42. $\sqrt{2x-1} - \sqrt{x-1} = 1$

43. $\dfrac{1}{\sqrt{x-2}} + \dfrac{3}{2} = \sqrt{x-2}$

44. $\dfrac{3}{\sqrt{3x-2}} - \dfrac{1}{\sqrt{x-1}} = \dfrac{1}{\sqrt{3x^2-5x+2}}$

45. $\sqrt{1-x} - \sqrt{4+x} = \sqrt{2x+7}$

46. $\sqrt{2x+3} - 2\sqrt{x-2} = \sqrt{4-x}$

47. $x^4 + 2x^2 - 2 = 0$

48. $x^6 - 7x^3 - 8 = 0$

49. $36x^{4/3} + 7x^{2/3} - 4 = 0$

50. $8x^{-6} + 19x^{-3} - 27 = 0$

---

7 Applications

In the application of mathematics to real-life situations problems are typically stated in words, not mathematical symbols. Learning to translate such verbal statements into mathematical terms is as important an aspect of the study of mathematics as is learning how to solve problems after they are formulated. The examples and exercises in this section provide practice in setting up these so-called "word problems" which lead to linear or quadratic equations.

Unfortunately, there is no magical road to success in setting up word problems. Guidelines can be given, but each problem has its own unique features. There are, however, general classes into which many problems can be categorized, and learning how to do one problem of a given class will usually help in solving other problems of that class. For example, in physical applications many problems deal with motion in a straight line in which the relation "distance equals rate times time" is applicable (where the rate, or velocity, is constant). Thus, the formula Distance = (Rate)(Time) or $d = rt$ is used in all such situations. Another class of problems has to do with the mixing of substances, as in chemistry experiments. These and other classes will be illustrated in the examples.

The following guidelines are suggested:

1. Read the problem through and identify what unknown quantity is to be determined.
2. Introduce some letter to designate the unknown quantity. The letter x is often used for historical reasons, but sometimes it is helpful to use a suggestive letter, such as d for distance or v for velocity. Be very specific about this; for example, a statement like "Let t = the time in hours required to complete the job" is typical.
3. Begin a careful rereading of the problem, phrase-by-phrase, and write down the relevant information that is given, expressing relationships with the

unknown when appropriate. Often, a sketch can be useful in looking for relationships.

4. Try to identify in the problem some equation that relates the unknown and the known information and write this down in terms of the symbols you have introduced. Here it is useful to observe that the words *is* and *are* often translate as *equals* in an equation.

5. Solve the equation obtained in Step 4, and check your answers to see if they are reasonable in the context of the original problem. Sometimes, one or more solutions must be eliminated because of physical limitations imposed by the problem.

When more than one unknown is involved, obvious modifications in these steps should be made. Also, there are occasions when it is best to introduce as the unknown a quantity related to, but not the same as, the quantity to be determined.

The importance of Steps 2 and 3 should be emphasized. A thorough and careful listing of the relevant given information and a precise identification of the unknown are often the keys to success in solving problems.

EXAMPLE 22   **Motion Problem.**   A man leaves town A by car and travels at a constant speed of 40 miles per hour toward town B, which is 100 miles away. One hour later a woman leaves town B and travels on the same highway toward town A at a constant speed of 50 miles per hour. Find how much time elapses before they meet.

Solution   Let

t = Number of hours elapsed from time man leaves until they meet

Then

$t - 1$ = Number of hours woman travels

We use the fundamental relationship

Distance = (Average rate)(Time)   or $d = rt$

to determine the distances for the man and woman.

$40t$ = Distance man travels before they meet

$50(t - 1)$ = Distance woman travels before they meet

Since the total distance is 100, we see from Figure 1 that

$$40t + 50(t - 1) = 100$$
$$40t + 50t - 50 = 100$$
$$90t = 150$$
$$t = \tfrac{150}{90} = \tfrac{5}{3}$$

So the man travels $1\tfrac{2}{3}$ hours, or 1 hour and 40 minutes.

Figure 1

EXAMPLE 23   **Geometry Problem.**   A flower bed is in the shape of a rectangle. Its length is twice its width. The bed is surrounded by a walkway 4 feet wide. If the area of the walk is exactly twice the area of the bed, find the dimensions of the bed.

Solution   In problems such as this a sketch such as Figure 2 is definitely helpful.

Figure 2

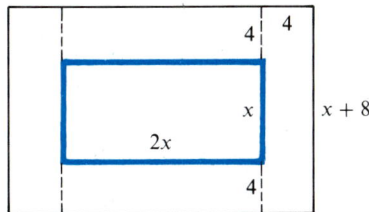

Let
$$x = \text{Width of bed in feet}$$
Then
$$2x = \text{Length of bed in feet}$$
$$\text{Area of bed} = (\text{Length})(\text{Width}) = (2x)(x) = 2x^2$$
$$\text{Area of walk} = 2 \cdot 4(x + 8) + 2 \cdot 4(2x)$$
$$= 8x + 64 + 16x$$
$$= 24x + 64$$

(This is obtained by dividing the walk into rectangles as shown in Figure 2.) Therefore,
$$24x + 64 = 2(2x^2)$$
or, on dividing both sides by 4 and rearranging,
$$x^2 - 6x - 16 = 0$$
$$(x - 8)(x + 2) = 0$$
$$x - 8 = 0 \quad | \quad x + 2 = 0$$
$$x = 8 \quad | \quad x = -2$$

Clearly, x cannot be negative, so the width of the bed is 8 feet and the length is $2x = 16$ feet.

EXAMPLE 24   **Mixing Problem.**   A large tank contains 100 gallons of pure water. How many gallons of a saline solution containing 25% salt must be added to obtain a solution that is 10% salt?

Solution   Let
$$x = \text{Number of gallons of 25\% solution that must be added}$$

Then

$$0.25x = \text{Number of gallons of salt added}$$
$$100 + x = \text{Total number of gallons of final solution}$$
$$0.10(100 + x) = \text{Number of gallons of salt in final solution}$$

Since the salt added is the only source of salt, it follows that the amount of salt added equals the amount of salt in the final solution. So we have the equation

$$0.25x = 0.10(100 + x)$$

Decimals can be eliminated by multiplying both sides by 100.

$$25x = 10(100 + x)$$
$$25x = 1{,}000 + 10x$$
$$15x = 1{,}000$$
$$x = \frac{1{,}000}{15} = \frac{200}{3}$$

So $66\frac{2}{3}$ gallons of the mixture must be added.

EXAMPLE 25   **Mixing Problem.**   A solution containing 80% sulfuric acid is to be mixed with a 65% solution to obtain a 75% solution. If 10 gallons of the final solution are desired, how many gallons of each of the original solutions should be used?

Solution   Let
$$x = \text{Number of gallons of 80\% solution}$$

Then

$$10 - x = \text{Number of gallons of 65\% solution}$$
$$0.80x = \text{Number of gallons of pure sulfuric acid in first solution}$$
$$0.65(10 - x) = \text{Number of gallons of pure sulfuric acid in second solution}$$
$$0.75(10) = \text{Number of gallons of pure sulfuric acid in final solution}$$

So, since the amount of pure sulfuric acid in the first solution plus the amount in the second solution must equal the amount in the final solution, we have

$$0.80x + 0.65(10 - x) = 0.75(10)$$
$$80x + 65(10 - x) = 750$$
$$80x + 650 - 65x = 750$$
$$15x = 100$$
$$x = \tfrac{100}{15} = \tfrac{20}{3}$$

And

$$10 - x = 10 - \tfrac{20}{3} = \tfrac{10}{3}$$

Thus, $6\frac{2}{3}$ gallons of the 80% solution and $3\frac{1}{3}$ gallons of the 65% solution should be used.

The basic idea in mixture problems is:

$$\begin{pmatrix} \text{Amount of pure} \\ \text{substance in the} \\ \text{first solution} \end{pmatrix} + \begin{pmatrix} \text{Amount of pure} \\ \text{substance in the} \\ \text{second solution} \end{pmatrix} = \begin{pmatrix} \text{Amount of pure} \\ \text{substance in the} \\ \text{final mixture} \end{pmatrix}$$

EXAMPLE 26

Falling Body Problem. In calculus it is proved that if air resistance is not considered, the distance s above the earth of a falling body after t seconds is given by the law

$$s = -\tfrac{1}{2}gt^2 + v_0 t + s_0$$

where g is the acceleration due to gravity (approximately 32 feet per second per second), v_0 is the initial velocity of the object, and s_0 is the initial distance above the earth. Here, s is measured positively upward from ground level. (This accounts for the negative sign on the first term, since acceleration is directed downward.) If a ball is thrown upward from the top edge of a 128 foot building with a velocity of 32 feet per second, find how long it will be before the ball strikes the ground.

Solution

In this problem the unknown t has already been introduced, and in fact the equation relating t to known information is given. All that remains is to interpret the data given in the problem in terms of the constants in the equation of motion. It is evident that $v_0 = 32$ and $s_0 = 128$. Furthermore, at the time the ball strikes the ground $s = 0$; so we have

$$0 = -\tfrac{1}{2}(32)t^2 + 32t + 128$$
$$16t^2 - 32t - 128 = 0$$
$$t^2 - 2t - 8 = 0$$
$$(t - 4)(t + 2) = 0$$
$$t = 4 \quad | \quad t = -2$$

Clearly, $t = 4$ is the only admissible solution. So the ball will strike the ground after 4 seconds.

EXAMPLE 27

Economics Problem. A theater has an average daily attendance of 400 with the current ticket price of $2.00. It is estimated that for each 10¢ decrease in the ticket price the average attendance will increase by 40 persons. What price should be charged to increase gross income by $100? What will be the new average attendance?

Solution

This is a situation in which it is best to use as the unknown something related to the ticket price rather than the ticket price itself.

Let

$$x = \text{Number of 10¢ reductions in price needed to}$$
$$\text{achieve desired increase in income}$$

Then

$$2.00 - 0.10x = \text{Price of each ticket in dollars}$$

$$40x = \text{Increase in average attendance}$$

$$400 + 40x = \text{New average attendance}$$

$$\text{Income in dollars} = \text{Price of each ticket in dollars times number attending}$$

$$\text{Present income in dollars} = (2.00)(400) = 800$$

$$\text{Income desired in dollars} = 800 + 100 = 900$$

So,

$$900 = (2.00 - 0.10x)(400 + 40x)$$

$$900 = 800 + 40x - 4x^2$$

$$4x^2 - 40x + 100 = 0$$

$$x^2 - 10x + 25 = 0$$

$$(x - 5)^2 = 0$$

$$x = 5$$

So the ticket price should be reduced by 5 increments of 10¢ for a new price of $1.50 per ticket. The new average attendance will be $400 + (40)(5) = 600$. (It can be shown by calculus that this is the optimum price, that is, any other price, either higher or lower, would produce less income under the stated assumptions.)

EXAMPLE 28   **Motion Problem.**   An airplane flies from city A to city B in 1 hour and 40 minutes against a headwind of 80 miles per hour. The return trip, with no shift in the wind, requires 1 hour. The pilot flew at the same indicated airspeed going and coming. Find his indicated airspeed.

Note.   The indicated airspeed is the speed the plane would move relative to the ground if there were no wind.

Solution   Let

$$v = \text{Indicated airspeed in miles per hour}$$

Then

$$v - 80 = \text{Actual speed going}$$

$$v + 80 = \text{Actual speed returning}$$

$$\text{Time going} = 1 \text{ hour } 40 \text{ minutes} = \tfrac{5}{3} \text{ hours}$$

$$\text{Time returning} = 1 \text{ hour}$$

$$\text{Distance} = (\text{Rate})(\text{Time})$$

$$\text{Distance from } A \text{ to } B = (v - 80)(\tfrac{5}{3})$$

$$\text{Distance from } B \text{ to } A = (v + 80)(1)$$

These distances are equal, so

$$(v - 80)\tfrac{5}{3} = (v + 80)(1)$$
$$5v - 400 = 3v + 240$$
$$2v = 640$$
$$v = 320$$

The indicated airspeed is 320 miles per hour.

EXAMPLE 29

Work Problem. A pump can fill a reservoir in 12 days. A second pump, operating independently, can fill the same reservoir in 8 days. How long will it take to fill the reservoir if both pumps operate simultaneously?

Solution   Let

x = Number of days required to fill the reservoir with both pumps in operation

$\frac{1}{12}$ = Fractional part of the job first pump does per day

$\frac{1}{8}$ = Fractional part of the job second pump does per day

So the fractional part of the job done by first pump in x days = $x/12$, and the fractional part of the job done by second pump in x days = $x/8$. Working together they do the entire job.

$$\frac{x}{12} + \frac{x}{8} = 1$$
$$8x + 12x = 96$$
$$20x = 96$$
$$x = 4.8$$

Thus, 4.8 days would be required to fill the reservoir with both pumps in operation.

EXAMPLE 30

Economics Problem. A vendor purchased a shipment of lamps for a total cost of $1,000. Company clerks damaged 4 of the lamps so that they could not be sold. The remaining lamps were sold at a profit of $25.00 each, and a total profit of $200 was realized when all the lamps were sold. How many lamps were purchased?

Solution   Let

x = Total number of lamps purchased

Then

$$x - 4 = \text{Number of lamps sold}$$

$$\frac{1,000}{x} = \text{Cost of each lamp in dollars}$$

$$\frac{1,200}{x - 4} = \text{Selling price of each lamp in dollars}$$

(Since total profit was $200, total selling price was $1,200.)

Profit per lamp = (Selling price per lamp) − (Cost per lamp)

$$25 = \frac{1,200}{x - 4} - \frac{1,000}{x}$$

$$25(x - 4)x = 1,200x - 1,000(x - 4)$$

$$x^2 - 4x = 48x - 40x + 160 \qquad \text{Dividing by 25}$$

$$x^2 - 12x - 160 = 0$$

$$(x - 20)(x + 8) = 0$$

$$x = 20 \quad | \quad x = -8$$

So 20 lamps were purchased.

In Example 30 we used the following fundamental property of business:

Profit = (Selling price) − (Cost)

This applies to all problems involving the sale of manufactured or purchased items.

It should be evident to the reader that the degree of practicality of these problems varies considerably. Some are designed solely for the purpose of giving practice in translating from a verbal statement to a mathematical one; others accomplish this purpose and at the same time show useful applications of algebra. The latter would seem to be more desirable, but sometimes efforts to achieve relevance to real-world situations result in such complication as to obscure the basic intention. Furthermore, without the use of calculus we are limited in the degree of practicality that can be achieved. Nevertheless, these problems and those that follow, however contrived some may seem, develop facility in setting up and solving mathematical models, which will prove useful in more complicated situations encountered later.

EXERCISE SET 7

In Problems 1–44 carry out these steps:

a. Introduce a variable name for an appropriate unknown quantity, and express all other relevant unknown quantities in terms of this variable.

b. Obtain an equation relating the known and unknown quantities, involving only the variable introduced in part a.

c. Solve the equation in part b, and answer any other questions posed in the problem.

A   1.   Train A leaves Washington for New York and goes at an average speed of 60 miles per hour. On a parallel track, train B (the Metroliner) leaves Washington a half hour later and travels at an average speed of 90 miles per hour. At what point will train B pass train A?

2.   Two cars leave from the same point and go in opposite directions on a straight road. The average speed of one car is 8 miles per hour greater than the other. After 2 hours the cars are 196 miles apart. Find the average speed of each car.

3.   A cyclist and a jogger leave at the same time and follow the same route for a distance of 4 kilometers. The cyclist arrives 15 minutes before the jogger. If the cyclist goes twice as fast as the jogger, find the speed of the jogger.

4.   A girl walked from her home into town at the rate of 4 miles per hour. She decided to return by bus, over the same route. The bus averaged 20 miles per hour, and the entire trip took 1 hour and 40 minutes, including a 10 minute wait for the bus. How far did the girl walk?

5.   A field is in the shape of a rectangle twice as long as it is wide. A fence costing $2.50 per foot is to be placed around the field, and another fence costing $1.00 per foot is to be placed across the middle so as to divide the area into two squares. If the total cost of the fencing is $584, find the dimensions of the field.

6.   The length of a rectangular flower bed is 10 feet greater than its width. The bed is surrounded by a walk that is 2 feet wide. The overall area of the bed and walk is 231 square feet. Find the dimensions of the bed.

7.   The length of a room is 3 feet less than twice its width, and the perimeter is 72 feet. Find its dimensions.

8.   A pasture is bounded by a river on one side. The farmer has 400 feet of fencing for enclosing a rectangular area of 15,000 square feet. Only three sides will be fenced, using the river as the boundary for the fourth side. There are two ways to do this. Find them.

9.   Find three consecutive odd numbers whose sum is 375.

10.   A student has grades of 63, 82, and 90 on the first three exams in a math course. What grade does the student need on the fourth exam to obtain an average of 80?

11.   A student's average grade on three exams is 78. What would the student need to make on the fourth exam to bring the average grade up to 80?

12.   A boy in a town 32 miles from his home got a ride for all but the last 2 miles, which he had to walk. The average speed of the car was 40 miles per hour, and the whole trip took 1 hour and 15 minutes. Find his rate of walking.

13.   At a baseball game the gross receipts were $63,943 from 22,796 paid admissions. If grandstand seats cost $3.50 and bleacher seats cost $2.00, how many of each kind of ticket were sold?

14.   Admission to an amusement park is $5.00 for adults and $2.50 for children. The total receipts on a certain day were $17,500 for 5,000 paid admissions. How many tickets were sold to adults and how many to children?

15.   By radar a highway patrolman observes a speeder going 80 miles per hour. The patrolman has difficulty starting his car so that 5 minutes elapse before he is able to begin pursuit. It is 20 miles to the state line. What average speed would the patrolman have to go to overtake the speeder before he crosses the state line?

16.   Coffee costing $3.50 per pound is to be mixed with coffee costing $4.25 per pound to obtain 30 pounds of a blend worth $4.00 per pound. How much of each type should be used?

17.   How many cubic centimeters of a 50% alcohol solution must be added to 200 cubic centimeters of a mixture that is 25% alcohol to obtain a 30% alcohol solution?

18.   A dairy wishes to obtain 200 gallons of milk that is 3.8% butterfat by mixing lowfat milk, which is 2% butterfat, with half-and-half, which is 11% butterfat. How much of each should be used?

19. From a helicopter hovering 6,400 feet above the ground a projectile is fired straight down with an initial velocity of 1,200 feet per second. When will the projectile strike the ground? (See Example 26.)

20. A room has an area of 180 square feet. If the length is 3 feet more than the width, find its dimensions.

21. A lady paid $87.50 for a dress that was reduced by 30%. What was the original price of the dress?

22. A 10 gallon container is filled with a salt solution containing 20% salt. How many gallons should be drained and replaced by pure water to reduce the salinity to 15%?

23. A woman invests $10,000 in two accounts, one an ordinary savings account yielding $5\frac{1}{2}\%$ annual interest and the other a certificate of deposit yielding 7% annual interest. At the end of 1 year the combined interest is $652. How much did she invest in each account?

24. An open-top box is to be made by cutting squares from the corners of a flat 10×12 inch piece of cardboard and folding up the sides (see sketch). What size square should be removed to produce a box having a total surface area of 95 square inches?

25. A farmer can buy feeder calves weighing 530 pounds on the average for $150 each. If it costs an average of 30¢ per pound added to fatten a calf, and they can be sold at an average of 42¢ per pound, how much weight would have to be added to each calf on the average to realize a profit of $150 per animal?

26. Machine A can produce parts at the rate of 3,000 per hour, and machine B can produce the same parts at the rate of 5,000 per hour. Machine A is started at the beginning of the day, and 2 hours later machine B is started. How long will it take for 50,000 parts to be produced?

27. A plumber charges $9.00 per hour, and his assistant, who is an apprentice, receives $5.00 per hour. The bill for a certain job was $81.00. This included $25.00 for parts and $12.00 for making the house call. If the assistant worked 1 hour less than the plumber, find how long each worked.

28. Find two consecutive positive odd integers whose product is 195.

29. The sum of the reciprocals of two consecutive even integers is $\frac{5}{12}$. Find the numbers.

30. The sum of the reciprocals of two consecutive even integers is $\frac{13}{84}$. Find the numbers.

31. Forty people charter a boat at a cost of $15 each. They are told that for every additional person they can get to go, the price of each ticket will be reduced by 25¢, provided the total does not exceed 60, which is the capacity of the boat. The net income to the boat operator is $625. How many people are going to take the boat ride?

32. A bookstore purchased a number of copies of a new book for a total cost of $750. The selling price per book was $2 greater than the cost. At the end of 1 month all but 5 copies had been sold, and the profit was $90. How many books did the bookstore purchase?

33. A picture is 10 inches taller than it is wide. It is framed with a matting 2 inches wide at each side and 3 inches wide at the top and bottom. The area of the picture plus the matting is 468 square inches. Find the dimensions of the picture.

34. A man rows 6 miles down a river and back in 2 hours and 15 minutes. If the rate of the current is 2 miles per hour, find how fast he can row in still water.

B **35.** A railroad company agrees to run an excursion train for a group under the following conditions. If 200 people or less go, the rate is $10 per ticket. The rate for all tickets will be reduced by 2¢ per ticket for each person in excess of 200. If the total intake by the railroad was $2,450, find how many people took the trip.

36. A group of 40 people charter a bus for an excursion. They are told that if they can get 15 additional people to go, the price of each ticket will be reduced by $7.50 (while the total cost for chartering the bus remains the same). Find what the cost of each ticket will be if they get the additional 15 passengers. What will it be if only the original 40 people go?

37. A certain city bus line charges 50¢ per ticket and has an average daily ridership of 200,000. The capacity is double this amount, and in order to provide an incentive for people to use public transportation, the company experiments with reducing the fare by 1¢ increments. They find that for each 1¢ fare reduction the number of riders each day increases by an average of 7,500. They also find that up to a certain point their income rises, but further reductions cause the income to decline. Their maximum income exceeds what it was before any fare reduction by $10,200. What fare did they charge to produce this income, and what was the average daily ridership with this fare?

38. It takes a small pump 4 hours longer to fill a tank than a large pump. If both pumps work together, the tank can be filled in 2 hours and 40 minutes. How long will it take each pump working alone to fill the tank?

39. The octane rating of gasoline is a number that measures its antiknock value. The octane rating of a fuel consisting of a mixture of normal heptane (which has a decided knocking tendency) and isooctane (which has a decided antiknocking tendency) is the percentage of isooctane in the mixture. Other fuels are rated in comparison with this mixture. For example, gasoline rated at 90 octane has the same antiknock qualities as a mixture of heptane and isooctane that is 90% isooctane. In working with octane ratings, then, we may treat the fuel as if it were a mixture of isooctane and heptane. If two batches of gasoline, one rated at 96 octane and the other at 87 octane, are to be mixed to obtain 200 gallons of 93 octane gasoline, find how many gallons of each should be used.

40. Fifty gallons of 88 octane gasoline are mixed with 75 gallons of 94 octane gasoline. What is the octane rating of the mixture? (See Problem 39.)

41. One pump can fill a reservoir in 8 days and another can do it in 6 days. If both pumps begin working together but the faster pump breaks down at the end of the third day, how long will it take to fill the reservoir?

42. A girl is in a boat on a lake 4 miles from the point nearest to her on the shore (point A). She wants to get to point B, 9 miles along the straight shore from A. She can row at an average of 6 miles per hour and walk at 4 miles per hour. She decides to row directly to a point C between A and B and walk from there. The total trip takes 2 hours and 20 minutes. How far is it from A to C?

43. Point A is on one bank of a river and B is on the other, directly opposite A. The river is 120 feet wide and is essentially straight at the area in question. An underground telephone cable is to go from A to a point C, which is at the river's edge on the same side as B and 150 feet from B. It costs $4 per foot to run the cable under the river and $2 per foot to place it underground. The cable is run under the river from A to a point D between B and C, and from there to C underground. If the total cost is $720, how far is it from B to D?

44. Bill can mow a large lawn with his rider mower in $3\frac{1}{2}$ hours, and Joanne can do the same job with her hand-operated power mower in 6 hours. How long will it take them working together?

45. A room containing 1,990 cubic feet is originally free of carbon monoxide. Cigarette smoke, containing 2.4% carbon monoxide, is then introduced into the room at the rate of 0.1 cubic feet per minute.

    a. Find a general expression for the concentration of carbon monoxide in the room in terms of the elapsed time t in minutes that the smoke has been entering the room.

    b. Extended exposure to concentrations of carbon monoxide as low as 0.00012 is harmful to the human body. Find the critical value of t at which this concentration is reached.

8   Linear Inequalities

It may come as a surprise to you that inequalities are used in mathematics almost as much as equations. The only difference in appearance of an inequality and an equation is that the equals sign is replaced by an inequality sign ($<$, $>$, $\leq$, or $\geq$). For example, $2x - 3 > 4$ is a linear inequality in one unknown, and $x^2 - 2x - 3 \leq 0$ is a quadratic inequality in one unknown. By the solution set of an inequality we mean the set of all values of the unknown (or unknowns) for which the inequality holds true. In this section and the next we consider the solution of linear inequalities. Quadratic inequalities will be discussed in Section 9, and inequalities involving more than one unknown will be taken up later, when we discuss systems of inequalities.

The order properties given in Section 3 of Chapter 1 provide the basis for solving inequalities of the first degree in one unknown. Briefly, these state that we can add the same number to, or subtract the same number from, both sides of an inequality. Also, we can multiply or divide by any *positive* number and retain the sense (that is, the direction of the inequality symbol) of the inequality. But multiplying or dividing by a *negative* number reverses the sense of the inequality. This last point requires special care, and this feature distinguishes the solution of linear inequalities from that of linear equations. We illustrate the technique with several examples.

EXAMPLE 31   Solve for x: $2x - 3 < 5x + 6$

Solution   We solve just as if it were an equation, collecting the x's together on one side of the inequality sign and the constants on the other. One way to do this is to add 3 to both sides and also to subtract $5x$, obtaining

$$-3x < 9$$

Now to get x we want to divide by -3 (or multiply by $-\frac{1}{3}$), but remember that dividing by a negative number reverses the sense of the inequality. So we get

$$x > -3$$

We write the solution set as

$$\{x: \quad x > -3\}$$

It consists not of just one value of x but *all* numbers greater than -3. This can be depicted on a number line, as shown in Figure 3.

Figure 3

Some people prefer to avoid dividing by negative numbers and so collect terms in such a way as to result in a positive coefficient for x. Thus, we could have added $-2x$ and -6 to each member in this example to get:

$$-9 < 3x$$
$$-3 < x$$

which can be turned around to read $x > -3$.

EXAMPLE 32   Solve the inequality: $\dfrac{2x-3}{5} \geq \dfrac{x}{2} - 1$

Solution   First, we clear fractions by multiplying by the LCD, which is 10.

$$4x - 6 \geq 5x - 10$$
$$4 \geq x$$
$$x \leq 4$$

So the solution set is $\{x: \ x \leq 4\}$. This can be depicted graphically as shown in Figure 4.

Figure 4

EXAMPLE 33   Find all x such that $-4 < 2x - 3 \leq 5$.

Solution   This is really the combination of two inequalities, $-4 < 2x - 3$ and $2x - 3 \leq 5$, and we are seeking the values of x that satisfy both inequalities at once. We could solve each inequality individually and find those values of x common to the two solution sets (that is, the intersection of the two solution sets). An easier way, however, is to work with the combined inequality as follows. Add 3 to every member and then divide by 2:

$$-1 < 2x \leq 8$$
$$-\tfrac{1}{2} < x \leq 4$$

The solution set is $\{x: \ -\tfrac{1}{2} < x \leq 4\}$. We can read this from the middle: x is greater than $-\tfrac{1}{2}$ and less than or equal to 4. Graphically, we show this in Figure 5.

Figure 5

EXERCISE SET 8

A   In Problems 1–25 find the solution sets and depict these on a number line.

1. $2x + 3 < 5$ **2.** $x - 3 < 4$

3. $3x + 4 < x + 8$ **4.** $3x + 5 < 11$

5. $2x - 3 > 5x + 4$ **6.** $2x + 1 < 3x - 2$

7. $4 - 2x < 6 - 3x$ **8.** $2(x + 3) \leq 5$

9. $3(x - 2) > 1$ **10.** $\dfrac{x + 2}{3} \geq \dfrac{5}{6}$

11. $\dfrac{x - 4}{3} < \dfrac{3x}{4}$ **12.** $\dfrac{x}{3} - \dfrac{1}{2} \leq \dfrac{3x}{4} + \dfrac{5}{6}$

13. $\dfrac{2x + 5}{4} > \dfrac{4 - 3x}{6}$ **14.** $\dfrac{x}{2} - \dfrac{3}{4} > \dfrac{5x}{6} - \dfrac{1}{3}$

15. $\dfrac{3x}{2} + \dfrac{1}{4} > \dfrac{5x}{8} - \dfrac{1}{2}$ **16.** $1 < x - 4 < 3$

17. $3 < 2x - 1 < 5$ **18.** $-1 < 3x - 4 \leq 7$

19. $-3 < 2x + 1 < 5$ **20.** $-2 \leq \dfrac{3x - 4}{5} < 3$

21. $0 < \dfrac{3x - 2}{4} \leq 2$ **22.** $-\dfrac{1}{2} < x - 2 < \dfrac{1}{2}$

23. $0 \leq \dfrac{3 - 2x}{4} \leq 1$ **24.** $-3 \leq \dfrac{5 - 3x}{2} < 6$

25. $-0.01 < 2x - 3 < 0.01$

26. A student has grades of 72, 83, and 78 on three tests. How high must he score on the fourth test to have an average of 80 or greater?

27. The temperature in degrees Fahrenheit (°F) ranges between 77 and 86 on a certain South Sea island. Celsius temperature (°C) is related to Fahrenheit temperature by the formula °C = $(\frac{5}{9})$(°F − 32). What is the Celsius temperature range on this island?

28. Apples keep best in cold storage if they are held above freezing but at no greater than 5°C, that is, $0 < °C \leq 5$. Find the corresponding range for the Fahrenheit temperature (°F). (See Problem 27.)

29. The perimeter of a rectangle with length 15 inches must be at least 42 inches but no greater than 60 inches. What is the allowable range of values of the width?

B   In Problems 30 and 31 solve the inequalities.

30. $\dfrac{2x - 5}{3} + \dfrac{3 - 2x}{12} \geq \dfrac{3x}{4}$ **31.** $3 > \dfrac{2(3 - 4x)}{7} \geq -2$

32. Explain why each of the following has no solution:
   a. $5 < x < 3$ **b.** $6 < 2x + 5 < -1$ **c.** $3 > x - 2 > 4$

33. Find all values of x that satisfy *either* $3x - 2 < 4$ *or* $4 + 3x > x + 10$, and depict this solution graphically. Write the solution set as the union of two sets.

34. Find the set of all numbers that satisfy either

$$\frac{3 - 2x}{4} \geq 5$$

or

$$\frac{4 - x}{2} < \frac{2x - 8}{3}$$

Depict the solution graphically. Write the solution set as the union of two sets.

35. The cost of manufacturing x microcomputers of a certain kind each week is given by $C = 2{,}000 + 50x$, and the revenue from selling these is given by $R = 75x$. How many microcomputers must be produced and sold in order to realize a profit?

9 Inequalities and Absolute Value

Inequalities often occur in combination with absolute value, such as $|x - 3| < 1$ or $|x - 2| > 3$. In order to see how to solve these, we first consider some further properties of absolute value.

Recall that when viewed geometrically $|a|$ can be interpreted as the distance between a and 0 on the number line. For example, $|-2| = 2$, and the point corresponding to -2 on the number line is 2 units from the origin. Similarly, $|a - b|$ can be interpreted as the distance between a and b on the number line. You can convince yourself of this by considering several possibilities of a and b on a number line.

The following further properties of absolute value are often useful:

Properties of Absolute Values

1. $|-x| = |x|$ **2.** $|xy| = |x||y|$

3. $|x| = \sqrt{x^2}$ **4.** $|x + y| \leq |x| + |y|$

We will not prove these in detail. You can convince yourself of the truth of properties 1 and 2 by considering the definitions of the quantities involved. For property 3, remember that $\sqrt{N}$, where $N \geq 0$, means the unique *nonnegative* number whose square is N. Since both $x \cdot x = x^2$ and $(-x) \cdot (-x) = x^2$, then $\sqrt{x^2} = x$ when x is nonnegative, and $\sqrt{x^2} = -x$ when x is negative, that is, $\sqrt{x^2} = |x|$. Property 4 is known as the **triangle inequality,** and is probably the most used inequality in all mathematics. Because of its importance, we will prove it. First, though, you should note that it is intuitively evident, because when x and y are both positive or both negative, the two sides are the same. For example $|5 + 2| = |5| + |2|$ and $|(-5) + (-2)| = |-5| + |-2|$, since in each case we get 7 on both sides of the equation. But when x and y are opposite in sign, the left-hand side really involves a subtraction, whereas the right-hand side always involves addition and hence is greater than the left. Thus $|5 + (-2)| = |5 - 2| = 3$, but $|5| + |-2| = 5 + 2 = 7$.

To prove property 4, observe that $-|x| \leq x \leq |x|$. In fact, this is an extreme inequality in the sense that the quantity in the middle always equals one or the other of the end points. For example, suppose $x = 2$. Then

$$-|2| \leq 2 \leq |2|$$

since this is the same as

$$-2 \leq 2 \leq 2$$

Or suppose $x = -3$. Then

$$-|-3| \leq -3 \leq |-3|$$

since this is the same as

$$-3 \leq -3 \leq 3$$

Now we write a similar inequality for y and add:

$$
\begin{array}{r}
-|x| \leq \quad x \quad \leq |x| \\
-|y| \leq \quad y \quad \leq |y| \\
\hline
-|x| - |y| \leq x + y \leq |x| + |y|
\end{array}
$$

or

$$-(|x| + |y|) \leq x + y \leq |x| + |y| \qquad (2)$$

The left-hand inequality can be rewritten after multiplying by -1:

$$-(x + y) \leq |x| + |y|$$

Since, by the right-hand inequality in (2), $(x + y) \leq |x| + |y|$, it follows that both $x + y$ and its negative are always less than or equal to $|x| + |y|$. But $|x + y|$ is either $x + y$ or its negative. So

$$|x + y| \leq |x| + |y|$$

Let us return now to the problems posed at the beginning of this section.

EXAMPLE 34   Find the solution set for the inequality $|x - 3| < 1$.

Solution   Since $|x - 3|$ can be interpreted as the distance between x and 3, we are seeking all numbers x whose distance from 3 is less than 1 unit. These are the numbers between 2 and 4, as shown on the number line in Figure 6. We can also obtain this without reference to geometry. Suppose first that $x > 3$. Then $x - 3$ is positive, and $|x - 3| = x - 3$. So $x - 3 < 1$ when $x < 4$, and all numbers

Figure 6

between 3 and 4 are in the solution set. Next suppose $x < 3$, so that $x - 3$ is negative. Then $|x - 3| = -(x - 3) = 3 - x$, and $3 - x < 1$ if $x > 2$. So all numbers between 2 and 3 are in the solution set. When $x = 3$, then $|x - 3| = 0$, and this is certainly less than 1. We therefore conclude that all numbers between 2 and 4 constitute the solution set, that is, $\{x : \ 2 < x < 4\}$.

EXAMPLE 35   Find the solution set for the inequality $|x - 2| > 3$.

Solution   Again we could reason in terms of distance. We are seeking all numbers whose distance from 2 is greater than 3. These are numbers that are either greater than 5 or else less than -1, as shown in Figure 7. So we can write the solution set as

$$\{x: \quad x < -1\} \cup \{x: \quad x > 5\}$$

Figure 7

Without reference to geometry, we can solve this inequality by considering two cases. First, if $x \geq 2$, then $|x - 2| = x - 2$. So the inequality becomes $x - 2 > 3$, or $x > 5$. On the other hand, if $x < 2$, then $x - 2$ is negative, so that $|x - 2| = -(x - 2) = 2 - x$, and the inequality becomes

$$2 - x > 3$$
$$x < -1$$

So, again, we see that the inequality is satisfied if either $x > 5$ or $x < -1$.

We wish to be able to solve inequalities like those in Examples 34 and 35 more rapidly, and toward this end we first consider the simple cases $|x| < b$ and $|x| > b$, where $b > 0$. As we saw in Chapter 1, the solution set to $|x| < b$ is the set of all numbers x whose distance from 0 on the number line is less than b. These are the numbers between $-b$ and b. That is,

$$|x| < b \qquad \text{is equivalent to} \qquad -b < x < b \qquad\qquad (3)$$

Similarly, the solution set of the inequality $|x| > b$ is the set of all numbers x whose distance from 0 on the number line is greater than b. These are the numbers that are greater than b, together with the numbers that are less than $-b$. That is,

$$|x| > b \qquad \text{is equivalent to} \qquad x > b \quad \text{or} \quad x < -b \qquad\qquad (4)$$

So in the future, if we have to solve an inequality of the form

$$|x - a| < b$$

we replace x by $x - a$ in inequality (3) and solve the equivalent inequality

$$-b < x - a < b$$

by adding a to all three members:

$$a - b < \quad x \quad < a + b$$

For example, let us again consider $|x - 3| < 1$, which is equivalent to

$$-1 < x - 3 < 1$$

We add 3 to all three members to get

$$2 < \quad x \quad < 4$$

So the solution set is $\{x: \quad 2 < x < 4\}$.

Similarly, an inequality of the form $|x - a| > b$ can be solved using inequality (4) and replacing x by $x - a$. The inequality $|x - a| > b$ is therefore equivalent to

$$x - a > b \qquad \text{or} \qquad x - a < -b$$

which, on adding a to both sides of each inequality, gives $x > a + b$ or $x < a - b$. For example, $|x - 2| > 3$ is equivalent to

$$x - 2 > 3 \qquad \text{or} \qquad x - 2 < -3$$

from which we get

$$x > 5 \qquad \text{or} \qquad x < -1$$

So the solution set is $\{x: \quad x > 5\} \cup \{x: \quad x < -1\}$.

A set of the form $\{x: \quad a < x < b\}$ is called an **open interval** and is sometimes designated as (a, b). A set of the form $\{x: \quad a \leq x \leq b\}$ is called a **closed interval** and may be designated as $[a, b]$. In a closed interval the end points are included, but in an open interval they are not. An interval that includes only one of the end points is called **half-open** (or **half-closed**). There are two types:

$$[a, b) = \{x: \quad a \leq x < b\} \qquad \text{and} \qquad (a, b] = \{x: \quad a < x \leq b\}$$

EXAMPLE 36   Illustrate on a number line the intervals $(-2, 1)$ and $[3, 4]$.

Solution   The interval $(-2, 1)$ is the set $\{x: \quad -2 < x < 1\}$, and $[3, 4]$ is the set $\{x: 3 \leq x \leq 4\}$. These are shown in Figure 8.

Figure 8

EXERCISE SET 9

A 1. Verify the four absolute value properties for each of the following:
   a. $x = 7, \quad y = 3$ b. $x = -12, \quad y = 5$
   c. $x = -4, \quad y = 10$ d. $x = -5, \quad y = -7$

   2. Verify on a number line that the distance between a and b is $|a - b|$ for each of the following:
   a. $a = 3, \quad b = 8$ b. $a = 6, \quad b = -2$
   c. $a = -8, \quad b = 2$ d. $a = -3, \quad b = -10$

   3. Show that $|a|^2 = a^2$. Is it also true that $|a|^3 = a^3$? Explain why or why not.

   Solve the inequalities in Problems 4–25.

   4. $|x - 2| < 3$ 5. $|x - 4| < 7$
   6. $|x + 5| < 8$ 7. $|x + 1| < \frac{1}{2}$
   8. $|x - 1| > 3$ 9. $|x - 2| > 1$

10. $|x + 3| \geq 2$

11. $|3x - 2| \leq 4$

12. $|4 - x| > 3$

13. $|2x - 3| > 4$

14. $|3 - 2x| \geq 2$

15. $|4x - 5| > 3$

16. $|x - a| < 5$
(*a* is a constant)

17. $|x - b| \geq 3$
(*b* is a constant)

18. $\left|\dfrac{x + 2}{3}\right| < 4$

19. $\left|\dfrac{2x - 5}{3}\right| \leq 1$

20. $\left|\dfrac{3 - x}{4}\right| > 2$

21. $\left|\dfrac{x - 5}{3}\right| < 6$

22. $\left|\dfrac{2 - 3x}{4}\right| \geq 3$

23. $|2 - x| < 0.01$

24. $|-3(2x - 4)| < 7$

25. $|-4(3 - 2x)| > 3$

26. Write out the meaning in set notation of each of the following intervals:
   a. $[2, 5]$ **b.** $(-1, 3]$ **c.** $(2, 4)$ **d.** $[-4, -1)$

27. Write in terms of an inequality involving absolute values:
   a. The distance between x and 2 is less than 1.
   b. x is closer than 1 unit to 2 but is not equal to 2.

B   **28.** Show that $|a - b| \leq |a| + |b|$.
   Hint. Write $a - b = a + (-b)$.

29. Show that $|a^{-1}| = |a|^{-1}$.
   Hint. Show that $|a^{-1}|$ fulfills the requirement of being the multiplicative inverse of $|a|$.

30. Use the result of Problem 29 to show that $|a/b| = |a|/|b|$.

31. Show that $|a + b + c| \leq |a| + |b| + |c|$.
   Hint. Write $a + b + c = (a + b) + c$.

32. **a.** In the triangle inequality, let $x = a$ and $y = b - a$ to obtain

$$|b - a| \geq |b| - |a|$$

   b. Similarly, let $x = b$ and $y = a - b$ to obtain

$$|a - b| \geq |a| - |b|$$

   c. Use the results of parts a and b to obtain the inequality

$$|a - b| \geq ||a| - |b||$$

Solve the inequalities in Problems 33–36.

33. $|x - a| < \delta$
(*a* and δ are constants)

34. $0 < |x - 2| < 1$

35. $0 < |2x + 3| \leq 5$

36. $0 < |x - 3| < \delta$
(δ is a constant)

---

10 Quadratic and Other Nonlinear Inequalities

Using the example $x^2 - 3x - 4x < 0$, we will illustrate one technique for solving a quadratic inequality. A second method, involving graphing, will be shown in Chapter 5.

First factor the left-hand side:

$$(x + 1)(x - 4) < 0 \tag{5}$$

Next show on a number line the points for which either factor is zero. These points divide the line into three regions, as in Figure 9. Test each region to see if the inequality is satisfied there.

Figure 9

To do this it is sufficient to substitute any one value from each region.

Region I: Using $x = -2$ as a test value, we see that both $(x + 1)$ and $(x - 4)$ are negative, so that their product is positive. Hence the expression cited above, inequality (5), is not satisfied.

Region II: With $x = 0$ as the test value, $(x + 1)$ is positive and $(x - 4)$ is negative, so that the product is negative. Thus region II is a part of the solution set of inequality (5).

Region III: Using $x = 5$ as a test value, we see that both factors are positive, as is their product. So we reject region III.

Finally, we check the critical numbers themselves. Since they cause the left-hand side to be 0, inequality (5) is not satisfied. We conclude that the solution set is region II:

$$\{x: \quad -1 < x < 4\}$$

In practice much of this process can be done mentally, and we only need to show a sketch such as Figure 10.

Figure 10

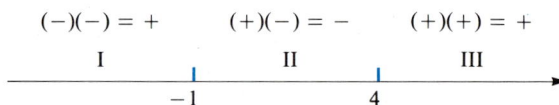

A Word of Caution.   It is tempting to try to solve inequality (5) just as if it were an equation and write

$$(x + 1)(x - 4) < 0$$

$$
\begin{array}{c|c}
x + 1 < 0 & x - 4 < 0 \\
x < -1 & x < 4
\end{array}
$$

You must resist this temptation, because this procedure *is not correct.* (Do you see why?)

A procedure similar to the one we used in this example can be used for any quadratic inequality and also any other inequality in which one side is zero and the other can be written as a product and/or quotient of linear factors. The numbers that make each of these factors zero are called **critical numbers.** These divide the number line into regions, each of which must be tested to see if the inequality is satisfied there. Note that it is also necessary to test the critical numbers themselves, since they may be part of the solution set. (This is possible when the inequality is of the type $\geq$ or $\leq$.)

Note.   For this procedure to work, it is essential that one side of the inequality be zero.

EXAMPLE 37   Solve the inequality: $x^2 - 2x > 8$

Solution   First add -8 to both sides to get 0 on the right, and factor the quadratic expression on the left:

$$x^2 - 2x - 8 > 0$$

$$(x - 4)(x + 2) > 0$$

The critical numbers are $x = 4$ and $x = -2$. Since for these values of x the left side is 0, the inequality is not satisfied for either value. The regions into which these divide the number line, and the signs of the factors in each region are shown in Figure 11. In regions I and III, the product is positive (>0), so the inequality is satisfied for all x values in either region. In region II, the product is negative, so the given inequality is not satisfied there. Hence, the solution set is $\{x: \ x < -2\} \cup \{x: \ x > 4\}$.

Figure 11

$$(-)(-) = (+) \qquad (-)(+) = (-) \qquad (+)(+) = (+)$$

I   II   III

-2 4

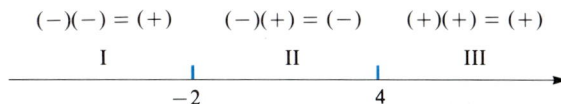

EXAMPLE 38   Solve the inequality: $\dfrac{x - 1}{x + 2} < 0$

Solution   The critical numbers are $x = 1$ and $x = -2$. These divide the number line into three regions, as shown in Figure 12. For any value of x in region I, both the numerator and denominator are negative, so the quotient is positive (>0). Therefore, region I is not a part of the solution set. In region II, the numerator is negative and the denominator is positive, so the quotient is less than 0. Therefore, region II is a part of the solution set. In region III, the numerator and denominator are both positive, so the quotient is positive, and region III is not in the solution set. Finally, we test the critical numbers themselves. For $x = -2$, the expression on the left is not defined, so $x = -2$ is not in the solution set. When $x = 1$, the expression is 0, so it is not less than 0, and $x = 1$ is not a part of the solution set. It follows, then, that the complete solution set is region II, that is, the interval $(-2, 1)$, or $\{x: \ -2 < x < 1\}$.

Figure 12

$$\frac{(-)}{(-)} = (+) \qquad \frac{(-)}{(+)} = (-) \qquad \frac{(+)}{(+)} = (+)$$

I   II   III

-2 1

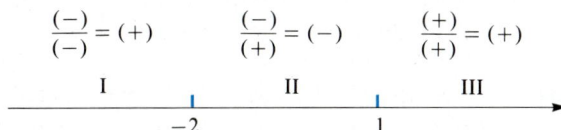

Note.   Since the solution set to an inequality typically involves one or more intervals, we may use the notation for intervals introduced in Section 8 to simplify the writing of the answer. A set of the form $\{x: \ x > a\}$ is called an **unbounded interval** and is designated (a, ∞). The symbol ∞ is read "infinity,"

and can be roughly translated "beyond all bound." Similarly, $(-\infty, a)$ is the set $\{x: \ x < a\}$, $[a, \infty)$ is the set $\{x: \ x \geq a\}$, and $(-\infty, a]$ is the set $\{x: \ x \leq a\}$. Since ∞ is not a number, the interval is never closed at the unbounded end. Using this notation, the solution to Example 37 can be written $(-\infty, -2) \cup (4, \infty)$.

EXAMPLE 39   Solve the inequality: $\dfrac{3x-4}{x+2} \leq 1$

Solution   We cannot simply clear of fractions by multiplying by the LCD as in an equation, because since the LCD involves the unknown x, we do not know if this LCD is positive or negative—and in multiplying both sides of an inequality, it is essential to know the sign of the multiplier. We can, however, combine the terms into one fraction. The first step is to add -1 to both sides, since for our procedure to work, we must have 0 on one side of the inequality:

$$\frac{3x-4}{x+2} - 1 \leq 0$$

Then we combine the left-hand side into one fraction:

$$\frac{3x - 4 - (x+2)}{x+2} \leq 0$$

$$\frac{2x-6}{x+2} \leq 0$$

$$\frac{2(x-3)}{x+2} \leq 0$$

The critical numbers are $x = 3$ and $x = -2$, as indicated in Figure 13. We observe at the outset that $x = 3$ is a part of the solution set, and $x = -2$ is not. Since region II is the only one for which the inequality is satisfied, it follows that the complete solution set is the interval $(-2, 3]$.

Figure 13

$$\frac{(-)}{(-)} = (+) \qquad \frac{(-)}{(+)} = (-) \qquad \frac{(+)}{(+)} = (+)$$

I   II   III

-2   3

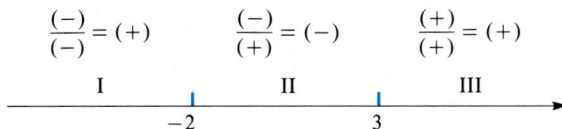

EXAMPLE 40   Find the set of values of x for which the following expression has real values:

$$\sqrt{\frac{x(x-2)}{x+3}}$$

Solution   The expression will be real provided

$$\frac{x(x-2)}{x+3} \geq 0$$

so we wish to solve this inequality. The critical numbers are $x = 0$, $x = 2$, and $x = -3$, as indicated in Figure 14. We note that $x = 0$ and $x = 2$ lie in the solution set, but $x = -3$ does not. Regions II and IV are parts of the solution set, so the complete solution set is $(-3, 0] \cup [2, \infty)$.

Figure 14

$$\frac{(-)(-)}{(-)} = (-) \qquad \frac{(-)(-)}{(+)} = (+) \qquad \frac{(+)(-)}{(+)} = (-) \qquad \frac{(+)(+)}{(+)} = (+)$$

$$\text{I} \qquad \qquad \text{II} \qquad \qquad \text{III} \qquad \qquad \text{IV}$$

$$-3 \qquad \qquad 0 \qquad \qquad 2$$

EXERCISE SET 10

A   Solve Problems 1–34 by the method shown in this section.

1. $x^2 - 2x - 3 < 0$
2. $x^2 - x - 6 > 0$
3. $x^2 - 3x - 4 \le 0$
4. $2x^2 - 9x + 4 \ge 0$
5. $x^2 - 4 < 0$
6. $x^2 - 2x < 8$
7. $x^2 + x - 12 < 0$
8. $2x^2 - 3x - 5 > 0$
9. $3x^2 - x - 2 \le 0$
10. $12x^2 - 7x - 10 \ge 0$
11. $x(x - 1) > 2$
12. $x(2x - 3) < 5$
13. $3x^2 \ge 4(1 - x)$
14. $6(x^2 + 3) \le 31x$
15. $\dfrac{x + 2}{x - 3} < 0$
16. $\dfrac{x}{x + 4} > 0$
17. $\dfrac{3 - x}{x + 2} < 0$
18. $(x - 1)(x + 2)(x - 4) \le 0$
19. $(2x - 1)(x + 4)(x - 3) \ge 0$
20. $\dfrac{x^2 - 16}{x + 1} < 0$
21. $\dfrac{x^2 - 9}{(x + 1)^2} < 0$
22. $\dfrac{x^2 - 1}{x^2 - 9} > 0$
23. $\dfrac{x^2 - 2x - 3}{x + 5} < 0$
24. $\dfrac{x - 2}{x^2 - 2x - 8} \ge 0$
25. $\dfrac{x^2 - x - 6}{2x^2 - 7x - 15} < 0$
26. $\dfrac{2x^2 - 3x - 2}{x^2 + x - 12} \le 0$
27. $\dfrac{3x + 1}{x - 2} > 2$
28. $\dfrac{2x - 3}{x - 1} \le 4$
29. $\dfrac{x + 2}{2x - 3} < 1$
30. $\dfrac{x + 1}{x - 2} < \dfrac{x + 3}{x - 4}$
31. $\dfrac{3}{x} + \dfrac{2x}{x - 2} < 1$
32. $\dfrac{x}{x - 1} + \dfrac{2}{x + 2} < 1$
33. $1 + \dfrac{x}{x + 1} < \dfrac{9}{x^2 - 2x - 3}$
34. $\dfrac{(x - 2)(x + 3)^2}{(x - 6)(x + 1)} \ge 0$

B   **35.**   Find all values of k for which the equation below will have real solutions.

$$kx^2 - 3kx + k - 2 = 0$$

36.   Find all values of a for which the solutions of the equation below will be real.

$$ax^2 - (a - 3)x + 1 = 0$$

37.   For what values of c will the solutions of the equation below be imaginary?

$$x^2 - 2cx - 2c + 3 = 0$$

38.   Solve the inequality:

$$\frac{x - 3}{x^2 + 3x + 2} + \frac{2x - 5}{x^2 + x - 2} < \frac{x - 3}{x^2 - 1}$$

39.   Solve the inequality:

$$\frac{x - 3}{2x^2 - x - 3} + \frac{x + 2}{2x^2 - 7x + 6} > \frac{x - 1}{x^2 - x - 2}$$

40.   For what values of x will the expression below be real?

$$\sqrt{\frac{(x - 2)(x + 1)}{x^3(x - 4)}}$$

41.   An object is thrown downward from the top of a building 256 feet high with an initial velocity of 16 feet per second. The formula for the distance s above the ground of the object at any time t is given by $s = -16t^2 - 16t + 256$ (see Example 26). Find the time interval during which the object will be at least 64 feet above the ground.

42.   The intensity I, in candlepower, of a certain light is given by $I = 6{,}400/d^2$, where d is the distance in feet from the source. For what range of distances will I satisfy the inequality $900 \le I \le 3{,}600$?

43.   The load L that can be safely supported by a wooden beam of length l with rectangular cross-section of width w and depth d is given by the formula

$$L = \frac{kwd^2}{l}$$

where k is a constant depending on the type of wood. A beam is to be 15 feet long and 4 inches wide, and it is known that for the material being used, $k = 120$. If the maximum load the beam will have to support is 3,200 pounds, find the minimum depth d that should be used.
Note.   The given value of k is for both w and d in inches and l in feet.

Review Exercise Set

A   In Problems 1–22 find the solution set.

1.   **a.** $2(3x - 4) = 6 - 7x$ **b.** $\dfrac{x}{2} - \dfrac{3}{4} = \dfrac{5(2 - 3x)}{6}$

2.   **a.** $4(x - 3) = 2(3 - 4x)$ **b.** $\dfrac{2x}{5} - \dfrac{1}{3} = \dfrac{2(4 - x)}{15}$

3. a. $\dfrac{2x-7}{3} = \dfrac{3}{8} - \dfrac{5x}{6}$ b. $\dfrac{3}{5}\left(\dfrac{1}{4} - \dfrac{x}{2}\right) = \dfrac{3x-7}{4}$

4. a. $x^2 - x - 6 = 0$ b. $3x^2 + 10x - 8 = 0$

5. a. $6x^2 + x - 15 = 0$ b. $12x^2 - 25x + 12 = 0$

6. a. $x(23 - 6x) = 20$ b. $4x^2 - 25 = 0$

7. a. $x^2 - 4x + 3 = 0$ b. $3y^2 - 2y - 4 = 0$

8. a. $9x^2 + 16 = 0$ b. $10x^2 - 3x = 18$

9. a. $2r^2 - 5r + 4 = 0$ b. $3y^2 + 2 = 4y$

10. a. $x^2 = 2(x - 2)$ b. $t^2 = \dfrac{4(t-1)}{5}$

11. a. $2(4 + m) = 15m^2$ b. $x^2 = 1 + \dfrac{4x}{3}$

12. a. $\dfrac{2}{x-2} - \dfrac{3}{x+1} = 0$ b. $\dfrac{2}{x} - \dfrac{5}{x+1} = \dfrac{4}{x^2+x}$

13. a. $\dfrac{4}{2x-3} - \dfrac{5}{4-x} = 0$ b. $\dfrac{x}{x+1} - \dfrac{2}{x-1} = \dfrac{x^2+3}{x^2-1}$

14. a. $\dfrac{x-1}{x+2} = \dfrac{x-3}{x+1} + \dfrac{2x}{x^2+3x+2}$ b. $\dfrac{x}{3x+4} - \dfrac{5}{2x-3} = \dfrac{7-3x}{6x^2-x-12}$

15. a. $\dfrac{x+1}{x-2} - \dfrac{x}{2x-3} = \dfrac{3x+5}{2x^2-7x+6}$ b. $\dfrac{x-1}{x-3} - \dfrac{2x}{x+2} = \dfrac{4x}{x^2-x-6}$

16. a. $\dfrac{x+1}{x-2} = 3 - \dfrac{x-1}{x+2}$ b. $\dfrac{x-1}{2x-3} - \dfrac{x}{x+1} = \dfrac{1}{3}$

17. a. $\sqrt{3-2x} = 4$ b. $\sqrt{x+2} - 2 = x$

18. a. $\sqrt{5x-2} = 3$ b. $1 - \sqrt{x-1} = x$

19. a. $\sqrt{x-2} = \sqrt{x+3} - 1$ b. $\dfrac{1}{\sqrt{2x-1}} + \sqrt{2x-1} = 2$

20. a. $\sqrt{2+x} - \sqrt{5-2x} + 3 = 0$ b. $\sqrt{x-1} = \sqrt{2x-1} - 1$

21. a. $9x^4 + 32x^2 - 16 = 0$ b. $12x^{-2} + x^{-1} - 6 = 0$

22. a. $2x^{2/3} + x^{1/3} - 15 = 0$ b. $4x^{-4} - 37x^{-2} + 9 = 0$

In Problems 23 and 24 perform the indicated operations and write the answer in the form $a + bi$.

23. a. $(2 + 3i)(4 - 5i)$ b. $\dfrac{3+2i}{4-3i}$ c. $(4 - 5i)^3$

24. a. $(3 + 4i)^{-1}$ b. $(3 - \sqrt{-4})^4$ c. $\dfrac{2i-4}{3+2i}$

Solve the equations in Problems 25 and 26 by completing the square.

25. a. $2x^2 - 5x + 4 = 0$ b. $3t^2 + 2t - 6 = 0$

26. a. $2x^2 + 4x + 3 = 0$ b. $4x^2 - 3 = 6x$

27. Without solving the equations below, determine whether the solutions are real and unequal, real and equal, or imaginary.
   a. $3x^2 - 7x + 12 = 0$ b. $9x^2 - 15x - 13 = 0$
   c. $12x(5 - 3x) = 25$ d. $8t^2 + 9t + 3 = 0$

28. Evaluate each of the following:

    a. i^{43} **b.** i^{-10} **c.** $\sqrt{-5}\sqrt{-10}$ **d.** $\dfrac{1}{i^{17}}$ **e.** $\dfrac{\sqrt{24}}{\sqrt{-6}}$

29. The length of a room is 6 feet more than its width, and its perimeter is 64 feet. Find the length and width.

30. After selling four-fifths of her stock of a certain type of winter jacket at $55 each, a store owner placed the others on sale at $40 each. If all the jackets were sold and the gross amount realized from them was $3,900, how many jackets did she sell at the regular price and at the sale price?

31. Two cars leave from the same point and travel the same route. The first car travels at an average speed of 65 kilometers per hour, and the second car, which leaves 30 minutes after the first, travels at an average speed of 90 kilometers per hour. How many kilometers will each car have gone when the second car overtakes the first?

32. By combining two types of candy, one costing $3.00 per pound and the other $4.00 per pound, a 2 pound box is prepared that costs $6.50. How much of each kind of candy is used?

33. A man has money invested in two types of savings accounts, one paying 5% and the other 6% annual interest. He has $5,000 more in the account paying 6% than in the account paying 5%. The interest at the end of 1 year is $1,180. How much does he have in each account?

34. A jetliner takes off from Washington for San Francisco and flies at an average speed of 440 miles per hour. Forty-five minutes later an Air Force jet leaves from the same airport and follows the same flight path. If the Air Force jet flies at an average speed of 800 miles per hour, how long will it take to overtake the jetliner? (Assume no change in the wind.)

35. A quantity of brine containing 25% salt is on hand, and it is desired to reduce the salinity to 10% by adding pure water. If 7 gallons of pure water are required, how many gallons of brine were there originally?

36. Two pumps working simultaneously can fill a water tank in 20 hours. The first one alone can fill it in 50 hours. How long would it take the second pump alone?

37. Driver M makes a trip of 220 miles. Driver N makes the same trip in 20 minutes less time, averaging 5 miles per hour faster than driver M. What is the average speed of each driver?

38. Pumps A and B working together can pump all the water out of a reservoir in 20 hours. Pump A could do the job alone 9 hours faster than pump B alone. How long would it take each pump alone?

39. A rain gutter is to be formed from a long, flat piece of tin, 10 inches wide, by bending up at a right angle a certain amount on each side (see the sketch). By calculus it is determined that the greatest amount of water can be accommodated when the cross-sectional area is 12.5 square inches. How many inches on each side should be turned up to produce the gutter?

40. The length of a rectangle is 14 inches greater than the width, and the diagonal is 26 inches. Find the dimensions of the rectangle.

41. How many kilograms of silver alloy containing 35% silver should be mixed with 12 kilograms of an alloy having 43% silver in order to obtain an alloy with 38% silver?

Find the solution sets for the inequalities in Problems 42–50.

42. **a.** $\dfrac{2x-5}{3} \geq \dfrac{x}{4} - 1$ **b.** $\dfrac{4-3x}{2} < \dfrac{2x+5}{3}$

43. **a.** $-1 \leq \dfrac{x-2}{3} < 1$ **b.** $0 < \dfrac{2x}{3} - \dfrac{1}{4} \leq 2$

44. **a.** $9x^2 - 6x - 8 < 0$ **b.** $x(2x+5) \geq 3$

45. **a.** $\dfrac{x+2}{x^2-9} \geq 0$ **b.** $\dfrac{x-4}{3} < \dfrac{x-6}{x+4}$

46. **a.** $\dfrac{3x^2+2x-8}{x^2-3x} \geq 0$ **b.** $\dfrac{2}{x+3} - \dfrac{1}{x-2} < 1$

47. **a.** $(x-2)(x+4)(3x-10) \leq 0$ **b.** $\dfrac{(x-1)(x-2)}{5-x} < 1$

48. **a.** $|x-2| < \tfrac{1}{2}$ **b.** $|2x+1| > 3$
49. **a.** $|3x-4| \leq 1$ **b.** $|2-x| > 3$

50. **a.** $\left|\dfrac{x+1}{3}\right| \geq 1$ **b.** $\left|\dfrac{1}{2} - \dfrac{x}{3}\right| \leq \dfrac{2}{3}$

51. Write in terms of an inequality involving absolute values:
  a. The distance between x and 5 is less than 2.
  b. x is closer to -3 than 1 unit but is not equal to -3.

52. A student has grades of 72, 63, 68, and 75 on the four hour exams in a course. The final exam is to count the equivalent of two hour exams. In what range should the final exam grade fall so that the student's average grade for the course will be greater than or equal to 70? Is it possible for the average to be 80 or better?

53. The temperature on a certain day in Los Angeles ranged between 59 and 86°F. What was the range in degrees Celsius?
  Note. $°C = (\tfrac{5}{9})(°F - 32)$

B 54. Solve for x:
  a. $2a^2x - 3b = b^2x + 4a$ **b.** $10a^2x^2 + 9abxy - 36b^2y^2 = 0$

55. **a.** Solve for y: $y^2 - 2ky + 2k^2 = 1, \quad k > 1$

  b. Solve for x: $\dfrac{2}{x} - \dfrac{1}{x-a} = \dfrac{1}{x-b}$

56. Find all values of k for which the equation below will have equal solutions.
$$kx^2 - 2(k-3)x + 3k + 1 = 0$$

For each value of k so determined, find the solutions of the equation.

57. For what values of k will the solutions of the equation below be real?
$$kx^2 + (k-2)x + 2 = k$$

58. Use a hand calculator to solve for x:
  a. $34.27x^2 + 28.39x - 52.76 = 0$ **b.** $3.258x^2 - 1.237x + 0.965 = 0$

In Problems 59–61 find the solution set.

59. $\sqrt{x+3} + \sqrt{2x+5} = 2$ **60.** $\sqrt{x-1} + \sqrt{x-4} = \sqrt{2x-1}$

61. $\dfrac{x+3}{2x^2+x-3} - \dfrac{3x}{2x^2+7x+6} = \dfrac{5x+1}{x^2+x-2}$ (Check all answers.)

62. Find the solution set for each and depict it graphically.

a. $-\dfrac{3}{2} < \dfrac{3(2x-4)}{5} \leq 2$ **b.** $\dfrac{x-1}{x+2} - \dfrac{x-3}{x+1} < 1$

63. Solve the inequality:

$$\frac{2x}{x^2-2x-3} + \frac{x+2}{1-x^2} \geq \frac{6}{x^2-4x+3}$$

64. Find the values of x for which the expression below will be real.

$$\sqrt{\frac{(x-1)^3(x+2)}{x^3+x^2}}$$

65. A group of 25 students rents a bus for a field trip at a cost of $8.00 per person. They learn that the price of each ticket will be reduced by 10¢ for each additional student they can recruit to go on the trip, provided that the total number does not exceed 45 (the capacity of the bus). If the final total cost of the bus was $251.60, find out how many students actually went and the price of each ticket.

66. A container to hold a piece of machinery is to be constructed with a square base and with height 2 feet more than the side of the base. The material for the top and bottom costs 50¢ per square foot and the material for the sides costs 25¢ per square foot. If the total cost is $24, find the dimensions of the container.

67. A motorist drives 300 kilometers, and after a 2 hour visit returns over the same route. His average speed on the return trip is 20 kilometers per hour greater than his average speed going. If the total elapsed time from the time he left until he returned was 10 hours and 45 minutes, find his average speed going and coming.

68. An 8 inch by 10 inch picture is to be surrounded by a matting of the same width on all sides. The total area of the picture plus matting is not to exceed 195 square inches. What is the maximum width of matting that may be used?

69. A group of people in New Orleans arrange for an all-day boat excursion on the Gulf for a total price of $1,080. They learn that the boat will accommodate 15 additional people, and they succeed in getting 15 more to go, which results in the cost per person being $1.00 less than it would have been without the extra people. How many people actually went on the excursion, and what was the cost per person?

Cumulative Review Exercise Set I (Chapters 1–3)

1. Perform the indicated operations and simplify:

$$\frac{(2x-1)(x+2) - 2(4x+5)}{x+4-(x-1)(4x+5)}$$

2. Simplify the expressions. Answers should not involve negative exponents, and there should be no fractions under the radical. All letters represent positive numbers.

   a. $\sqrt{\dfrac{2x^{-3}y^5z^0}{3x^{-2}y^3}}$ **b.** $\sqrt{a^{-1}b - 2 + b^{-1}a}$

3. Prove that if $a < b$ and $c < d$, then $ac < bd$ provided b and c are positive. Show by examples that the conclusion is not necessarily true if b and c are not both positive.

4. A 50% alcohol solution is to be combined with a 25% alcohol solution to obtain 50 cubic centimeters of a solution having 35% alcohol. How much of each solution should be used?

5. **a.** Express 0.2135135135. . . . as the ratio of two integers.
   b. If a, b, and c are integers, with $a \neq 0$, show that regardless of the nature of the roots of the equation $ax^2 + bx + c = 0$, their sum and their product are always rational numbers.

6. Solve for x:
   a. $3x^2 - 8x + 6 = 0$ **b.** $(3+x)(14-3x) = 30$

7. Perform the indicated operations and simplify:

$$\frac{x^2 - 2x + 1}{2x^2 + x - 3} \cdot \frac{8x^2 + 6x - 9}{3x^2 + x - 4} - \frac{6x^2 + 5x - 4}{4x^2 + 5x - 6} \cdot \frac{2x^2 + 5x + 2}{1 - 4x^2}$$

8. Solve for t: $\sqrt{2t+5} - \sqrt{2-t} = 1$

9. A flower garden in the shape of a rectangle 8 feet wide by 12 feet long is surrounded by a walkway of uniform width. If the combined area of the bed and walk is 221 square feet, find the width of the walk.

10. Perform the indicated operations and simplify:

   a. $\dfrac{\dfrac{3}{2} - \left(-\dfrac{5}{4}\right)\left(1 - \dfrac{2}{3}\right)}{\dfrac{5}{6}\left(\dfrac{3}{4} - 2\right)}$ **b.** $\dfrac{\dfrac{x}{2} - 1}{x - 1 - \dfrac{2}{x}}$

11. **a.** Rationalize the numerator: $\dfrac{\sqrt{2x+2h-3} - \sqrt{2x-3}}{h}$

   b. Simplify and combine terms. Leave no fraction under a radical and no radical in a denominator.

$$\sqrt{\frac{3}{2}} - \frac{1}{3}\sqrt{24} + \frac{3}{2}\sqrt{\frac{32}{3}} - \frac{5}{2\sqrt{6}}$$

12. Solve for x and give a careful justification for each step based on fundamental properties:

$$\frac{2(1-x)}{3} + \frac{1}{2} = \frac{3x}{4}$$

13. Factor completely with integer coefficients:
   a. $4xy + 3x^2 - x^3y - 12$ **b.** $72x^3 + 10x^2y - 48xy^2$

14. **a.** Expand and simplify: $\left(x^2 - \dfrac{2}{x}\right)^6$

   b. Find the first four terms of the expansion of $(2x + 3y)^{10}$. **115**

15. a. Solve for s: $F = \dfrac{rs - 1}{r + 2s}$

   b. Solve for t: $s = \frac{1}{2}gt^2 + v_0 t$ $(s \geq 0, t \geq 0)$

16. Solve the inequalities and show the solution sets on a number line.

   a. $x(3x + 14) \geq 24$ **b.** $\left| \dfrac{3x - 4}{5} - \dfrac{3x}{4} \right| < \dfrac{1}{2}$

17. a. Simplify, and express the answer with positive exponents only:

$$\left(\frac{25a^{-2}b^{4/3}}{\sqrt[3]{16\, a^{8/3}b^2 c^0}} \right)^{-3/2}$$

   b. Evaluate using scientific notation:

$$\frac{(0.000003)\sqrt{250{,}000{,}000{,}000}}{2 \times 10^{-3} + 5 \times 10^{-4}}$$

18. Solve for x: $\dfrac{2x}{x - 2} - \dfrac{3x - 1}{x + 1} = 4$

19. Simplify, and write the answer with positive exponents only:

$$\frac{\sqrt[3]{(x^2 - 1)^2} - \dfrac{4x^2}{3}(x^2 - 1)^{-1/3}}{(x^2 - 1)^{4/3}}$$

20. A woman drove a distance of 120 kilometers to do some research in the Library of Congress. She stayed 4 hours and 24 minutes before returning home. On the return trip she encountered rush hour traffic, and as a result her average speed on the return trip was 15 kilometers per hour less than on the trip going. If the total elapsed time from leaving home until returning was 8 hours, find her average speed going and returning.

21. Solve the inequalities:

   a. $\dfrac{x}{x - 1} - \dfrac{1}{x + 3} \leq 1$ **b.** $\dfrac{2}{x - 1} \geq \dfrac{x + 3}{x + 11}$

22. For $a = \pm 1$ and $b = \pm 2$ show that $a + bi$ satisfies the equation $x^4 + 6x^2 + 25 = 0$. Also, solve the equation by the quadratic formula. Verify that the solutions are the same.

23. A tank can be filled by two pumps working together in 6 hours. The larger pump alone can fill the tank in 5 hours less time than it would take the smaller pump alone. How long would it take each pump working alone to fill the tank?

24. Perform the indicated operations and simplify:

   a. $\dfrac{\dfrac{1}{x - 1} - \dfrac{2}{x + 2}}{\dfrac{18}{x^2 + x - 2} - 1}$ **b.** $\dfrac{x + 2}{x} - \dfrac{8}{4x - x^3} - \dfrac{x}{x + 2}$

25. A men's clothing store owner had a month long 20% off sale on suits of a certain type. His gross income from the sale of these suits during the month of the sale was $15,120. During the preceding month, when the suits were full price, his gross income from selling 30 fewer of these suits was $12,600. Find how many of this type of suit he sold during the month of the sale. What was the original price of the suit?

4   Functions and Graphs

The concept of a function is so basic to mathematics that it is difficult to find any area in which mathematics is applied that this concept does not enter in, at least implicitly. The following excerpt from an economics textbook* explains the basic idea of a function as well as certain differences between the mathematical model and the true situation.

Consider two examples, one from a natural science and one from economics. The gravitational attraction of two bodies depends on their mass and the distance separating them, attraction increasing with size and diminishing with distance; the amount of a commodity that people would like to buy depends on (among other things) the price of the commodity, purchases increasing as price falls. When mathematicians wish to say that one variable depends on another, they say that one variable is a function of another . . . .

When we say that the world behaves so that $Y = f(X)$ we do not expect that knowing X will tell us *exactly* what Y will be but only if it will tell us what Y will be *within some margin of error* . . . . When, for example, we say that the demand for butter is a function of the price of butter, $D_b = f(p_b)$, we know that other factors will also influence this demand. A change in the price of margarine will certainly affect the demand for butter, even though the price of butter does not change. Thus we do not expect to find a perfect relation between D_b and p_b that will allow us to predict D_b exactly from a knowledge of p_b.

In this chapter we will examine the function concept and become familiar with functional notation, such as $Y = f(X)$. Graphs will also be studied, with special emphasis on graphs of functions.

---

* Richard G. Lipsey and Peter O. Steiner, *Economics*, 5th ed. (New York: Harper & Row, 1978), pp. 854, 855. Copyright © 1978 by Richard G. Lipsey and Peter O. Steiner. Reprinted by permission of Harper & Row, Publishers, Inc.

1   The Cartesian Coordinate System

The French mathematician and philosopher René Descartes (1596–1650) is usually given credit for the idea of representing points in a plane by ordered pairs of numbers. By an **ordered pair** is meant a pair of numbers (a, b) in which the position of each number is important.* Thus, (2, 3) and (3, 2) are two different ordered pairs. As is so often the case in mathematical discoveries, the same concept was obtained independently at about the same time by Pierre de Fermat (1601–1665), also a Frenchman, and a jurist as well as a mathematician. Descartes's book, *Geometry*, appeared in 1635, and was his only book on mathematics, but it had a profound influence on the subsequent development of mathematics because it provided an essential prerequisite for the invention of calculus. The approach to geometry introduced by Descartes forms the basis of what is now referred to as **analytic geometry.**

The method employed by Descartes makes use of the so-called **rectangular** or **cartesian** (after Descartes) **coordinate system.** Although this system is familiar to many students from high school mathematics, we will review its essential elements. We consider two number lines perpendicular to each other, one vertical and one horizontal, so that the point of intersection corresponds to 0 on each line; this point is called the **origin.** It is customary to have positive numbers to the right on the horizontal line and along the top part of the vertical line. The two lines are called the **horizontal and vertical axes.** It is also customary (but not essential) to name the horizontal axis the **x axis** and the vertical axis the **y axis.** These axes divide the plane into four parts, called **quadrants,** numbered I, II, III, and IV counterclockwise, as shown in Figure 1. Corresponding to

Figure 1

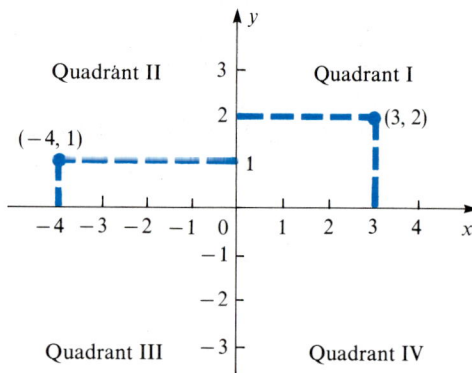

each ordered pair (x, y) of real numbers is a point in the plane determined as follows: Starting from the origin, we move x units along the x axis (right or left, depending on whether x is positive or negative) and from there move y

---

* The context will usually make clear whether (a, b) designates an open interval or a point in a plane.

units parallel to the y axis (up or down, depending on whether y is positive or negative). The resulting point is said to have **coordinates** (x, y); for brevity we often say "the point (x, y)." The points having coordinates $(3, 2)$ and $(-4, 1)$ are pictured in Figure 1. The first number of the ordered pair is called the **x coordinate,** or **abscissa,** of the point, and the second number is called the **y coordinate,** or **ordinate.**

If a point in the plane is given, then that point has unique coordinates (x, y) determined by erecting lines through the point and perpendicular to the x and y axes. So the coordinate system provides a one-to-one correspondence between all points in the plane (geometric objects) and all ordered pairs of real numbers (algebraic objects).

2 Graphs of Equations

Equations such as

$$y = 2x + 3 \qquad x^2 + y^2 = 4 \qquad y^2 = \frac{x - 1}{x + 3}$$

are said to be **equations in two variables.** In this section we will define what is meant by the graph of an equation of this type. In the equation $y = 2x + 3$ we may substitute any real number for x, but then the value of y is completely determined. In this case, then, we say that x is the **independent variable** and y is the **dependent variable.** Alternatively, we could solve this equation for x in terms of y, getting $x = \frac{1}{2}y - 3$, and then y would be the independent variable and x would be the dependent variable.

An ordered pair of numbers (a, b) is said **to satisfy an equation** if when a is substituted for x and b is substituted for y, **the equation becomes an identity.** For example, the equation $y = 2x + 3$ is satisfied by the pair $(1, 5)$, since when $x = 1$, we have $y = 2(1) + 3 = 5$. Similarly, this equation is satisfied by $(-2, -1)$, $(-1, 1)$, $(0, 3)$, $(\frac{1}{2}, 4)$, $(2, 7)$, and infinitely many other ordered pairs. Figure 2 shows these points, and they are seen to lie on a straight line.

Figure 2

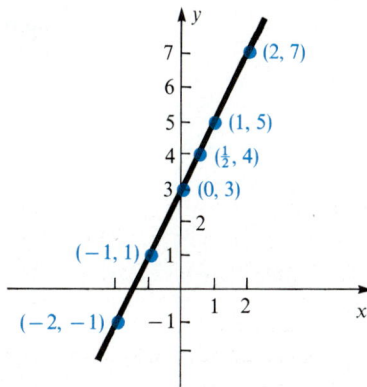

The graph of an equation is the collection of all points with coordinates x and y that satisfy the equation. Usually, it is impossible to locate (that is, to **plot**) every point with coordinates that satisfy an equation, because in most cases there are an infinite number of them. For the equations we will consider, a reasonably accurate graph can be drawn by plotting several points and joining these with a smooth curve. For many other equations, however, a more detailed analysis, such as would be studied in a calculus course, is needed. The next three examples illustrate how to draw graphs by plotting points.

EXAMPLE 1   Draw the graph of $y = 1/x^2$.

Solution   We make a table of values showing ordered pairs that satisfy the equation. We arbitrarily select several values of x and determine the corresponding y values. The graph is shown in Figure 3.

x	1	2	3	4	$\frac{1}{2}$	$\frac{1}{3}$	-1	-2	-3	-4	$-\frac{1}{2}$	$-\frac{1}{3}$
y	1	$\frac{1}{4}$	$\frac{1}{9}$	$\frac{1}{16}$	4	9	1	$\frac{1}{4}$	$\frac{1}{9}$	$\frac{1}{16}$	4	9

Figure 3

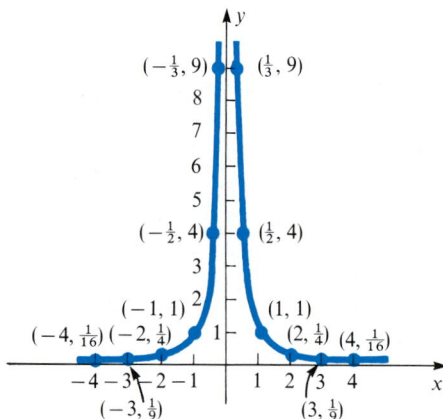

EXAMPLE 2   Draw the graph of $y = x^2 - 4$.

Solution

x	0	± 1	± 2	± 3
y	-4	-3	0	5

Here we have used the $\pm$ sign for x to shorten the table, since the value of y is the same when x is a given number or its negative. The graph is shown in Figure 4. (This is an example of a **parabola,** which we will study in Chapter 5.)

Figure 4

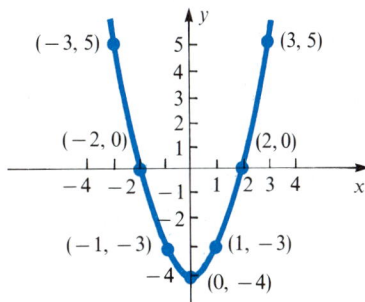

EXAMPLE 3   Draw the graph of $x^2 + y^2 = 36$.

Solution

x	0	± 1	± 2	± 3	± 4	± 5	± 6
y	± 6	$\pm\sqrt{35}$ $\approx \pm 5.92$	$\pm\sqrt{32}$ $\approx \pm 5.65$	$\pm\sqrt{27}$ $\approx \pm 5.20$	$\pm\sqrt{20}$ $\approx \pm 4.47$	$\pm\sqrt{11}$ $\approx \pm 3.32$	0

The graph is shown in Figure 5. (This is a **circle of radius 6,** as we shall show in Chapter 5.)

Figure 5

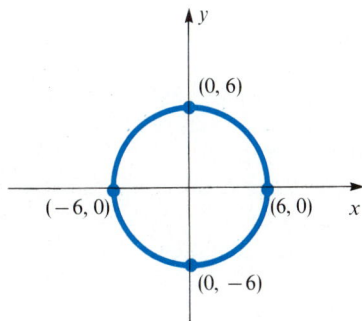

EXERCISE SET 2

A   In Problems 1–21 make a table of values and draw the graph.

1. **a.** $y = x + 1$ **b.** $y = x - 2$
2. **a.** $y = 3x - 4$ **b.** $y = 3 - x$

3. **a.** $y = 2x$ **b.** $y = 3 + x$
4. **a.** $y = 2x - 5$ **b.** $x = 3 - y$
5. **a.** $x + y = 1$ **b.** $x - y = 2$
6. **a.** $2x + 3y = 4$ **b.** $3x - y = 2$
7. **a.** $5x - 3y = 4$ **b.** $4x + 5y + 7 = 0$
8. **a.** $y = -3x$ **b.** $x = 2y - 3$
9. **a.** $y = x$ **b.** $x + y = 0$
10. **a.** $x = 2$ **b.** $y = 3$
11. **a.** $x - 3 = 0$ **b.** $y + 1 = 0$
12. **a.** $y = \sqrt{x}$ **b.** $y = 1/x$
13. **a.** $y = x^2$ **b.** $y = 4 - x^2$
14. **a.** $y = |x|$ **b.** $y = |1 - x|$

B 15. **a.** $y^2 = x$ **b.** $x^2 + y^2 = 25$
16. **a.** $y = x^3/4$ **b.** $y = 2\sqrt[3]{x}$

17. **a.** $y = \dfrac{1}{1 + x^2}$ **b.** $y = \sqrt{36 - x^2}$

18. **a.** $y = x^2 - 2x$ **b.** $y = (x + 1)(x - 3)$

19. **a.** $y = x^3 - x$ **b.** $y = \dfrac{x - 1}{x}$

20. **a.** $y = |2x + 3|$ **b.** $y = 4 - |x|$
21. **a.** $|x + y| = 1$ **b.** $|x| + |y| = 1$
22. A farmer estimates that if he plants x pounds of seed in a plot of land, the yield per pound of seed will be $50 - 2x$ pounds of produce. The total yield y from the plot is the number of pounds of seed planted multiplied by the yield per pound. Find the equation for y and graph that portion of the equation for which $x \geq 0$ and $y \geq 0$.

3 The Function Concept

The concept of a **function** occupies a central place in most branches of mathematics. A formal definition will be given below, but we will precede it with some examples.

To say that a certain thing is a function of another can be interpreted as meaning the first thing depends on the second. This terminology is often used in nonmathematical situations. For example, one might say "the size of the wheat crop is a function of the weather." Of course, it is a function of many other things as well. The mathematical use of the phrase "is a function of" is consistent with its everyday use, but the meaning is more precisely defined. We might say that the circumference of a circle is a function of its radius. Given the length of the radius, the circumference can be determined; the circumference depends on the radius. In this case, we can state precisely the nature of the dependence by means of the equation $C = 2\pi r$, where C represents the circumference and r is the radius.

Or, consider a car traveling at a constant speed of 45 miles per hour. The distance d the car travels is a function of the time t elapsed. In this case, $d = 45t$.

As another example, if money is invested at compound interest, the accumulated amount of money A after t years is given by

$$A = P(1 + r)^t$$

where P is the original amount invested (the principal) and r is the annual interest rate. Suppose \$1,000 is invested at compound interest for 5 years. Then we can express A as a function of r by

$$A = 1,000(1 + r)^5$$

It is not always easy, and sometimes it is not possible, to express the dependence given by a functional relationship by means of an equation. Try, for example, to write an equation expressing precisely how the cost of mailing a first class letter is a function of its weight. It is easier in this case to state the relationship in words. Sometimes a table can be used to describe a function. For example, it is known that the number of deaths annually in the United States resulting from highway accidents is a function of the maximum speed limit. A table showing this relationship might look like the following:

Speed limit in miles per hour	50	55	60	65	70	Unlimited
Number of deaths annually	42,000	45,000	52,000	66,000	75,000	85,000

Whether given by an equation, stated in words, or shown by a table, there is always implicit in a functional relationship some sort of rule whereby the value of one quantity is determined by the value of another (or others). Moreover, each of these quantities assumes values ranging over some prescribed set. For example, in the equation relating the circumference of a circle to its radius, $C = 2\pi r$, the value of r may be chosen arbitrarily, but only from the set of positive real numbers. For each choice of r the value of C is uniquely determined, and the totality of values of C as r ranges over all positive real numbers also constitutes a set of positive numbers. In fact, it can be shown that C also assumes every positive real number value.

So the basic ingredients of a function are these: two sets and a rule relating the elements of one of the sets to elements in the other.

DEFINITION 1　　Let A and B designate two nonempty sets. A function from A to B is a rule whereby each element in A is made to correspond to exactly one element in B.

The set A in this definition is called the **domain** of the function, and the set of elements of B that correspond, under the rule, to elements in A is called the

range of the function. Note that the range may or may not be all of *B*. If the range is all of *B*, we say the function is from *A* **onto** *B*. The set *B* is sometimes called the **codomain** of the function. It is customary to designate functions by letters such as *f*, *g*, *F*, or ϕ. If *f* is a function from *A* to *B*, and *x* is an element of *A*, then the element of *B* that corresponds to *x* is called the **image of *x* under *f*,** and is designated *f*(*x*), read "*f* of *x*." The set of all such images of elements of *A* is the range of *f*. If *y* designates an element in the range of *f*, and *x* is an element in *A* for which *f*(*x*) = *y*, then we say that *x* is a **preimage** of *y*. Depending on the nature of the function, an element of the range may have more than one preimage. This is in contrast to the fact that each element of the domain has exactly one image in the range.

The term *variable* is appropriate in speaking of functions. If *x* stands for an arbitrary value in the domain of a function *f*, and *y* designates the image of *x* under *f*—that is, *y* = *f*(*x*)—then *x* is the independent variable and *y* is the corresponding dependent variable. Any number in the domain may be substituted for the independent variable; the corresponding value for the dependent variable is then uniquely determined by means of the function.

To make these ideas more concrete, let us consider the function *f* with domain being the set of all real numbers, and value at *x* being $2x^2 + 3$. That is,

$$f(x) = 2x^2 + 3$$

This function is now completely defined. The set of images lies in *R*, and specifically the range of *f* is the subset of *R* consisting of those positive real numbers greater than or equal to 3:

$$\text{Range of } f = \{y: \ y \geq 3\} \qquad \textbf{Why?}$$

We have, for example, *f*(0) = 3, since $f(0) = 2 \cdot (0)^2 + 3 = 2(0) + 3 = 3$. Also, *f*(1) = 5, *f*(4) = 35, and *f*(−2) = 11.

An equation such as $y = 2x^2 + 3$ implicitly defines a function, even though no letter is specified for the function. The equation is the rule, and the domain is assumed to be the largest subset of *R* such that for *x* in this subset, the corresponding value of *y* will be real. In this example, the domain, then, is all of *R*. Such an assumption about the domain of functions we use will always be made unless the domain is explicitly stated. In the function implied by the equation $y = \sqrt{x}$, then, we would assume the domain to be the set of all nonnegative real numbers.

To reiterate, we may write

$$f(x) = 2x^2 + 3$$

or

$$y = 2x^2 + 3$$

to define the same function. The first way has the advantage that it assigns a letter *f* to name the function, and images of various values of *x* are easily indicated, for example, *f*(0) = 3 and *f*(1) = 5. The second way has the advantage that a name, *y*, is assigned to the dependent variable. Both methods are useful and will be employed throughout the remainder of this text. It should be noted, too, that the particular letters used to designate the function or the variables are not important in themselves; the form is the important part. For example, the function g defined by

$$g(t) = 2t^2 + 3$$

is the very same function as f described previously, because both functions give the same result for each value of the independent variable. For this reason, we can write $f = g$. When the variables represent certain physical quantities, suggestive letters are often used, such as $v = f(t)$ for the velocity v in terms of time t.

EXAMPLE 4   Let $f(x) = \dfrac{x}{x+1}$.   Find:

    a. $f(2)$ **b.** $f(0)$ **c.** $f(\frac{2}{3})$ **d.** $f(x-1)$ **e.** $f(x+h)$

Solution   **a.** $f(2) = \dfrac{2}{2+1} = \dfrac{2}{3}$ **b.** $f(0) = \dfrac{0}{0+1} = \dfrac{0}{1} = 0$

    c. $f(\frac{2}{3}) = \dfrac{\frac{2}{3}}{\frac{2}{3}+1} = \dfrac{2}{2+3} = \dfrac{2}{5}$ **d.** $f(x-1) = \dfrac{(x-1)}{(x-1)+1} = \dfrac{x-1}{x}$

    e. $f(x+h) = \dfrac{x+h}{x+h+1}$

Note.   Whatever occurs in the parentheses following f is substituted for x wherever x appears.

EXAMPLE 5   Let $g(x) = x^2 + 2x - 3$.   Find:

    a. $g(4)$ **b.** $g(-2)$ **c.** $g(a)$ **d.** $g(x + \Delta x)$

Solution   **a.** $g(4) = 4^2 + 2(4) - 3 = 16 + 8 - 3 = 21$
    b. $g(-2) = (-2)^2 + 2(-2) - 3 = 4 - 4 - 3 = -3$
    c. $g(a) = a^2 + 2a - 3$
    d. $g(x + \Delta x) = (x + \Delta x)^2 + 2(x + \Delta x) - 3$
                 $= x^2 + 2x(\Delta x) + (\Delta x)^2 + 2x + 2(\Delta x) - 3$

Note.   The symbol Δx is read "delta x," and has historically been used in calculus. It is treated as a unit and does not mean the product of Δ and x.

EXAMPLE 6   Find the domain and range of the function f.

    a. $f(x) = x^2 + 4$ **b.** $f(x) = \dfrac{1}{\sqrt{x-1}}$

Solution

a. The domain of f is all of R, since $x^2 + 4$ is finite for all real x. Since $x^2 \geq 0$, we see that $f(x) \geq 4$. Furthermore, any number ≥ 4 is the image of at least one x in the domain. For example, to find an x such that $f(x) = 7$, we solve the equation $7 = x^2 + 4$ for x and get $x = \pm\sqrt{3}$. More generally, for any number $k \geq 4$, putting $f(x) = k$ gives $k = x^2 + 4$, and this has the solutions $x = \pm\sqrt{k^2 - 4}$. This proves that the range of f is the set of all numbers ≥ 4—that is,

$$\text{Range of } f = \{y: \quad y \geq 4\}$$

b. For $f(x)$ to be real, we must have $x > 1$. So the domain of $f = \{x: \quad x > 1\}$. It is clear that $f(x) > 0$ for all x in the domain. To prove that the range of f is the set of all positive real numbers, let k be any positive number and see if the equation $f(x) = k$ can be solved for x:

$$\frac{1}{\sqrt{x-1}} = k$$

$$\sqrt{x-1} = \frac{1}{k}$$

$$x - 1 = \frac{1}{k^2}$$

$$x = 1 + \frac{1}{k^2}$$

Since this is a number in the domain, we have shown that

$$\text{Range of } f = \{y: \quad y > 0\}$$

EXAMPLE 7   Let $f(x) = \dfrac{1}{\sqrt{x}}$.   Find: $\dfrac{f(x + h) - f(x)}{h}$

Solution
$$\frac{f(x + h) - f(x)}{h} = \frac{\dfrac{1}{\sqrt{x+h}} - \dfrac{1}{\sqrt{x}}}{h} = \frac{\sqrt{x} - \sqrt{x+h}}{h\sqrt{x}\sqrt{x+h}}$$

In calculus, where this type of calculation is important, it is essential that the numerator be rationalized:

$$\frac{\sqrt{x} - \sqrt{x+h}}{h\sqrt{x}\sqrt{x+h}} \cdot \frac{\sqrt{x} + \sqrt{x+h}}{\sqrt{x} + \sqrt{x+h}} = \frac{x - (x + h)}{h\sqrt{x}\sqrt{x+h}\,(\sqrt{x} + \sqrt{x+h})}$$

$$= \frac{-h}{h\sqrt{x}\sqrt{x+h}\,(\sqrt{x} + \sqrt{x+h})}$$

$$= \frac{-1}{\sqrt{x}\sqrt{x+h}\,(\sqrt{x} + \sqrt{x+h})}$$

Sometimes the rule for a function is given by more than one expression, as the next example shows.

EXAMPLE 8   Let

$$f(x) = \begin{cases} -1 & \text{if} & x < 0 \\ x & \text{if} & 0 \le x < 2 \\ 1 - x^2 & \text{if} & x \ge 2 \end{cases}$$

Find:

a. $f(1)$ **b.** $f(2)$ **c.** $f(-2)$ **d.** $f(0)$ **e.** $f(3)$

Solution
a. When $0 \le x < 2$, $f(x) = x$. So $f(1) = 1$.
b. When $x \ge 2$, $f(x) = 1 - x^2$. So $f(2) = 1 - 4 = -3$.
c. When $x < 0$, $f(x) = -1$. So $f(-2) = -1$.
d. Since 0 is in the interval $0 \le x < 2$, for which $f(x) = x$, it follows that $f(0) = 0$.
e. When $x \ge 2$, $f(x) = 1 - x^2$. So $f(3) = 1 - 9 = -8$.

EXAMPLE 9   Express the area A of a circle as a function of its radius r.

Solution
$$A = \pi r^2$$

EXAMPLE 10   A woman invests \$1,000 at 5% simple interest. Express the interest earned I as a function of time t in years.

Solution   Using the formula Interest = Principal × Rate × Time for simple interest, we get

$$I = (1,000)(0.05)t = 50\,t$$

EXAMPLE 11   A rectangle is inscribed in a circle of radius 2. Express the area of the rectangle as a function of its base.

Solution   Here it is helpful to draw a sketch, as shown in Figure 6. Since the radius of the circle is 2, its diameter is 4. Divide the rectangle into two triangles as shown by means of a diagonal. This diagonal is a diameter of the circle. Designate the base

Figure 6

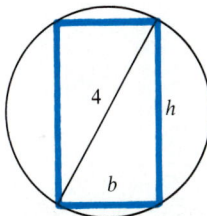

of the rectangle by b and its height by h. The area is $b \cdot h$, but to obtain this as a function of b only we need to express h in terms of b. This can be done by means of the Pythagorean theorem. For our triangle, this says that

$$b^2 + h^2 = 4^2$$

So $h^2 = 16 - b^2$, and $h = \sqrt{16 - b^2}$. Finally, then, the area A is given by

$$A = b\sqrt{16 - b^2}$$

EXERCISE SET 3

A   In Problems 1–11 find the specified functional values for the given functions.

1. For $f(x) = 2x - 1$, find:
    a. $f(0)$ **b.** $f(1)$ **c.** $f(-2)$ **d.** $f(5)$

2. For $h(t) = t^2 + 2t - 1$, find:
    a. $h(-1)$ **b.** $h(2)$ **c.** $h(4)$ **d.** $h(-3)$

3. For $F(x) = \dfrac{x+1}{x-1}$, find:

    a. $F(2)$ **b.** $F(0)$ **c.** $F(-1)$ **d.** $F(-3)$

4. For $g(x) = \sqrt{2x^2 - 3x - 5}$, find:
    a. $g(3)$ **b.** $g(-2)$ **c.** $g(6)$ **d.** $g(-4)$

5. For $f(x) = \sqrt{x-1}$, find:
    a. $f(2)$ **b.** $f(5)$ **c.** $f(1)$ **d.** $f(2x)$

6. For $f(t) = t^3 - 4t - 5$, find:
    a. $f(2)$ **b.** $f(-1)$ **c.** $f(4)$ **d.** $f(-3)$

7. For $f(x) = \dfrac{2x-3}{3x+4}$, find:

    a. $f(-2)$ **b.** $f(\tfrac{1}{2})$ **c.** $f(\tfrac{5}{6})$ **d.** $f(-\tfrac{2}{3})$

8. For $g(x) = \dfrac{x-1}{x+2}$, find:

    a. $g(1)$ **b.** $g(-3)$ **c.** $g(0)$ **d.** $g\left(\dfrac{1}{x}\right)$

9. For $f(x) = 2x^2 - 4$, find:
    a. $f(1)$ **b.** $f(-2)$ **c.** $f(a)$ **d.** $f(x+1)$ **e.** $f(x+h)$

10. For $f(t) = 1/t$, find:

    a. $f(2)$ **b.** $f(\tfrac{1}{2})$ **c.** $f\left(\dfrac{1}{a}\right)$ **d.** $\dfrac{f(t+h) - f(t)}{h}$

11. For $h(t) = \sqrt{1 - t^2}$, find:

    a. $h(1)$ **b.** $h(1-t)$ **c.** $h\left(\dfrac{1}{t}\right)$ **d.** $h(t + \Delta t)$

In Problems 12–15 find the domain and range of f.

12. **a.** $f(x) = 2x$ **b.** $f(x) = x^2$

13. **a.** $f(x) = x^3$ **b.** $f(x) = \dfrac{1}{x}$

14. **a.** $f(x) = \sqrt{x-4}$ **b.** $f(x) = \dfrac{1}{x+2}$

15. **a.** $f(x) = \sqrt{1-x^2}$ **b.** $f(x) = \dfrac{x}{x-4}$

16. For $f(x) = \begin{cases} x & \text{if } x \geq 0 \\ 1-x & \text{if } x < 0 \end{cases}$ find:

   a. $f(0)$ **b.** $f(1)$ **c.** $f(-1)$ **d.** $f(2)$

17. For $g(x) = \begin{cases} x^2 & \text{if } x > 1 \\ 0 & \text{if } x = 1 \\ -1 & \text{if } x < 1 \end{cases}$ find:

   a. $g(2)$ **b.** $g(-2)$ **c.** $g(0)$ **d.** $g(1)$

18. For $f(x) = \begin{cases} x^2 - 4 & \text{if } x \geq 1 \\ \dfrac{1-2x}{3} & \text{if } x < 1 \end{cases}$ find:

   a. $f(5)$ **b.** $f(-2)$ **c.** $f(1)$

19. For $\phi(x) = \begin{cases} 1 & \text{if } x \text{ is rational} \\ 0 & \text{if } x \text{ is irrational} \end{cases}$ find:

   a. $\phi(1)$ **b.** $\phi(0)$ **c.** $\phi(\sqrt{2})$ **d.** $\phi(\pi)$

20. Let $F(x) = \sqrt{x}$. Show that

$$\frac{F(x+h) - F(x)}{h} = \frac{1}{\sqrt{x+h} + \sqrt{x}}$$

21. Let $\phi(x) = x/(x-3)$. Find

$$\frac{\phi(4+h) - \phi(4)}{h}$$

   and simplify your result.

22. Find the domain of f if:
   a. $f(x) = \sqrt{2x - 4x^2}$ **b.** $f(x) = \sqrt{x^2 - 2x - 3}$

23. Find the domain of g if

   a. $g(x) = \sqrt{\dfrac{x-1}{x+2}}$ **b.** $g(t) = \sqrt{t^2 - 4}$

24. Express the area of a triangle of base 10 as a function of its altitude h.

25. Express the perimeter of a rectangle of length 12 as a function of its width w.

26. Express the area of a circle as a function of its diameter d.

27. Express the circumference of a circle as a function of its diameter d.

28. The sum of \$600 is invested at $5\frac{1}{2}\%$ simple interest for t years. Express the total interest earned as a function of t.

29. Express the amount of money accumulated from investing \$10,000 at 7% compounded annually as a function of the number of years t.

30. Express the amount of money accumulated from investing \$500 at compound interest (compounded annually) for 10 years as a function of the annual interest rate r.

31. A can is in the form of a right circular cylinder with the height twice the radius of the base. Express the following as functions of the radius of the base:
   a. Volume   **b.** Lateral surface area   **c.** Total surface area
   Hint. The volume of a right circular cylinder is the area of the base times the

altitude, and the lateral surface area is the circumference of the base times the altitude.

32. Express the Celsius temperature (°C) as a function of the Fahrenheit temperature (°F). **Hint.** Write °F = a(°C) + b and find a and b from the fact that when °C = 100, °F = 212, and when °C = 0, °F = 32.

33. Let $f(x) = (x + 2)/(2x + 1)$. Show that if $x \neq 0$, then

$$f\left(\frac{1}{x}\right) = \frac{1}{f(x)}$$

34. Let $f(x) = 2x$. Show that for any real number k, $f(kx) = k \cdot f(x)$.

35. A function is said to be **even** if $f(-x) = f(x)$ for all x in the domain, and it is said to be **odd** if $f(-x) = -f(x)$ for all x in the domain. Determine in each of the following whether the function is even, odd, or neither:
   a. $f(x) = x^2$ b. $f(x) = x^3$ c. $f(x) = x^2 + 2x$
   d. $g(x) = x - 1$ e. $h(x) = 2x^2 - 3$

36. Follow the instructions in Problem 35 for the following:

   a. $f(x) = \dfrac{x}{x^2 + 1}$ b. $g(x) = \dfrac{1}{x^3 - 2x}$ c. $h(t) = \dfrac{t + 2}{t - 1}$

   d. $\phi(x) = \dfrac{x^2 - 1}{x^2 + 4}$ e. $F(t) = |t|$

37. A piece of manufacturing equipment is purchased for $200,000. For tax purposes the value is decreased by $40,000 times the number of years x since the equipment was purchased. Let $f(x)$ be the value of the equipment x years after purchase.
   a. Write the rule for the function f.
   b. Find the domain of f if the value of the equipment cannot be negative.

38. If a price of $\$x$ per unit is charged for a certain product, the number of units sold will be $1,000 - 25x$. Let $f(x)$ be the revenue when the price is x, where revenue is the price per unit times the number of units sold.
   a. Write the rule for the function f.
   b. Find the domain of f if the revenue is to be nonnegative.

B Find the domain of each of the functions in Problems 39 and 40.

39. $f(x) = \sqrt{\dfrac{x^2 - 2x - 8}{x + 5}}$ 40. $g(t) = \sqrt{\dfrac{t + 4}{t^3 - t^2 - t + 1}}$

41. Express the area of an equilateral triangle as a function of one of its sides s. **Hint.** Use the Pythagorean theorem.

42. An isosceles triangle of base x is inscribed in a circle of radius 2. Express the area of the triangle as a function of x. **Hint.** Use the Pythagorean theorem.

43. A right circular cylinder is inscribed in a sphere of radius a. Express the volume of the cylinder as a function of its base radius r.

44. A rectangle is inscribed in an isosceles triangle of height 4 and base 6. Express the area of the rectangle as a function of its base. **Hint.** Use similar triangles.

45. A pyramid has a square base 4 feet on a side, and its height is 10 feet. Express the area of a cross-section, parallel to the base, that is h feet above the base as a function of h.

46. A storage tank is in the form of a cylinder x feet long and y feet in diameter, with hemispheres at both ends (see sketch).

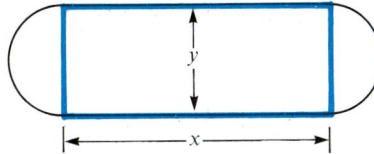

a. Express the volume of the tank as a function of x and y.
b. Express the surface area of the tank as a function of x and y.
c. If $x = 4y$, express the volume and the surface area as functions of x only.

47. An organization issuing credit cards charges the card holder interest of $1\frac{1}{2}\%$ per month for the first $1,000 unpaid balance after 30 days and 1% a month on the unpaid balance above $1,000. Let $f(x)$ be the interest charged per month on an unpaid balance of $\$x$, and find the rule for f.

48. A company deducts 2% of gross salary from each employee's pay as the employee's contribution to the pension fund. However, no employee pays more than $400 into the fund in a single year. Let $f(x)$ be the contribution of an employee with gross salary of $\$x$ a year. Write the rule for f.

49. A right circular cone is inscribed in a sphere of radius a. Express the volume of the cone as a function of its base radius r.
   Hint. The volume of a cone is one-third the area of its base times its altitude.

50. Let f denote any function, and define g and h as follows:

$$g(x) = \frac{f(x) + f(-x)}{2} \qquad h(x) = \frac{f(x) - f(-x)}{2}$$

a. Show that g is even and h is odd. (See Problem 35.)
b. Show that $f(x) = g(x) + h(x)$. (This proves that every function can be expressed as the sum of an even function and an odd function.)

51. Prove that the range of the function $f(x) = 1 + \sqrt{x}$ is the set $\{y: \ y \geq 1\}$.
52. Prove that the range of the function $f(x) = 2x/(x^2 + 1)$ is the set $\{y: \ |y| \leq 1\}$.

4 Graphs of Functions

Let f be a function from A to B, where A and B are subsets of R. If x is an element in A, let y denote its image under f, that is, $y = f(x)$. Thus, f establishes a pairing of values (x, y) with x in A and y in B. The totality of such pairs as x varies over all of A can be plotted in a cartesian coordinate system, and the result is called the **graph of f.** If the rule for f is given in the form of an equation, the graph of f is identical to the graph of this equation as defined in Section 2. For example, the graph of the function f for which $f(x) = 2x + 3$ is the same as the graph of the equation $y = 2x + 3$. However, an important distinction must be made. Not all graphs of equations in two variables are graphs of functions. This is because of the requirement that in the case of a function, each x in the domain determines exactly one value y in the range. **Geometrically, this amounts to the requirement that a vertical line through any point on the x axis strikes the graph of f at no more than one point** (Figure 7).

As a specific example of an equation that does not define y as a function of x, consider $y^2 = x$. If we solve for y, we get $y = \pm\sqrt{x}$, so that each $x > 0$

Figure 7

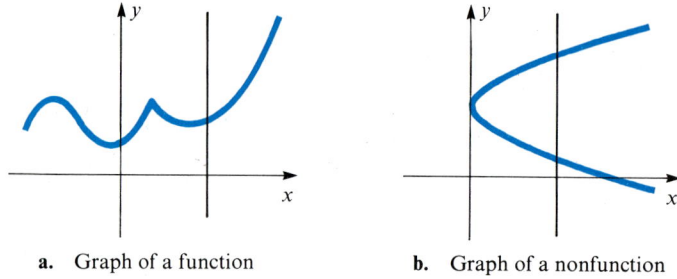

a. Graph of a function   **b.** Graph of a nonfunction

Figure 8

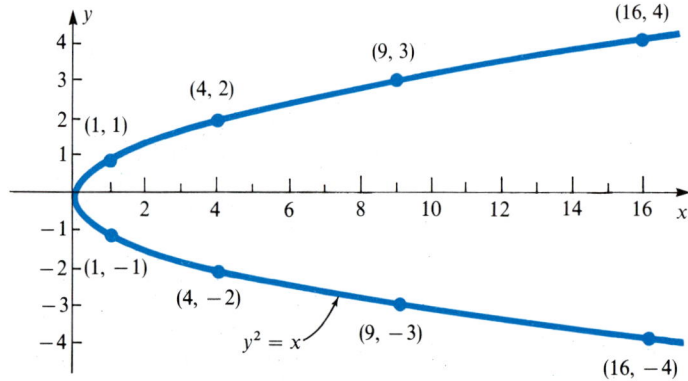

determines two values of y, which cannot happen in the case of a function. The graph of $y^2 = x$ (Figure 8) can be obtained by making a table of values, as follows:

x	1.	4	9	16
y	± 1	± 2	± 3	± 4

It is possible to view the equation $y = \pm\sqrt{x}$ as defining two different functions, say,

$$y_1 = \sqrt{x} \quad \text{and} \quad y_2 = -\sqrt{x}$$

corresponding to the upper and lower halves, respectively, of Figure 8.* In a similar way, it is often possible to consider an equation whose graph is not a single function as defining more than one function.

---

* There are, in fact, various other ways to define functions from the equation, but the way given is the natural decomposition. We could, for example, let

$$y_1 = \begin{cases} \sqrt{x} & \text{if } x \text{ is rational and } \geq 0 \\ -\sqrt{x} & \text{if } x \text{ is irrational and } > 0 \end{cases} \qquad y_2 = \begin{cases} -\sqrt{x} & \text{if } x \text{ is rational and } \geq 0 \\ \sqrt{x} & \text{if } x \text{ is irrational and } > 0 \end{cases}$$

but it is unlikely that this would be very useful.

EXAMPLE 12   Determine which of the graphs in Figure 9 are graphs of functions and which are not.

Figure 9

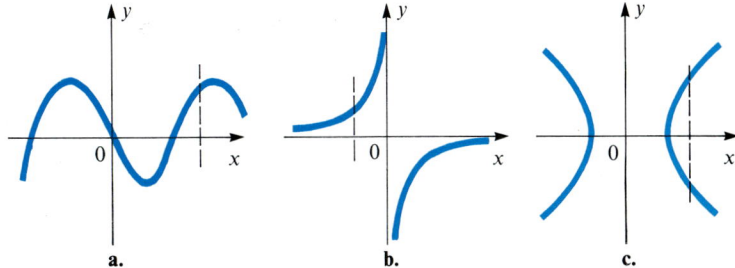

a.   b.   c.

Solution   **a.**   This a function since each vertical line cuts the curve in only one point.
   b.   Each vertical line cuts the curve at most in one point, so this is a function.
   c.   Some vertical lines cut the curve in two points, so this is not a function.

EXAMPLE 13   Draw the graph of the function f defined by

$$f(x) = \begin{cases} 1 - x & \text{if} & x \leq 0 \\ 1 & \text{if} & 0 < x < 2 \\ \sqrt{x - 2} & \text{if} & x \geq 2 \end{cases}$$

Solution   We set $y = f(x)$ and make a table of values, including points in each of the intervals on which the various parts of the function are defined. The graph is given in Figure 10.

x	-3	-2	-1	0	1	2	3	6	11
y	4	3	2	1	1	0	1	2	3

Notice the break in the graph at $x = 2$. The function is said to be *discontinuous* there. Even though the graph is made up of three distinct parts, it is still the graph of the single function f.

Figure 10

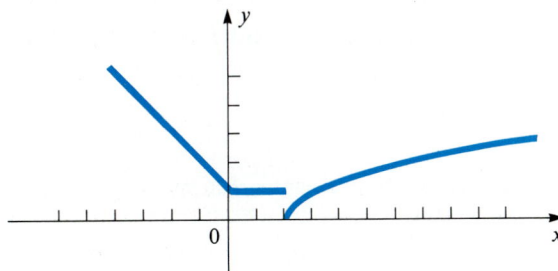

A function is said to be *increasing* on an interval if for any x_1 and x_2 on the interval, with $x_1 < x_2$, it is true that $f(x_1) < f(x_2)$. If when $x_1 < x_2$, it is true that $f(x_1) > f(x_2)$, then f is *decreasing* on the interval. Figure 11 illustrates increasing and decreasing functions.

Figure 11

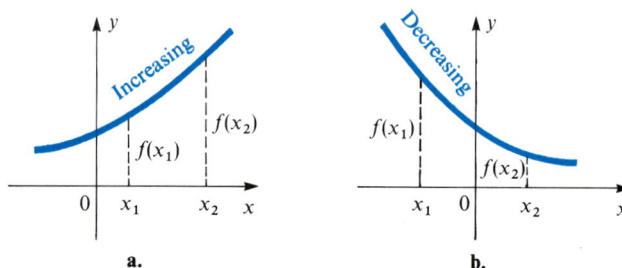

a.   b.

It is useful to be able to identify from the graph of a function the intervals on which it is increasing and those on which it is decreasing. The next example illustrates this.

EXAMPLE 14   Determine the intervals on which the function whose graph is shown in Figure 12 is increasing and decreasing.

Figure 12

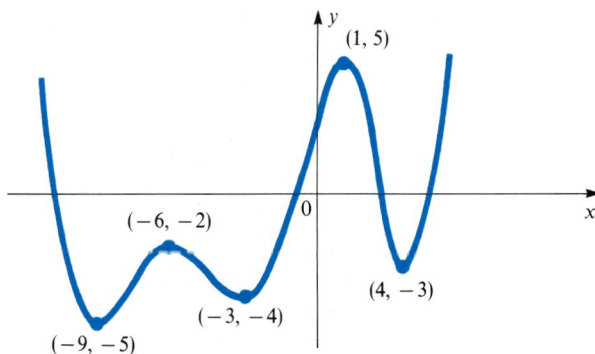

Solution   Increasing on the intervals $[-9, -6]$, $[-3, 1]$, and $[4, \infty)$.
Decreasing on the intervals $(-\infty, -9]$, $[-6, -3]$, and $[1, 4]$.

EXERCISE SET 4

A   Graph the functions in Problems 1–18.

1. $f(x) = x - 2$
2. $f(x) = 3x + 4$
3. $f(x) = 2x - 1$
4. $g(x) = 2 - 5x$
5. $f(x) = \dfrac{2x + 5}{3}$
6. $g(x) = \dfrac{4 - 3x}{5}$

7. $f(x) = x^2 - 2x$

8. $h(x) = x^3 - 1$

9. $g(x) = \sqrt{x - 1}$

10. $F(x) = \sqrt{4 - x}$

11. $f(x) = \dfrac{4}{x^2}$

12. $g(x) = \sqrt{4 - x^2}$

13. $f(x) = \dfrac{3}{2x}$

14. $h(x) = \dfrac{1}{x - 1}$

15. $f(x) = \begin{cases} x & \text{if } x \geq 0 \\ -1 & \text{if } x < 0 \end{cases}$

16. $g(x) = \begin{cases} x^2 & \text{if } x > 1 \\ 0 & \text{if } x = 1 \\ 2 - x & \text{if } x < 1 \end{cases}$

17. $F(x) = \begin{cases} 2x & \text{if } & x \geq 2 \\ 1 - x & \text{if } & -1 \leq x < 2 \\ 2 & \text{if } & x < -1 \end{cases}$

18. $h(x) = \begin{cases} \sqrt{x - 4} & \text{if } x \geq 4 \\ 1 - \dfrac{x}{4} & \text{if } x < 4 \end{cases}$

In Problems 19 and 20 determine which of the graphs are graphs of functions and which are not.

19. **a.**

b.

c.

d.

e.

f.

20. **a.**

b.

c.

d.

e.

f.

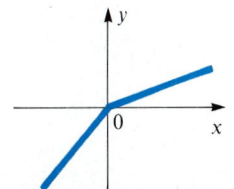

In Problems 21 and 22 determine the intervals on which the function whose graph is shown is increasing and those on which it is decreasing.

21.

22.

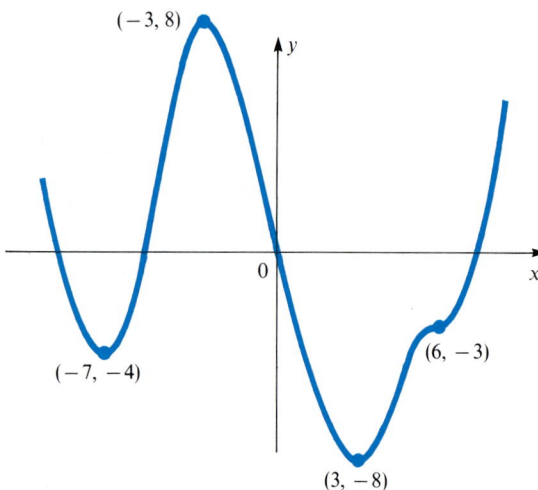

B In Problems 23–26 exhibit two functions defined by the given equation and graph each function.

23. $x^2 + y^2 = 4$ **24.** $y^2 = 1 - x$

25. $x = \sqrt{1 + y^2}$ **26.** $|x| + |y| = 1$

27. Graph the function f defined by

$$f(x) = \begin{cases} x^3 - 1 & \text{if} & x > 1 \\ 1 - x & \text{if} & 0 < x \le 1 \\ 2 & \text{if} & x = 0 \\ 1 - x^2 & \text{if} & x < 0 \end{cases}$$

28. A model for the operation of a hydroelectric plant determines the function f below, which gives the amount of water that should be allowed to pass through the turbines if the amount of water in the reservoir is x. It is assumed that a steam generating plant supplying k units of energy is available to supplement the hydroelectric plant. If the total power required in a given period of time is A, then there are water levels a and b so that

$$f(x) = \begin{cases} x & \text{if} & 0 \le x < A - k \\ A - k & \text{if} & A - k \le x < a \\ \dfrac{k}{b-a}(x-b) + A & \text{if} & a \le x < b \\ A & \text{if} & x \ge b \end{cases}$$

Given that $A = 100$, $k = 70$, $a = 42$, and $b = 74$, graph the function f.

5 One-to-One Functions

As we saw in Section 4 the graph of a function has the property that a vertical line intersects the curve in at most one point. It is entirely possible, however, that a horizontal line might intersect the graph in two or more points. Consider, for example, the graph of the function f defined by $f(x) = x^2$, shown in Figure 13. In this case any horizontal line above the x axis intersects the curve in two points. So there are distinct points in the domain having the same function value. For example, $f(2) = f(-2)$. More generally, when a horizontal line intersects the graph of a function in two or more points, we can always find two numbers x_1 and x_2 in the domain for which $f(x_1) = f(x_2)$ but $x_1 \ne x_2$. In this section we study an important class of functions for which this situation cannot occur. These are called *one-to-one* functions (written 1–1).

Figure 13

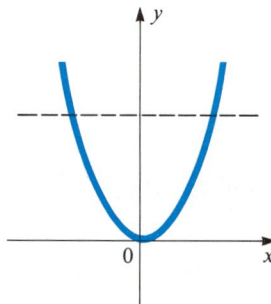

DEFINITION 2 A function f is said to be **one-to-one** provided that whenever $f(x_1) = f(x_2)$, then $x_1 = x_2$.

Note. An equivalent formulation is to say that f is one-to-one if two distinct points x_1 and x_2 in the domain of f have distinct images, $f(x_1) \ne f(x_2)$. Geometrically, this definition requires that each horizontal line intersect the graph of f in at most one point.

Figure 14

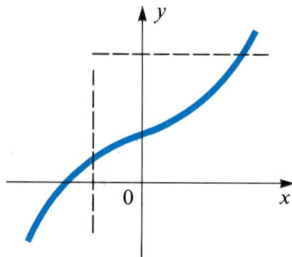

Figure 14 illustrates a 1–1 function. We conclude that for a graph to be that of a 1–1 function, it must pass both the vertical and horizontal line tests: *Every vertical line and every horizontal line must intersect the graph in at most one point.*

We cannot rely solely on the graphical method for determining whether a function is 1–1, since the graph may be difficult to draw with accuracy. The next three examples show how to use the definition in making this determination.

EXAMPLE 15   Let $f(x) = 3x + 4$. Show that f is 1–1.

Solution   Suppose $f(x_1) = f(x_2)$, that is, $3x_1 + 4 = 3x_2 + 4$. Then $3x_1 = 3x_2$, and hence $x_1 = x_2$. So f is 1–1.

EXAMPLE 16   Show that the function g defined by $g(x) = \sqrt{x}$ is 1–1 on its domain.

Solution   Note that the domain consists of all nonnegative real numbers, that is, the set $\{x: \ x \geq 0\}$. Suppose $g(x_1) = g(x_2)$, that is, $\sqrt{x_1} = \sqrt{x_2}$. Squaring both sides yields immediately that $x_1 = x_2$. Thus, g is 1–1.

EXAMPLE 17   Show that the function ϕ defined by $\phi(t) = t^2 - 2t - 3$ is 1–1 on the domain $\{t: \ t \geq 1\}$.

Solution   If $\phi(t_1) = \phi(t_2)$, then $t_1^2 - 2t_1 - 3 = t_2^2 - 2t_2 - 3$. We rearrange and factor:

$$t_1^2 - t_2^2 - 2t_1 + 2t_2 = 0$$
$$(t_1 - t_2)(t_1 + t_2) - 2(t_1 - t_2) = 0$$
$$(t_1 - t_2)(t_1 + t_2 - 2) = 0$$

So either $t_1 = t_2$ or $t_1 + t_2 = 2$. But the only way the latter equation can be true when t_1 and t_2 are greater than or equal to 1 is for both t_1 and t_2 to equal 1. In both cases, then, $t_1 = t_2$, so that ϕ is 1–1 on the specified domain.

The next example illustrates how we can sometimes restrict the domain of a function to make it 1–1.

EXAMPLE 18   Let $h(x) = 4 - x^2$. Show that h is not 1–1, but find a suitable restriction on the domain so that it will be 1–1.

Solution   To show that h is not 1–1 we can take any value of x (other than zero) and its negative—for example, $h(1) = 3$ and $h(-1) = 3$. Since $1 \neq -1$, the definition is not satisfied. From Figure 15 we can see that the graph fails the horizontal line test.

   If we restrict the domain to nonnegative values of x only, that is, to the set $\{x: \ x \geq 0\}$, it appears from the graph that the function is then 1–1. In fact if x_1 and x_2 are nonnegative and $h(x_1) = h(x_2)$, we have

$$4 - x_1^2 = 4 - x_2^2$$
$$x_1^2 = x_2^2$$
$$x_1 = x_2$$

since neither x_1 nor x_2 is negative. So by Definition 2, h is 1–1 on this restricted domain.

Figure 15

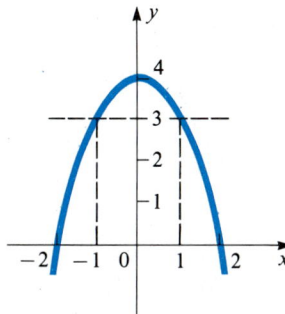

EXERCISE SET 5

A   **1.**   Which of the graphs in Problem 19 of Exercise Set 4 are graphs of 1–1 functions?
    2.   Which of the graphs in Problem 20 of Exercise Set 4 are graphs of 1–1 functions?

In Problems 3–14 use Definition 2 to show that the functions are 1–1 on R.

3. $f(x) = 2x$ 　　　　　　　　　　　　　　　　　**4.** $f(x) = x + 4$
5. $g(x) = 3x - 2$ 　　　　　　　　　　　　　　**6.** $h(x) = 2 - x$
7. $f(t) = 2t - 3$ 　　　　　　　　　　　　　　　**8.** $F(x) = 5x + 3$

9. $\phi(x) = \dfrac{3x}{4} + \dfrac{2}{3}$ 　　　　　　　　　　　**10.** $g(t) = t^3$

11. $f(x) = \dfrac{2(3 - x)}{5}$ 　　　　　　　　　**12.** $g(x) = \dfrac{1 - 2x}{3}$

13. $h(t) = \dfrac{2t}{3} - \dfrac{1}{4}$ 　　　　　　　　　**14.** $f(s) = \dfrac{4s - 5}{7}$

15.   Let $\phi(x) = 1/x$. What are the domain and range of ϕ? Determine whether ϕ is 1–1.

16. What is the domain of the function $f(x) = \sqrt{x - 1}$? Is f a 1–1 function on this domain?

17. Let $\phi(x) = |x|$. Is ϕ a 1–1 function? Draw the graph of ϕ.

18. Let $h(x) = |x - 2|$. Is h a 1–1 function? Draw the graph of h.

19. Let $g(x) = 1/\sqrt{x}$. Show that g is a 1–1 function from R^+ to R^+.
(Recall that R^+ means the set of all positive real numbers.)

20. Let h be the function from R to R defined by $h(x) = x^3 - x$. Show that h is not 1–1.
Hint. Find two or more numbers that have 0 as their image.

21. Let $f(t) = t/(t + 1)$. What is the domain of f? Determine whether f is 1–1.

22. Let $f(t) = (2t - 1)/(2t + 1)$. What is the domain of f? Determine whether f is 1–1.

23. Determine whether the function ϕ defined by $\phi(t) = t^2 - 2t - 8$ is 1–1.

24. Let $g(x) = (1 - 2x)/(3x - 4)$. What is the domain of g? Determine whether g is 1–1.

25. Let $h(x) = 2 + \sqrt{x - 1}$. Find the domain of h, and prove that h is 1–1.

26. Show that if $f(x) = |3x - 5|$, then f is not 1–1 on R. Find a suitable restriction on the domain so that f will be 1–1.

B 27. **a.** Show that the function f defined by $f(x) = 1 - x^2$ is not 1–1.
b. Restrict the domain of f in a suitable way so that it will be 1–1.

28. Let $g(x) = x^2 - 2x$. Show that g is not 1–1 on all of R but that it is 1–1 on the domain $\{x: \ x \geq 1\}$.

29. Show three distinct values of x that have the same image for the function $f(x) = x^3 - 4x^2 - x + 4$. What conclusion can you draw?

30. In Exercise Set 4 an even function was defined as one for which $f(-x) = f(x)$ and an odd function as one for which $f(-x) = -f(x)$, for all x in the domain. Show that an even function cannot be 1–1. Show by means of examples that an odd function may or may not be 1–1.

31. Show that if f is either increasing on its domain or decreasing on its domain, then f is 1–1.

32. A function f is said to be **periodic** if there exists a positive real number k such that $f(x + k) = f(x)$ for all x in the domain of f. Show that a periodic function cannot be 1–1.

33. To show that f is a function from A onto B, it is sufficient to show that whatever element y in B is chosen, there is some element x in A for which $f(x) = y$. Show that the function f for which $f(x) = \sqrt[3]{x}$ is a 1–1 function from R onto R.

34. Show that if $g(x) = (3 - 2x)/4$, then g is a 1–1 function from R onto R.

35. Let $f(x) = (x + 1)/(x - 1)$.
a. Show that f is 1–1 on its domain.
b. The set of images of f is contained in the set $\{y: \ y \geq 0\}$. Is f a 1–1 function from its domain onto this set?

36. The notation $[x]$ is defined to mean the greatest integer less than or equal to x. For example, $[2.3] = 2$, $[5\frac{3}{4}] = 5$, $[6] = 6$, and $[-1.5] = -2$. Show that the function f defined by $f(x) = [x]$ from R to R is neither 1–1 nor onto.

6 Composite Functions and Inverses

Functions are often compared to machines. For example, a value of x from the domain is fed into the machine. The machine (the function) then operates on x and out comes $f(x)$,* as shown in Figure 16. Now it frequently happens

---
* A calculator can be thought of as such a function machine.

Figure 16

Figure 17

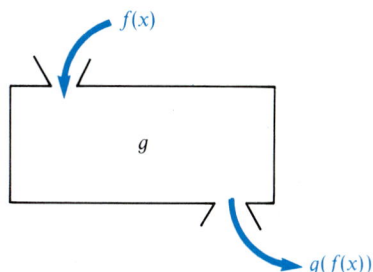

that having applied the function f to a number x and obtained $f(x)$ as an output, we then input $f(x)$ into a second function machine, say, g, as illustrated in Figure 17. The output of g would then be designated $g(f(x))$. When we first apply f and then g to the result, the overall effect on x is to produce $g(f(x))$. We could consider a new machine (a new function) that does this all at once, and this is usually designated $g \circ f$, as indicated in Figure 18. It is called the **composite** of g and f. For example, suppose that $f(x) = 2x^2 + 3$ and $g(x) = \sqrt{x}$. Then $g(f(x)) = \sqrt{2x^2 + 3}$.

Note. Observe that $g \circ f$ and $f \circ g$ need not be—and usually are not—equal. In this example, the function $f \circ g$ has the following effect on x:

$$(f \circ g)(x) = f(g(x)) = 2(\sqrt{x})^2 + 3 = 2x + 3$$

Care must be exercised in specifying the domain of a composite function. Since $(g \circ f)(x) = g(f(x))$, the (maximum) domain of $g \circ f$ consists of those values of x in the domain of f for which $f(x)$ lies in the domain of g; we cannot input $f(x)$ into the g function unless $f(x)$ lies in the domain of g. In our example above, where $f(x) = 2x^2 + 3$ and $g(x) = \sqrt{x}$, this was no problem, since the range of f consists of real numbers greater than or equal to 3, and these are

Figure 18

included in the domain of g. However, if we had been given $f(x) = x^2 - 4$ and $g(x) = \sqrt{x}$, then we would have $(g \circ f)(x) = \sqrt{x^2 - 4}$, so that the domain of $g \circ f$ would be restricted to those values of x for which $x^2 - 4 \geq 0$, or equivalently $(x - 2)(x + 2) \geq 0$. Using the technique for solving quadratic inequalities given in Chapter 3, we find the solution set to be $\{x: \ x \geq 2\} \cup \{x: \ x \leq -2\}$. This, then, is the domain of $g \circ f$.

We now wish to introduce the concept of the **inverse** of a function. We will see that this has a direct relationship with composite functions. Roughly speaking, two functions are inverses of one another if each undoes what the other does. Thus, if $f(x) = 2x$ and $g(x) = x/2$, then f and g are inverses; f doubles any given number in its domain, whereas g halves numbers in its domain. So the effect of first applying f and then g, or vice versa, to a given number x is that there is no net change. This is typical of functions and their inverses.

DEFINITION 3   We say that f and g are inverses of one another provided that

$$\text{Range of } g = \text{Domain of } f$$
$$\text{Range of } f = \text{Domain of } g$$

and

$$(f \circ g)(x) = x$$
$$(g \circ f)(x) = x$$

EXAMPLE 19   Show that f and g, defined by $f(x) = 2x + 1$ and $g(x) = (x - 1)/2$, are inverses.

Solution   Both f and g have all of R as domain and range. Furthermore,

$$(f \circ g)(x) = f(g(x)) = 2\left(\frac{x - 1}{2}\right) + 1 = x$$

$$(g \circ f)(x) = g(f(x)) = \frac{(2x + 1) - 1}{2} = x$$

So f and g are inverses.

EXAMPLE 20   Show that if the domain of the function f defined by $f(x) = x^2$ is restricted to be $\{x: \ x \geq 0\}$, then if g is defined by $g(x) = \sqrt{x}$, f and g are inverses.

Solution   The range of f consists of all nonnegative numbers, which is precisely the domain of g, and the range of g consists of the set of nonnegative numbers, which by the given restriction is the domain of f. Also,

$$(f \circ g)(x) = f(g(x)) = (\sqrt{x})^2 = x$$
$$(g \circ f)(x) = g(f(x)) = \sqrt{x^2} = x$$

Note.   We have $\sqrt{x^2} = x$ since $x \geq 0$.

Figure 19

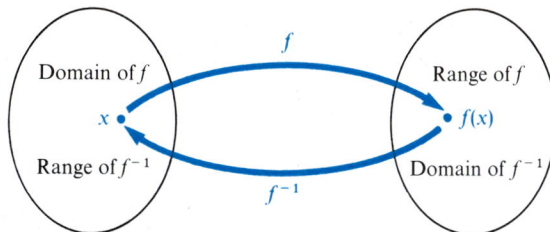

The symbol f^{-1} is customarily used to denote the inverse of f. So we always have

$$(f \circ f^{-1})(x) = (f^{-1} \circ f)(x) = x$$

We could say that $f \circ f^{-1}$ (or $f^{-1} \circ f$) is the **identity function,** because it leaves a number unchanged. Figure 19 shows how f and f^{-1} are related.

For the inverse of a function f to exist, it must be true that each element of the range of f is the image of precisely one element in the domain. If we begin with an x in the domain of f, its image is $f(x)$. Now if f^{-1} exists, it must make $f(x)$ correspond to x and to nothing else:

$$f^{-1}(f(x)) = x$$

But the requirement that each element in the range of f be the image of exactly one element in the domain is just the requirement that f be one-to-one.

Suppose now that f is 1–1. We will show that it has an inverse. All we need to do is to define f^{-1} as that function having domain equal to the range of f and for which

$$f^{-1}(y) = x$$

where $y = f(x)$. This is a valid definition, since each such y uniquely determines an x.

So we have the following result:

> A function has an inverse if and only if it is 1–1.

Suppose we determine that a given function does have an inverse. How do we go about actually finding the inverse? Let

$$y = f(x)$$

Now apply f^{-1} to both sides:

$$f^{-1}(y) = f^{-1}(f(x)) = x$$

So

$$x = f^{-1}(y)$$

It appears, then, that to find an equation defining f^{-1}, we solve the equation $y = f(x)$ for x in terms of y. That is, we reverse the roles of dependent and independent variables. Consider, for example, the problem of finding the inverse of the function f defined by $f(x) = 2x + 3$. We can show that f is 1–1, so it has an inverse. Now set $y = 2x + 3$ and solve for x:

$$2x = y - 3$$

$$x = \frac{y - 3}{2}$$

So $f^{-1}(y) = (y - 3)/2$. This adequately defines the function f^{-1}; it is the function that subtracts 3 from the input value and then divides the result by 2. The particular letter used in the defining equation for a function is not important. We could just as well write

$$f^{-1}(t) = \frac{t - 3}{2} \quad \text{or} \quad f^{-1}(u) = \frac{u - 3}{2} \quad \text{or} \quad f^{-1}(x) = \frac{x - 3}{2}$$

Each of these in effect tells us what the function f^{-1} does. Since it is customary to use the letter x as the independent and y as the dependent variable in a functional relationship, this suggests the following procedure for finding the inverse of a 1–1 function f:

1. Set $y = f(x)$.
2. Solve the equation for x in terms of y.
3. Interchange x and y.

Again, consider the example $f(x) = 2x + 3$. We write

$$y = 2x + 3$$

$$x = \frac{y - 3}{2}$$

So,

$$y = \frac{x - 3}{2} = f^{-1}(x)$$

Two points should be emphasized regarding the procedure given above for finding the inverse. First, before attempting to apply the procedure it should be determined that the inverse actually exists. However, if this is not done in advance, the procedure itself will generally show this. For example, consider $f(x) = x^2 + 1$. We set $y = x^2 + 1$, solve for x:

$$x = \pm \sqrt{y - 1}$$

and interchange x and y:

$$y = \pm \sqrt{x - 1}$$

But the ambiguity of sign shows that no unique inverse exists.

Second, a major problem with the procedure is that it is not always possible to solve for x. For example, try to solve $y = x^5 + x - 1$ for x!

EXAMPLE 21   Show that if $f(x) = \sqrt{x - 1}$, then f has an inverse on the domain $\{x: \; x \geq 1\}$, and find that inverse.

Solution We show first that f is 1–1. Suppose $f(x_1) = f(x_2)$, so that $\sqrt{x_1 - 1} = \sqrt{x_2 - 1}$. It follows by squaring both sides that $x_1 - 1 = x_2 - 1$, or $x_1 = x_2$. Thus, f is 1–1 and hence has an inverse. Now set

$$y = \sqrt{x - 1}$$

Squaring and solving for x yields

$$y^2 = x - 1$$
$$x = y^2 + 1$$

Finally, the rule for f^{-1} is

$$y = x^2 + 1$$

that is,

$$f^{-1}(x) = x^2 + 1$$

But we must carefully state the domain of f^{-1}. It is precisely the range of f. Since $f(x) = \sqrt{x - 1}$, the range is contained in the set of nonnegative real numbers; in fact, this is the range of f. If we take any nonnegative real number k, we can find an x for which $f(x) = k$ as follows:

$$\sqrt{x - 1} = k$$
$$x - 1 = k^2$$
$$x = 1 + k^2$$

This value of x does work, since

$$f(x) = f(1 + k^2) = \sqrt{1 + k^2 - 1} = \sqrt{k^2} = k$$

Therefore, the domain of f^{-1} is the set of all nonnegative real numbers.

We can now see the geometrical relationship between a function and its inverse. Let f be a 1–1 function from A onto B, where A and B are subsets of R. In order to obtain the equation $y = f^{-1}(x)$, we solve the equation $y = f(x)$ for x and then interchange the roles of x and y. It follows that if (a, b) is a point on the graph of $y = f(x)$, then (b, a) is on the graph of $y = f^{-1}(x)$. The situation is shown in Figure 20. The graph of $y = f^{-1}(x)$ is the reflection of

Figure 20

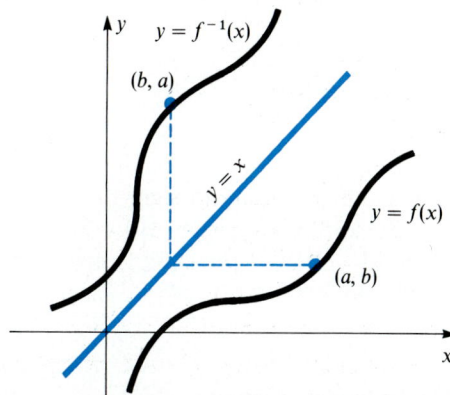

the graph of $y = f(x)$ in the line through the origin making a 45° angle with the x axis. On this line the x coordinate and the y coordinate of any point are equal, and this holds true only for points on this line. Thus, the equation of the line is $y = x$. We say that the graphs of a 1–1 function and its inverse are **symmetric with respect to the line $y = x$.**

EXERCISE SET 6

A   In Problems 1–12 find $f \circ g$ and $g \circ f$.

1. $f(x) = x - 1, \quad g(x) = 2x + 1$

2. $f(x) = 2x, \quad g(x) = x + 3$

3. $f(x) = 3x - 5, \quad g(x) = 2 - x$

4. $f(x) = 3x + 4, \quad g(x) = \dfrac{2x - 1}{3}$

5. $f(x) = 2x^2, \quad g(x) = x + 2$

6. $f(x) = \sqrt{x - 2}, \quad g(x) = x^2 + 4$

7. $f(x) = \dfrac{1}{x + 1}, \quad g(x) = \dfrac{1}{x - 3}$

8. $f(x) = x^3, \quad g(x) = x^2$

9. $f(x) = x^2 - 2x + 1, \quad g(x) = 2x - 3$

10. $f(x) = 1/x, \quad g(x) = 3x + 4$

11. $f(x) = \dfrac{x}{x - 1}, \quad g(x) = \dfrac{2}{x}$

12. $f(x) = 2, \quad g(x) = x^2 - 4$

In Problems 13–15 find $f \circ g$ and $g \circ f$, and give the domain of each.

13. $f(x) = \sqrt{x - 1}, \quad g(x) = x^2$

14. $f(x) = 2x^2 - 1, \quad g(x) = \sqrt{x}$

15. $f(x) = \sqrt{x^2 - 1}, \quad g(x) = 2x - 3$

16. Let $f(x) = x^2 - 1$. Find $(f \circ f)(x)$.

17. Let $f(x) = (2x - 3)/5$, $g(x) = x^2 - 3$, and $h(x) = (5x + 3)/2$. Find:
  a. $f(g(x))$ **b.** $g(f(x))$ **c.** $f(h(x))$ **d.** $h(f(x))$ **e.** $g(h(x))$

In Problems 18–32 show that an inverse exists, and find it.

18. $f(x) = x - 1$

19. $f(x) = 2x + 5$

20. $f(x) = 3x + 7$

21. $g(x) = \dfrac{x}{2} + 4$

22. $h(x) = \dfrac{2x - 5}{3}$

23. $G(x) = \dfrac{3x - 4}{7}$

24. $f(t) = \sqrt{t + 4}$

25. $g(x) = \dfrac{1}{x + 2}$

26. $F(x) = x^3$

27. $G(x) = \sqrt{x}$

28. $f(t) = \dfrac{1}{t}$

29. $h(t) = \dfrac{t}{t + 3}$

30. $g(t) = 1 + t^2, \quad t \geq 0$

31. $F(z) = \sqrt{z^2 - 4}, \quad z \geq 2$

32. $\phi(x) = \dfrac{x - 1}{x + 1}$

In Problems 33–38 show that each function is 1–1. Graph each function and its inverse on the same set of axes.

33. $f(x) = \dfrac{x+1}{3}$

34. $g(x) = x^2, \quad x \ge 0$

35. $f(x) = 2x - 5$

36. $g(x) = \sqrt{x-2}$

37. $h(x) = \dfrac{3x+4}{5}$

38. $\phi(x) = \sqrt{1-x}$

In Problems 15 and 16 the graph of a function is given. On the same set of axes sketch the graph of the inverse.

39. **a.**

b.

40. **a.**

b.

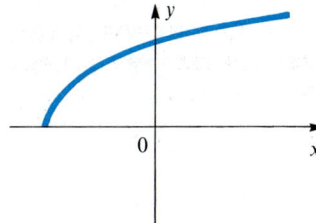

B In Problems 41–44 show that an inverse does not exist. Then place a suitable restriction on the domain so that an inverse does exist, and find it.

41. $f(x) = x^2 - 4$

42. $g(x) = \dfrac{1}{x^2 + 1}$

43. $h(x) = x^2 - 2x$

44. $y = \sqrt{4 - x^2}$

45. Let $f(x) = (x + a)/(x + b)$, where $a \ne b$. Show that f has an inverse, and find it. What are the domain and range of f and of f^{-1}? Show that $f(f^{-1}(x)) = x$ and $f^{-1}(f(x)) = x$.

46. Let $f(x) = x^2 - 1$, $g(x) = 2x + 3$, and $h(x) = 1/(x + 1)$. Find $[f \circ (g \circ h)](x)$ and $[(f \circ g) \circ h](x)$. In general, if f, g, and h are arbitrary functions (with suitably restricted domains), what do you conjecture about $f \circ (g \circ h)$ and $(f \circ g) \circ h$?

47. If a satellite of mass m is at a distance $f(t)$ from the center of the earth at time t, then the force of gravity exerted by the earth on the satellite is $(h \circ f)(t)$, where $h(t) = km/t^2$, $k = gR$, g is the force of gravity at the surface of the earth, and R is the radius of the earth. If $f(t) = 6{,}400 + 4t - 0.0001t^2$, $g = 9.81$, and $R = 6{,}400$, find the rule for $h \circ f$.

7 Variation

The following experiment demonstrates a recurrent type of functional relationship in physical science, as well as in the social and life sciences: An experiment in physics consists of attaching various weights to a spring and measuring the amount by which the spring is stretched; this is called the **elongation.** The object of the experiment is to determine a functional relationship between elongation and weight. Suppose that for a certain spring the measurements in Table 1 were found. From these data we would expect the pattern of each additional pound stretching the spring another 0.5 inch to continue, so long as the elastic limit of the spring is not exceeded. (At this limit the spring is stretched so much that it will not return to its original shape.)

Table 1

Weight (pounds)	Elongation (inches)
1	0.5
2	1.0
3	1.5
4	2.0

Let us designate the weight by w and the elongation by x. The functional relationship between w and x can be determined if we extend our table to include the ratio of w to x, as shown in Table 2. Since the ratio is constant for these four values, we assume it remains constant, so that for all x less than the elastic limit of the spring, $w/x = 2$, or $w = 2x$. This is an example of what is called **direct variation,** or **direct proportion.** The fact that w/x is constant is an expression of what is known as **Hooke's law.** The particular constant depends on the spring and is called the **spring constant.**

Table 2

w	x	w/x
1	0.5	2
2	1.0	2
3	1.5	2
4	2.0	2

In other types of situations we may find that instead of the ratio of two quantities being constant, it is their product that is constant, and this leads to what is known as **inverse variation,** or **inverse proportion.** The following experiment in chemistry illustrates this: The experiment consists of measuring the pressure (p) of a gas occupying varying volumes (v) while held at constant temperature. The data are given in Table 3. Note that as the volume decreases, the pressure increases. It appears that for this gas at the given constant temperature, $pv = 6$, or $p = 6/v$.

Table 3

Pressure, p (millimeters of mercury)	Volume, v (cubic centimeters)	$p \cdot v$
2	3.00	6
3	2.00	6
5	1.20	6
8	0.75	6

The expressions *varies directly as* and *varies inversely as* are used to describe such situations as these two experiments illustrate. For example, Hooke's law says that the weight necessary to stretch a given spring (within its elastic limit) *varies directly* as the amount it is stretched beyond its natural length. As we saw, this means that $w = kx$. Also, we can say that for a gas at constant temperature the pressure *varies inversely* as the volume. As another example, Newton's law of gravitation states that the force of attraction between two bodies *varies jointly* as their masses and inversely as the square of the distance between them. Also, in biology we know from experiment that within certain limits the rate of growth of a bacteria culture is *proportional to* the number of bacteria present.

These concepts are made more precise by the following definition:

DEFINITION 4   The statement **y varies directly as x** means there is a real number $k \neq 0$ such that

$$y = kx$$

The statement **y varies inversely as x** means there is a real number $k \neq 0$ such that

$$y = \frac{k}{x}$$

The statement **w varies jointly as x and y** means there is a real number $k \neq 0$ such that

$$w = kxy$$

Instead of saying y varies directly as x we sometimes say y is **directly proportional** to x, and this is understood to mean the same thing. Similarly, inverse variation and joint variation can be stated using the language of proportionality. If the word *directly* is omitted, it is understood, but *inversely* and *jointly* must always be explicitly stated. There can be combined statements, such as "y varies jointly as x and the square of t and inversely as v^3," which means

$$y = \frac{kxt^2}{v^3}$$

The real number k in each case is called the **constant of variation,** or the **constant of proportionality.** Often, sufficient information is available to find k, in which case a completely defined functional relationship is determined and various values of the dependent variable can be found. The examples below should help to make these ideas clearer.

EXAMPLE 22   Translate each of the following into an appropriate mathematical statement:

  a.   The temperature T of a gas in a container of fixed volume varies directly as the pressure p.
  b.   The force F necessary to stop a body that is moving in a straight line varies directly as the square of the velocity v.
  c.   The time t required for a satellite traveling in a circular orbit around the earth to complete its orbit is inversely proportional to its velocity v.
  d.   The drag force F on an airplane varies jointly as the total cross-sectional area A and the square of the velocity v.

Solution   **a.** $T = kp$ **b.** $F = kv^2$ **c.** $t = \dfrac{k}{v}$ **d.** $F = kAv^2$

EXAMPLE 23   It is known that y varies directly as x and that when $x = 2$, then $y = 10$. Find y when $x = 7$.

Solution   The variational statement translates to $y = kx$. Now we know one pair of values satisfying this equation, namely $x = 2$, $y = 10$. So we substitute these to find k:

$$10 = k \cdot 2$$
$$k = 5$$

Therefore, the specific functional relationship is

$$y = 5x$$

From this we can find y for any other value of x. The problem asks for y when $x = 7$:

$$y = 5(7) = 35$$

Note that one set of values of the variables is sufficient to determine k, because k is constant. Having found it for one set of the variables, it is determined once and for all.

The preceding example is typical of most variation problems. There are four steps to their solution:

  1.   Translate the variational statement into a mathematical equation using Definition 4.
  2.   Substitute the given set of values for all the variables involved, and solve for k.

3. Substitute the value of k into the original equation. This gives an explicit functional relationship.
4. Solve for the unknown requested by substituting the corresponding known value (or values).

EXAMPLE 24   If w varies directly as t^2 and inversely as v, and $w = 15$ when $t = 2$ and $v = 3$, find w when $t = 6$ and $v = 8$.

Solution   We have

$$w = k \cdot \frac{t^2}{v}$$

$$15 = k \frac{(2)^2}{3}$$

$$15 = \frac{4k}{3}$$

$$4k = 45$$

$$k = \tfrac{45}{4}$$

So the original equation becomes

$$w = \frac{45}{4} \cdot \frac{t^2}{v}$$

Substituting $t = 6$ and $v = 8$, we get

$$w = \frac{45}{\underset{1}{4}} \cdot \frac{\overset{9}{\cancel{36}}}{8} = \frac{405}{8}$$

EXAMPLE 25   The kinetic energy E of a moving object is jointly proportional to its weight w and the square of its velocity v. If an object weighing 32 pounds and moving with a velocity of 60 feet per second has a kinetic energy of 1,800 foot-pounds, find the kinetic energy of an object weighing 96 pounds and traveling at 20 feet per second.

Solution   The given statement translates to

$$E = kwv^2$$

We find k by substituting the known set of values:

$$1,800 = k \cdot (32)(60)^2$$

$$1,800 = k(32)(3,600)$$

$$k = \tfrac{1}{64}$$

So the equation becomes

$$E = \tfrac{1}{64} wv^2$$

Finally, we substitute $w = 96$ and $v = 20$:

$$E = \tfrac{1}{64} \cdot (96)(20)^2$$
$$= \tfrac{3}{2} \cdot 400 = 600 \text{ foot-pounds}$$

EXERCISE SET 7

A In Problems 1–10 translate the given statement into a mathematical equation.

1. u varies directly as v
2. w varies inversely as t
3. z varies jointly as x and y
4. y is directly proportional to x^2
5. s is inversely proportional to $\sqrt{t}$
6. w varies directly as x and inversely as y
7. F is jointly proportional to m_1 and m_2 and inversely proportional to r^2
8. The force required to stretch a spring x units beyond its natural length is proportional to x.
9. The distance s traveled by a freely falling object varies directly as the square of the time t it has fallen.
10. The volume V occupied by a gas varies directly as the temperature T and inversely as the pressure P.

11. If y varies directly as x, and $y = 4$ when $x = 12$, then find y when $x = 20$.
12. If s varies inversely as r, and $s = 5$ when $r = 8$, then find s when $r = 3$.
13. If u varies jointly as x and y, and $u = 12$ when $x = 6$ and $y = 8$, then find u when $x = 4$ and $y = 12$.
14. If w varies directly as u and inversely as v, and $w = 6$ when $u = 4$ and $v = 2$, then find w when $u = 10$ and $v = 6$.
15. If x is jointly proportional to y and t^2, and $x = 108$ when $y = 4$ and $t = 3$, then find x when $y = 7$ and $t = 4$.
16. The volume of a sphere varies as the cube of its radius. A sphere of radius 3 has a volume of 36π. Find the constant of variation. Write the general formula for the volume of a sphere. What is the volume of a sphere of radius 5?
17. The weight of a body on or above the surface of the earth varies inversely as the square of the distance from the center of the earth. If a body weighs 50 pounds on the earth's surface, how much would it weigh 1,000 miles above the surface of the earth? (Assume the radius of the earth is 4,000 miles.)
18. A printing company has found that for orders between 5,000 and 50,000 the unit cost of printing a college catalogue is inversely proportional to the number printed. If the cost of printing 10,000 of these catalogues is 80¢ per copy, what is the unit cost of printing 25,600 copies?
19. According to Ohm's law the current I in a wire varies directly as the potential E and inversely as the resistance R of the wire. When $R = 20$ ohms and $E = 220$ volts, it is found that $I = 11$ amperes. Find I when $E = 110$ volts and $R = 5$ ohms.
20. The resistance R of a wire varies directly as its length l and inversely as the square of its diameter d. A certain type of wire 60 feet long and with diameter 0.02 inch has a resistance of 15 ohms. What would be the resistance of 90 feet of the same type of wire with cross-section 0.01 inch?
21. The volume of a right circular cone varies jointly as the height h and the square of the base radius r. A cone of base radius 2 and height 6 has volume 8π. Find the constant of variation, and write the general formula for the volume of any right circular cone. What is the volume of a cone of height 10 and base radius 6?

22. The force of the wind on a wall is jointly proportional to the area of the wall and the square of the wind velocity. When the wind is blowing at 20 miles per hour, the force on a wall having area 100 square feet is 180 pounds. Find the force on a wall of area 400 square feet caused by a wind blowing at 50 miles per hour.

23. Newton's law of cooling states that the rate r at which a body cools is proportional to the difference between the temperature T of the body and the temperature T_0 of the surrounding medium. A thermometer registering 70°F is taken outside where the temperature is 40°F, and at that instant the rate of cooling, r, is 18°F per minute. Find the rate of cooling when the thermometer reads 50°F.

24. The vibrating frequency (pitch) of a string varies directly as the square root of the tension in the string. If when the tension is 4 pounds, the frequency of vibration is 240 times per second, find the frequency of vibration when the tension is 16 pounds.

25. One mathematical model of the spread of an infectious disease in a community says that if x is the number of persons already infected and y is the number not infected, then the rate r at which additional persons become infected is jointly proportional to x and y. In a community of 500 persons, when 20 already have a certain infectious disease, the rate of spread is 2 additional cases per day. What will be the rate of spread when 80 persons in the community have the disease? (This model fails to take into consideration such things as quarantine and the duration of the disease.)

B **26.** The intensity of light varies inversely as the square of the distance from the source. The intensity of a certain light is 200 candlepower at a point 8 feet from the source. At what distance from the source will the intensity be 100 candlepower?

27. Kepler's third law states that the square of the time it takes a planet to complete its orbit around the sun varies directly as the cube of its mean distance from the sun. The mean distance of Mars from the sun is approximately $1\frac{1}{2}$ times that of the earth. Find the approximate time (in "earth days") it takes Mars to complete its orbit.

28. The force of attraction between two bodies of masses m_1 and m_2, respectively, is jointly proportional to m_1 and m_2 and inversely proportional to the square of the distance d between them. What will be the effect on the force if m_1 is doubled, m_2 is tripled, and the distance d is cut in half?

29. The weight that can be safely supported by a wooden beam of rectangular cross-section varies jointly as the width and square of the depth of the cross-section and inversely as the length of the beam. A beam of length 12 feet with cross-section 4 inches wide by 8 inches deep will safely support 2,000 pounds. How much weight can be safely supported by a beam of the same material that is 8 feet long and has cross-section 2 inches wide by 4 inches deep?

30. The pressure P of a gas varies directly as its absolute temperature T and inversely as its volume V. Gas at pressure 200 pounds per square inch is at a temperature of 47°C and occupies a volume of 500 cubic feet. If the gas is allowed to expand so that its pressure is reduced to 20 pounds per square inch and its temperature is 17°C, find the volume it occupies.
   Note. **Absolute temperature** is measured through positive values from absolute 0, which is equivalent to -273°C, and one degree on the absolute scale equals one degree on the Celsius scale.

31. The mass of a spherical body varies jointly as its density and the cube of its radius. Find the ratio of the mass of Jupiter to that of the earth if the density of Jupiter is $\frac{5}{22}$ that of the earth and its radius is 11 times that of the earth.

32. The time of exposure necessary to photograph an object varies directly as the square of the distance d of the object from the light source and inversely as the intensity of illumination I. When the light source is 10 feet from the object, the correct exposure time for a certain type of film is $\frac{1}{30}$ second. For the same film, if the intensity of the light is doubled and the distance from the light to the object is cut in half (to 5 feet), what will be the correct exposure time?

Review Exercise Set

A   In Problems 1–6 make a table of values and draw the graph.

1. **a.** $y = 2x - 1$ **b.** $2x + 3y = 4$
2. **a.** $x - 2y + 3 = 0$ **b.** $y - 3 = 0$
3. **a.** $5x - 2y = 4$ **b.** $x + 2 = 0$
4. **a.** $\dfrac{x + 2y}{4} = 3$ **b.** $\dfrac{y - 3}{2} = x$
5. **a.** $f(x) = 1 - x^2$ **b.** $g(x) = 1 - \sqrt{1 - x}$
6. **a.** $F(x) = \dfrac{1}{x + 2}$ **b.** $h(x) = \sqrt{x^2 + 4}$

7. Let $f(x) = x^2 - 1$. Find:
    a. $f(0)$ **b.** $f(-1)$ **c.** $f(4)$ **d.** $f(a)$ **e.** $f(x + h)$
8. Let $f(x) = x/(x - 2)$. Find:
    a. $f(1)$ **b.** $f(0)$ **c.** $f(3)$ **d.** $f(-5)$ **e.** $f(2.1)$
9. Let $g(t) = 2t/(t - 3)$. What is the domain of g? Find:
    a. $g(1)$ **b.** $g(-2)$ **c.** $g(1/t)$ **d.** $g(t + \Delta t)$
10. Let $g(x) = \sqrt{9 - x^2}$. What is the domain of g? Find:
    a. $g(0)$ **b.** $g(-3)$ **c.** $g(2)$ **d.** $g(\tfrac{12}{5})$ **e.** $g(-\tfrac{9}{5})$
11. Let

$$h(t) = \begin{cases} 2t^2 - 1 & \text{if} & t \geq 2 \\ 4 - t & \text{if} & 0 \leq t < 2 \\ 0 & \text{if} & t < 0 \end{cases}$$

Find:
    a. $h(5)$ **b.** $h(-1)$ **c.** $h(0)$ **d.** $h(2)$ **e.** $h(1)$
12. Let $f(t) = t - (1/t)$. Find:
    a. $f(1)$ **b.** $f\left(-\dfrac{1}{2}\right)$ **c.** $f\left(\dfrac{1}{t}\right)$ **d.** $\dfrac{1}{f(t)}$

13. Let $f(x) = 1/x^2$. Find $[f(x) - f(2)]/(x - 2)$ and simplify your result.

14. Let $f(x) = x/(x + 1)$. Find $[f(x) - f(-2)]/(x + 2)$ and simplify your result.

15. Let $F(x) = \sqrt{x - 1}$. Show that

$$\frac{F(x + h) - F(x)}{h} = \frac{1}{\sqrt{x + h - 1} + \sqrt{x - 1}}$$

16. Find the domain of each of the following:
    a. $f(x) = \sqrt{2x^2 - 3x - 5}$ **b.** $g(x) = \sqrt{\dfrac{x + 1}{x - 3}}$

17. Express the length of the diagonal of a square as a function of one of its sides s.
18. Express the diameter of a circle as a function of its area.
19. The sum of $5,000 is invested in an account yielding 6% interest compounded annually. Express the total amount accumulated at the end of t years as a function of t.
20. Express the altitude h of an equilateral triangle as a function of one of its sides s.
21. The costs of renting a truck for 1 day are: $25 rental fee, 20¢ for each mile driven, $5.50 for insurance, 10¢ for each mile driven for gasoline. Let $C(x)$ be the total cost for driving x miles in a day. Write the rule for $C(x)$.

In Problems 22 and 23 show that each function is 1–1.

22. **a.** $f(x) = 3x - 7$ **b.** $f(x) = \dfrac{2x + 7}{3}$

23. **a.** $g(x) = 8 - 5x$ **b.** $h(x) = \dfrac{x + 1}{x}$

24. Show that the function f defined by $f(x) = 4 - x^2$ is not 1–1 on R. Find a suitable restriction on the domain of f so that it will be 1–1.

25. Determine which of the following functions are even, which are odd, and which are neither even nor odd (see Problem 31, Exercise Set 4):
  a. $f(x) = x^4 - 2x^2 + 1$ **b.** $g(x) = x(x^2 - 1)$ **c.** $h(t) = t^3 + 2t - 4$
  d. $F(x) = x - \dfrac{1}{x}$ **e.** $G(x) = \sqrt{\dfrac{4}{1 - x^2}}$

26. Show that the function $f(x) = |x - 1|$ is not 1–1 on R. Find a suitable restriction on the domain of f so that it will be 1–1.

27. Let $\phi(x) = (2x - 3)/5$ and $\psi(x) = (4 - 2x)/7$. Find $\phi \circ \psi$ and $\psi \circ \phi$.

28. Let $f(x) = x^2$ and $g(x) = \sqrt{x - 4}$. Find $f \circ g$ and $g \circ f$, and determine the domain of each.

29. Let $f(t) = t^2 - 3$ and $g(t) = \sqrt{1 - t}$. Find $f \circ g$ and $g \circ f$, and determine the domain of each.

30. Let $g(t) = 1/(t - 1)$ and $h(t) = 1/(t + 2)$. Find $g \circ h$ and $h \circ g$, and determine the domain of each.

31. At temperature x the thermal conductivity of a wall is given by $f(x) = k(1 + ax)$, where k and a are constants (k is the thermal conductivity at temperature 0°C). Write the rule for the thermal resistance $g \circ f$, given that $g(x) = T/(Ax)$, where T is the thickness of the wall and A is its cross-sectional area.

In Problems 32–39 show that an inverse exists, and find it.

32. $f(x) = 4x - 5$ **33.** $f(x) = \dfrac{5x + 7}{3}$

34. $g(x) = 1 - \dfrac{2x}{3}$ **35.** $h(t) = \dfrac{2 - 3t}{5}$

36. $F(z) = 1 - \dfrac{2}{z}$ **37.** $g(x) = \dfrac{1}{\sqrt{x - 2}}$

38. $f(t) = \dfrac{1}{\sqrt{t}}$ **39.** $h(x) = \dfrac{x + 2}{x - 3}$

In Problems 40 and 41 determine which graphs are graphs of functions and which are not. For those that are graphs of functions, state whether an inverse exists.

40. **a.**

b.

c.

d.

e.

f.

41. a.

b.

c.

d.

e.

f.

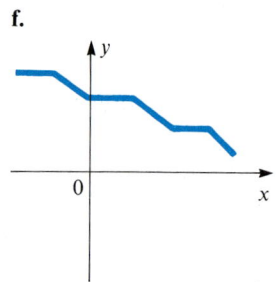

In Problems 42 and 43 draw f and f^{-1} on the same set of axes.

42. $f(x) = \dfrac{3x - 5}{2}$

43. $f(x) = \sqrt{x + 1}$

44. Determine the intervals on which the function whose graph is shown is increasing and those on which it is decreasing.

a.

b.

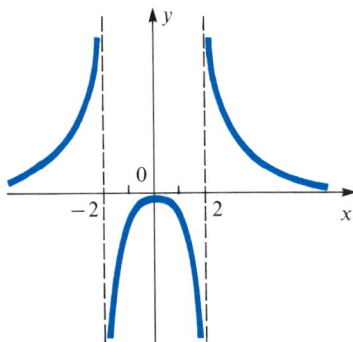

45. If y varies directly as x and inversely as the square root of t, and $y = 5$ when $x = 3$ and $t = 4$, find y when $x = 8$ and $t = 9$.

46. If a body is dropped and falls freely for t seconds, the distance through which it falls varies directly as the square of t (neglecting air resistance). If after 2 seconds a body has fallen 64 feet, how far will it fall in 10 seconds?

47. The surface area S of a sphere is proportional to the square of its radius. If a sphere of radius 3 has a surface area of 36π, find a formula for the surface area of any sphere. What is the surface area of a sphere of diameter 10?

48. If the temperature is constant, the volume of a gas varies inversely as its pressure. A gas with a pressure of 150 pounds per square inch occupies a volume of 25 cubic feet. What volume will it occupy when the pressure is 45 pounds per square inch, assuming the temperature is held constant?

B **49.** Make a table of values and draw the graph of each of the following:
   a. $y^2 = 18 - 2x^2$ **b.** $f(x) = 2 - x - x^2$

50. Find the domain of each of the following functions:

   a. $f(x) = \dfrac{2x + 3}{x^3 - 3x^2 - 4x + 12}$ **b.** $g(x) = \sqrt{\dfrac{4 - x^2}{x^3 + 4x^2}}$

51. Let

$$f(x) = \begin{cases} \sqrt{x^2 - 9} & \text{if} \quad x \geq 3 \\ 2 - x & \text{if} \quad 0 \leq x < 3 \\ -1 & \text{if} \quad x < 0 \end{cases}$$

Draw the graph of f and find:
   a. $f(5)$ **b.** $f(-1)$ **c.** $f(0)$ **d.** $f(3)$ **e.** $f(1)$

52. A rectangle of base b and altitude h is inscribed in an isosceles triangle of altitude 10 and base 6, as shown in the sketch. Express h as a function of b.

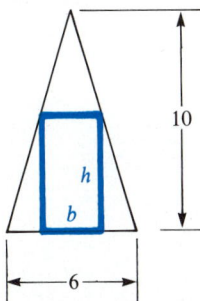

53. A circle is inscribed in an equilateral triangle. Express the area of the circle as a function of the length of a side of the triangle.

54. Let $f(x) = 4x - x^2$. Show that f is not 1–1 on R but that it is 1–1 on the domain $\{x: \ x \geq 2\}$. Find f^{-1} for this restricted domain.

55. Show that no inverse exists for the function defined by

$$f(x) = \frac{4}{(x-2)^2}$$

but that by a suitable restriction on the domain an inverse does exist. Find this inverse.

56. Let $g(x) = x^2 - 4x - 5$. Show that g is not 1–1 on R but that it is 1–1 on the domain $\{x: \ x \leq 2\}$.

57. The strength of a beam of rectangular cross-section is jointly proportional to the width w and the square of the depth d of the cross-section and inversely proportional to the length l of the beam. What will be the effect on the strength if w and d are each doubled and l is cut in half?

5 Linear and Quadratic Functions

Many mathematical models make use of linear and quadratic functions. The following example illustrates one such model from the field of economics.* Unless you have studied economics, you will not understand all the terms used, but the fact that linear and quadratic functions are employed is clear.

The fourth proposition of the Keynesian hypothesis, that MPC (marginal propensity to consume) declines as income increases, cannot be illustrated with the linear consumption function, because straight lines have constant slopes. However, a relatively simple nonlinear function, a second-degree polynomial, may be employed to illustrate proposition 4. Consider the following:

$$C = 506 + .92Y - .000014Y^2 \qquad (1)$$

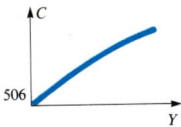

(These parameter values were actually estimated by Ralph Husby . . . .) Calculation of the marginal propensity to consume yields:

$$\text{MPC} = .92 - .000028Y \qquad (2)$$

MPC is a linear function of income and as income increases MPC declines. Figure 2 illustrates this consumption function. Keynes believed MPC would tend to decline during a boom and rise during slowdowns for two reasons. First, during a boom as employment increases relative to available capital, diminishing returns to labor set in. Income to property, relative to labor, increases. Keynes felt that entrepreneurs, whose relative share of income would rise, tend to have a low marginal propensity to consume. Consequently, aggregate MPC would decline during booms. Second, during downturns in the cycle transfer payments are relatively high, and the propensity to spend such income by unemployed and those on public relief would be high in Keynes' view.

Figure 2

$C = 506 + .92Y - .000014Y^2$

C

506

Y

Linear and quadratic functions are among the most important in applications. In this example, equation (1) illustrates a quadratic function and equation (2) a linear function. We will analyze both these types of functions in detail in this chapter. The concept of *marginal propensity to consume* (MPC) is encountered in economics courses as well as in business-oriented calculus courses. It is shown there that MPC is found from the consumption function C by the calculus operation known as *differentiation*.

---

* Frank C. Wykoff, *Macroeconomics: Theory, Evidence, and Policy*, © 1976, pp. 84–85. Reprinted by permission of Prentice-Hall, Inc., Englewood Cliffs, New Jersey.

1 Introduction

A function of the form

$$f(x) = a_n x^n + a_{n-1} x^{n-1} + \cdots + a_1 x + a_0 \qquad (a_n \neq 0)$$

where n is a nonnegative integer, is a **polynomial function** of degree n in the variable x. If $n = 1$, the function is **linear**; and if $n = 2$, it is **quadratic.** In this chapter we will study these two cases in some detail. The word *linear*, as you would expect, has some relationship to a straight line. In order to understand this more fully we begin by studying straight lines.

We know from plane geometry (and intuition) that a straight line is uniquely determined by two points. A line is also determined by one point and the "inclination," or **slope,** of the line. The next section makes this more precise.

2 The Equation of a Line

Suppose we are given a nonvertical straight line l and know any two points on the line, say, $P_1(x_1, y_1)$ and $P_2(x_2, y_2)$, as shown in Figure 1. Then we have the definition below.

Figure 1

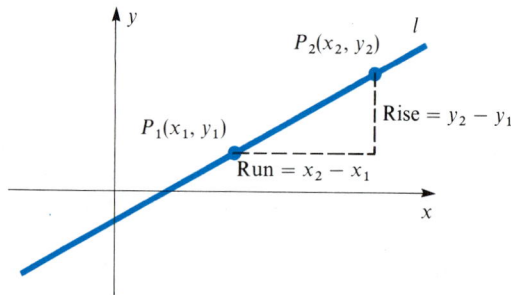

DEFINITION 1   The slope m of line l is defined as

$$m = \frac{y_2 - y_1}{x_2 - x_1}$$

(Can you see why we restricted l to be nonvertical?)

The slope is the vertical displacement from P_1 to P_2 divided by the horizontal displacement (sometimes described as the **rise** divided by the **run**). It does not matter which point is labeled P_1 and which is labeled P_2, since

$$\frac{y_2 - y_1}{x_2 - x_1} = \frac{y_1 - y_2}{x_1 - x_2} \qquad \textbf{Why?}$$

It can also be shown, using similar triangles, that it does not matter which particular two points on the line are chosen. The value found for the slope will always be the same.

EXAMPLE 1   A line passes through the points (1, 2) and (5, 4). Find the slope of the line.

Solution   We will let P_1 be the point (1, 2) and P_2 be (5, 4), but we could equally well reverse these. By Definition 1, we have

$$m = \frac{y_2 - y_1}{x_2 - x_1} = \frac{4 - 2}{5 - 1} = \frac{2}{4} = \frac{1}{2}$$

We can think of this as saying that for every 2 units we go horizontally to the right, the line rises 1 unit vertically, or for every 1 unit we go horizontally to the right, the line rises $\frac{1}{2}$ unit vertically. The graph is shown in Figure 2.

Figure 2

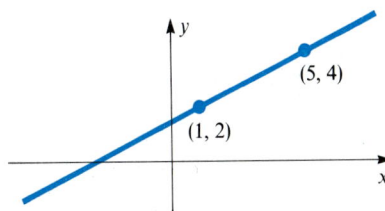

An examination of the definition of the slope of a line will show that lines that go upward to the right have positive slopes and those that go upward to the left have negative slopes (Figure 3). Also, a small numerical value for the slope indicates a line that is close to horizontal, whereas a large numerical value indicates a line that is nearly vertical. (What would a slope of 1 indicate? What about -1?) Horizontal lines have a slope of 0 (why?), and slope is not defined for vertical lines.

Figure 3

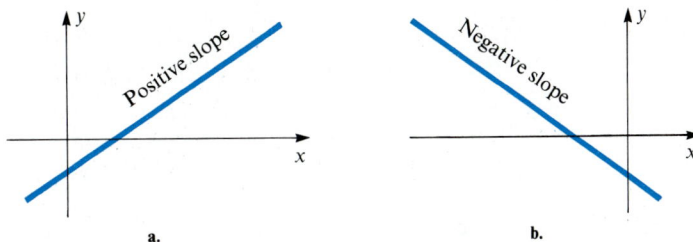

a.

b.

Let l be a nonvertical line passing through a given point $P_1(x_1, y_1)$ and having slope m. Any other point $P(x, y)$ will lie on l if and only if

$$\frac{y - y_1}{x - x_1} = m$$

If we clear this equation of fractions, we obtain

$$y - y_1 = m(x - x_1) \tag{1}$$

All points (including P_1) that lie on l have coordinates that satisfy this equation, and this is true for those points only. Thus, equation (1) is the equation of l. It is called the **point–slope form** of the equation of a line.

EXAMPLE 2   Find the equation of the line having slope $\frac{3}{4}$ and passing through the point $(-2, 5)$.

Solution   We simply substitute in equation (1), using $x_1 = -2$ and $y_1 = 5$:

$$y - 5 = \tfrac{3}{4}(x + 2)$$
$$4y - 20 = 3x + 6$$
$$3x - 4y + 26 = 0$$

Note.   In applying equation (1), x_1 and y_1 represent the coordinates of the given point and so will be specific numbers. On the other hand, x and y will remain in the equation as variables.

EXAMPLE 3   Find the equation of the line joining $(-6, -2)$ and $(2, 5)$.

Solution   First we must calculate the slope:

$$m = \frac{5 - (-2)}{2 - (-6)} = \frac{7}{8}$$

We may choose either point as (x_1, y_1) for the purpose of substituting in equation (1), so we select $(2, 5)$:

$$y - 5 = \tfrac{7}{8}(x - 2)$$
$$8y - 40 = 7x - 14$$
$$7x - 8y + 26 = 0$$

A special case of equation (1) results when the point (x_1, y_1) is taken as the point where the line crosses the y axis. The y coordinate of this point is called the **y intercept** and is usually denoted by b. Substituting $(0, b)$ for (x_1, y_1) in equation (1), we obtain

$$y - b = m(x - 0)$$

or

$$y = mx + b$$

This is called the **slope–intercept form** of the equation of a line (*intercept* is understood to mean the y intercept).

Note.   The x coordinate of the point at which a line crosses the x axis is called its *x* **intercept** and is usually denoted by a. For a form of the equation of a line that uses both the x intercept and the y intercept, see Problem 27, Exercise Set 2.

EXAMPLE 4   Show that the equation $2x - 3y + 6 = 0$ is the equation of a line, and find the slope and y intercept of the line. Graph the line.

Solution   If we can put the equation in the form $y = mx + b$, we will know it is a line. This is done by solving for y:

$$3y = 2x + 6$$
$$y = \tfrac{2}{3}x + 2$$

Therefore, this is the equation of a line with slope $\tfrac{2}{3}$ and y intercept 2. We can use the slope to find another point on the line as follows: From $(0, 2)$ if we move 3 units in the x direction and 2 units in the y direction, we must come to another point on the line. This results in the point $(3, 4)$. The line can now be drawn as shown in Figure 4. An easier way to get a second point on the line is to find the x intercept by letting $y = 0$. This gives

$$0 = \tfrac{2}{3}x + 2$$
$$2x = -6$$
$$x = -3$$

So $(-3, 0)$ is another point on the line.

Figure 4

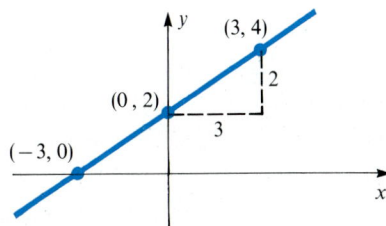

In either the point–slope form, $y - y_1 = m(x - x_1)$, or the slope–intercept form, $y = mx + b$, of the equation of a line, if the terms are rearranged, the result can be written in the form

$$Ax + By + C = 0 \tag{2}$$

But do all equations of this form have straight lines as graphs? The answer is yes, as we now show.

We suppose that A and B are not both 0, because if they were, then C would also have to be 0, and the equation would read $0 = 0$, which is true but not of much interest. Now let us consider the case in which $B \neq 0$ (A may or may not be 0). We can solve for y to get

$$y = -\frac{A}{B}x + \left(-\frac{C}{B}\right)$$

This is in the form $y = mx + b$, with

$$m = -\frac{A}{B} \quad \text{and} \quad b = -\frac{C}{B} \tag{3}$$

So this represents a line with slope $-A/B$ and y intercept $-C/B$.

In the special case where $A = 0$ (but $B \neq 0$), we see from the above that

$$y = -\frac{C}{B}$$

or

$$y = b$$

Since this equation places no restriction on x, it follows that all points with coordinates of the form (x, b) satisfy the equation, and therefore the graph is a horizontal line. The slope is 0.

One final case needs to be considered, and that is the case in which $B = 0$ but $A \neq 0$. Equation (2) then has the form

$$Ax + C = 0$$

$$x = -\frac{C}{A}$$

If we let $a = -C/A$, this can be written

$$x = a$$

and this is the equation of a vertical line, since all points with coordinates of the form (a, y), where y can be anything whatsoever, satisfy the equation. Slope is not defined for a vertical line.

EXAMPLE 5   Draw the graphs of the lines:

a. $y = 3$ **b.** $x = -2$

Solution

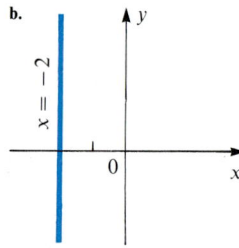

Note. A common mistake is to suppose that $y = 3$ means only the single point $(0, 3)$ or that $x = -2$ means just the point $(-2, 0)$. In the context of two dimensions both of these represent lines, not points.

Since equation (2) always represents a line, it is called the **general equation of a line.** It is also called the **general linear equation in two variables.**

EXERCISE SET 2

A 1. Find the slopes of the lines joining the pairs of points given. Sketch the lines.
    a. $(2, -1)$ and $(3, 4)$ **b.** $(-3, -2)$ and $(5, 4)$
    c. $(3, -4)$ and $(-2, 3)$ **d.** $(-5, 3)$ and $(-2, 0)$

2. The points $A(3, -2)$, $B(-6, -8)$, and $C(12, 4)$ all lie on a line. Calculate the slope of the line using three different pairs of points, and verify that the results are the same.

3. Find the slopes of the sides of the triangle with vertices at $A(3, 2)$, $B(-5, 4)$, and $C(-2, -3)$. Draw the triangle.

4. Find the slopes of the two diagonals of the quadrilateral with vertices at the points $(5, 6)$, $(-1, 3)$, $(-4, 0)$, and $(2, -2)$. Draw the figure.

5. What is the horizontal displacement between $(-3, -5)$ and $(2, -1)$? What is the vertical displacement?

6. In each of the following a line passes through the given point with the given slope. Find a second point on the line, and draw a sketch.
    a. $(-1, -3)$, slope $\frac{3}{4}$ **b.** $(2, -4)$, slope $-\frac{1}{2}$

7. The slope of the line passing through $(2, 3)$ and $(-4, y)$ is $-\frac{2}{3}$. Find y.

8. The slope of the line passing through $(x, 2)$ and $(6, 8)$ is $\frac{3}{5}$. Find x.

9. A quadrilateral has vertices $A(3, 2)$, $B(7, 5)$, $C(-1, 3)$, and $D(-5, 0)$. Find the slope of each of the sides. Does your result suggest anything special about this quadrilateral? Explain. Sketch the figure.

In Problems 10–18 find the equations of the lines satisfying the given conditions.

10. Slope $\frac{2}{5}$, passing through $(-2, -5)$ **11.** Slope -2, passing through $(3, -4)$
12. Passing through $(3, 4)$ and $(-1, -2)$ **13.** Passing through $(-1, 3)$ and $(2, -5)$
14. Passing through $(2, -3)$ and $(-6, 2)$ **15.** Passing through $(-3, 0)$ and $(0, 4)$
16. Slope $-\frac{1}{2}$ and y intercept -3 **17.** Slope $\frac{2}{3}$ and y intercept 2
18. Slope 3 and y intercept $-\frac{1}{2}$

In Problems 19–24 find the slope m and the y intercept b. Draw the graph.

19. $y = 3x - 4$ **20.** $3x + 5y - 2 = 0$
21. $2x + 6y = 7$ **22.** $2y - 3x + 4 = 0$
23. $y = \dfrac{3x - 4}{5}$ **24.** $\dfrac{4y - 5}{2} = x$

In Problems 25 and 26 write the equation of each horizontal or vertical line, as indicated.

25. **a.** y intercept 2, horizontal   **b.** x intercept 3, vertical
    c. Passing through $(-1, -3)$, horizontal   **d.** Passing through $(-1, -3)$, vertical

26. **a.** x intercept -4, vertical   **b.** y intercept -3, horizontal
    c. Passing through $(-3, 4)$, vertical   **d.** Passing through $(-3, 4)$, horizontal

27. Derive the **two-intercept form** of the equation of a line:

$$\frac{x}{a} + \frac{y}{b} = 1$$

    Hint. You know two points on the line.

28. Use the result of Problem 27 to find the equations of the lines that have the given intercepts.
    a. x intercept 2, y intercept -3 **b.** x intercept $-\frac{3}{4}$, y intercept $\frac{5}{6}$

B   In Problems 29–31 show in two ways that the given points are **collinear** (that is, they lie on the same line).

29. $(2, 2), (-1, -7), (3, 5)$ 30. $(6, 2), (-2, -4), (2, -1)$
31. $(0, -3), (2, 1), (-1, -5)$

32. The line l_1 passes through the points $(2, 3)$ and $(-4, 6)$. Line l_2 passes through the point $(-1, -2)$ and has the same slope as l_1. Line l_3 passes through $(-1, -2)$, and its slope is the negative of the reciprocal of the slope of l_1. Find a second point on each of the lines l_2 and l_3, and sketch all three lines on the same set of axes. What relationship appears to exist among the three lines?

33. **a.** A line has slope $\frac{3}{2}$. Its equation can be written in the form $3x - 2y + C = 0$. Explain why this is so.
    b. If the line of part a passes through the point $(-5, 1)$, we can find C by substituting -5 for x and 1 for y in the equation $3x - 2y + C = 0$. Do this. After finding C, write the equation of the line.

34. Use the procedure of Problem 33 to find the equation of the line with slope $-\frac{3}{4}$ and passing through $(2, 3)$.

35. Find by two methods (see Problem 33 for one method) the equation of the line with slope $\frac{1}{2}$ and passing through $(3, -4)$.

36. What can you say about the relationship between the lines $3x - 4y + 7 = 0$ and $3x - 4y - 9 = 0$? Also compare $6x - 8y + 23 = 0$ with these two. How can you generalize your findings?

37. We may consider the equation $2x - 3y + C = 0$ as defining a **family of lines,** one line for each value of C. What can you conclude about each member of this family? What is the geometric significance of this?

38. A salesperson works for a fixed base weekly salary of $\$b$, plus a commission of $\$c$ for each unit sold. Write the weekly salary y as a function of the number x of units sold. Suppose the salesperson receives $\$300$ in a week in which 10 units were sold and $\$375$ in a week in which 15 units were sold. Find the person's base salary b and commission c. What will the person's salary be in a week in which 18 units are sold?

3   Distance and Midpoint Formulas

It is often useful to be able to find the length of a line segment in the plane when we know the coordinates of the end points. Suppose P_1 and P_2 are the end points, having coordinates (x_1, y_1) and (x_2, y_2) respectively. As shown in Figure 5 we introduce the point Q with coordinates (x_2, y_1).

Figure 5

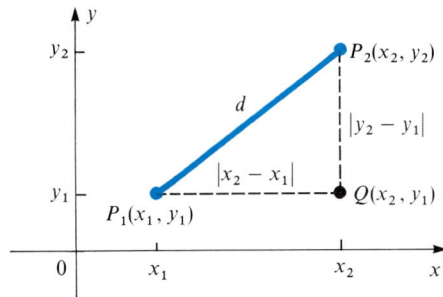

Then the triangle P_1QP_2 is a right triangle. We now make use of the Pythagorean theorem, which states that in a right triangle the square of the length of the hypotenuse equals the sum of the squares of the lengths of the legs. In our triangle the legs are P_1Q, with length $|x_2 - x_1|$ and P_2Q, with length $|y_2 - y_1|$. So if d is the length of the hypotenuse P_1P_2, we have

$$d^2 = |x_2 - x_1|^2 + |y_2 - y_1|^2 = (x_2 - x_1)^2 + (y_2 - y_1)^2$$

The last equality follows since for any real number a, $|a|^2 = a^2$. Taking square roots we obtain the desired result. This is known as the *distance formula*.

The Distance Formula

$$d = \sqrt{(x_2 - x_1)^2 + (y_2 - y_1)^2}$$

For example, the distance between the points $(-1, 3)$ and $(7, 5)$ is

$$d = \sqrt{[7 - (-1)]^2 + (5 - 3)^2} = \sqrt{8^2 + 2^2} = \sqrt{68} = 2\sqrt{17}$$

Notice that it makes no difference which point is labeled (x_1, y_1) and which is (x_2, y_2).

Another useful result is the formula for the coordinates of the midpoint of the line segment joint P_1 and P_2. Again label the points (x_1, y_2) and (x_2, y_2). respectively, and let (x, y) designate the unknown coordinates of the midpoint M.

Figure 6

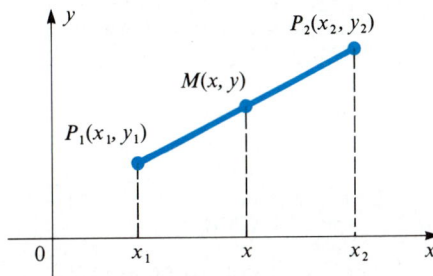

We project each of the points to the x axis as in Figure 6. From plane geometry we know that the projected segments on the x axis are in the same ratio as the segments on the line. Thus, since M divides P_1P_2 into equal parts, we must have the distance from x_1 to x the same as the distance from x to x_2. That is,

$$x - x_1 = x_2 - x$$
$$2x = x_1 + x_2$$
$$x = \frac{x_1 + x_2}{2}$$

By projecting to the y axis we can show in a similar way that $y = (y_1 + y_2)/2$. So we have the following result.

The Midpoint Formula

Midpoint of $P_1P_2 = \left(\dfrac{x_1 + x_2}{2}, \dfrac{y_1 + y_2}{2} \right)$

For example, the midpoint of the line segment joining $(-1, 3)$ and $(7, 5)$ is

$$\left(\frac{-1 + 7}{2}, \frac{3 + 5}{2} \right) = (3, 4)$$

Observe that each coordinate of the midpoint is the *average* of the corresponding coordinates of the end points.

EXERCISE SET 3

A   In Problems 1–8 find (a) the distance between the two points and (b) the midpoint of the segment joining them.

1. $(-1, 3)$ and $(2, 7)$
2. $(4, 2)$ and $(-3, 4)$
3. $(0, 2)$ and $(2, -1)$
4. $(3, -2)$ and $(-3, 6)$
5. $(-2, -1)$ and $(3, 11)$
6. $(-3, 4)$ and $(5, 0)$
7. $(-9, 3)$ and $(6, -5)$
8. $(2, -3)$ and $(-1, -6)$

9. The distance between $(3, 4)$ and $(x, -2)$ is 10. Find x. (There are two solutions.)
10. The distance between $(-1, -2)$ and $(3, y)$ is $2\sqrt{5}$. Find y. (There are two solutions.)
11. One end point of a line segment has coordinates $(-1, 3)$, and the midpoint has coordinates $(2, -4)$. Find the coordinates of the other end point.
12. The point $(3, 4)$ is the midpoint of the line segment joining $(x, 2)$ and $(5, y)$. Find x and y.

Problems 13 and 14 make use of the converse of the Pythagorean theorem, which states that if $c^2 = a^2 + b^2$, where a, b, and c are the lengths of the sides of a triangle, then the triangle is a right triangle.

13. Prove that the triangle with vertices $(-2, 4)$, $(3, -6)$, and $(6, -2)$ is a right triangle.
14. An isosceles triangle is one in which two sides are equal. Show that the triangle with vertices $(-7, 5)$, $(-3, -2)$, and $(4, 2)$ is an isosceles right triangle.
15. Show that the triangle with vertices $(-4, -3)$, $(-3\sqrt{3}, 4\sqrt{3})$, and $(4, 3)$ is equilateral (all sides equal).

16. A right triangle is formed by the x axis, the y axis, and the line $3x + 4y = 18$. Find: **(a)** the length of the hypotenuse and **(b)** the midpoint of the hypotenuse.

17. Find the equation of the line joining the point $(2, -3)$ and the midpoint of the segment from $(5, 4)$ to $(3, -2)$.

18. The vertices of a quadrilateral are $(5, 10)$, $(-9, 2)$, $(-3, -8)$, and $(7, -4)$. Prove that the line segments joining successive midpoints of the sides of the quadrilateral form a parallelogram. *Note:* The line segments joining the midpoints of the sides of *any* quadrilateral form a parallelogram.

B 19. A *median* of a triangle is a line segment from a vertex to the midpoint of the opposite side. Find the equations of the medians of the triangle with vertices $(2, 5)$, $(0, -3)$, and $(-6, 1)$.

20. Show that the points $(-1, 2)$, $(2, 4)$, $(3, -4)$, and $(6, -2)$ are vertices of a rectangle. Do this in two ways: **(a)** using distances and **(b)** using slopes.

21. The midpoints of the sides of a triangle are $(1, 0)$, $(2, 5)$, and $(4, 2)$. Find the coordinates of the vertices.

22. Write and simplify an equation which specifies that the distance from (x, y) to $(3, 4)$ is 6. How would you describe the set of all points (x, y) satisfying this condition?

23. Coordinates are introduced into a town planner's map. One boundary of the town's limits corresponds to the graph of the equation $y = 2x + 1$, while the entrance to the fire station is at the point with coordinates $(3, 4)$. Find the formula, in terms of x, for the distance from the fire station entrance to each point on that boundary of the town.

---

4 Parallel and Perpendicular Lines

It is intuitively obvious that two lines having the same slope are parallel, and conversely, if two lines are parallel, they have the same slope. This can be proved formally, but we will not do so here. (The proof will be called for in Problem 28, Exercise Set 4.)

But it is not obvious what the relationship is between slopes of perpendicular lines. If either line is horizontal, the other must be vertical; so we will consider only the case in which neither line is horizontal. Let $y = mx + b$ be the equation of such a line. We wish to find the slope of lines perpendicular to this one. First, we consider a line through the origin and parallel to the given line, since any line perpendicular to the original line will be perpendicular to all lines parallel to it, and vice versa (Figure 7). The equation of the line parallel to $y = mx + b$ and passing through the origin O is $y = mx$. We work with this line instead of the original, since it simplifies our computations. Designate this line by l_1.

Figure 7

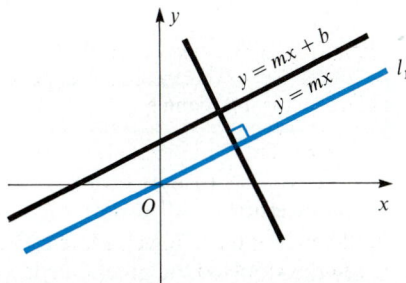

We find a second point on l_1 by letting $x = 1$. This gives $(1, m)$ as a point on the line. Let P be the point $(1, m)$ and let A be $(1, 0)$, as shown in Figure 8. Now consider a line through the origin and perpendicular to the line $y = mx$. Call this l_2. Draw the vertical line $x = -m$ and designate by B and Q the points of intersection with the x axis and l_2, respectively. The triangles OAP and QBO are congruent (since the sides are perpendicular and $\overline{OB} = \overline{AP}$). Thus, corresponding sides are equal in length. In particular, $\overline{BQ} = \overline{OA} = 1$. The coordinates of Q must therefore be $(-m, 1)$. Hence, the slope of l_2 is

$$\frac{1 - 0}{-m - 0} = -\frac{1}{m}$$

which is the result we were seeking.

Figure 8

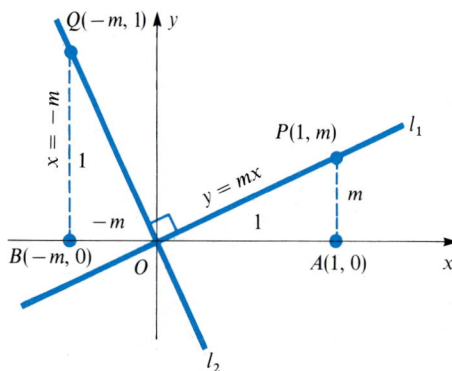

The slope of any line perpendicular to $y = mx + b$ is $-1/m$.

If the argument used above is reversed, we conclude that any line with slope $-1/m$ is perpendicular to any line with slope m.

Note. In the figures we have indicated that m is positive. The result is also true if m is negative, and the steps of the argument would be identical; only the figures would look different.

The number $-1/m$ is the **negative reciprocal** of m. Using this terminology, we can state our result as follows:

Perpendicular Lines

Two lines, neither of which is horizontal, are perpendicular if and only if their slopes are negative reciprocals of each other.

EXAMPLE 6   Find the slope of all lines perpendicular to the line $y = 2x + 3$.

Solution   Since the slope of the given line is 2, all lines perpendicular to it have slope $-\frac{1}{2}$.

Remark. The set of all lines satisfying a given condition is called a **family of lines.** So we could conclude in this case that the family of lines perpendicular to the given line is given by

$$y = -\tfrac{1}{2}x + C$$

where C can be any real number.

EXAMPLE 7   Find the equation of the line that passes through $(1, 3)$ and is perpendicular to the line $y = (2x/3) - 4$.

Solution   The line $y = (2x/3) - 4$ has slope $\tfrac{2}{3}$, so the line we are seeking has slope $-\tfrac{3}{2}$. Now we can use the point–slope form $y - y_1 = m(x - x_1)$ to find the desired equation:

$$y - 3 = -\tfrac{3}{2}(x - 1)$$
$$2y - 6 = -3x + 3$$
$$3x + 2y - 9 = 0$$

EXAMPLE 8   Find the equation of the family of all lines perpendicular to the line with equation $3x - 4y + 3 = 0$.

Solution   We know from equation (3) that the slope of the given line is $\tfrac{3}{4}$, so the slope of all lines perpendicular to it is $-\tfrac{4}{3}$. Since the slope of a line $Ax + By + C = 0$ is $-A/B$, we can let $A = 4$ and $B = 3$ to get

$$4x + 3y + C = 0$$

as the equation of the desired family. The constant C can take on any real value, and for each such choice, the line will be perpendicular to $3x - 4y + 3 = 0$.

If P and Q are two points on a curve, the line joining them is called a **secant line** for the curve. If P is held fixed and Q comes closer and closer to P, the secant lines through P and Q may approach some line as a limit; if so, this line is called the **tangent** to the curve at P. Figure 9 illustrates this.

Figure 9

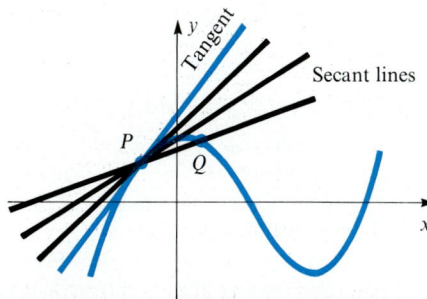

EXAMPLE 9   In calculus it is shown that the curve defined by $y = x^2 - 3x$ has a tangent at each point (x, y) whose slope is given by $m = 2x - 3$. Find the equation of the tangent line to this curve at the point for which $x = 2$.

Solution   When $x = 2$, $y = 2^2 - 3(2) = 4 - 6 = -2$. Also, the slope $m = 2(2) - 3 = 1$. So the equation is

$$y + 2 = 1(x - 2)$$
$$x - y - 4 = 0$$

The graph is shown in Figure 10.

Figure 10

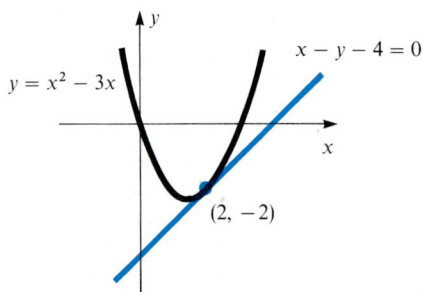

$y = x^2 - 3x$

$x - y - 4 = 0$

$(2, -2)$

EXERCISE SET 4

A   In Problems 1–16 find the equations of the lines satisfying the given conditions.

1.   Passing through $(5, -3)$ and parallel to $3x - 4y = 12$
2.   Passing through $(0, 4)$ and parallel to $x - y = 4$
3.   Passing through $(-1, 2)$ and perpendicular to $y = 3x - 5$
4.   Passing through $(3, -1)$ and perpendicular to $2x - 3y - 4 = 0$
5.   Passing through $(0, 0)$ and parallel to $5x - 2y + 3 = 0$
6.   Passing through $(-2, -3)$ and parallel to $y = (x - 3)/4$
7.   Passing through $(6, 1)$ and perpendicular to $3y - 4x = 7$
8.   Passing through $(-2, 6)$ and perpendicular to $4x + 7y = 13$
9.   Parallel to the line joining $(3, 2)$ and $(-1, 5)$, passing through the point $(0, 2)$
10.   Perpendicular to the line joining $(-2, -3)$ and $(3, 5)$, passing through $(2, -4)$
11.   Passing through $(7, -3)$ and parallel to the line joining $(5, 4)$ and $(-1, -2)$
12.   Passing through $(3, 5)$ and perpendicular to the line joining $(-1, 3)$ and $(3, -5)$
13.   Parallel to $x + 2 = 0$ and passing through $(3, 5)$
14.   Parallel to $2y - 3 = 0$ and passing through $(-1, 4)$
15.   Perpendicular to $y = 4$ and passing through $(2, 3)$
16.   Perpendicular to $3x - 5 = 0$ and having y intercept 3
17.   Find the equation of the line perpendicular to $5x - 2y = 3$ and having the same y intercept as this line.
18.   Find the equation of the line parallel to $3x - 5y - 6 = 0$ and with x intercept that is the negative of the x intercept of this line.

19. By using slopes show that the points $(2, 1)$, $(6, 9)$, and $(-2, 3)$ are vertices of a right triangle.
20. Show that the points $(3, -1)$, $(5, 4)$, $(-5, 8)$, and $(-7, 3)$ are vertices of a rectangle.
21. Show that the points $(2, 2)$, $(0, -1)$, $(-4, 1)$, and $(-2, 4)$ are the vertices of a parallelogram.
22. Find the equation of the family of lines parallel to the line $5x - 4y = 6$. Find the equation of the member of this family that goes through the point $(4, 2)$.
23. Find the equation of the family of lines perpendicular to the line $4x + 3y - 8 = 0$. Find the equation of the member of this family that has the same y intercept as that of the given line.

In Problems 24–26 find the equation of the perpendicular bisector of the line segment joining the two points.

24. $(3, 4)$ and $(-1, 2)$ 25. $(5, -7)$ and $(-3, -1)$ 26. $(-6, 3)$ and $(5, 4)$

27. An *altitude* of a triangle is a line from a vertex perpendicular to the opposite side. Find the equations of the altitudes of the triangle with vertices $(2, -5)$, $(-3, 4)$, and $(1, 6)$.

B 28. Let $y_1 = m_1 x + b_1$ and $y_2 = m_2 x + b_2$. Carry out the details of the argument outlined here to prove that the corresponding lines are parallel if and only if $m_1 = m_2$. We know that two lines are parallel if and only if they do not intersect. If $m_1 = m_2$, show that the lines do not intersect (unless they coincide). If $m_1 \neq m_2$, show that the lines do intersect.
29. A line parallel to $x - 2y - 4 = 0$ crosses the negative x axis and positive y axis so that the line and these axes form a right triangle of area 9. Find the equation of the line.
30. Prove that the points $(-2, 9)$, $(-4, -2)$, $(1, -12)$, and $(3, -1)$ are vertices of a rhombus (a parallelogram with all sides equal in length). Show that the diagonals are perpendicular.
31. A physicist describes the results of an experiment on a plane coordinate system. Two magnets have centers at the points with coordinates $(0, -\frac{1}{2})$ and $(2, \frac{3}{2})$, respectively. The path of a particle in the experiment is the perpendicular bisector of the line segment joining the centers of the magnets. Find the equation of the path of the particle.
32. **a.** It can be shown by calculus that the slope of the tangent line to the curve $y = x^2 - 4$ at any point (x, y) is given by $m = 2x$. Find the equation of the tangent line at the point for which $x = 1$.
    b. The line perpendicular to the tangent line of a curve is called the **normal** line. Find the equation of the normal to the curve of part **a** at the given point. Draw the graph of $f(x) = x^2 - 4$, showing the tangent and normal at the given point.
33. The slope of the tangent line to the curve $y = x^3 - 2x^2 + 3$ at any point (x, y) can be shown by calculus to be given by the formula $m = 3x^2 - 4x$. Find the equation of the tangent line and of the normal line to this curve at the point for which $x = 2$. (See Problem 32.)

5 Linear Functions

In Section 1 we defined a linear function as a polynomial function of degree 1, that is, a function of the form $f(x) = a_1 x + a_0$, with $a_1 \neq 0$. The reason for calling this *linear* should now be clear. If we put $y = f(x)$, we get

$$y = a_1 x + a_0$$

which is of the form $y = mx + b$, where $m = a_1$ and $b = a_0$. It follows that the graph of every linear function is a straight line. The requirement that $a_1 \neq 0$ ensures that the line is not horizontal. If $a_1 = 0$, the function would be of the form $f(x) = a_0$, which is called a **constant function.** Its graph is the horizontal line having the equation $y = a_0$. So even though the graph is a line, the function is not called linear in this case.

We can now conclude that every linear equation in two variables,

$$Ax + By + C = 0$$

in which *neither A nor B is 0*, defines a linear function. The rule for the function is obtained by solving for y:

$$y = -\frac{A}{B} x + \left(-\frac{C}{B} \right)$$

or in functional notation,

$$f(x) = -\frac{A}{B} x + \left(-\frac{C}{B} \right)$$

Polynomial equations of the first degree in more than two variables are also called *linear*, although their graphs are no longer straight lines. For example, the equation $2x - 3y + 4z - 7 = 0$ is a linear equation in three variables. Graphing this equation requires three dimensions. Can you guess what sort of graph this equation would have? Equations such as this will be considered later, when we discuss systems of equations.

EXAMPLE 10   A clothing store owner is able to sell 60 jackets of a certain type per week if the price is \$55 per jacket. He finds that if he reduces the price to \$40, he is able to sell 90 of the jackets per week. Assume that the number $N(x)$ sold per week is a linear function of the price x, and express $N(x)$ in terms of x. How many of the jackets could he expect to sell if the price were \$50?

Solution   We assume

$$N(x) = mx + b$$

From the given information $N(55) = 60$ and $N(40) = 90$. If we let $y = N(x)$, the points $(55, 60)$ and $(40, 90)$ are on the graph. So the slope m is

$$m = \frac{90 - 60}{40 - 55} = \frac{30}{-15} = -2$$

Therefore, $y = -2x + b$. To find b we can substitute either point. Putting $x = 40$ and $y = 90$ gives

$$90 = -2(40) + b$$
$$b = 170$$

Therefore, the functional relationship is

$$N(x) = -2x + 170$$

To find how many would be sold if the price were $50, put $x = 50$:

$$N(50) = -2(50) + 170 = 70$$

So he could expect to sell 70 jackets at this price.

EXERCISE SET 5

A   **1.** Let $f(x) = 3x - 2$. Identify and draw the graph of this function.

      2. Let g be the linear function defined by $g(x) = (2 - x)/3$. What is the slope of the graph of g? Draw the graph.

      3. Let $f(x) = (5x - 4)/3$. What are the slope and y intercept of the graph of f? Draw the graph.

      4. Graph the constant function defined by $f(x) = 5$.

      5. For a certain linear function f, we are given that $f(1) = 2$ and $f(-2) = 4$. Find $f(x)$.

      6. For a certain linear function f, the slope of the graph is 2 and $f(0) = -5$. Find $f(x)$.

      7. If g is a linear function with $g(0) = -1$ and $g(2) = 3$, find $g(x)$.

      8. If $g(0) = \frac{2}{3}$, g is linear, and the slope of the graph of g is $-\frac{1}{2}$, find $g(x)$.

      9. If h is linear, with $h(2) = 1$ and $h(-1) = 3$, find $h(x)$.

     10. If f is a linear function with $f(0) = 4$ and $f(-2) = 0$, find $f(x)$.

     11. For a function f it is known that $f(-2) = 3$ and $f(4) = 3$. Can f be linear? Explain. If f is a polynomial function of degree less than or equal to 1, find $f(x)$.

     12. The function g is a polynomial function of degree less than 2, having the property that $g(0) = -5$ and $g(-3) = -5$. Find $g(x)$.

     13. A car rental agency charges $18 per day, plus 20¢ per mile for renting a certain model car. Express the daily cost of renting this type of car as a function of the number of miles driven. What is the cost for driving 375 miles?

     14. If P are invested at simple interest r, then the amount of money $A(t)$ accumulated at the end of t years is a linear function of t. Find this function. Find $A(10)$ if $P = $2,000$ and $r = 0.08$.

     15. According to Hooke's law, the force $F(x)$ required to stretch a spring x inches beyond its natural length is a linear function of x. If for a certain spring it takes 40 pounds to stretch it 5 inches, find $F(x)$, and determine the force necessary to stretch the spring 8 inches.
     Note. When $x = 0$, $F(x) = 0$.

     16. The owner of a hamburger stand finds that she can sell an average of 200 hamburgers per day if she charges 95¢ per hamburger but only 170 hamburgers per day if she charges $1.10 per hamburger. Assuming the relationship is linear, express the number $N(x)$ sold per day as a function of the price x. How many hamburgers could the owner expect to sell per day if she charged $1.00 per hamburger?

     17. Show that the composition of two linear functions is also a linear function.
     Hint. Let $f(x) = a_1 x + a_0$ and $g(x) = b_1 x + b_0$, and consider $f \circ g$.

18. Let $f(x) = 2x - 3$ and $g(x) = (4 - x)/3$. Find $f \circ g$ and $g \circ f$. Give the slopes of the graphs of both $f \circ g$ and $g \circ f$, and draw their graphs.

B **19.** Show that every linear function is 1–1 from R onto R.

20. What is the relationship between the slope of the graph of a linear function f and that of its inverse f^{-1}?

21. If f and g are linear functions with graphs that are perpendicular, show that the slopes of the graphs of $f \circ g$ and of $g \circ f$ are both -1.

22. A common practice in business and industry is for capital equipment to be **depreciated linearly** over a specified period of years. If we let $V(t)$ represent the value of the equipment t years after purchase, this means that $V(t) = at + b$, where a and b are constants determined by the following conditions: When $t = 0$, $V(t) = C$, the original cost. When $t = N$, $V(t) = 0$, where N is the number of years over which the equipment is being depreciated. Find the constants a and b in terms of C and N. What is the value after 8 years of an item originally costing \$10,000 which is to be depreciated linearly to 0 in 20 years?

23. In Problem 22, it is reasonable to assume that certain items will not depreciate to 0 but will have some residual value (at least as junk) after N years. If the residual value is R, find $V(t)$ in terms of C, N, and R. If the \$10,000 item in Problem 22 has a residual value of \$500 after 20 years, what is its value after 8 years?

24. A certain nonlinear function $L(x)$ is tabulated for x values given to two decimal places between $x = 1.00$ and $x = 9.99$. It is common practice to use **linear interpolation** to approximate $L(x)$ for x expressed to the nearest thousandth, that is, to assume $L(x)$ is linear between consecutive entries in the table. If $L(2.13) = 0.3284$ and $L(2.14) = 0.3304$, use linear interpolation to approximate $L(2.137)$.

25. A nonlinear function $C(x)$ is tabulated so that two consecutive entries in the table are $C(0.5992) = 0.8258$ and $C(0.6021) = 0.8241$. It is desired to find $C(0.6000)$. Use linear interpolation to approximate this. (See Problem 24.)

6 Quadratic Functions

As we indicated in Section 1, a polynomial function of degree 2 is called a *quadratic* function. So the general form is $f(x) = a_2x^2 + a_1x + a_0$, or as it is more customarily written,

$$f(x) = ax^2 + bx + c \qquad (a \neq 0) \qquad (4)$$

Let us consider several special cases and look at their graphs. The simplest case is $f(x) = x^2$. Denote the dependent variable by y, so that

$$y = x^2$$

The smallest value y can have is 0, which occurs when $x = 0$, because if $x \neq 0$, then $x^2 > 0$. Furthermore, a given value of x and its negative produce the same value of y, since $(-x)^2 = x^2$. Finally, we see that when $|x| > 1$, y increases more rapidly than x; for example, when x goes from 2 to 3, y goes from 4 to 9. With these facts, and by plotting a few points, we can draw a reasonably accurate graph, as shown in Figure 11. The graph is called a **parabola.** The low point on the parabola is called its **vertex,** and the y axis is the **axis** of the parabola.

The parabola is said to be **symmetric** to its axis because the part of the curve to the left of the axis is the mirror image of the part to the right.

Figure 11

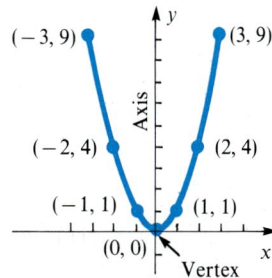

x	0	±1	±2	±3
y	0	1	4	9

We consider next the effect of a coefficient other than 1 on x^2:

$$y = ax^2$$

This causes every y coordinate to be multiplied by a. If $a > 0$, the general shape of the curve is the same as in Figure 11, but with the y coordinates stretched (if $a > 1$) or shortened (if $a < 1$). If $a < 0$, then each y value becomes negative, and the curve opens downward. In each case the curve is still a parabola with vertex at the origin and axis coinciding with the y axis. Figure 12 shows $y = 2x^2$, $y = \frac{1}{2}x^2$, and $y = -\frac{3}{2}x^2$ on the same set of axes.

Figure 12

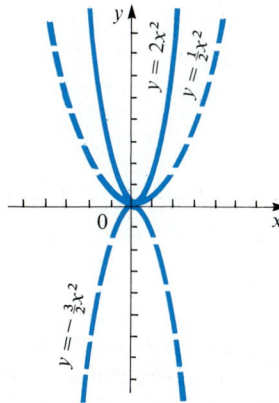

If a constant k is added, so that $y = ax^2 + k$, this has the effect of moving each y value upward (if $k > 0$) or downward (if $k < 0$). The vertex is shifted to the point $(0, k)$. Figure 13 shows the graph of $y = 2x^2 + 3$.

Figure 13

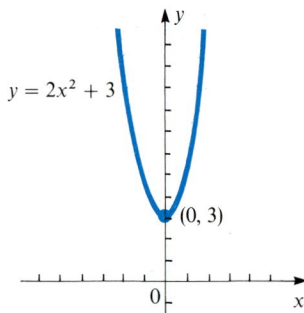

$y = 2x^2 + 3$

$(0, 3)$

Finally, we consider a function of the form

$$y = a(x - h)^2 + k$$

for example,

$$y = 2(x - 1)^2 + 3$$

In this case, y takes on its smallest value, 3, when $x = 1$, since for all other values of x, the term $2(x - 1)^2$ will be positive and so when added to 3 causes y to be greater than 3. Also, we note that if x is to the right or left of 1 by the same amount, the y value is the same. For example, if $x = 2$, then $y = 2(1)^2 + 3 = 5$, and when $x = 0$, then $y = 2(-1)^2 + 3 = 5$. We conclude that the curve is a parabola whose vertex is at the point $(1, 3)$ and whose axis is the line $x = 1$. In fact, this is the same parabola as in Figure 13 shifted one unit to the right, as shown in Figure 14.

Figure 14

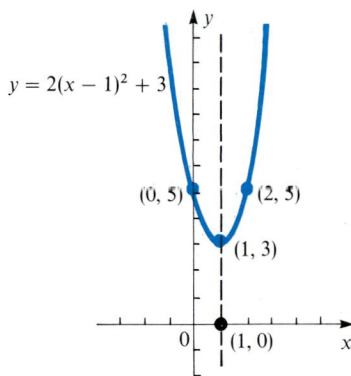

$y = 2(x - 1)^2 + 3$

$(0, 5)$ $(2, 5)$

$(1, 3)$

$(1, 0)$

Generalizing this, we can say that the graph of

$$y = a(x - h)^2 + k \tag{5}$$

is the same as the graph of

$$y = ax^2 + k$$

shifted h units horizontally. If $h > 0$, the shift is to the right, and if $h < 0$, it is to the left. In summary, we conclude that the graph of equation (5) is a parabola with the following properties:

---

1. Its vertex is at (h, k).
2. Its axis is the line $x = h$.
3. It opens upward if $a > 0$ and downward if $a < 0$.

Remark.   If we write equation (5) in the form

$$y - k = a(x - h)^2$$

we can observe that shifting the parabola whose equation is $y = ax^2$ so that the vertex is at (h, k) results in x being replaced by $x - h$ and y being replaced by $y - k$. Such a shift is called a **translation,** and the result holds true for other curves as well. That is, **if the equation of a curve is known, and the curve is then translated h units horizontally and k units vertically, the new equation is obtained from the old by replacing x by $x - h$ and y by $y - k$.**

Now let us return to the general quadratic function (4). Let $y = f(x)$. We factor out the coefficient a from the first two terms and complete the square on x:

$$y = a\left(x^2 + \frac{b}{a}x\right) + c$$

$$= a\left(x^2 + \frac{b}{a}x + \frac{b^2}{4a^2}\right) + c - \frac{b^2}{4a}$$

$$= a\left(x + \frac{b}{2a}\right)^2 + \frac{4ac - b^2}{4a}$$

Note that we added $b^2/4a^2$ inside the parentheses (the square of one-half of the coefficient of x), which had the effect of adding $b^2/4a$ after multiplying by a, so we subtracted this same amount to balance what we added.

If we let

$$h = -\frac{b}{2a} \quad \text{and} \quad k = \frac{4ac - b^2}{4a} \tag{6}$$

we can finally write

$$y = a(x - h)^2 + k$$

Therefore, the graph of

$$y = ax^2 + bx + c$$

is a parabola with vertex at (h, k), where h and k are given by equations (6). Its axis is the line $x = h$, and the parabola opens upward if $a > 0$ and downward if $a < 0$. Rather than memorize the values of h and k given in equations (6), it is probably better in each case to complete the square.

As a further aid in sketching the graph of a parabola we can make use of the x and y intercepts. The x intercept is found by setting $y = 0$; the y intercept is found by setting $x = 0$. For example, for the parabola

$$y = x^2 - 2x - 3$$

we immediately see that the y intercept is -3. To get the x intercepts we set $y = 0$ and factor:

$$(x - 3)(x + 1) = 0$$

So 3 and -1 are the x intercepts. If the quadratic function is not factorable with rational coefficients, the quadratic formula can be employed and the x intercepts approximated.

EXAMPLE 11   Find the vertex and the axis of the parabola with equation $y = x^2 - 2x + 3$.

Solution   We write

$$\begin{aligned} y &= x^2 - 2x + 3 \\ &= (x^2 - 2x + 1) + 3 - 1 \\ &= (x - 1)^2 + 2 \end{aligned}$$

We added 1 inside the parentheses to complete the square and subtracted 1 outside the parentheses to balance this off. Comparing this with equation (5), we conclude that the vertex is (1, 2) and the axis is line $x = 1$. There are no x intercepts, since $(x - 1)^2 + 2 > 0$ for all x. The y intercept is 3. We make a table of values and show the graph (Figure 15).

Figure 15

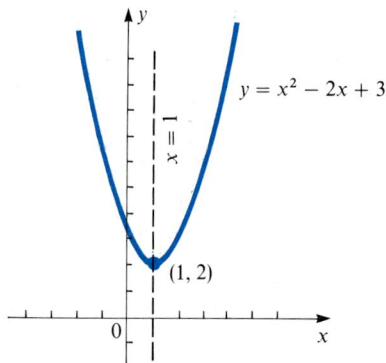

x	0	1	2	3	-1
y	3	2	3	6	6

EXAMPLE 12 Find the largest value of the function $f(x) = 1 - 8x - 2x^2$. Draw the graph.

Solution Let $y = f(x)$ and complete the square on x in order to put the equation in the form of equation (5):

$$y = -2x^2 - 8x + 1$$
$$= -2(x^2 + 4x) + 1$$
$$= -2(x^2 + 4x + 4) + 1 + 8$$
$$= -2(x + 2)^2 + 9$$

Notice that when we added 4 inside the parentheses to complete the square, we were actually adding -8 to the expression because of the factor -2, and so we had to balance this by adding $+8$.

The graph is a parabola, with vertex $(-2, 9)$, opening downward since the coefficient of the squared factor is negative. The y intercept is 1. The x intercepts, found by applying the quadratic formula, are approximately -4.12 and 0.12 (check this). Its graph is shown in Figure 16. The highest point on the graph is the vertex $(-2, 9)$, so the largest value of y, that is $f(x)$, is 9.

Figure 16

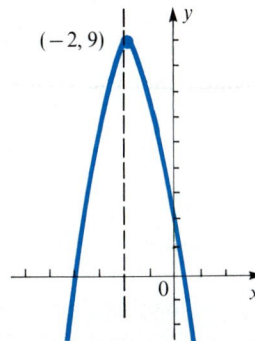

x	0	-1	-3	-4
y	1	7	7	1

Example 12 illustrates a technique for finding **maximum and minimum values** of quadratic functions. Since the graph is a parabola, its vertex is the lowest point on the curve if it opens upward and the highest point if it opens downward. When a curve attains such a highest or lowest point, this is called a **maximum point or minimum point**, respectively, of the curve, and the corresponding y coordinate is the **maximum or minimum value of the function**. More general techniques for finding maximum and minimum values of a much broader class of functions are studied in calculus. The next example illustrates an application of finding the maximum value of a function.

EXAMPLE 13   The average nightly attendance at a certain movie theater is 100 when the ticket price is $3.00. The manager finds that for each 10¢ reduction in price the average attendance goes up by 10 persons. If x represents the number of 10¢ reductions, the revenue $R(x)$ is given by

$$(20x - x^2) \geq 0$$
$$x(20 - x) \geq 0 \text{ FOR LIMIT}$$

$$R(x) = 300 + 20x - x^2$$

$$(\# PEOPLE)(PRICE)$$
$$(100 + 10x)(3 - x(.1))$$

Find the value of x that gives the maximum revenue, and determine the maximum revenue. What is the price per ticket and the average attendance for maximum revenue? (*Note:* You will be asked to verify the formula for $R(x)$ in Problem 35 of Exercise Set 6.)

Solution   We want to maximize $R(x)$, so we look for the highest point on the graph of $y = R(x)$:

$$y = -x^2 + 20x + 300$$
$$= -(x^2 - 20x) + 300$$
$$= -(x^2 - 20x + 100) + 300 + 100$$
$$= -(x - 10)^2 + 400$$

The parabola opens downward, and so has its maximum point at its vertex (10, 400), as shown in Figure 17. Therefore, the maximum value of the revenue is $400, and this occurs when $x = 10$. So there should be 10 reductions in price of 10¢ each, making the cost of each ticket $2.00. Since the average attendance increases by 10 for each such reduction in price, the average attendance for maximum revenue is 200.

Figure 17

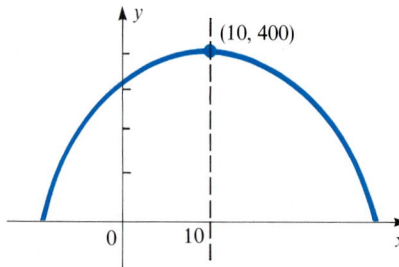

EXERCISE SET 6

A   In Problems 1–20 find the vertex and axis of the parabola, and draw the graph.

1. $y = x^2/2$
2. $y = -2x^2$
3. $y = x^2 + 4$
4. $y = 3 - x^2$
5. $y = (x - 2)^2 + 1$
6. $y = -(x + 1)^2 + 2$
7. $y = 2(x - 3)^2 - 1$
8. $y = -\frac{3}{2}(x - 1)^2 - 2$
9. $y = x^2 + 4x + 5$
10. $y = 3 - 2x - x^2$
11. $y = 2x^2 - 4x + 7$
12. $y = 2x^2 + 3x - 1$
13. $y = 3x - x^2$
14. $y = 4 - 5x - 2x^2$
15. $y = 3x^2 - 2x + 4$
16. $y = 2x - 3x^2$
17. $y = \dfrac{x^2}{2} + x + 5$
18. $y = \dfrac{-3x^2 + 5}{2} - 3x$
19. $y = 2x(x - 3) - 5$
20. $y = x(1 - 2x) - \frac{3}{2}$

In Problems 21–28 find the maximum or minimum value of each function, and state the value of x that gives this maximum or minimum value.

21. $f(x) = 2x - x^2$
22. $f(x) = x^2 - 4x + 3$
23. $g(x) = 2x^2 - 6x + 3$
24. $h(x) = 5 - 3x - 2x^2$
25. $F(x) = 5x^2 - 2x - 3$
26. $G(x) = 4x^2 - 6x + 5$
27. $\phi(x) = 8x - 3x^2$
28. $\psi(x) = 6x(x - 2) + 25$

29. For a small manufacturing firm the cost in dollars of producing x items per day is given by the function
$$C(x) = x^2 - 120x + 4,000$$
How many items should be produced per day to minimize cost? What is the minimum cost?

30. A company that produces computer terminals analyzes its production and finds that the profit in dollars from selling x terminals per month is given by
$$P(x) = 160x - 0.1x^2 - 20,000$$
How many terminals should be sold per month to produce the maximum profit? What is the amount of the maximum profit?

31. An object is projected vertically upward from the ground at an initial velocity of 192 feet per second. If air resistance is neglected, its distance $s(t)$ in feet above the ground after t seconds is given by $s(t) = 192t - 16t^2$. Find the maximum height the object will rise.

32. An object is propelled vertically upward at time $t = 0$ in such a way that its height y above the ground at time t is given by
$$y = -16t^2 + \tfrac{247}{6}t + 4$$
Draw the graph of y. How long will the object remain in the air?

B   33. Prove that if $f(x) = a(x - h)^2 + k$, then $f(h + t) = f(h - t)$.
   Note.   This proves that the parabola is symmetric to its axis, $x = h$.

34. A farmer wants to fence off a rectangular field that is bounded by a river on one side, so only three sides need to be fenced. He has 1,000 feet of fencing. What are the dimensions of the field if the area is to be a maximum?

35. Derive the formula for $R(x)$ in Example 13 from the information given there.

36. A restaurant has a fixed price of $10.00 for a complete dinner. The average number of customers per evening is 120. The owner estimates on the basis of prior experience that for each 50¢ increase in the price of the dinner, there will be 4 fewer customers per evening on the average. What should be charged for the dinner to obtain the maximum income?

37. A manufacturer sets the price of a certain item depending on the number sold per week, as follows:

$$\text{Selling price (dollars) per item} = 100 - 0.05x$$

where x is the number of items sold in a week. The total cost of producing x of these items in a week is given by

$$\text{Cost (dollars) of producing } x \text{ items} = 10{,}000 + 10x$$

Express the profit $P(x)$ obtained by selling x items in a week as a function of x. Find the value of x that maximizes the profit. What should the selling price be for maximum profit?

7 Graphical Solution of Quadratic Inequalities

We will see in the next two examples how quadratic inequalities can be solved by using graphs. For this purpose we need to know the x intercepts, but a rough sketch is all that is required otherwise. Since we know that the graph of a quadratic function $ax^2 + bx + c$ is a parabola, opening upward if $a > 0$ and downward if $a < 0$, the x intercepts provide us with the only other information we need for a rough sketch.

EXAMPLE 14   Solve the inequality $x^2 - 12x < 0$ by graphical means.

Solution   We consider the function

$$y = x^2 - 12x = x(x - 12)$$

We know the graph is a parabola that opens upward, since the coefficient of x^2 is positive. From the factored form of the right-hand side, the x intercepts are seen to be $x = 0$ and $x = 12$. From this we sketch the parabola, as shown in Figure 18, without attempting to locate the vertex exactly. All we want to know are the x values for which y is negative, that is, for which the curve lies *below* the x axis. We can see from the figure that the answer is those values of x for which $0 < x < 12$. Or we could say the solution set is $\{x:\ 0 < x < 12\}$.

Figure 18

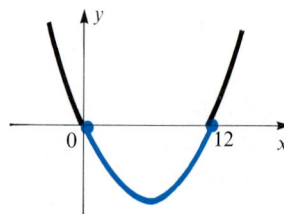

EXAMPLE 15   Solve by graphical means: $5 - 3x - 2x^2 \leq 0$

Solution   Let $y = 5 - 3x - 2x^2$. We will make a sketch of the graph and determine where $y \leq 0$. To find the x-intercepts, we set $y = 0$ and factor:

$$5 - 3x - 2x^2 = 0$$

$$(5 + 2x)(1 - x) = 0$$

$5 + 2x = 0$	$1 - x = 0$
$x = -\frac{5}{2}$	$x = 1$

We know the graph is a parabola that opens downward, since the coefficient of x^2 is negative, and we draw it, as shown in Figure 19. So $y \leq 0$ when $x \geq 1$ or $x \leq -\frac{5}{2}$, that is, the solution set is $\{x: \ x \geq 1\} \cup \{x: \ x \leq -\frac{5}{2}\}$

Figure 19

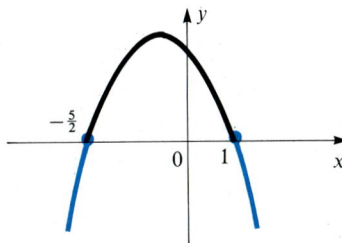

Note.   This graphical technique is not limited to solving quadratic inequalities. It will work whenever we can graph the function in question.

EXERCISE SET 7

A   In Problems 1–17 use the graphical method to solve the inequalities.

1. $x^2 - 2x > 0$
2. $x^2 - 3x - 4 \leq 0$
3. $x^2 + 4x - 5 \leq 0$
4. $x^2 - x - 12 > 0$
5. $3x^2 - 5x - 2 < 0$
6. $6 - x - x^2 \geq 0$
7. $2x^2 + 5x - 12 \geq 0$
8. $6x^2 + 7x - 20 < 0$
9. $2x^2 - x > 3$
10. $x(2x + 1) \leq 15$
11. $2(1 - 3x^2) \geq x$
12. $3(x^2 - 4) \leq 5x$
13. $10x(x - 2) < 3(x - 4)$
14. $x(3x + 10) \geq 8$
15. $4x(3x - 2) > 15$
16. $x^2 - 2x \leq 4$
17. $x(x + 2) \geq 1$

B   Use graphical techniques to find the domains of the functions in Problems 18 and 19.

18. $f(x) = x + \sqrt{12x^2 + x - 20}$

19. $g(x) = \dfrac{2x - 1}{\sqrt{18 - 3x - 15x^2}}$

20. Solve the inequality below by graphical means.

$$x^3 - x^2 - 9x + 9 < 0$$

Hint. First factor the left-hand side to find the x intercepts, and then plot a few points.

21. The revenue from the sale of x units of a certain commodity is 38 times the number of units sold. The cost of producing x units is $105 + 12x + x^2$. Write the profit function and find the range of values of x for which the profit is positive. What value of x produces the maximum profit, and what is that profit?

In Problems 22 and 23 prove that the inequality is satisfied for all values of x.

22. $3x^2 - 5x + 4 > 0$ **23.** $x(1 - x) \leq \frac{1}{4}$

---

8 Other Second-Degree Equations; Conic Sections

We saw in Section 6 that the graph of an equation of the form

$$y = ax^2 + bx + c \qquad (a \neq 0) \tag{7}$$

is a parabola with a vertical axis, opening upward if $a > 0$ and downward if $a < 0$. By completing the square we found that we could write the equation in the form $y = a(x - b)^2 + k$. Now, for consistency with what follows, we choose to write this in the equivalent form

$$y - k = a(x - h)^2 \tag{8}$$

The vertex is (h, k), and the axis is the line $x = h$.

If in equation (7) we interchange the roles of x and y, we obtain

$$x = ay^2 + by + c \qquad (a \neq 0) \tag{9}$$

which is the equation of a parabola with horizontal axis, opening to the right if $a > 0$ and to the left if $a < 0$. Completing the square yields the following equation, which is analogous to equation (8):

$$x - h = a(y - k)^2 \tag{10}$$

Again the vertex is (h, k). The axis is the horizontal line $y = k$.

EXAMPLE 16   Sketch the graph of the equation $4y^2 - x - 8y + 2 = 0$.

Solution   First we solve for x, obtaining an equation in the form of equation (9):

$$x = 4y^2 - 8y + 2$$

We complete the square in y and write the equation in the form of equation (10):

$$x = 4(y^2 - 2y + 1) + 2 - 4$$
$$= 4(y - 1)^2 - 2$$
$$x + 2 = 4(y - 1)^2$$

So $h = -2$ and $k = 1$. These are the coordinates of the vertex. The axis is the line $y = 1$, and the parabola opens to the right, as shown in Figure 20.

Figure 20

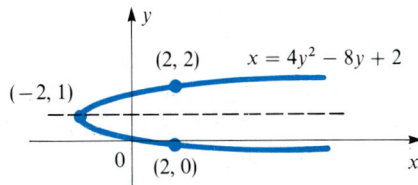

It should be emphasized that an equation of the form (9) does not define y as a function of x, since there are vertical lines that intersect the graph in more than one point.

The equations (7) and (9) each involves the square of *one* of the variables x or y, but not both. We now want to examine briefly some equations that involve the square of both x and y. The first of these is the equation of a **circle,** which we will derive.

A circle with radius r and center (h, k) is the set of all points whose distance from (h, k) equals r (Figure 21). A point (x, y) therefore lies on the circle if and only if

$$\sqrt{(x - h)^2 + (y - k)^2} = r$$

or equivalently,

$$(x - h)^2 + (y - k)^2 = r^2 \qquad (11)$$

Equation (11) is called the **standard form of the equation of a circle.** If the center is at the origin, it assumes the particularly simple form

$$x^2 + y^2 = r^2 \qquad (12)$$

Figure 21

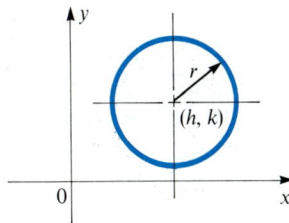

EXAMPLE 17   Identify and draw the graph of the equation $x^2 + y^2 - 6x + 4y + 9 = 0$.

Solution   We complete the square in both x and y to bring the equation to the standard form (11).

$$(x^2 - 6x + 9) + (y^2 + 4y + 4) = -9 + 9 + 4$$
$$(x - 3)^2 + (y + 2)^2 = 4$$

This is the equation of a circle with center $(3, -2)$ and radius 2, as shown in Figure 22.

Figure 22

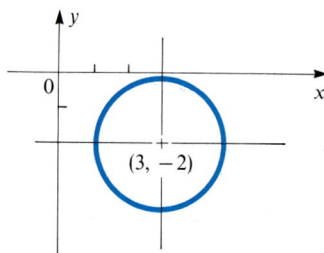

If we divide both sides of equation (12) by r^2, we get

$$\frac{x^2}{r^2} + \frac{y^2}{r^2} = 1$$

A closely related equation is of the form

$$\frac{x^2}{a^2} + \frac{y^2}{b^2} = 1 \tag{13}$$

where a and b have different values. This is the equation of an **ellipse** with center at the origin. The x intercepts are $\pm a$, and the y intercepts are $\pm b$. If $a > b$, the ellipse is elongated on the x axis, and if $b > a$, it is elongated on the y axis. Figure 23 illustrates both cases. The line segments joining the intercepts

Figure 23

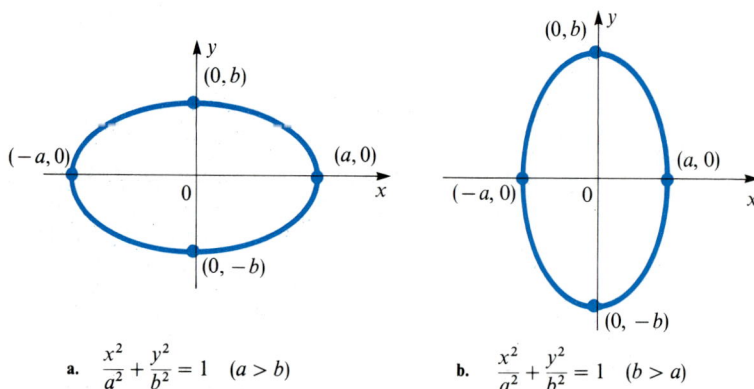

a. $\dfrac{x^2}{a^2} + \dfrac{y^2}{b^2} = 1 \quad (a > b)$

b. $\dfrac{x^2}{a^2} + \dfrac{y^2}{b^2} = 1 \quad (b > a)$

on the respective axes are called the **axes** of the ellipse. The longer axis is the **major axis** and the shorter one is the **minor axis.**

If the center of the ellipse is at the point (h, k), the standard equation of the ellipse is

$$\frac{(x - h)^2}{a^2} + \frac{(y - k)^2}{b^2} = 1 \tag{14}$$

EXAMPLE 18   Identify and sketch the graph of the equation $4x^2 + 9y^2 - 36 = 0$.

Solution   We write the equation in the form of equation (13) by adding 36 to both sides and then dividing both sides by 36.

$$\frac{x^2}{9} + \frac{y^2}{4} = 1$$

This is an ellipse with center at the origin and major axis along the x axis. Since $a^2 = 9$ and $b^2 = 4$, the x intercepts are ± 3 and the y intercepts are ± 2. These are the end points of the major and minor axes, respectively, as shown in Figure 24. We could find additional points on the graph by solving for y:

$$y = \pm\tfrac{2}{3}\sqrt{9 - x^2}$$

and substituting values for x. For a sketch, however, it is usually sufficient to use only the end points of the major and minor axes.

Figure 24

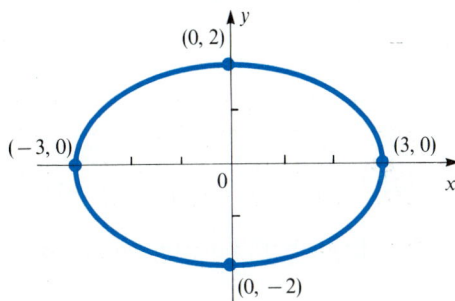

If instead of the sum of the squares as in equation (13), we have the difference

$$\frac{x^2}{a^2} - \frac{y^2}{b^2} = 1 \tag{15}$$

or

$$\frac{y^2}{b^2} - \frac{x^2}{a^2} = 1 \tag{16}$$

then the graph is that of a **hyperbola.** Figure 25 illustrates these two situations. The lines $y = bx/a$ and $y = -bx/a$ are called **asymptotes** of the hyperbola. The hyperbola approaches these lines more and more closely as the curve recedes indefinitely. An easy way to draw the asymptotes is to mark the points $(\pm a, 0)$ and $(0, \pm b)$ and draw a rectangle with vertical and horizontal lines, respectively, through them, as shown in Figure 25. This is called the **fundamental rectangle.** The asymptotes are the diagonals of this rectangle.

Figure 25

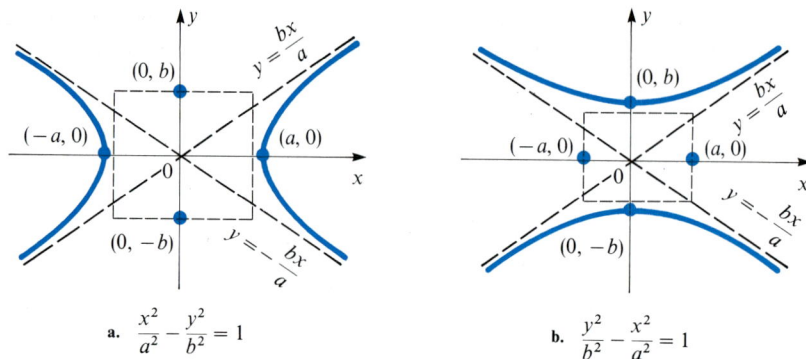

a. $\dfrac{x^2}{a^2} - \dfrac{y^2}{b^2} = 1$

b. $\dfrac{y^2}{b^2} - \dfrac{x^2}{a^2} = 1$

If the center is at (h, k), the two equations become

$$\frac{(x - h)^2}{a^2} - \frac{(y - k)^2}{b^2} = 1 \tag{17}$$

and

$$\frac{(y - k)^2}{b^2} - \frac{(x - h)^2}{a^2} = 1 \tag{18}$$

In this case, the asymptotes are the lines

$$y - k = \pm\frac{b}{a}(x - h)$$

EXAMPLE 19   Identify and sketch the graph of the equation $16x^2 - 9y^2 = 144$.

Solution   We divide both sides by 144 to obtain

$$\frac{x^2}{9} - \frac{y^2}{16} = 1$$

So the graph is a hyperbola with center at the origin. The intercepts on the x axis are ± 3. There are no y intercepts; $y = 4x/3$ and $y = -4x/3$ are asymptotes.

Figure 26

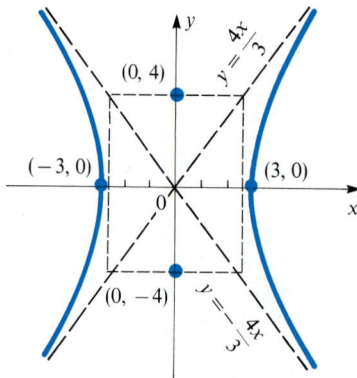

The circle, ellipse, parabola, and hyperbola are called **conic sections** (or simply **conics**) because they may be formed by the intersection of a plane with a right circular cone, as shown in Figure 27.

Figure 27

a. Plane perpendicular to axis of cone; intersection is a circle

b. Plane parallel to element of cone; intersection is a parabola

c. Plane parallel to axis of cone; intersection is a hyperbola

d. Any plane other than those in parts a, b, or c; intersection is an ellipse

EXERCISE SET 8

A   In Problems 1–16 identify the curve, and sketch its graph.

1. $y^2 - 4x = 0$

2. $y^2 + 2x = 0$

3. $x^2 + y^2 - 9 = 0$

4. $x^2 + 4y^2 = 4$

5. $x^2 - y^2 = 1$

6. $4x^2 - 9y^2 + 36 = 0$

7. $4x^2 + 4y^2 = 25$

8. $9x^2 - 4y = 0$

9. $y^2 = \dfrac{16(9 - x^2)}{9}$

10. $y^2 = \dfrac{16(x^2 - 25)}{25}$

11. $x = 1 + y^2$

12. $(x - 1)^2 + (y - 2)^2 = 4$

13. $(x - 3) = -2(y + 2)^2$

14. $\dfrac{(x + 3)^2}{16} + \dfrac{(y - 2)^2}{25} = 1$

15. $\dfrac{(x + 2)^2}{4} - \dfrac{(y + 1)^2}{1} = 1$

16. $\dfrac{(y - 3)^2}{9} - \dfrac{(x + 2)^2}{16} = 1$

In Problems 17–22 graph the function by first squaring both sides and writing the result in a standard form. The graph must be appropriately restricted as dictated by the given equation.

17. $y = \sqrt{4 - x^2}$

18. $y = -\sqrt{1 - x}$

19. $y = \dfrac{2\sqrt{9 - x^2}}{3}$

20. $y = \dfrac{2\sqrt{9 + x^2}}{3}$

21. $f(x) = \sqrt{x + 2}$
Hint. First let $y = f(x)$.

22. $g(x) = \sqrt{x^2 - 1}$

B In Problems 23–34 write the equation in a standard form, identify, and sketch the graph.

23. $y^2 - 2x - 6y + 13 = 0$
24. $x^2 + y^2 + 2x - 4y + 1 = 0$
25. $4x^2 + 9y^2 - 16x - 20 = 0$
26. $16x^2 - 9y^2 - 32x - 54y + 79 = 0$
27. $2y^2 - 16y + x + 35 = 0$
28. $x^2 + y^2 - 3x + 5y - 21 = 0$
29. $4x^2 - y^2 + 8x - 4y - 4 = 0$
30. $25x^2 + 16y^2 + 100x - 32y - 284 = 0$
31. $3(x^2 + y^2) - 8x + 10y - 7 = 0$
32. $9x^2 + 36x + 4y + 32 = 0$
33. $16x^2 + 9y^2 - 64x + 18y + 37 = 0$
34. $36x^2 - 16y^2 - 180x - 16y + 365 = 0$

Review Exercise Set

A   **1.** Find the slopes of the lines joining the following pairs of points:
a. $(-1, 3)$ and $(5, -4)$ **b.** $(-2, -6)$ and $(-4, 2)$

2. In each of the following a line passes through the given point and has the given slope. Find a second point on the line.
a. $(2, 5)$, slope $\frac{2}{3}$ **b.** $(-3, 2)$, slope $-\frac{5}{2}$

3. Find the unknown if the line joining the two points has the given slope.
a. $(5, -3)$ and $(7, y)$; slope 3 **b.** $(-4, 2)$ and $(x, -6)$; slope $-\frac{4}{3}$

In Problems 4–7 find the equations of the lines satisfying the given conditions.

4. a. Slope $-\frac{1}{2}$, passing through $(-5, 3)$
  b. Passing through $(-1, -4)$ and $(2, -6)$
5. a. Slope $\frac{3}{2}$, y intercept -2
  b. Passing through $(2, 7)$ and $(-1, 4)$
6. a. Slope $\frac{3}{4}$, passing through $(-1, -5)$
  b. Passing through $(-2, 4)$ and $(5, 7)$
7. a. y intercept 3, slope $\frac{3}{7}$
  b. Passing through $(5, -3)$ and $(-2, 6)$

In Problems 8 and 9 give the slope, x intercept, and y intercept, and draw the graphs.

8. a. $5x - 4y + 20 = 0$ **b.** $3(y - 4) = 6 - 2x$

9. a. $3(x - 4) = 2(y + 3)$ **b.** $\dfrac{2x - 3}{5} = \dfrac{1 - y}{3}$

10. Find the length of the line segment joining the given points.
a. $(-2, 1)$ and $(3, -4)$ **b.** $(0, 3)$ and $(4, 0)$ **c.** $(4, -2)$ and $(-1, 10)$
d. $(6, 9)$ and $(-2, -6)$ **e.** $(7, -5)$ and $(-2, 3)$
11. Find the midpoint of each line segment in Problem 10.
12. Find y so that the distance between $(-3, 2)$ and $(5, y)$ is 10. (There are two solutions.)
13. Show that the triangle with vertices $(-1, 5)$, $(3, -2)$, and $(-2, -3)$ is isosceles.

In Problems 14–16 find the equations of the lines satisfying the given conditions.

14. a. Passing through $(3, 5)$ and parallel to $2x - 4y + 3 = 0$
  b. Passing through $(-1, 2)$ and perpendicular to $x + 5y - 6 = 0$

15. a. Perpendicular to the line joining $(2, 6)$ and $(-3, 2)$ and passing through $(1, -1)$
     b. Parallel to the line joining $(1, 4)$ and $(-3, 7)$ and passing through $(2, -5)$

16. a. Parallel to the line joining $(-1, 2)$ and $(5, 4)$ and passing through the origin
     b. Perpendicular to the line $3x + 2y - 4 = 0$ and having x intercept -1

17. For the triangle with vertices at $A(3, -2)$, $B(-1, 4)$, and $C(5, 6)$, find the following:
     a. The equation of the line through C and parallel to the side AB
     b. The equation of the altitude drawn from C

18. The line through $(-4, -1)$ and $(2, y)$ is parallel to the line $5x + 2y + 4 = 0$. Find y.

19. Find the equation of the perpendicular bisector of the line segment joining $(2, 7)$ and $(-4, -3)$.

20. a. Find the equation of the family of lines parallel to $3x - 5y + 2 = 0$. Find the equation of the member of this family that has y intercept 2.
     b. Find the equation of the family of lines perpendicular to $2x + 3y - 4 = 0$. Find the equation of the member of this family that has an x intercept at the same point as that of the given line.

21. a. Find the equation of the family of lines parallel to the line $8x + 3y + 7 = 0$. Find the equation of the member of this family that passes through the point $(2, -3)$.
     b. Find the equation of the family of lines perpendicular to the line $y = 3x - 4$. Find the equation of the member of this family that passes through the point $(-1, 5)$.

22. For a certain linear function f it is given that $f(2) = -1$ and $f(5) = 3$. Find $f(x)$ and draw the graph of f.

23. If g is a polynomial function of degree 1, and $g(0) = -3$ and $g(2) = -1$, find $g(x)$. What is the slope of the graph of g?

24. For a certain linear function f it is given that $f(-1) = 2$ and $f(3) = -4$. Find $f(x)$ and draw the graph of f.

25. Let $f(x) = (3x + 4)/5$ and $g(x) = 2 - 3x$. Find $f \circ g$ and $g \circ f$, and draw their graphs.

26. Let $g(x) = 4x - 5$ and $h(x) = (x - 2)/3$. Find $g \circ h$ and $h \circ g$, and draw their graphs.

27. The temperature of the air diminishes approximately linearly with altitude h, for altitudes of up to 6 miles, dropping about $2°F$ for each 1,000 feet of altitude. If T_0 is the temperature on the ground, write the temperature T as a linear function of the altitude h (feet). If $T_0 = 72°F$, find T at an altitude of 18,000 feet.

28. A bicycle shop owner sells an average of 20 ten-speed bicycles a month when the price is \$175. When the price is reduced by 20%, sales go up by 50%. Assuming a linear relationship between price p and number of sales n, find the equation relating them. How many ten-speed bicycles should the shop owner expect to sell per month if the price is reduced by 10% from the original price?

In Problems 29 and 30 find the vertex and the axis of the parabola, and draw its graph.

29. a. $y = x^2 - 6x + 4$ b. $y = -2x^2 + 4x - 3$

30. a. $y = 4x - x^2$ b. $y = \dfrac{x^2}{2} + 2x + 3$

In Problems 31 and 32 find the maximum or minimum value of each function and state the value of x that gives this maximum or minimum value.

31. a. $f(x) = 3x^2 - 9x + 4$ b. $g(x) = 8 - 4x - x^2$

32. a. $F(x) = 2x^2 - 3x + 7$ b. $h(x) = 3x(2 - x) + 4$

33. The cost of producing x parts per month for a certain piece of equipment is given by the formula

$$C(x) = 2x^2 - 400x + 30,000$$

How many parts should be produced to minimize cost? What is the minimum cost?

34. The profit function $P(x)$ from producing and selling a certain type of pocket calculator is given by

$$P(x) = -0.02x^2 + 60x - 35,000$$

where x is the number produced and sold per week, and $P(x)$ is given in dollars. How many calculators should the manufacturer produce and sell each week to maximize profits? What is the maximum profit?

In Problems 35–37 solve the inequalities by the graphical method.

35. a. $x^2 - x - 2 < 0$ **b.** $3 - 2x - x^2 > 0$
36. a. $3x^2 - 5x - 2 \geq 0$ **b.** $2x^2 - 5x + 2 \leq 0$
37. a. $2(3x^2 + 2) \geq 11x$ **b.** $8 \geq x(2 + 3x)$

In Problems 38–42 identify the curve and draw its graph.

38. a. $x^2 + y^2 = 25$ **b.** $16x^2 + 25y^2 = 400$
39. a. $4x^2 - y^2 = 4$ **b.** $y^2 - x^2 = 1$
40. a. $y^2 + 2x = 0$ **b.** $x - 2 = \frac{1}{4}(y + 1)^2$
41. a. $(x - 3)^2 + (y + 3)^2 = 4$ **b.** $9(x - 1)^2 + 4(y + 2)^2 = 36$
42. a. $9(x - 3)^2 - 4(y + 1)^2 = 36$ **b.** $x = 3 - 4y - 2y^2$

B   **43.** Show that the points $(-5, 2)$, $(-3, -2)$, $(6, 1)$, and $(4, 5)$ are the vertices of a parallelogram. Find the equations of the sides.

44. For the triangle with vertices at $(0, 5)$, $(-4, -3)$, and $(6, 1)$ find the equations of the following:
     a. The altitudes   **b.** The medians
     (See Problem 19, Exercise Set 3.)

45. A space shuttle is placed in a circular orbit around the earth. When its engine is fired, it will move in a straight line tangent to the orbit. If with respect to a certain coordinate system for the plane of the orbit the center of the earth is at $(-1, 2)$ and the engine is fired when the spacecraft is at $(2, 3)$, what is the equation of the line along which the space shuttle will move?
     Note. The tangent to the circle at a point is perpendicular to the radius drawn to that point.

46. By calculus it can be shown that the slope of the tangent line to the curve $y = x^4 - 2x^2 + 3x - 7$ at any point (x, y) is given by $m = 4x^3 - 4x + 3$. Find the equations of the tangent line and the normal line (the line perpendicular to the tangent) at the point for which $x = -1$.

47. In calculus it can be shown that the slope of the tangent line at any point (x, y) on the curve $y = 1/x$ is given by the formula $m = -1/x^2$. Find the equations of the tangent line and the normal line at the point for which $x = -1$. Draw the graph, showing the tangent and normal.

48. Use the graphical method to solve the inequality $x^3 + 4x^2 - x - 4 \geq 0$.

In Problems 49 and 50 write the equation in standard form, and identify and draw the graph.

49. a. $x^2 + y^2 - 2x + 4y + 1 = 0$ **b.** $x^2 + 4y^2 + 6x - 16y + 21 = 0$
50. a. $4x^2 - 9y^2 - 16x - 18y + 43 = 0$ **b.** $25x^2 + 16y^2 - 192y + 176 = 0$

51. Prove that the line $3x - 4y + 15 = 0$ is tangent to the circle $x^2 + y^2 - 4x + 2y - 20 = 0$ at the point $(-1, 3)$.

52. At a certain movie theater the price of admission is \$3.00, and the average daily attendance is 200. As an experiment the manager reduces the price by 5¢ and finds that the average attendance increases by 5 people per day. Assuming that for each further 5¢ reduction the average attendance would rise by 5, find the number of 5¢ reductions that would result in the maximum revenue.

53. A railroad company agrees to run an excursion train for a group under the following conditions: If 200 people or less go, the rate will be $10 per ticket. The rate for each ticket will be reduced by 2¢ for each person in excess of 200 who go. What number of people will produce the maximum revenue for the railroad?

54. Find the dimensions of the rectangle of maximum area that can be inscribed in an isosceles triangle of altitude 8 and base 6.

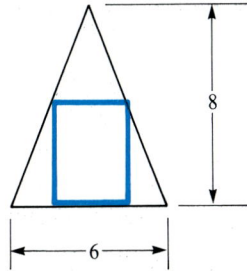

Hint. In a sketch use similar triangles to express the height of the rectangle in terms of its base.

6 Polynomial Functions of Higher Degree

The following example is taken from a mathematics textbook that emphasizes applications in economics and business.* You are not expected to understand the first step, which involves calculus, but the other steps of the example involve only algebra.

Now suppose the machine has a salvage value at time t of

$$S(t) = \frac{6480}{6+t}$$

where $S(t)$ is in units of \$10,000 and t is years. Then the company will maximize its net earnings if it disposes of the machine at time T when the net earnings after T equals the salvage value at T . . . .

Net earnings after T equals salvage value at T if

$$\frac{6480}{6+T} = \int_T^{10} (225 - \tfrac{9}{4}t^2)\,dt$$

$$\frac{6480}{6+T} = 1500 - 225T + \tfrac{3}{4}T^3$$

$$6480 = 9000 - 1350T + \tfrac{9}{2}T^3 + 1500T - 225T^2 + \tfrac{3}{4}T^4$$

$$0 = 2520 + 150T - 225T^2 + \tfrac{9}{2}T^3 + \tfrac{3}{4}T^4$$

$$= (T - 4)(\tfrac{3}{4}T^3 + \tfrac{15}{2}T^2 - 195T - 630)$$

Thus the machine should be disposed of after 4 years.

The symbol $\int_T^{10}$ that appears on the right-hand side of the equation is called an *integral sign* and signifies an operation of calculus. The important thing for you to note is the fourth-degree equation in the next-to-last line, and the factorization that follows. In this chapter you will learn how to discover this factorization, which then leads to the solution.

---

* Jean E. Draper and Jane S. Klingman, *Mathematical Analysis, Business and Economic Applications*, 2d ed., revised edition by Jean Draper Weber (New York: Harper & Row, 1972), pp. 435, 436. Copyright © 1967, 1972 by Jean E. Draper and Jane S. Klingman. Reprinted by permission of Harper & Row, Publishers, Inc.

1 Historical Note

The problem of trying to find formulas analogous to the quadratic formula for the roots of polynomial equations of degree greater than 2 occupied mathematicians for centuries. For the cases $n = 3$ and $n = 4$, called the **cubic** and **quartic** equations, respectively, formulas were obtained around 1540 by the Italian mathematicians Tartaglia (cubic) and Ferrari (quartic). Attempts over the next two centuries to solve the general **quintic** (degree 5) equation all met with failure. Finally, in 1824, the brilliant Norwegian mathematician Niels Henrik Abel (1802–1829), at the age of 22, made the remarkable discovery that no such general formula for the solutions of polynomial equations of degree higher than 4 could be found. This settled the matter once and for all, but in a surprising way. It is indeed a curious fact that algebraic formulas for the solutions of degree n equations in terms of their coefficients exist for the cases $n = 1, 2, 3, 4$ but not for $n \geq 5$. It is not simply that no one has been able to find these formulas—it is *impossible* for anyone ever to find them because they do not exist. This is not to say that *no* equation of degree 5 or higher can be solved in terms of its coefficients; in some cases this can be done. The special case $ax^5 + b = 0$ can certainly be solved for one of its roots, namely, $x = \sqrt[5]{-b/a}$. Furthermore, we will show in this chapter a technique for finding the rational roots of polynomial equations (with integral coefficients) of arbitrary degree and also a way of approximating the irrational roots to any desired degree of accuracy. So the situation is not hopeless. As a matter of fact, the formulas developed by Tartaglia and Ferrari are of little practical importance. Cubic and quartic equations are typically solved not by their formulas but by the techniques to be presented here (or by numerical techniques with the aid of the computer). The quadratic formula, on the other hand, is used extensively because of its simplicity.

2 The Remainder Theorem and the Factor Theorem

Let $P_n(x)$ denote a polynomial function of degree n:

$$P_n(x) = a_n x^n + a_{n-1} x^{n-1} + \cdots + a_1 x + a_0$$

When this is set equal to 0, it becomes a polynomial equation, and we will be seeking ways to solve such equations for $n > 2$. Recall that we use the terms **root** and **solution** interchangeably, and if r is a root of the equation, then r is also called a **zero** of the polynomial, and conversely. For example, we may say that the roots of the polynomial equation $x^2 - x - 2 = 0$ are 2 and -1, or equivalently, that the zeros of the polynomial $x^2 - x - 2$ are 2 and -1. The zeros of a polynomial are the x intercepts of its graph.

If we divide $P_n(x)$ by $x - r$, we obtain a quotient of degree $n - 1$ and a constant term as remainder. For example, let us divide $2x^3 - 3x + 4$ by $x - 2$:

$$\begin{array}{r} 2x^2 + 4x\ + 5 \\ x - 2\overline{)\ 2x^3 \qquad\quad - 3x +\ \ 4} \\ \underline{2x^3 - 4x^2} \\ 4x^2 - 3x \\ \underline{4x^2 - 8x} \\ 5x +\ \ 4 \\ \underline{5x - 10} \\ 14 \quad \text{Remainder} \end{array}$$

The quotient $2x^2 + 4x + 5$ is one degree less than the dividend, and the remainder 14 is a constant. We could write in this case

$$\frac{2x^3 - 3x + 4}{x - 2} = 2x^2 + 4x + 5 + \frac{14}{x - 2}$$

and obtain from multiplication by $(x - 2)$

$$2x^3 - 3x + 4 = (x - 2)(2x^2 + 4x + 5) + 14$$

This is an identity in x, that is, it is true for all values of x. In a similar way, if we denote the quotient on dividing $x - r$ into $P_n(x)$ by $Q(x)$ and the remainder by R, we obtain the identity

$$P_n(x) = (x - r)Q(x) + R \qquad\qquad (1)$$

Two results can now be obtained, and these are stated as theorems.

THE REMAINDER THEOREM

When the polynomial $P_n(x)$ is divided by $x - r$, the remainder is equal to $P_n(r)$.

Proof   In equation (1) substitute $x = r$. We obtain

$$P_n(r) = (r - r)Q(r) + R$$
$$= 0 + R$$
$$= R$$

For example, if we let $P(x) = 2x^3 - 3x + 4$, we can conclude from the division problem above that $P(2) = 14$, since when we divided by $x - 2$, we obtained 14 as the remainder. We emphasize that to get $P(2)$ we divide by $x - 2$ and read off the *remainder* as the answer.

THE FACTOR THEOREM

The polynomial $x - r$ is a factor of the polynomial $P_n(x)$ if and only if r is a root of the polynomial equation $P_n(x) = 0$, or equivalently, if and only if r is a zero of the polynomial $P_n(x)$.

For example, consider the polynomial $P(x) = x^3 - x^2 + x - 1$. By inspection we see that $x = 1$ is a root of the equation $P(x) = 0$. By the factor theorem it follows that $x - 1$ is a factor of $P(x)$. We can see this is true by factoring as follows:

$$x^3 - x^2 + x - 1 = x^2(x - 1) + (x - 1)$$
$$= (x^2 + 1)(x - 1)$$

Conversely, since $x - 1$ is a factor of $P(x)$, by putting $x = 1$, the polynomial equals 0.

These two theorems, although very simple, play a fundamental role in the solution of equations. The second theorem shows that the problem of finding roots of a polynomial equation and the problem of factoring a polynomial are essentially the same.

3 Synthetic Division

Since division will play a prominent role in the rest of this discussion, we will pause here to describe a shortened version of long division known as **synthetic division.** Consider a typical long division problem in which the divisor is of the special form $x - r$. For example, let us repeat the division of $2x^3 - 3x + 4$ by $x - 2$, shown in Section 2:

$$
\begin{array}{r}
2x^2 + 4x\ + 5 \\
x - 2{\overline{\smash{\big)}\,2x^3\qquad\ \ - 3x +\ \ 4}} \\
-\underline{\left(2x^3 - 4x^2\right)} \\
4x^2 - 3x \\
-\ \underline{\left(4x^2 - 8x\right)} \\
5x + 4 \\
-\underline{\left(5x - 10\right)} \\
14
\end{array}
$$

We will go through a series of steps that simplifies this procedure. First, there really is no need to write down the terms that have been circled above. We know that by subtraction the result will be 0. Leaving these out, we have

$$
\begin{array}{r}
2x^2\ + 4x\ + 5 \\
x - 2{\overline{\smash{\big)}\,2\,x^3\qquad\ - 3x +\ \ 4}} \\
-\ 4x^2 \\
\underline{} \\
4\,x^2 - 3x \\
-\ 8x \\
\underline{} \\
5\,x +\ 4 \\
-\ 10 \\
\underline{} \\
14
\end{array}
$$

Next, note that the circled terms in the above display are the same as the coefficients in the quotient; this is because the coefficient of x in the divisor is unity. With this observation, then, we can leave out the x in the divisor. Also, we can dispense with the powers of x everywhere and let the position of the coefficient indicate the associated power of x. The display now takes the form

$$
\begin{array}{r}
2 \quad\; 4 \quad\;\; 5 \\
-2)\overline{2 \quad\; 0 \;\; -3 \quad\;\; 4} \\
-4 \\
\overline{\quad 4 \;\; \boxed{-3}} \\
-8 \\
\overline{\quad 5 \quad\;\; \boxed{4}} \\
-10 \\
\overline{\quad\;\; 14}
\end{array}
$$

Note that we have written a 0 for the coefficient of the missing power. The first coefficient 2 in the quotient is the same as the first coefficient in the dividend. Each succeeding coefficient is obtained by multiplying the preceding coefficient by the -2 of the divisor and subtracting the result from the appropriate coefficient in the dividend. This can be simplified by changing the sign of the -2 in the divisor to $+2$ and *adding* rather than subtracting. Also, there is no need to repeat the circled terms above, because they occur in the dividend. This will enable us to compress the entire display as follows:

$$
\begin{array}{r}
2 \quad\; 4 \quad\;\; 5 \\
2)\overline{2 \quad\; 0 \;\; -3 \quad\;\; 4} \\
4 \quad\;\; 8 \quad 10 \\
\overline{4 \quad\;\; 5 \quad 14}
\end{array}
$$

Finally, if we bring down the initial coefficient 2 of the dividend to the bottom line, we see that the answer can be read from that line, so that we can omit the top line entirely. So we have

$$
\begin{array}{r}
\underline{2} \;\;\; | \quad 2 \quad\; 0 \;\; -3 \quad\;\; 4 \\
\downarrow \;\; 4 \quad\;\; 8 \quad 10 \\
\overline{2 \quad\; 4 \quad\;\; 5 \quad 14}
\end{array}
$$

Recall that the second line is obtained by multiplying the 2 in the divisor position by the numbers 2, 4, and 5, respectively, of the bottom line. Thus, $4 = 2 \cdot 2$, $8 = 2 \cdot 4$, and $10 = 2 \cdot 5$. The entries in the third line are obtained by adding the two entries above them. Finally, the answer is read, from right to left, as the remainder, constant term, coefficient of x, and coefficient of x^2.

Caution. Although 2 appears in the divisor position, the divisor is $x - 2$.

While the procedure was illustrated with a specific example, the method is general. Note carefully that the divisor must be of the form $x - r$, and r then is the number that appears in the position of the divisor. For example, if the divisor were $x + 2$, then this must be thought of as $x - (-2)$, so that -2 is in the divisor position. Remember, too, that since the positions of the coefficients indicate the powers of x, these coefficients must be arranged according to descending powers of x, and a 0 must be supplied as the coefficient of any missing power.

EXAMPLE 1   Divide $4x^4 - 15x^3 + 8x^2 - x + 7$ by $x - 3$.

Solution

$$
\begin{array}{r|rrrrr}
3 & 4 & -15 & 8 & -1 & 7 \\
  &   & 12 & -9 & -3 & -12 \\
\hline
  & 4 & -3 & -1 & -4 & -5
\end{array}
$$

Thus, the quotient is $4x^3 - 3x^2 - x - 4$, and the remainder is -5.

EXAMPLE 2   Divide $x^5 - 2x^4 + x$ by $x + 2$.

Solution

$$
\begin{array}{r|rrrrrr}
-2 & 1 & -2 & 0 & 0 & 1 & 0 \\
   &   & -2 & 8 & -16 & 32 & -66 \\
\hline
   & 1 & -4 & 8 & -16 & 33 & -66
\end{array}
$$

Thus, the quotient is $x^4 - 4x^3 + 8x^2 - 16x + 33$, and the remainder is -66.

Let us now consider the problem of evaluating a polynomial function $P_n(x)$ at a particular value of x, say $x = r$. There are two ways of doing this:

1. **The direct method:** Substitute r for x wherever x appears.
2. **Use the remainder theorem:** Divide $P_n(x)$ by $x - r$ using synthetic division; the answer sought is the remainder.

Consider, for example, the polynomial used previously, $P(x) = 2x^3 - 3x + 4$, and evaluate this by each method when $x = 2$. By the direct method,

$$P(2) = 2(2)^3 - 3(2) + 4 = 16 - 6 + 4 = 14$$

To apply method 2 we divide $P(x)$ by $x - 2$ using synthetic division and read off the remainder as the answer.

$$
\begin{array}{r|rrrr}
2 & 2 & 0 & -3 & 4 \\
  &   & 4 & 8 & 10 \\
\hline
  & 2 & 4 & 5 & \boxed{14 = P(2)}
\end{array}
$$

Remark.   Method 2 is especially well-suited to the use of a hand calculator. When the coefficients are messy (as is usually the case in practical applications), the use of a calculator is particularly helpful.

EXERCISE SET 3

A   In Problems 1–17 use synthetic division to divide the first polynomial by the second.

1. $x^2 - 2x - 4$ by $x - 1$
2. $3x^2 - 4x + 5$ by $x - 4$
3. $x^3 + 2x^2 - x + 3$ by $x - 2$
4. $2x^3 - 3x^2 + 4x - 5$ by $x + 1$
5. $x^3 + x^2 - 4$ by $x - 3$
6. $2x^3 - 5x^2 + 4$ by $x - 2$

7. $3x^3 - 4x + 5$ by $x + 2$
8. $2x^3 - 3x^2 + x - 7$ by $x - 3$
9. $2x^3 - 3x + 10$ by $x + 2$
10. $5x^3 + 2x - 3$ by $x + 3$
  (What can you conclude?)
11. $x^4 - 2x^3 - 25$ by $x - 3$
12. $x^4 - 3x^3 + 2x^2 - x - 3$ by $x - 1$
13. $x^5 - 2x^4 + 3$ by $x - 1$
14. $5x^3 - 4x^2 + x$ by $x + 4$
15. $3x^4 - 14x^3 - 6x^2 + 7x - 15$ by $x - 5$
16. $x^5 - 8x^3 - 6x^2 + 20$ by $x + 3$
17. $x^5 - 81$ by $x + 2$

In Problems 18–36 make use of synthetic division and the remainder theorem to find the indicated function values.

18. $P(x) = 3x^2 - 5x + 7$; find $P(4)$
19. $P(x) = x^3 - 2x^2 + 3x + 5$; find $P(2)$
20. $P(x) = x^3 + 7x^2 + 8x - 10$; find $P(-2)$.
21. $f(x) = 2x^3 - 10x - 8$; find $f(3)$
22. $P(x) = 2x^3 - 3x^2 + 4x - 7$; find $P(-3)$
23. $g(t) = t^4 - 2t^2 - 6$; find $g(-2)$
24. Let $f(x) = 3x^4 - 10x^3 - 24x - 16$; find $f(4)$. Also find $f(4)$ by substitution. Which method is easier?
25. Evaluate the polynomial $x^5 - 8x^3 + 10x + 12$ when $x = 2$.
26. $Q(t) = 4t^3 - 8t^2 - 9$; find $Q(-3)$
27. $P(x) = x^4 - 16$; find $P(3)$
28. $F(x) = 3x^4 - 8x^3 - 12x^2 + 5x - 9$; find $F(2)$
29. $P(y) = y^4 - 6y^2 + 3$; find $P(5)$
30. $P(x) = x^4 + 2x^3 - 3x^2 - 4x - 8$; find $P(2)$
31. $g(x) = 5x^4 - 20x^3 - 12x^2 + 10$; find $g(-2)$
32. $P(x) = x^5 - 2x^3 + 7$; find $P(3)$
33. $Q(s) = 3s^4 + 2s^3 - s^2 - 5s$; find $Q(-4)$
34. $P(x) = 3 - x - 2x^3 - x^4$; find $P(3)$
35. $Q(x) = x^5 + 12x^4 + 24x^3 - 10x^2 - 5$; find $Q(-3)$
36. $P(t) = 10 + x^2 - 3x^3 - 2x^4$; find $P(-2)$

B Use synthetic division to perform the divisions in Problems 37–40.

37. $(4x^4 - 3x^3 + x - 4) \div (x - \frac{1}{2})$
38. $(2x^4 + 3x^2 - 5x) \div (x + \frac{3}{2})$
39. $(x^3 - 5x^2 + 3x - 4) \div (2x - 1)$
  Hint. Write $(2x - 1) = 2(x - \frac{1}{2})$. Divide first by $x - \frac{1}{2}$, using synthetic division, and then divide the final quotient by 2.
40. $(2x^4 - 3x^3 + 2x - 5) \div (3x + 2)$ (See hint to Problem 39.)

41. Show by two methods that $x = -3$ is a zero of the polynomial $P(x) = 2x^4 - x^3 - 8x^2 + 34x - 15$.
42. Determine by two methods whether $x = 4$ is a root of the equation $3x^4 - 2x^3 - 50x^2 + 32x + 32 = 0$.
43. Show that $x + 6$ is a factor of $2x^4 + 11x^3 - 6x^2 + x + 6$ using synthetic division.
44. Let $P(x) = x^5 - 4x^4 - 5x^3 + 20x^2 + 4x - 16$. Use synthetic division and the remainder theorem to show that $P(4) = 0$. Show the complete factorization of $P(x)$.
45. Find $f(\frac{1}{2})$ using synthetic division if $f(x) = 4 - 2x + 3x^2 - x^4$.
46. Let $P(x) = 2x^4 - 3x^3 + 5x - 7$. Find $P(-\frac{3}{2})$ using synthetic division.
47. Let $Q(x) = 16x^4 - x^2 - 3x + 4$. Find $Q(\frac{3}{4})$ using synthetic division.
48. Show by synthetic division that $x = 4$ is a zero of the polynomial $x^3 - 6x^2 + 9x - 4$. Factor this polynomial completely. What are its other zeros?

49. Show by synthetic division that $x = -3$ is a root of the equation $x^3 + 2x^2 - 2x + 3 = 0$. What are the factors of the left-hand side? Are there any other real roots? Explain.

In Problems 50 and 51 find the specified function values using synthetic division and a hand calculator.

50. If $f(x) = 2.035x^3 - 1.768x^2 - 9.251x + 6.347$, find:
    a. $f(5.623)$ **b.** $f(-1.037)$

51. If $g(t) = 25.76 - 13.42t + 7.059t^3 - t^4$, find:
    a. $g(0.3254)$ **b.** $g(-2.167)$

4   The Fundamental Theorem of Algebra and Its Corollaries

As its name implies, the following theorem is fundamental to the theory of equations. Its proof is beyond the scope of this course, but two important corollaries will be proved.

THE FUNDAMENTAL THEOREM OF ALGEBRA   **Every polynomial equation $P_n(x) = 0$ has at least one root in the field of complex numbers.**

Our interest will center on polynomials with real, and usually integral, coefficients, but this theorem is valid when the coefficients are any complex numbers. The root that is asserted to exist, however, cannot be assumed to be real, even when the coefficients are. For example, the equation $x^2 + 4 = 0$ has the root $x = 2i$ (also $x = -2i$), which is not real, even though the coefficients are integers. As a corollary to the fundamental theorem, we have the following:

COROLLARY 1   **A polynomial of degree n can be factored into n (not necessarily distinct) linear factors over the complex number field.**

Proof   By the factor theorem, we know that $x - r$ is a factor of $P_n(x)$ if and only if $P_n(r) = 0$, that is, if and only if r is a root of the polynomial equation $P_n(x) = 0$. By the fundamental theorem, we know that $P_n(x)$ does have a root, say, r_1. Thus,

$$P_n(x) = (x - r_1)P_{n-1}(x)$$

where $P_{n-1}(x)$ is the quotient of $P_n(x)$ divided by $x - r$, and hence is of degree $n - 1$ and has the same leading coefficient, say, a_n, as $P_n(x)$. Further, $P_n(x) = 0$ if and only if

$$(x - r_1)P_{n-1}(x) = 0$$

So, applying the factor theorem and the fundamental theorem to $P_{n-1}(x)$, we know there is a root, say r_2, of $P_{n-1}(x) = 0$, so that

$$P_{n-1}(x) = (x - r_2)P_{n-2}(x)$$

and thus,

$$P_n(x) = (x - r_1)(x - r_2)P_{n-2}(x)$$

where $P_{n-2}(x)$ is of degree $n - 2$ and has the same leading coefficient as $P_{n-1}(x)$ and hence as $P_n(x)$. We continue this process until arriving at the stage

$$P_n(x) = (x - r_1)(x - r_2) \cdot \cdots \cdot (x - r_{n-1})P_1(x)$$

where $P_1(x)$ is of degree 1 and has the same leading coefficient as $P_n(x)$. That is, $P_1(x) = a_n x + b = a_n[x + (b/a_n)]$. If we write $r_n = -b/a_n$, we have finally,

$$P_n(x) = a_n(x - r_1)(x - r_2) \cdot \cdots \cdot (x - r_n) \tag{2}$$

and the proof is complete.

It must be emphasized that the factors in the above corollary may not all be distinct, which is equivalent to saying that the r_k's are not necessarily distinct. Each factor $(x - r_k)$ corresponds to a root of $P_n(x) = 0$, according to the factor theorem. We therefore have another corollary.

COROLLARY 2   **A polynomial equation of degree n has at most n roots.**

There will, in fact, be exactly n roots if all the r_k's are distinct. If, in the factorization given in equation (2), $(x - r_k)$ occurs as a factor m times, then r_k is said to be a **root of multiplicity m** of the equation $P_n(x) = 0$.
Suppose now that the coefficients in

$$P_n(x) = a_n x^n + a_{n-1} x^{n-1} + \cdots + a_1 x + a_0$$

are all real, and suppose $x = r$ is an imaginary root of the equation $P_n(x) = 0$. We will show that the conjugate $\bar{r}$ is also a root. For

$$\overline{P_n(r)} = \overline{a_n r^n + a_{n-1} r^{n-1} + \cdots + a_1 r + a_0}$$
$$= \bar{a}_n \bar{r}^n + \bar{a}_{n-1} \bar{r}^{n-1} + \cdots + \bar{a}_1 \bar{r} + \bar{a}_0$$

where we have used the properties of conjugates repeatedly. Now, since the coefficients are real, conjugation leaves them unaltered; that is,

$$\overline{P_n(r)} = a_n \bar{r}^n + a_{n-1} \bar{r}^{n-1} + \cdots + a_1 \bar{r} + a_0 = P_n(\bar{r})$$

Finally, since $P_n(r) = 0$ by hypothesis and 0 is a real number,

$$\overline{P_n(r)} = \bar{0} = 0 = P_n(\bar{r})$$

So $\bar{r}$ is a root of $P_n(x) = 0$ as asserted. This result shows that **in polynomial equations with real coefficients, imaginary roots always occur in conjugate pairs.** Thus, if $2 + 3i$ is a root of such an equation, then $2 - 3i$ is also.

EXERCISE SET 4

A   In Problems 1–5 verify the factorizations by making use of synthetic division.

1. $2x^3 - x^2 - 7x + 6 = 2(x - 1)(x + 2)(x - \frac{3}{2})$
2. $4x^3 - 21x^2 + 18x + 27 = 4(x + \frac{3}{4})(x - 3)^2$
3. $3x^3 + 4x^2 - 12x - 16 = 3(x + 2)(x - 2)(x + \frac{4}{3})$
4. $x^4 + 3x^3 - 6x^2 - 28x - 24 = (x - 3)(x + 2)^3$
5. $3x^4 - 2x^3 + 11x^2 - 8x - 4 = 3(x - 1)(x + \frac{1}{3})(x - 2i)(x + 2i)$

6. Construct a polynomial with integer coefficients whose only zeros are 2, -1, and $\frac{1}{2}$.
7. Find a polynomial equation with roots 3, 2, and -2
8. Construct a polynomial with integer coefficients whose only zeros are -3, 4, and $\frac{3}{4}$.
9. Find a polynomial with 2 as a zero of multiplicity 3 and whose other zero is -1.
10. Find a polynomial equation with -3 as a root of multiplicity 2 and whose only other root is 4.
11. Show by direct substitution that both $1 + i$ and its conjugate are roots of the equation $5x^3 - 7x^2 + 4x + 6$.
12. Show by synthetic division that both $3i$ and $-3i$ are roots of the equation $x^4 - 5x^3 + 5x^2 - 45x - 36 = 0$.
13. Give an example of a quadratic equation with:
    a. No real roots   b. Two real roots   c. Exactly one real root

B   14. Show that every polynomial of *odd* degree with real coefficients has at least one real root.
15. Verify that $x = 2$ is a root of multiplicity 3 of the equation $x^4 - 4x^3 + 16x - 16 = 0$. What is the other root?
16. Find a polynomial whose only zeros are $2 + 3i$, $2 - 3i$, and 4.
17. Find a polynomial of fourth degree with integer coefficients two of whose zeros are $3 - 4i$ and $2 + i$.
18. Two of the roots of a certain fourth-degree polynomial equation with integer coefficients are $1 + 2i$ and $4 - 3i$. Find the equation.

5 Rational Roots

If the polynomial equation $P_n(x) = 0$ has rational numbers as coefficients, it is equivalent to one with integer coefficients. This can be seen by multiplying both sides of the equation by the LCD of the coefficients. For example, by multiplying both sides of

$$\tfrac{2}{3}x^3 - \tfrac{1}{4}x^2 + \tfrac{5}{6}x - 1 = 0$$

by 12, we obtain the equivalent equation

$$8x^3 - 3x^2 + 10x - 12 = 0$$

For this reason we will concentrate our attention on polynomial equations with integer coefficients. When the coefficients are irrational, the roots can be approximated to any desired degree of accuracy using numerical techniques. A hand calculator is very helpful in this situation.

Even when the coefficients are integers, the roots are not necessarily rational, or even real (for example, $x^2 + 1 = 0$ has imaginary roots). However, if there *are* rational roots, there is a procedure for finding them, which we now describe.

A rational number can always be written in the form p/q, where p and q are relatively prime integers (that is, they have in common no integer factor other than ± 1). Suppose p and q are relatively prime and $x = p/q$ is a root of the equation

$$P_n(x) = a_n x^n + a_{n-1} x^{n-1} + \cdots + a_1 x + a_0 = 0$$

where now it is assumed that all coefficients are integers. Then we have

$$a_n \frac{p^n}{q^n} + a_{n-1} \frac{p^{n-1}}{q^{n-1}} + \cdots + a_1 \frac{p}{q} + a_0 = 0 \qquad (3)$$

We multiply both sides of (3) by q^n and obtain

$$a_n p^n + a_{n-1} p^{n-1} q + a_{n-2} p^{n-2} q^2 + \cdots + a_1 p q^{n-1} + a_0 q^n = 0 \qquad (4)$$

We rewrite (4) in two equivalent forms. First, subtract $a_0 q^n$ from both sides and factor the common factor p from each term remaining on the left:

$$p(a_n p^{n-1} + a_{n-1} p^{n-2} q + \cdots + a_1 q^{n-1}) = -a_0 q^n$$

From this we see that p is a factor of the left-hand side and hence also of the right-hand side. But p and q are relatively prime; hence, p is not a factor of q^n.* So p must divide a_0.

Now write equation (4) in another way—this time subtracting $a_n p^n$ from both sides and factoring q from what remains on the left:

$$q(a_{n-1} p^{n-1} + a_{n-2} p^{n-2} q + \cdots + a_0 q^{n-1}) = -a_n p^n$$

Reasoning as above, we see that q must divide a_n. These results are summarized as a theorem.

THEOREM   The only possible rational roots of the polynomial equation with integral coefficients

$$a_n x^n + a_{n-1} x^{n-1} + \cdots + a_0 = 0$$

are of the form p/q, where p is a factor of the constant term a_0 and q is a factor of the leading coefficient a_n.

---

* Although this really requires more proof, it is intuitively clear; we will not go into more detail here.

EXAMPLE 3   Find all roots of the equation $3x^3 - 8x^2 + 5x - 2 = 0$.

Solution   The possible numerators of rational roots are factors of 2, namely ± 1 and ± 2. The possible denominators are factors of 3, that is, 1 or 3. We need not consider negative denominators, since we get all possible signs by allowing the numerator only to vary. Thus, a listing of all possible rational roots is

$$\pm \tfrac{1}{3} \qquad \pm \tfrac{2}{3} \qquad \pm 1 \qquad \pm 2$$

We do not know whether any of these is actually a root, but at least the list of those we have to try is finite. There are various strategies for the order in which to test the possible rational roots. One way is to order them according to size and start with the smallest positive one and work up until (1) a root is found, (2) the list of positive possibilities is exhausted, or (3) it becomes evident that there is no need to proceed further. When a root r is encountered, we usually look for further roots in the so-called **depressed equation,** which is the quotient (on dividing by $x - r$) set equal to 0. If the depressed equation is quadratic, then the quadratic formula (or simple factorization) is used. If situation (2) or (3) above is encountered before finding all roots, then we can try the negative possibilities, working in reverse order.

For this problem the procedure is as follows:

$$
\begin{array}{r|rrrr}
\tfrac{1}{3} & 3 & -8 & 5 & -2 \\
  &   & 1 &   &   \\
\hline
  & 3 & -7 &   &   \\
\end{array}
$$

This is not carried further since all remaining multiplications result in non-integers, and thus there is no possibility of getting a 0 remainder.

$$
\begin{array}{r|rrrr}
\tfrac{2}{3} & 3 & -8 & 5 & -2 \\
  &   & 2 & -4 &   \\
\hline
  & 3 & -6 & 1 &   \\
\end{array}
$$

$$
\begin{array}{r|rrrr}
1 & 3 & -8 & 5 & -2 \\
  &   & 3 & -5 & 0 \\
\hline
  & 3 & -5 & 0 & -2 \\
\end{array}
$$

$$
\begin{array}{r|rrrr}
2 & 3 & -8 & 5 & -2 \\
  &   & 6 & -4 & 2 \\
\hline
  & 3 & -2 & 1 & 0 \\
\end{array}
$$

Now we have met with success. We have found that $x = 2$ is a root of the equation, since on division by $x - 2$ we have a remainder of 0. The polynomial can be factored as $(x - 2)(3x^2 - 2x + 1)$. Thus, all other roots are those of the depressed equation

$$3x^2 - 2x + 1 = 0$$

Since this is quadratic, we solve it by the quadratic formula:

$$x = \frac{2 \pm \sqrt{4 - 12}}{6} = \frac{1 \pm i\sqrt{2}}{3}$$

Note here, as we expected, the imaginary roots are conjugates. Now we have the complete solution set:

$$\left\{ 2, \quad \frac{1 + i\sqrt{2}}{3}, \quad \frac{1 - i\sqrt{2}}{3} \right\}$$

We also have the factorizations:

$$3x^3 - 8x^2 + 5x - 2 = (x - 2)(3x^2 - 2x + 1)$$

over the reals, and

$$3x^3 - 8x^2 + 5x - 2 = 3(x - 2)\left(x - \frac{1 + i\sqrt{2}}{3} \right)\left(x - \frac{1 - i\sqrt{2}}{3} \right)$$

over the complex numbers.

Before we go to another example of finding rational roots, we will illustrate a tabular arrangement which is convenient when we have several divisions to perform on the same polynomial. We also give two further ways of limiting the trials when seeking roots of a polynomial equation.

Consider the polynomial

$$P(x) = 2x^3 - 5x^2 - 8x + 11$$

We will find the value of $P(r)$ for various values of r, using synthetic division and the remainder theorem. Suppose, for example, that we want $P(2)$ and $P(-3)$. Instead of showing the synthetic divisions in the usual way, namely

$$
\begin{array}{r|rrrr}
2 & 2 & -5 & -8 & 11 \\
  &   & 4 & -2 & -20 \\
\hline
  & 2 & -1 & -10 & -9
\end{array}
$$

and

$$
\begin{array}{r|rrrr}
-3 & 2 & -5 & -8 & 11 \\
   &   & -6 & 33 & -75 \\
\hline
   & 2 & -11 & 25 & -64
\end{array}
$$

therefore obtaining $P(2) = -9$ and $P(-3) = -64$, we compress these into one table, as shown in Table 1. We have written the coefficients of $P(x)$ only once, and we have deleted the second line of the synthetic division process, carrying out the additions mentally. The numbers r whose function values we are seeking are listed in the first column, and the remainders, that is, the values of $P(r)$ corresponding to the value of r on the left, are listed in the right-hand column.

Table 1

r				$P(r)$
0	2	-5	-8	11
2	2	-1	-10	-9
-3	2	-11	25	-64

Table 2

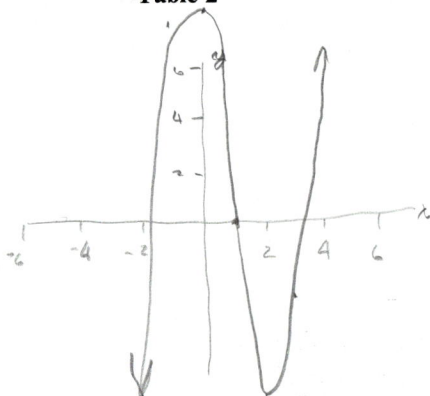

r				P(r)
0	2	−5	−8	11
1	2	−3	−11	0
2	2	−1	−10	−9
3	2	1	−5	−4
4	2	3	4	27
5	2	5	17	96
−1	2	−7	−1	12
−2	2	−9	10	−9
−3	2	−11	25	−64

Now we extend the table, as shown in Table 2, and make some additional observations. Note first the sign change from $P(3)$ to $P(4)$. Now it can be proved that the graph of every polynomial function has no breaks in it (it is **continuous**). It follows that $P(x)$ must be 0 for some value of x between $x = 3$ and $x = 4$, since $P(x)$ is negative when $x = 3$ and positive when $x = 4$. Therefore, $P(x)$ has a zero between $x = 3$ and $x = 4$, or equivalently, a root of the equation $P(x) = 0$ occurs between $x = 3$ and $x = 4$. By the same sort of reasoning we can conclude that $P(x)$ has a zero between $x = -1$ and $x = -2$, since $P(-1)$ is positive, and $P(-2)$ is negative.

Our next observation is that 1 is a zero of $P(x)$. The line corresponding to $r = 1$ tells us that $P(x)$ can be factored as

$$P(x) = (x - 1)(2x^2 - 3x - 11)$$

So if we are interested in solving the equation $P(x) = 0$, we have

$$(x - 1)(2x^2 - 3x - 11) = 0$$

and thus either $x - 1 = 0$ or $2x^2 - 3x - 11 = 0$. So $x = 1$ is one root, and all other roots are contained in the equation $2x^2 - 3x - 11 = 0$. In this case the depressed equation is quadratic and can be solved by the quadratic formula:

$$x = \frac{3 \pm \sqrt{9 + 88}}{4} = \frac{3 \pm \sqrt{97}}{4} \approx \frac{3 \pm 9.85}{4}$$

So the two roots of the depressed equation are approximately 3.21 and -1.71, which agrees with our earlier conclusion that there were roots between 3 and 4 and between -1 and -2.

More generally, if we have found a root $x = r$ of a polynomial equation $P_n(x) = 0$, then the polynomial can be factored in the form

$$(x - r)P_{n-1}(r)$$

and the equation $P_{n-1}(x) = 0$ is the depressed equation corresponding to the root $x = r$. All other roots of the original equation are found by solving the depressed equation.

Returning now to Table 2, we want to make two more observations. Notice that all entries in the line corresponding to $r = 4$ are positive, as are the entries in the next line. We could have anticipated that the entries corresponding to $r = 5$ would also be positive, in fact, because they were positive when 4 was the multiplier, and so will be even larger when 5 is the multiplier. We can conclude from this that there are no roots of $P(x) = 0$ larger than $x = 4$. The number 4 is therefore an **upper bound** to the roots of $P(x) = 0$. Of course, since we have already actually found all roots in this particular problem, we get no new useful information by finding this upper bound, but we want to obtain a general result, which in some problems can be quite helpful.

Similarly, since the multiplier -2 is negative, and the signs of the entries in its row *alternate*, they will continue to alternate when a negative number greater in absolute value is used, as can be seen in the line corresponding to $r = -3$. Thus, we can conclude that -2 is a **lower bound** to the roots of $P(x)=0$.

More generally, if the result of dividing a polynomial by $x - r$ using synthetic division yields all positive numbers when $r > 0$, then r is an upper bound to the roots of the equation $P_n(x) = 0$. If $r < 0$ and the signs alternate, then r is a lower bound to the roots. (Note that for this test, 0 may be treated as either positive or negative.)

In addition to limiting trials of possible roots using upper and lower bounds, the following rule is often useful.

Descartes' Rule of Signs

Let $P_n(x)$ be a polynomial with real coefficients, of degree $n \geq 1$, with terms arranged in descending (or ascending) powers of x. The number of positive real roots of the equation $P_n(x) = 0$ is either equal to the number of sign changes between successive terms of $P_n(x)$ or fewer than this by an even number. The number of negative real roots is found by applying the same rule to $P_n(-x)$.

Note. In Descartes' rule a root of multiplicity m is counted m times. Observe that the rule gives information on the number of real roots, but these roots need not be rational.

We illustrate how to apply Descartes' rule with the equation

$$P(x) = 2x^3 - 5x^2 - 8x + 11 = 0$$

sign   sign
change   change

There are two sign changes between successive terms of $P(x)$, so there are either two or zero positive real roots. Now consider $P(-x)$:

$$P(-x) = 2(-x)^3 - 5(-x)^2 - 8(-x) + 11$$
$$= -2x^3 - 5x^2 + 8x + 11$$

sign
change

Since there is only one sign change, there must be exactly one negative real root to the original equation. (We cannot have fewer than one by an even number.) All the concepts discussed in this section are employed in the next two examples.

EXAMPLE 4   Find all rational roots of $2x^4 - 7x^3 - 10x^2 + 33x + 18 = 0$.

Solution   The possible numerators are ± 1, ± 2, ± 3, ± 6, ± 9, ± 18 and possible denominators are 1, 2. Therefore, the possible rational roots are $\pm\frac{1}{2}$, ± 1, $\pm\frac{3}{2}$, ± 2, ± 3, $\pm\frac{9}{2}$, ± 6, ± 9, ± 18. By Descartes' rule of signs we find that there are either two or zero positive real roots and two or zero negative real roots.

From Table 3, we see that $x = 3$ is a root. Now that a root has been found, we seek the remaining roots from the depressed equation

$$2x^3 - x^2 - 13x - 6 = 0$$

First, we observe that since the original polynomial can now be factored as

$$(x - 3)(2x^3 - x^2 - 13x - 6)$$

any root of the depressed equation is also a root of the original; so we know there is no need to try possible rational roots that have already been rejected. However, it is possible that $x = 3$ is a root of multiplicity 2 or greater, and so we test $x = 3$ in the depressed equation. This procedure is general; **when a root has been found, test this same number to see if it is a root of the depressed equation.**

Table 3

r					$P(r)$
0	2	-7	-10	33	18
$\frac{1}{2}$	2	-6	-13		
1	2	-5	-15	18	36
$\frac{3}{2}$	2	-4	-16	9	
2	2	-3	-16	1	20
3	2	-1	-13	-6	0

Table 4

r					$P(r)$
0	2	-7	-10	33	18
$\frac{1}{2}$	2	-6	-13		
1	2	-5	-15	18	36
$\frac{3}{2}$	2	-4	-16	9	
2	2	-3	-16	1	20
3	2	-1	-13	-6	0
3	2	5	2	0	

This is important, because otherwise multiple roots may not show up. Note, too, that the coefficients of the depressed equation are the last ones in Table 3, so we can simply continue the table, writing the remainder one column to the left. The entire table is repeated in Table 4 to illustrate this. And from Table 4, we see that $x = 3$ is a double root. We could continue testing the remaining possibilities in the new depressed equation

$$2x^2 + 5x + 2 = 0$$

but since this is quadratic, we can solve it by other means. In this case, it can be factored as

$$(2x + 1)(x + 2) = 0$$

So, $x = -\frac{1}{2}$ or $x = -1$. The complete solution set is

$$\{3, \quad -\tfrac{1}{2}, \quad -2\}$$

with 3 a root of multiplicity 2.

EXAMPLE 5   Find all rational roots of $x^5 - 8x^3 - 10x^2 + 12x - 20 = 0$.

Solution   The possible rational roots are $\pm 1, \pm 2, \pm 4, \pm 5, \pm 10, \pm 20$. There are either three or one positive real roots and two or zero negative real roots.

Table 5

r						$P(r)$	
0	1	0	−8	−10	12	−20	
1	1	1	−7	−17	−5	−25	**Note**
2	1	2	−4	−18	−24	−68	**sign**
Upper bound → 4	1	4	8	22	100	380	**change**
−1	1	−1	−7	−3	15	−35	
−2	1	−2	−4	−2	16	−52	
Lower bound → −4	1	−4	8	−42	180	−740	

Since we have tried all possible rational roots in Table 5 and none is actually a root, we conclude that there are no rational roots for this equation. We observe the sign change between $P(2)$ and $P(4)$, however, and conclude that $P(x) = 0$ for some value of x between 2 and 4. We find $P(3)$ in order to narrow the bounds on the root:

$$
\begin{array}{r|rrrrr}
3 & 1 & 0 & -8 & -10 & 12 & -20 \\
  &   & 3 & 9 & 3 & -21 & -27 \\
\hline
  & 1 & 3 & 1 & -7 & -9 & -47
\end{array}
$$

So $P(3) = -47$, which shows that the root lies between 3 and 4. In the next section we will see how we can obtain the root to any desired degree of accuracy.

We now summarize the procedure we have discussed for finding the rational roots of a polynomial equation $P_n(x) = 0$ having integral coefficients.

Step 1.   List in order all numbers of the form $\pm p/q$, where p is a factor of the constant term of $P_n(x)$ and q is a factor of the leading coefficient.

Step 2.   Apply Descartes' rule of signs to determine the possible numbers of positive and negative real roots.

Step 3.   By synthetic division or otherwise, begin trying the positive numbers obtained in Step 1. Stop if (a) a root is found, (b) a bound on the roots is found, or (c) the possibilities are exhausted.

Step 4.   If a root is found and the depressed equation is of degree 2, solve for all other roots (rational, irrational, and imaginary) by use of the quadratic formula or by factoring. If the depressed equation is of degree 3 or higher, continue testing in this equation all possibilities not previously rejected, beginning with the successful root just found. Use the same stopping criteria given in Step 3.

Step 5.   When stopping criterion 3(b) or 3(c) is operative, begin testing negative possibilities in the current depressed equation until 3(a), 3(b), or 3(c) occurs.

Step 6.   Repeat Step 4.

This procedure will always yield all rational roots, and in case the depressed equation at any stage is quadratic, all roots can be found. Even when it is not possible to find all roots, by observing changes in sign in the values of $P_n(x)$, we can roughly locate irrational roots.

EXERCISE SET 5

A   In Problems 1 and 2 list all possible rational roots. (Do not test the possibilities.)

1.   **a.** $4x^4 - 8x^3 + 2x^2 - 3x + 3 = 0$ **b.** $6x^5 - 5x^3 + x^2 - 8x - 20 = 0$

2.   **a.** $15x^5 - 17x^3 + 5x^2 - 8x - 12 = 0$ **b.** $8x^4 + 12x^2 - 3x + 30 = 0$

In Problems 3 and 4 find upper and lower bounds for the roots. Indicate roots between consecutive integers when possible.

3. $2x^3 + 3x^2 - 12x - 24 = 0$ 4. $x^4 - 6x^3 - 5x^2 + 2x - 7 = 0$

In Problems 5 and 6 use Descartes' rule of signs to determine the possible numbers of positive and negative real roots.

5.   **a.** $2x^4 - 3x^3 - 2x + 4 = 0$ **b.** $3x^5 - 2x^3 + 4x^2 + 2x + 1 = 0$

6.   **a.** $3x^5 + 2x^4 - 7x^3 - 5x^2 + x - 8 = 0$ **b.** $x^4 + 2x^3 - 3x^2 + 5 = 0$

In Problems 7–19 find all rational roots. When the depressed equation is quadratic, find all roots.

7. $x^3 - 3x - 2 = 0$
8. $x^3 - x^2 - 8x + 12 = 0$
9. $x^3 - 2x^2 - 6x - 8 = 0$
10. $2x^3 - 7x^2 + 9 = 0$
11. $4x^3 - 5x^2 + 10x + 12 = 0$
12. $3x^3 - 4x^2 - 17x + 6 = 0$
13. $2x^3 + 3x^2 - 14x - 15 = 0$
14. $8x^3 + 14x^2 - 33x - 9 = 0$
15. $x^4 - x^2 + 2x + 2 = 0$
16. $x^3 - 19x - 30 = 0$
17. $x^4 - 5x^3 + 20x - 16 = 0$
18. $x^4 - 2x^3 - 4x^2 - 8x - 32 = 0$
19. $x^4 - 6x^2 - 8x - 3 = 0$

In Problems 20–27 factor completely over the reals.

20. $3x^3 - x^2 - 8x - 4$
21. $x^3 - 13x + 12$
22. $6x^3 - x^2 - 27x - 20$
23. $x^4 - 2x^3 + x^2 - 8x - 12$
24. $5x^4 - 2x^3 - 35x^2 - 16x + 12$
25. $x^4 - 5x^2 - 10x - 6$
26. $x^4 + 2x^3 - 5x^2 - 18x - 36$
27. $4x^4 - 19x^2 + 3x + 18$

B In Problems 28–30 find all roots.

28. $6x^3 + 5x^2 - 34x - 40 = 0$
29. $3x^3 + 22x^2 + 32x - 32 = 0$
30. $4x^5 - 18x^4 + 21x^3 - 14x^2 + 60x - 72 = 0$

31. Show that the equation $2x^4 + 13x^3 - 40x - 24 = 0$ has only one rational root. How many real roots does it have? Justify your answer.

6   Irrational Roots

The following example illustrates a technique for approximating irrational roots to any desired degree of accuracy. There are other methods requiring calculus which are more efficient in that they provide the same accuracy in fewer steps, but the method we present has the advantage of being straightforward and easily remembered. It is a definite advantage to use a calculator.

EXAMPLE 6   Approximate the real solution of the equation $x^3 - 3x^2 + 3x - 4 = 0$ to two decimal places of accuracy.

Solution   A quick check will show that there are no rational roots. By synthetic division we locate the root between consecutive integers (Table 6). If we denote the polynomial by $f(x)$, we see that $f(2) = -2$ and $f(3) = 5$, so there is a root between 2 and 3. Since 3 is an upper bound and 0 is a lower bound, there are no other real roots. On the interval $[2, 3]$ we approximate the graph of $y = f(x)$ by the line joining the two points $(2, -2)$ and $(3, 5)$, as shown in Figure 1. The

Table 6

Lower bound → 0	1	−3	3	−4
1	1	−2	1	−3
2	1	−1	1	−2 ⎫
Upper bound → 3	1	0	3	5 ⎭ Note sign change

Figure 1

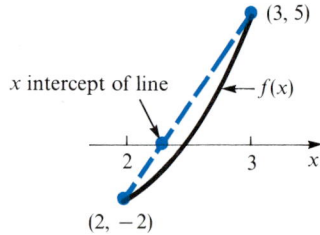

x intercept of this line is then an approximation of the zero of $f(x)$. This process is called **linear interpolation.** The slope of this line is 7, and its equation is

$$y + 2 = 7(x - 2)$$

or

$$y = 7x - 16$$

Setting $y = 0$, we find the *x* intercept to be $2\frac{2}{7}$, or approximately 2.3. So we try this as our next approximation to the root. We want to locate the root between consecutive tenths. Note from Table 7 that the approximation 2.3 found by linear interpolation was not quite as good an approximation as we might have hoped, since the actual root turns out to be between 2.4 and 2.5. This sometimes happens, but linear interpolation nevertheless provides a good starting point.

Now we use linear interpolation again. The line joining $(2.4, -0.26)$ and $(2.5, 0.38)$ has *x* intercept 2.44 (check this), which is our next approximation (Table 8). Then, in order to obtain two-place accuracy, we need to carry the process one more step and then round off. By linear interpolation we find the next approximation to be 2.442 (Table 9). The root is therefore between 2.442 and 2.443, so the answer correct to two decimal places is 2.44.

Table 7

	1	-3	3	-4	
2.3	1	-0.7	1.39	-0.80	
2.4	1	-0.6	1.56	-0.26	**Note sign change**
2.5	1	-0.5	1.75	0.38	

Table 8

	1	-3	3	-4
2.44	1	-0.56	1.634	-0.0140
2.45	1	-0.55	1.652	0.0486

Table 9

	1	-3	3	-4
2.442	1	-0.558	1.6374	-0.00156
2.443	1	-0.557	1.6392	0.00469

We can summarize this procedure as follows. Suppose we have found that a root of $f(x) = 0$ lies between x_1 and x_2 (which may be consecutive integers, consecutive tenths, hundredths, etc.). The line joining $(x_1, f(x_1))$ and $(x_2, f(x_2))$

has the equation

$$y - f(x_1) = m(x - x_1)$$

where

$$m = \frac{f(x_2) - f(x_1)}{x_2 - x_1}$$

This line is used to approximate the actual graph of $y = f(x)$ on the interval $[x_1, x_2]$, and its x intercept provides an approximation to the root. This intercept is found by setting $y = 0$ in the equation of the line, which gives

$$x = x_1 - \frac{f(x_1)}{m} \tag{5}$$

The root is then approximated to any desired degree of accuracy by repeated application of the following two steps:

Step 1. If $f(x_1)$ and $f(x_2)$ are opposite in sign, where x_1 and x_2 are consecutive n-place decimals $(n = 0, 1, 2, \ldots)$, find x by equation (5) and round off to $n + 1$ decimal places.

Step 2. Test the value of x found in Step 1 and move forward or backward, as required, by consecutive $(n + 1)$-place decimals to locate new values of x_1 and x_2 for which $f(x_1)$ and $f(x_2)$ are opposite in sign.

The process is stopped when the root is located between consecutive decimals having *one more decimal place of accuracy than is desired*. The answer is found by rounding back one place.

EXAMPLE 7   Find the real root of $x^3 - x^2 - 2x + 3 = 0$ correct to two decimal places.

Solution   From Table 10, the root is between -1.546 and -1.547, so the answer is -1.55, correct to two decimal places.

Table 10

	0	1	-1	-2	3	
	1	1	0	-2	1	
Upper bound →	2	1	1	0	3	
	-1	1	-2	0	3	$\left. \right\} m = 8, \quad x = -2 - \frac{-5}{8} = -1.4$
	-2	1	-3	4	-5	
	-1.4				1.096	
	-1.5				0.375	$\left. \right\} m = 8.31, \quad x = -1.6 - \frac{0.456}{8.31} = -1.54$
	-1.6				-0.456	
	-1.54				0.0561	$\left. \right\} m = 8.25, \quad x = -1.55 - \frac{-0.0264}{8.25} = -1.547$
	-1.55				-0.0264	
	-1.547				-0.001503	
	-1.546				0.00676	

In this example we made use of a calculator beginning with the entry -1.4, and so we did not show the intermediate steps of the synthetic division. For example, in Table 10 the function value for $x = -1.4$ can be obtained using the following sequence of calculator keystrokes:

1.4 [+/−] [STO] [−] [1] [=] [×] [RCL] [−] [2] [=]

[×] [RCL] [+] [3] [=] 1.096

Remark. In solving an equation it is best to look for rational roots first. If any are found, go to the depressed equation. Only if there are no rational roots or if the depressed equation is of degree 3 or greater should the method of this section be used.

EXERCISE SET 6

A   In Problems 1–5 find the specified irrational root correct to two decimal places.

1. The real root of $x^3 - x^2 + 2x - 3 = 0$
2. The real root of $x^3 + 2x^2 + 3x - 10 = 0$
3. The real root of $x^3 - x + 4 = 0$
4. The negative root of $2x^3 - x^2 - 12x + 10 = 0$
5. The largest positive root of $2x^4 + x^3 - 13x^2 - 4x + 12 = 0$

In Problems 6–15 find all rational and irrational roots, expressing irrational roots correct to two decimal places.

6. $x^4 + x^3 - 2x^2 - 7x - 5 = 0$ 7. $x^4 - 4x^3 + 4x^2 + 8x - 16 = 0$
8. $2x^4 - 3x^3 - 3x^2 + 8x - 3 = 0$ 9. $x^4 + x^3 - 7x^2 - 4x - 3 = 0$
10. $2x^4 + x^3 - 12x^2 + 27x - 27 = 0$

B   11. $x^3 + x^2 - 7x - 5 = 0$ 12. $x^3 - 2.34x^2 - 5.16x - 4.87 = 0$
13. $x^4 - 2x^2 + 5x - 8 = 0$
14. $x^5 - 6x^4 + 7x^3 + 11x^2 - 16x - 4 = 0$
15. $2x^5 - 8x^4 - 11x^3 + 21x + 20 = 0$

7 Graphing Polynomial Functions

We can use the method of Section 5 to make a table of values to be used in graphing a polynomial function, $y = P(x)$. The zeros of the polynomial are particularly helpful, and if these are rational, we know how to find them. Real zeros that are irrational can at least be located between consecutive integers.

As we indicated earlier, the graph of a polynomial function is a smooth curve, with no breaks. The graph of a second-degree polynomial is a parabola, as we know. The graph of a third-degree polynomial typically has both a maximum point and a minimum point and looks like one of the curves shown in Figure 2. However, the "humps" may be straightened out, as in Figure 3.

Figure 2

Figure 3 N^3

Figure 4 N^4

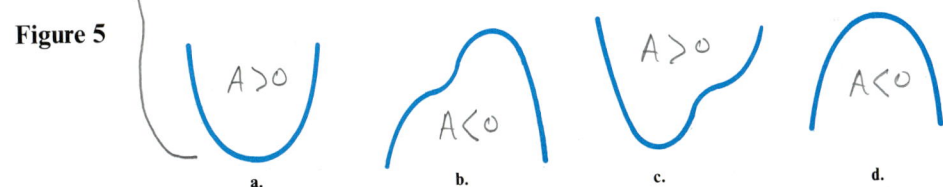

Figure 5

Fourth-degree polynomials usually add one more maximum or minimum point, as shown in Figure 4. But again, some of the humps may not be present. The shape could be any of those shown in Figure 5.

This pattern continues. The number of maximum points and minimum points is at most 1 less than the degree of the polynomial.

The sign of the coefficient of the highest power of x tells us the sign of the function when x is very large in absolute value. For example, in

$$y = 2x^3 - 15x^2 - 30x - 100$$

when x is very large, y will be positive, because the term $2x^3$ will dominate all other terms. Similarly, for x negative but large in absolute value, y will be negative. Thus, the general shape of the graph will be that of Figure 2a. By locating the real zeros and a few more points we can draw the graph with reasonable accuracy.

EXAMPLE 8   Graph the function $y = 2x^3 - 5x^2 - 8x + 11$.

Solution   This is the function we used as an illustration in Section 5. We can summarize the function values found in Table 2 as follows:

x	0	1	2	3	4	5	-1	-2	-3
y	11	0	-9	-4	27	96	12	-9	-64

Furthermore, we know that $x = 1$ is a zero of the polynomial, and that the other two zeros are between 3 and 4, and -1 and -2, respectively. In fact, we found these other two zeros to be approximately 3.21 and -1.71. The graph is shown in Figure 6. The exact location of the maximum and minimum points can be determined by the use of procedures studied in calculus.

Figure 6

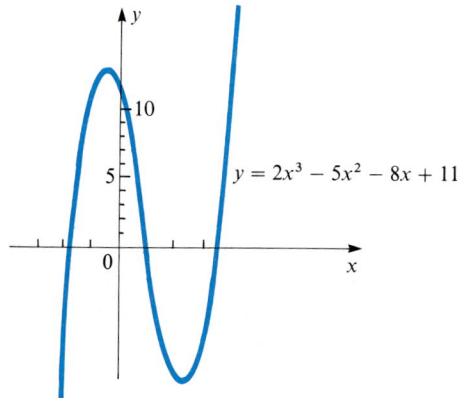

$y = 2x^3 - 5x^2 - 8x + 11$

EXAMPLE 9   Graph the function $y = x^4 - x^3 - 5x^2 + 12$.

Solution   We set up Table 11 using synthetic division. We find that 2 is a zero of the function, and we can write y in the factored form

$$y = (x - 2)(x^3 + x^2 - 3x - 6)$$

Table 11

	x					y
	0	1	-1	-5	0	12
	1	1	0	-5	-5	7
	2	1	1	-3	-6	0
Upper bound →	3	1	2	1	3	21
	-1	1	-2	-3	3	9
Lower bound →	-2	1	-3	1	-2	16

We test to see if 2 is also a zero of the second factor.

$$\begin{array}{r|rrrr} 2 & 1 & 1 & -3 & -6 \\ & & 2 & 6 & 6 \\ \hline & 1 & 3 & 3 & 0 \end{array}$$

This shows that 2 is a zero of the second factor and hence is a zero of multiplicity 2 of the original function. We can now factor y further as

$$y = (x - 2)^2(x^2 + 3x + 3)$$

Since the discriminant $b^2 - 4ac$ of the factor $x^2 + 3x + 3$ is $9 - 12 = -3$, it follows that there are no other real zeros.

The graph is shown in Figure 7. The significance of the fact that 2 is a zero of multiplicity 2 is that the curve is *tangent to the x axis* at $x = 2$.

Figure 7

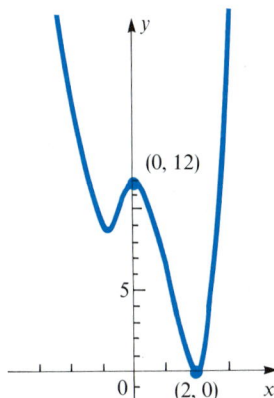

$(0, 12)$

0 $(2, 0)$ x

In Example 9 we indicated that the significance of the factor $(x - 2)^2$ occurring in the factored form of the polynomial was that the graph was tangent to the x axis at $x = 2$. **More generally, if a factor of the form $(x - r)^k$ occurs in the factored form of a polynomial, where $k \geq 2$, then the graph will be tangent to the x axis at $x = r$.** If k is even, then in the vicinity of $x = r$, the graph will have an appearance similar to one of the forms shown in Figure 8. If k is odd, the curve will look generally like one of the forms shown in Figure 9. The larger the exponent k is, the flatter the curve will be near the point of tangency.

Figure 8

a.   b.

Figure 9

a.   b.

EXAMPLE 10   Graph the function $y = 4 + 3x^2 - x^4$.

Solution   The polynomial can be factored as

$$y = (4 - x^2)(1 + x^2) = (2 - x)(2 + x)(1 + x^2)$$

So the only real zeros are ± 2. Since the variable x in the polynomial appears only to even powers, it follows that substituting a given value for x or its negative will produce the same value of y. Since the function is a simple one,

Figure 10

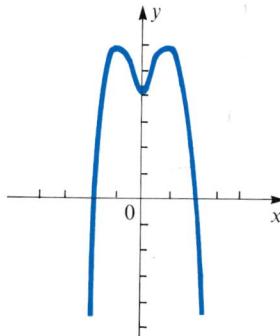

we will use direct substitution to make a table of values:

x	0	± 1	± 2	± 3
y	4	6	0	-50

EXERCISE SET 7

A In Problems 1–21 find the rational zeros, locate other real zeros between consecutive integers, make a table of values, and graph the function.

1. $y = x^3 - 1$
2. $y = x^3 - x^2 - 6x$
3. $y = x^3 - x^2 - 9x + 9$
4. $y = 1 - x^4$
5. $y = 4x - x^3$
6. $y = (x - 4)(x + 1)(x + 3)$
7. $y = (2x - 5)(x - 6)(x + 2)$
8. $y = (x - 1)(2x + 3)(x - 3)^2$
9. $y = (x + 1)^2(2x - 1)(x - 4)$
10. $y = \frac{1}{4}(x + 2)^3(x - 1)^2$
11. $y = x^3 - 3x + 2$
12. $y = 2x^3 - 7x^2 + 9$
13. $y = x^3 + x^2 - 10x - 12$
14. $y = x^4 - 10x^2 + 9$
15. $y = 8x^2 + 2x^3 - x^4$
16. $y = 12 - 3x + 4x^2 - x^3$
17. $y = x^4 + x^3 - 13x^2 - x + 12$
18. $y = 2x^4 - 5x^3 + 10x - 12$
19. $y = 2x^4 - 5x^3 + 10x - 12$
20. $y = x^5 - 4x^3$
21. $y = x^4 + 2x^3 - 12x^2 - 8x + 32$

In Problems 22–27 solve the inequalities by graphical means.

22. $(x - 3)(2x + 5)(x - 7)^3 \leq 0$
23. $(x + 4)^2(3x - 4)(x - 5)(x + 6) > 0$
24. $x^3 - 3x^2 - x + 3 < 0$
25. $x^3 - 5x^2 + 2x + 8 \geq 0$
26. $x^3 - 2x^2 - 5x + 6 \leq 0$
27. $x^4 - 9x^2 - 4x + 12 > 0$

Find the domain of each of the functions in Problems 28 and 29.

28. $f(x) = \sqrt{2x^3 - 9x^2 + x + 12}$

29. $g(x) = \dfrac{1}{\sqrt{x^4 - 9x^2 + 4x + 12}}$

B In Problems 30 and 31 solve the inequalities by graphical means.

30. $2x^4 - 7x^3 - 26x^2 + 49x + 30 < 0$

31. $x(x^3 - 4x^2 + 3) \geq 14(1 + x)$

Graph the functions in Problems 32–36.

32. $y = x^4 - 3x^3 - 8x^2 + 10x + 12$

33. $y = x^4 - 2x^3 - 5x^2 + 6x$

34. $y = 3x^4 - 5x^3 - 8x^2 + 10x + 7$

35. $y = x^5 - x^4 - 15x^3 + x^2 + 38x + 24$

36. $y = 2x^5 - 5x^4 - 11x^3 + 23x^2 + 8x - 15$

8 Rational Functions

A function of the form

$$f(x) = \frac{P(x)}{Q(x)}$$

where $P(x)$ and $Q(x)$ are polynomials, is called a **rational function.** We will assume that $P(x)$ and $Q(x)$ have no nonconstant factor in common. The zeros of $f(x)$ are the same as those of $P(x)$, since if the numerator of a fraction is 0 and the denominator not 0, the fraction is 0. These zeros are the x intercepts of the graph of f. The y intercept, if any, is found by putting $x = 0$.

The zeros of $Q(x)$ are not in the domain of f, but the behavior of $f(x)$ for x near these zeros is particularly useful in drawing the graph of f. The next example illustrates how to analyze this behavior.

EXAMPLE 11 Examine the nature of the function below near $x = 2$:

$$f(x) = \frac{x + 1}{x - 2}$$

Solution We set $y = f(x)$ and make a table of values for x close to 2.

x	1	1.5	1.9	1.99	3	2.5	2.1	2.01
y	-2	-5	-29	-299	4	7	31	301

As x approaches 2 from the left, y is negative but becomes arbitrarily large in absolute value. Similarly, when x approaches 2 from the right, y becomes arbitrarily large through positive values. The graph in the neighborhood of

$x = 2$ is shown in Figure 11. The line $x = 2$ is called an **asymptote** to the curve, and the curve is said to be **asymptotic to this line.**

Figure 11

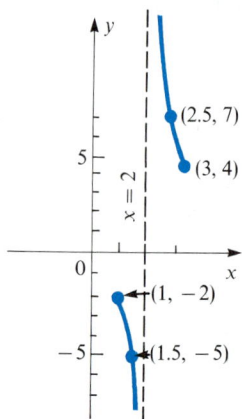

This example illustrates the general result that **if r is a zero of $Q(x)$, then the line $x = r$ is a vertical asymptote to the graph of f.**

Rational functions may also have horizontal asymptotes, and these can be determined by examing the behavior of $f(x)$ when x becomes arbitrarily large in absolute value. The next example illustrates a way of doing this.

EXAMPLE 12   Examine the behavior of the function

$$f(x) = \frac{2x^2 + x}{x^2 - 4}$$

as x becomes arbitrarily large in absolute value.

Solution   Let $y = f(x)$ and divide numerator and denominator by the highest power of x—in this case, x^2:

$$y = \frac{2x^2 + x}{x^2 - 4} = \frac{2 + (1/x)}{1 - (4/x^2)} \qquad (x \neq 0)$$

Now as x gets arbitrarily large in absolute value, the terms $1/x$ and $4/x^2$ both approach 0. So y approaches $\frac{2}{1} = 2$. For large values of $|x|$, the graph has the appearance shown in Figure 12. The line $y = 2$ is a horizontal asymptote.

Figure 12

More generally, to find horizontal asymptotes, we divide numerator and denominator by the highest power of x that appears in either place and then see if y approaches some finite constant b as x becomes arbitrarily large in absolute value. If so, then the line $y = b$ is a horizontal asymptote.

Remark. A rational function may have many vertical asymptotes (one for each zero of the denominator), but it can have at most one horizontal asymptote.

In the next example we make use of both intercepts and asymptotes to draw the graph.

EXAMPLE 13   Find the intercepts and asymptotes, and draw the graph of

$$y = \frac{2x - 3}{x^2 - 9}$$

Solution   The x intercept is $\frac{3}{2}$ and the y intercept is $\frac{1}{3}$. By factoring the denominator $x^2 - 9 = (x + 3)(x - 3)$, we see that the vertical asymptotes are $x = 3$ and $x = -3$. To determine whether a horizontal asymptote exists, we write

$$y = \frac{2x - 3}{x^2 - 9} = \frac{(2/x) - (3/x^2)}{1 - (9/x^2)} \qquad (x \neq 0)$$

As x increases without limit in absolute value, y approaches $\frac{0}{1} = 0$. So $y = 0$ is a horizontal asymptote. We now need only a few additional points:

x	1	2	4	-1	-2	-4
y	$\frac{1}{8}$	$-\frac{1}{5}$	$\frac{5}{7}$	$\frac{5}{8}$	$\frac{7}{5}$	$\frac{-11}{7}$

Figure 13

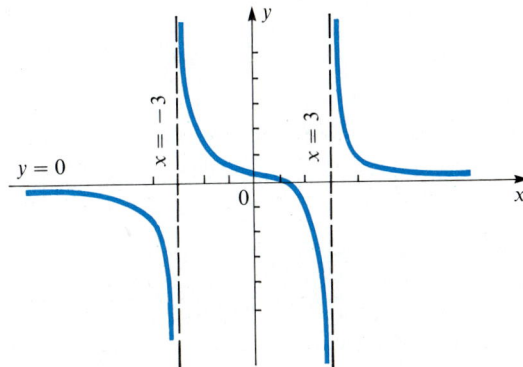

EXERCISE SET 8

A   In Problems 1–6 find all vertical asymptotes.

1. **a.** $y = \dfrac{x + 3}{x - 4}$ **b.** $y = \dfrac{1}{x^2 - 1}$

2. **a.** $f(x) = \dfrac{x + 2}{x^2 - 3x - 4}$ **b.** $g(x) = \dfrac{2x^2 - 1}{x^2 - 4x + 4}$

3. **a.** $y = \dfrac{x^3 + 4x - 1}{2x^2 - 3x - 5}$ **b.** $y = \dfrac{3x^2 + 4x + 6}{x^2 - 5x}$

4. **a.** $g(x) = \dfrac{x^2 + 1}{x^3 - 8}$ **b.** $h(x) = \dfrac{2x + 3}{x^3 - x^2 - x + 1}$

5. **a.** $y = \dfrac{x^2 + 3x - 7}{x^3 - 4x^2 - 9x + 36}$ **b.** $y = \dfrac{1}{x^4 + x}$

6. **a.** $y = \dfrac{2x - 1}{x^3 - 3x - 2}$ **b.** $y = \dfrac{1 - x}{x^3 - 7x - 6}$

In Problems 7–12 find the horizontal asymptote or show that there is none.

7. **a.** $y = \dfrac{x + 1}{x - 2}$ **b.** $y = \dfrac{x - 3}{2x + 1}$

8. **a.** $f(x) = \dfrac{2x}{1 - x^2}$ **b.** $g(x) = \dfrac{x^2 - 1}{x^2 - 4}$

9. **a.** $y = \dfrac{2 - x^2}{x^2 + 2x + 1}$ **b.** $y = \dfrac{x^2 - 1}{x + 3}$

10. **a.** $y = \dfrac{2x^2 + 4}{x^3 + 1}$ **b.** $y = \dfrac{2x^2 + 5}{1 - x - 3x^2}$

11. **a.** $F(x) = \dfrac{x^2 + 4x - 5}{2x + 3}$ **b.** $G(x) = \dfrac{x^2}{x^3 - 1}$

12. **a.** $y = \dfrac{2x - x^2}{3x^2 + 4}$ **b.** $y = \dfrac{1 - x^3}{1 + x^3}$

In Problems 13–20 find intercepts, vertical and horizontal asymptotes, and draw the graph.

13. $f(x) = \dfrac{2x + 3}{x - 1}$ 14. $g(x) = \dfrac{2}{x + 2}$

15. $y = \dfrac{x - 1}{x^2 - 9}$ 16. $y = \dfrac{2x}{x^2 + 1}$

17. $y = \dfrac{x - 2}{x^2 - 2x - 3}$ 18. $y = \dfrac{x^2 - 1}{x^2 - 4}$

19. $y = \dfrac{x^2 - 2x - 8}{x^2 - 2x}$ 20. $y = \dfrac{x^2 - 3x}{x^2 - 4}$

B   In Problems 21–23 find all vertical and horizontal asymptotes.

21. $y = \dfrac{1 - x - 2x^3}{x^3 - 3x^2 - 6x + 8}$ 22. $y = \dfrac{3x^3 + 4x - 7}{x^4 - 11x^2 + 18x - 8}$

23. $y = \dfrac{x^5 + 2}{x^4 - 4x^3 + 3x^2 + 4x - 4}$

In Problems 24–27 find intercepts, horizontal and vertical asymptotes, and draw the graph.

24. $y = \dfrac{x - 2}{x^2 + 4x}$

25. $f(x) = \dfrac{3 - 2x - x^2}{x^2 - x - 6}$

26. $y = \dfrac{2x + 5}{x^2 - 1}$

27. $y = \dfrac{x^2 - 1}{x + 2}$

28. Let $f(x) = P(x)/Q(x)$. If the degree of $P(x)$ is m and the degree of $Q(x)$ is n, prove that:
   a. If $m < n$, then $y = 0$ is a horizontal asymptote
   b. If $m = n$, there is a horizontal asymptote $y = b$, with $b \neq 0$. What can you conclude about the value of b?
   c. If $m > n$, there is no horizontal asymptote.

9 Partial Fractions

There are times, especially in calculus, when it is important to write a complicated rational fraction as a sum of simpler fractions. That is, we sometimes want to do just the opposite of adding fractions together. When we do this, we say that we have *resolved* (or *decomposed*) the original fraction into partial fractions. Consider the following example of adding two fractions:

$$\frac{2}{x - 1} + \frac{3}{x + 2} = \frac{2(x + 2) + 3(x - 1)}{(x - 1)(x + 2)} = \frac{5x + 1}{x^2 + x - 2}$$

Now suppose we are given the final fraction only and are asked to find the two original fractions that add to give this result. Of course we know the answer in this case, but you might try covering up those original fractions and see if you can find a way of discovering what they should be.

A systematic way of doing this problem is as follows. Write

$$\frac{5x + 1}{x^2 + x - 2} = \frac{5x + 1}{(x - 1)(x + 2)} = \frac{A}{x - 1} + \frac{B}{x + 2} \bigg] \text{LCD} \qquad (6)$$

where A and B are to be determined. Notice that we first factor the denominator and then indicate the sum of two fractions, each having one of these factors as its denominator, and with an unknown constant on the numerator. To find A and B we multiply both sides of the last equation in (6) by the LCD to obtain

$$5x + 1 = A(x + 2) + B(x - 1)$$

We want to determine A and B so that this equation is an identity in x. By substituting, in turn, the particular values $x = 1$ and $x = -2$, we get

$x = 1$: $\quad 6 = A \cdot 3 + B \cdot 0$

$\qquad\qquad 6 = 3A$

$\qquad\qquad A = 2$

$x = -2$: $\quad -9 = A \cdot 0 + B(-3)$

$\qquad\qquad -9 = -3B$

$\qquad\qquad B = 3$

Thus we have the partial-fraction decomposition

$$\frac{5x + 1}{x^2 + x - 2} = \frac{2}{x - 1} + \frac{3}{x + 2}$$

This example illustrates the basic idea of partial fractions, but certain complications can arise. First, the method will work only if the original fraction is *proper*, which means that the degree of the numerator must be less than the degree of the denominator. If this is not the case, then divide until you obtain a remainder with lower degree than the denominator. Suppose, for example, that $P_m(x)$ and $P_n(x)$ are polynomials of degree m and degree n, respectively, and that $m \geq n$. Then by long division we obtain a quotient $Q(x)$ and a remainder $R(x)$ such that

$$\frac{P_m(x)}{P_n(x)} = Q(x) + \frac{R(x)}{P_n(x)}$$

where either $R(x) = 0$ or deg $R < n$. Then we resolve $R(x)/P_n(x)$ into partial fractions. We will illustrate this procedure in Example 15.

The second complication is that the factors of the denominator may not be so simple as in our example. We know that (in theory, at least) every real polynomial can be factored into linear or quadratic factors over the reals, where one or more factors may have multiplicity greater than 1 (in which case we say the factors are *repeated*). It is useful to classify partial-fraction problems by the nature of the factors of the denominator:

Case I: All linear factors, none repeated
Case II: All linear factors, one or more repeated
Case III: At least one irreducible quadratic factor, not repeated
Case IV: At least one repeated irreducible quadratic factor

Note.   In cases III and IV linear factors, repeated or not, may be present.

Our example was a case I problem, and the technique we used for determining the unknown constants A and B is called the **method of substitution.** This method works on all case I problems. In the other three cases the method of substitution will not suffice to find all unknown constants, but it is still useful whenever linear factors are present. A second method, called **comparison of coefficients,** can then be used to find the remaining constants. We will see how this method works in the next example.

**EXAMPLE 14
(CASE II)**

Resolve

$$\frac{x^2 - 13x + 20}{(x - 1)(x - 3)^2}$$

into partial fractions.

Solution   First note that the fraction is proper. The appropriate form of the partial-fraction decomposition is

$$\frac{x^2 - 13x + 20}{(x - 1)(x - 3)^2} = \frac{A}{x - 1} + \frac{B}{x - 3} + \frac{C}{(x - 3)^2} \qquad (7)$$

Notice in particular the second term on the right. We must allow for its presence, since a fraction of this type could be involved when the common denominator is $(x - 1)(x - 3)^2$. More generally, when a linear factor of multiplicity m is present, say $(x - a)^m$, we must include fractions with denominators of the form $(x - a)^k$ for *all* positive integers $k \leq m$.

We now clear equation (7) of fractions, obtaining

$$x^2 - 13x + 20 = A(x - 3)^2 + B(x - 1)(x - 3) + C(x - 1) \qquad (8)$$

We use the method of substitution, first putting $x = 1$ and then $x = 3$:

$$x = 1: \quad 8 = A(-2)^2 \qquad\qquad x = 3: \quad -10 = 2C$$
$$4A = 8 \qquad\qquad\qquad\qquad C = -5$$
$$A = 2$$

This is as far as we can go substituting numbers that cause one or the other of the factors on the right to be zero. So we turn to the comparison of coefficients. We expand the right-hand side of equation (8) and collect like terms, obtaining

$$x^2 - 13x + 20 = (A + B)x^2 + (-6A - 4B + C)x + (9A + 3B - C)$$

Since this is to be an identity, the coefficient of each power of x on the left-hand side must be equal to the coefficient of the corresponding power of x on the right. Comparing coefficients of x^2 gives

$$1 = A + B$$

and since $A = 2$, we conclude that $B = -1$. Although we could compare the other coefficients, there is no need to do so, since we now know A, B, and C. The partial-fraction decomposition is therefore

$$\frac{x^2 - 13x + 20}{(x - 1)(x - 3)^2} = \frac{2}{x - 1} - \frac{1}{x - 3} - \frac{5}{(x - 3)^2}$$

Remarks. The method of comparison of coefficients can be used without first using the method of substitution, and it will always work. However, it is usually easier to get as much information as possible by using substitution and then turning to the comparison of coefficients.

In comparing coefficients it is not always necessary to expand the right-hand side and collect like terms, since this can sometimes be done mentally, especially for the highest power. For example, we can look at the right-hand side of equation (8) and determine that the coefficient of x^2 is $A + B$.

**EXAMPLE 15
(CASE III)**

Resolve

$$\frac{x^3 + 7x - 2}{x^3 - 2x - 4}$$

into partial fractions.

Solution   The fraction is improper, so we divide and get

$$\frac{x^3 + 7x - 2}{x^3 - 2x - 4} = 1 + \frac{9x + 2}{x^3 - 2x - 4} \qquad \text{(Check this)}$$

and we concentrate on the last term. Using the methods of this chapter we factor the denominator in the form $(x - 2)(x^2 + 2x + 2)$. The factor $x^2 + 2x + 2$ is irreducible over the reals since its discriminant $b^2 - 4ac$ is negative. The proper form of the partial-fraction decomposition in this case is

$$\frac{9x + 2}{(x - 2)(x^2 + 2x + 2)} = \frac{A}{x - 2} + \frac{Bx + C}{x^2 + 2x + 2} \qquad (9)$$

This form is typical of case III problems. When the denominator is an irreducible quadratic polynomial, we must allow for an unknown linear polynomial in the numerator.

Now we clear equation (9) of fractions and then substitute $x = 2$:

$$9x + 2 = A(x^2 + 2x + 2) + (Bx + C)(x - 2) \qquad (10)$$

$$x = 2: \quad 20 = A(10)$$

$$A = 2$$

Next we expand the right-hand side of equation (10), collect like terms, and compare coefficients:

$$9x + 2 = (A + B)x^2 + (2A - 2B + C)x + (2A - 2C)$$

Coefficient of x^2: $0 = A + B$

$B = -A = -2$

(Observe that since x^2 does not appear on the left, its coefficient is zero.)

Coefficient of x: $9 = 2A - 2B + C$

$9 = 4 + 4 + C$

$C = 1$

The final answer is

$$\frac{x^3 + 7x - 2}{x^3 - 2x - 4} = 1 + \frac{2}{x - 2} + \frac{-2x + 1}{x^2 + 2x + 2}$$

$$= 1 + \frac{2}{x - 2} - \frac{2x - 1}{x^2 + 2x + 2} \qquad \text{(Note how the signs are handled.)}$$

**EXAMPLE 16
(CASE IV)**   Resolve

$$\frac{2x - 3}{x^5 + 2x^3 + x}$$

into partial fractions.

Solution   The denominator in factored form is $x(x^2 + 1)^2$, and just as with repeated linear factors we must allow for fractions with $x^2 + 1$ as well as $(x^2 + 1)^2$ in the denominator. The proper form is therefore

$$\frac{2x - 3}{x(x^2 + 1)^2} = \frac{A}{x} + \frac{Bx + C}{x^2 + 1} + \frac{Dx + E}{(x^2 + 1)^2}$$

We clear of fractions and substitute $x = 0$:

$$2x - 3 = A(x^2 + 1)^2 + (Bx + C)x(x^2 + 1) + (Dx + E)x$$

$$x = 0: \quad -3 = A$$

To compare coefficients we expand and collect terms on the right:

$$2x - 3 = (A + B)x^4 + Cx^3 + (2A + B + D)x^2 + (C + E)x + A$$

Coefficient of x^4: $\quad 0 = A + B$

$$B = -A = 3$$

Coefficient of x^3: $\quad 0 = C$

Coefficient of x^2: $\quad 0 = 2A + B + D$

$$0 = -6 + 3 + D$$

$$D = 3$$

Coefficient of x: $\quad 2 = C + E$

$$2 = 0 + E$$

$$E = 2$$

Thus

$$\frac{2x - 3}{x^5 + 2x^3 + x} = \frac{-3}{x} + \frac{3x}{x^2 + 1} + \frac{3x + 2}{(x^2 + 1)^2}$$

EXERCISE SET 9

A   Resolve each of the following into partial fractions.

1. $\dfrac{5x + 7}{x^2 + 2x - 3}$

2. $\dfrac{6x - 7}{x^2 + x - 6}$

3. $\dfrac{x - 17}{x^2 + x - 12}$

4. $\dfrac{19 - x}{x^2 - 3x - 10}$

5. $\dfrac{3x + 10}{x^2 + 5x + 6}$

6. $\dfrac{x - 4}{x^2 - 3x + 2}$

7. $\dfrac{-2}{x^2 - 9x + 20}$

8. $\dfrac{3}{x^2 - 7x + 12}$

9. $\dfrac{3x^2 + 32x + 44}{(x + 3)(x - 2)(x + 4)}$

10. $\dfrac{2x^2 + 19x - 45}{(x - 1)(x - 3)(x + 2)}$

11. $\dfrac{3x^2 - 7x - 2}{x^3 - x}$

12. $\dfrac{10x + 4}{4x - x^3}$

13. $\dfrac{x^2 + 4x - 2}{x^2 + x - 2}$

14. $\dfrac{2x^2 - x - 20}{x^2 - x - 6}$

15. $\dfrac{x^3 + x^2 - 10x - 14}{x^2 + 4x + 3}$

16. $\dfrac{2x^3 - x^2 - 4x + 5}{x^2 - 1}$

17. $\dfrac{5x + 1}{(x + 2)(x - 1)^2}$

18. $\dfrac{x^2 - 6x + 23}{(x + 3)(x - 2)^2}$

19. $\dfrac{4x^2 - 10x + 9}{(x - 1)^3}$

20. $\dfrac{x^2 + x}{(x + 2)^3}$

21. $\dfrac{4 + 4x - x^2}{x^3 + 2x^2}$

22. $\dfrac{2x^2 - 6x + 12}{x^3 - 4x^2 + 4x}$

23. $\dfrac{5x + 6}{(x - 2)(x^2 + 4)}$

24. $\dfrac{x^2 + x - 7}{(x^2 + 1)(x + 2)}$

25. $\dfrac{3 + 4x - 3x^2}{(x + 1)^2(x^2 + 3)}$

26. $\dfrac{x^3 - 4x^2 + 5x - 2}{x^4 - x^3 + x^2}$

27. $\dfrac{6 - 12x}{x^3 - 2x^2 - 5x + 6}$

28. $\dfrac{2x^2 + 17x + 5}{x^3 - 13x - 12}$

29. $\dfrac{x^2 + 3x + 6}{x^3 + x - 2}$

30. $\dfrac{6x - 3}{x^3 - 3x - 2}$

B   **31.** $\dfrac{ad - bc}{(ax + b)(cx + d)}$

32. $\dfrac{2rs(x + 1)}{r^2x^2 - s^2}$

33. $\dfrac{6x^2 + 20x + 28}{x^3 + 3x^2 - 4}$

34. $\dfrac{3x^4 - 3x^3 + 5x^2 - 6x + 13}{(x + 3)(x^2 + 1)^2}$

35. $\dfrac{11x^3 - 41x^2 + 72x - 32}{x(x^2 - 3x + 4)^2}$

36. $\dfrac{12x^2 + 2x - 41}{6x^2 + x - 12}$

37. $\dfrac{10x^3 - 9x^2 + 7x + 14}{10x^2 + x - 3}$

38. $\dfrac{5x^2 - 6x + 58}{6(x^3 + 4x^2 + 2x + 8)}$

39. $\dfrac{3x^2 - 4}{x^4 - 4x^3 + 8x^2 - 16x + 16}$

40. $\dfrac{3x - 5}{12x^3 - 4x^2 - 5x + 2}$

41. $\dfrac{x^3 - 3x^2 - 5x}{(x^2 + 1)(x^2 + 4)}$

Review Exercise Set

A   In Problems 1–3 use synthetic division to perform the indicated divisions.

1. a. $2x^3 + 3x^2 - 4x + 5$ by $x - 2$ **b.** $x^3 - 3x + 4$ by $x + 3$

2. a. $x^4 - 3x^3 + 5x - 7$ by $x - 3$ **b.** $3x^5 - 12x^3 + 10x^2 + 22x + 4$ by $x + 2$ (What can you conclude?)

3. a. $3x^4 - 2x^3 + x - 5$ by $x + 4$ **b.** $2x^5 - 10x^3 + 16$ by $x - 2$ (What can you conclude?)

4. a. Show by synthetic division that $x + 5$ is a factor of $x^5 + 4x^4 - 7x^3 - 9x^2 - 25$.
    b. Let $P(x) = 2x^4 - x^3 - 27x^2 + 36x$. Show that $P(3) = 0$ by synthetic division and give the complete factorization of $P(x)$.

5. Find a polynomial whose only zeros are $-2, \frac{3}{2}, 3i, -3i$.

6. Find a polynomial equation having 4 as a root of multiplicity 2 and whose only other root is -2.

7. Without testing for actual roots, list all possible rational roots and use Descartes' rule of signs to determine the possible numbers of positive and negative real roots of each of the following:

   a. $3x^5 - 2x^3 + 4x^2 - 8 = 0$ **b.** $10x^4 + 7x^3 - 3x^2 - 5x + 12 = 0$

In Problems 8–13 find all rational roots, and if the depressed equation is quadratic, find all roots.

8. $2x^3 - 7x^2 + 9 = 0$

9. $x^3 - 4x^2 - 3x + 18 = 0$

10. $x^4 - 8x^2 - 24x - 32 = 0$

11. $6x^4 + 5x^3 + 20x^2 + 20x - 16 = 0$

12. $2x^4 + 6x^3 + 3x^2 + 4x + 12 = 0$

13. $4x^4 - 19x^2 + 3x + 18 = 0$

In Problems 14–16 factor completely over the reals.

14. $x^3 + 9x^2 + 15x - 25$

15. $2x^3 - 9x^2 + 18x - 20$

16. $2x^4 - 6x^3 + 7x^2 - 9x + 6$

In Problems 17–21 draw the graph.

17. $y = 2x^3 - 3x^2 - 5x$

18. $y = 25 + 21x^2 - 4x^4$

19. $y = (x - 3)^2(2x + 1)(x + 4)$

20. $y = x^3 - 12x - 16$

21. $y = 2x^4 + x^3 - 19x^2 - 9x + 9$

In Problems 22–24 solve the inequalities by graphical means.

22. $12x - x^2 - x^3 \geq 0$ 23. $x(x^2 - 3) < 2$ 24. $x^3 > 7x - 6$

25. Find the domain of the function $f(x) = \sqrt{2x^3 - 5x^2 + 18}$.

In Problems 26–30 find intercepts and asymptotes, and draw the graph.

26. $f(x) = \dfrac{2x + 3}{x - 4}$

27. $g(x) = \dfrac{4x}{1 - x^2}$

28. $y = \dfrac{x^2 - 4}{x^2 - 1}$

29. $y = \dfrac{2x^2 - 3x - 2}{x^2 - 5x}$

30. $y = \dfrac{1 - x^2}{(x - 2)^2}$

In Problems 31–36 resolve into partial fractions.

31. $\dfrac{x + 10}{x^2 + 2x - 8}$

32. $\dfrac{x^2 + 2x + 12}{x^2 - 4}$

33. $\dfrac{7 - 2x - x^2}{(x^2 - 1)(x - 1)}$

34. $\dfrac{2x^2 - 5x + 16}{x^3 - 2x^2 + 4x}$

35. $\dfrac{8x^2 + 6x - 8}{(x + 2)^2(x^2 + 2)}$

36. $\dfrac{x^4 - x^3 - 7x^2 + 11x}{x^3 - 3x^2 - x + 3}$

37. Find the real root of $2x^3 - 10x + 9 = 0$ correct to two decimal places.

38. Find the largest positive root of $2x^4 + x^3 - 13x^2 - 4x + 12 = 0$ correct to two decimal places.

B   **39.** Construct a polynomial of fourth degree with integral coefficients three of whose zeros are -2, $\frac{5}{2}$, and $3 - 2i$.

In Problems 40 and 41 find all roots.

40. $6x^4 - 13x^3 + 2x^2 - 4x + 15 = 0$ **41.** $6x^4 + x^3 + 2x - 24 = 0$

Draw the graphs of the functions in Problems 42 and 43.

42. $y = (2x - 1)(x + 3)^3(x - 4)^2$ **43.** $P(x) = x^4 + 2x^3 + 7x - 6$
Discuss the nature of the zeros of this polynomial.

44. Solve the inequality $x^4 - 9x^2 + 4x + 12 > 0$.
45. Find the domain of the function

$$f(x) = \sqrt{\frac{x^3 - 4x^2}{x^3 - 7x + 6}}$$

In Problems 46–48 find the intercepts and asymptotes and draw the graph.

46. $y = \dfrac{x^2}{x^2 - 2x - 8}$ **47.** $y = \dfrac{x^2 + x}{x - 1}$ **48.** $y = \dfrac{x^3 - 27}{x^4 - 16}$

In Problems 49 and 50 resolve into partial fractions.

49. $\dfrac{20 - 5x^2}{4x^4 + 9x^2 - 11x + 3}$ **50.** $\dfrac{6x^4 - 5x^3 - 3x^2 - 3}{6x^3 - 5x^2 + 6x - 5}$

51. Find all real roots of $x^3 - 3x^2 - 4x + 2 = 0$ correct to two decimal places.
52. Find the real root of $x^4 - 2.013x^3 + 0.025x^2 + 8.976x + 3.164 = 0$ correct to three decimal places.

7

Exponential and Logarithmic Functions

The functions we will study in this chapter are indispensable in applications of mathematics to many fields, especially where growth and decay are involved. The following excerpt from an ecology textbook* shows how an exponential function enters into a study of the decomposition of litter on a forest floor.

In a forest litter falls to the forest floor and accumulates. The litter is broken down into minerals and simple organic compounds, and the energy is lost in respiration. Rarely does litter continue to accumulate, as it must have once in the Carboniferous coal forests. If litter does not accumulate, an equilibrium of some sort has been reached where the amount of energy entering the decomposer cycle is matched by the energy lost in respiration. The change in litter ΔX during some interval of time Δt can be expressed by the simple difference

$$\frac{\Delta X}{\Delta t} = \text{(income for the interval)} - \text{(loss for the interval)}$$

. . . . As the interval of time becomes infinitely small, the difference equation becomes the differential equation

$$\frac{dX}{dt} = L - kX \qquad (17\text{-}1)$$

where L is the steady income of litter, X is the amount of litter present, and k is a constant instantaneous rate of litter decay. If litter is continuously added at a constant rate throughout the year and decays at a constant rate, Eq. (17-1) has the solution

$$X_t = \frac{L}{k}\,(1 - e^{-kt})$$

To understand this example fully requires calculus, but we will learn the meaning of the final equation in this chapter and we will see how to graph such a function.

---

* Robert W. Poole, *An Introduction to Quantitative Ecology* (New York: McGraw-Hill Book Company, 1974), pp. 489, 490. Reprinted by permission.

1   The Exponential Function

One of the very important functions that we have not yet studied is the **exponential function.** A typical example of such a function is given by

$$f(x) = 2^x$$

having as domain the set of all real numbers. We know how to evaluate this function for any integer x (positive, negative, or 0), and, in fact, for any rational number x. For example,

$$f(\tfrac{3}{2}) = 2^{3/2} = \sqrt{2^3} = \sqrt{2^2 \cdot 2} = 2\sqrt{2} \approx 2.828$$

(since $\sqrt{2} \approx 1.414$). How do we evaluate it for any irrational number x? For example, what is the meaning of $f(\pi) = 2^\pi$? Unfortunately, we cannot answer these questions in an entirely satisfactory way without more knowledge of limiting procedures. Nevertheless, it is not difficult to gain an intuitive feeling for the meaning of such expressions as 2^x, where x is an irrational number.

It can be shown that every irrational number can be approximated to any desired degree of accuracy by a rational number. This is a fundamental property of the real number system. Consider the irrational number we symbolize by π, for example. We can approximate it by 3.14, 3.142, 3.1416, and so on, and these numbers are rational, since they are terminating decimals. We *define* the number 2^π, then, as the number that is *approached* by $2^{3.14}$, $2^{3.142}$, $2^{3.1416}$, and so on. The fact that a unique number is approached more and more closely as the exponent approximates π with increasing accuracy, we will have to ask the reader to accept on faith at this stage.

More generally, let a be any positive number other than 1. (We exclude 1, since $1^x = 1$ for every x.) Now we define the function

$$f(x) = a^x \tag{1}$$

When x is rational, this is a well-defined number, and when x is irrational, we define a^x to mean the number approached by a^r as r takes on rational values that approach x arbitrarily closely. The function defined by equation (1) is called the **exponential function with base a.** The domain of the function consists of all real numbers, and the range is the set of all positive real numbers. While we cannot at this stage prove the latter assertion, it is intuitively reasonable that the range is at least a subset of R^+. Since roots, powers, and reciprocals of positive numbers are positive, then for a rational and positive x, say, $x = p/q$,

$$a^x = a^{p/q} = \sqrt[q]{a^p}$$

is positive, since $a > 0$. And since $a^{-x} = 1/a^x$, this too is positive. If x is irrational, then the value of a^x is approximated arbitrarily closely by numbers of the form a^r (with r rational), which is positive. It follows, then, that a^x also is positive. Finally, if $x = 0$, we know that $a^x = 1$.

It would lead to trouble to allow the base a to be either 0 or a negative number. If $a = 0$, then $a^x = 0$ for all $x > 0$, but a^x would be undefined for $x \leq 0$. If

Figure 1

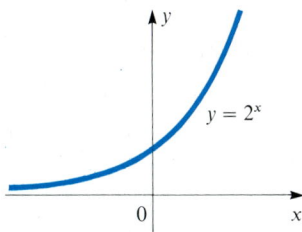

x	0	1	2	3	4	-1	-2	-3	-4	-5	-10
2^x	1	2	4	8	16	$\frac{1}{2}$	$\frac{1}{4}$	$\frac{1}{8}$	$\frac{1}{16}$	$\frac{1}{32}$	$\frac{1}{1,024}$

$a < 0$, then a^x would lead to imaginary numbers for infinitely many values of x (for example, for $x = \frac{1}{2}, \frac{3}{4}$, and so on).

A table of values for $f(x) = 2^x$ and the graph of f (Figure 1) are shown. Notice that as x gets larger and larger positively, the function increases very rapidly, and when x is negative and getting larger and larger in absolute value, the function gets closer and closer to 0, that is, the graph approaches the negative x axis more and more closely as we move to the left. The curve is said to become **asymptotic** to the negative x axis, and the x axis is said to be an **asymptote** to the curve.

The most common bases are those that are greater than 1. In fact, if $0 < a < 1$, then $a^x = (1/a)^{-x}$, and $1/a > 1$; so it really is sufficient to consider bases greater than 1. Figure 2 illustrates several exponential functions on the same coordinate system. The functions all have the following features in common.

Figure 2

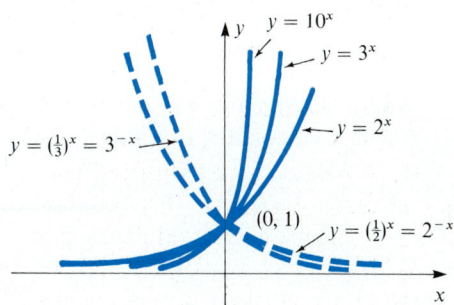

1. The y intercept is 1.
2. For $a > 1$, the negative x axis is an asymptote, and for $a < 1$, the positive x axis is an asymptote.
3. For $a > 1$, the curves all rise steadily as we move from left to right, and for $a < 1$, they all fall steadily from left to right.

Using these basic facts, we can graph more complex exponential functions, as the next example shows.

EXAMPLE 1   Draw the graph of the function defined by $y = 2^{1-|x|}$.

Solution   First we make a table of values:

x	0	± 1	± 2	± 3	± 4
y	2	1	$\frac{1}{2}$	$\frac{1}{4}$	$\frac{1}{8}$

Notice that we can substitute both a given value of x and its negative at once, since the absolute values are the same. Also observe that as x increases in absolute value, y approaches zero. So the x axis is an asymptote. The graph is shown in Figure 3.

Figure 3

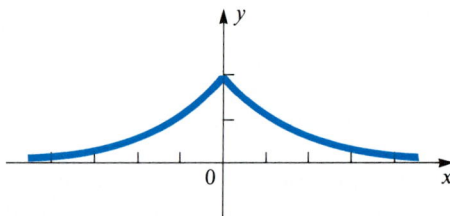

Among all possible bases one stands out as being far and away the most important in advanced courses in mathematics and in applications to real-world phenomena. It is an irrational number that is universally designated by the letter e, and its value is approximately 2.71828. The following is one way of defining the number e: Let us consider the expression

$$\left(1 + \frac{1}{n}\right)^n$$

where n designates any positive integer. We evaluate this for a few values of n (using a calculator) in Table 1. This should be fairly convincing evidence (but

Table 1

n	$\left(1 + \dfrac{1}{n}\right)^n$
1	2.00000
2	2.25000
3	2.37037
4	2.44141
5	2.48832
10	2.59374
100	2.70481
1,000	2.71692
10,000	2.71815
1,000,000	2.71828

it is not a proof) that as n becomes larger and larger, $[1 + (1/n)]^n$ approaches more and more closely some number whose first few digits are 2.718. We say that the **limit** of $[1 + (1/n)]^n$ as n becomes infinite is e, and write

$$e = \lim_{n \to \infty} \left(1 + \frac{1}{n}\right)^n \qquad (2)$$

One way in which this number e arises in a practical situation concerns money invested at compound interest. If a certain principal amount P is invested, and interest is compounded annually at an interest rate of r per year (for example, if the interest rate is 5%, then $r = 0.05$), the amount A of money in the account at the end of t years can be shown to be

$$A = P(1 + r)^t$$

If the interest is compounded semiannually, the formula becomes

$$A = P\left(1 + \frac{r}{2}\right)^{2t}$$

and if quarterly,

$$A = P\left(1 + \frac{r}{4}\right)^{4t}$$

More generally, if interest is compounded k times a year, the amount after t years is

$$A = P\left(1 + \frac{r}{k}\right)^{kt} \qquad (3)$$

For example, some banks make a big point of the fact that their interest is compounded daily. In this case equation (3) becomes

$$A = P\left(1 + \frac{r}{365}\right)^{365t}$$

Suppose that we wish to determine what the formula becomes when interest is compounded *continuously*. Some banks actually calculate their interest this way. What we must do is to let k become larger and larger in equation (3). That is, we want to find the limit of the expression on the right side of the equation as k gets arbitrarily large. In symbols, we want

$$\lim_{k \to \infty} P\left(1 + \frac{r}{k}\right)^{kt}$$

To find what this limit is, we manipulate the expression $[1 + (r/k)]^{kt}$ somewhat. First, let us make the substitution

$$n = \frac{k}{r}$$

Thus, $k = nr$. The substitution yields

$$\left(1 + \frac{r}{k}\right)^{kt} = \left(1 + \frac{1}{n}\right)^{nrt}$$

Now, as k gets larger and larger, so does n, and vice versa. So we can write the limit as*

$$\lim_{k \to \infty} P\left(1 + \frac{r}{k}\right)^{kt} = \lim_{n \to \infty} P\left(1 + \frac{1}{n}\right)^{nrt}$$

$$= P\left[\lim_{n \to \infty}\left(1 + \frac{1}{n}\right)^{n}\right]^{rt}$$

The expression in brackets is just the same as the right side of equation (2), and hence equals e. So, finally, our formula for the amount accumulated at the end of t years when the interest is compounded continuously is

$$A = Pe^{rt}$$

It should be emphasized that r is the annual interest rate, and t is the number of years.

EXAMPLE 2

If $1,000 is placed in a savings account yielding interest at 6%, find the amount accumulated after 5 years if interest is compounded:
a. Annually   **b.** Semiannually   **c.** Quarterly
d. Daily   **e.** Continuously

Note. To illustrate how problems such as this can be done on a calculator, we show keystroke displays for parts **d** and **e**.

Solution

a. $A = 1,000(1 + 0.06)^5 = 1,000(1.06)^5 = 1,000(1.33822) = \$1,338.22$

b. $A = 1,000\left(1 + \dfrac{0.06}{2}\right)^{5(2)} = 1,000(1.03)^{10} = 1,000(1.34392) = \$1,343.92$

c. $A = 1,000\left(1 + \dfrac{0.06}{4}\right)^{5(4)} = 1,000(1.015)^{20} = 1,000(1.34686) = \$1,346.86$

d. $A = 1,000\left(1 + \dfrac{0.06}{365}\right)^{5(365)} = 1,000(1.000164)^{1,825} = 1,000(1.34982)$

$= \$1,349.82$

By calculator:

$1,000\ \boxed{\times}\ \boxed{(}\ 1\ \boxed{+}\ .06\ \boxed{\div}\ 365\ \boxed{)}\ \boxed{y^x}\ \boxed{(}\ 5\ \boxed{\times}\ 365\ \boxed{)}$
$\boxed{=}\ 1,349.8257$

e. $A = 1,000e^{(0.06)5} = 1,000(e^{0.3}) = 1,000(1.34986) = \$1,349.86$

By calculator:

$1,000\ \boxed{\times}\ .3\ \boxed{e^x}\ \boxed{=}\ 1,349.8588$

---

* We use certain properties of limits here that are shown to be true in calculus.

The next example illustrates what is known as **exponential growth.** If y represents the size of a quantity at time t, then that quantity grows exponentially if it obeys the formula

$$y = Ce^{kt}$$

where C and k are positive constants. Under ideal conditions a culture of bacteria grows approximately exponentially for limited time intervals. Other applications of this law occur in chemistry, economics, and physics.

EXAMPLE 3   A culture of bacteria originally numbers 1,000, and after 2 hours the number has quadrupled. Assuming the law of exponential growth,

$$y = Ce^{kt}$$

find the number of bacteria after 6 hours.

Solution   We know that when $t = 0$, $y = 1,000$, so that

$$1,000 = C \cdot e^{k(0)}$$

giving $C = 1,000$. So our formula becomes

$$y = 1,000e^{kt} \tag{4}$$

We also know that when $t = 2$, $y = 4,000$, so that

$$4,000 = 1,000 \cdot e^{k(2)}$$
$$4 = e^{k(2)} \tag{5}$$

Instead of solving for k at this point, we solve for e^k. We take the square root of both sides of equation (5), or equivalently, raise both sides to the power $\frac{1}{2}$.

$$4^{1/2} = (e^{k(2)})^{1/2}$$
$$2 = e^k$$

Now we can substitute this in equation (4) to get

$$y = 1,000e^{kt} = 1,000(e^k)^t = 1,000 \cdot 2^t$$

This is the formula we need. It expresses the number y of bacteria in terms of the time t in hours. So when $t = 6$, we have

$$y = 1,000 \cdot 2^6 = 1,000 \cdot 64 = 64,000$$

In the case of radioactive substances, which exhibit **exponential decay,** a common measure of the rate of decay is the **half-life** of the substance. This is defined as the time required for the substance to diminish to one-half of the original amount. This is a property inherent in the particular substance and is independent of the amount present initially. Theoretically, a radioactive substance never decomposes completely, so it is not possible to give the "whole life." The basic formula (which is derived in calculus) for the amount y of a substance that decays exponentially is

$$y = Ce^{-kt}$$

where t represents time, and C and k are positive constants that are determined by the data in a particular instance.

EXAMPLE 4   A certain radioactive substance has a half-life of 50 years. How much of 100 grams will remain after 200 years?

Solution   The relevant data are:

$$\text{When} \quad t = 0, \quad y = 100$$
$$\text{When} \quad t = 50, \quad y = 50 \qquad \text{Since half-life is 50 years}$$
$$\text{When} \quad t = 200, \quad y = ?$$

First we substitute $t = 0$ and $y = 100$ in the exponential decay equation, $y = Ce^{-kt}$:

$$100 = Ce^{-0} = C$$

So the constant C is 100. The formula for y is therefore

$$y = 100e^{-kt} \tag{6}$$

Now we substitute $t = 50$, $y = 50$:

$$50 = 100e^{-k(50)}$$
$$\tfrac{1}{2} = e^{-k(50)}$$

Again, we do not attempt to solve for the constant k but rather solve for e^{-k} by raising both sides of this equation to the power $\frac{1}{50}$. This gives

$$\left(\frac{1}{2}\right)^{1/50} = e^{-k}$$

Formula (6) now becomes

$$y = 100e^{-kt} = 100(e^{-k})^t = 100\left(\frac{1}{2}\right)^{t/50}$$

Finally, we let $t = 200$:

$$y = 100\left(\frac{1}{2}\right)^4 = 100\left(\frac{1}{16}\right) = \frac{25}{4} = 6.25$$

So after 200 years, 6.25 grams of the original 100 remain.

Finally, we list for reference the laws of exponents given in Chapter 1. Proofs of these for irrational exponents require greater sophistication than we wish to employ here, but the truth of these laws for rational exponents, together with the knowledge that a^x for any irrational x is approximated arbitrarily closely by numbers of the form a^r with r rational, should provide a degree of confidence in their truth in general. We assume $a > 0$ and $b > 0$.

Laws of Exponents

1. $a^0 = 1$	**2.** $a^{-x} = \dfrac{1}{a^x}$
3. $a^x \cdot a^y = a^{x+y}$	**4.** $\dfrac{a^x}{a^y} = a^{x-y}$
5. $(a^x)^y = a^{xy}$	**6.** $(ab)^x = a^x b^x$

EXERCISE SET 1

Note. In this and in other exercises in this chapter a calculator or tables will be needed for certain problems.

A   In Problems 1 and 2 use a calculator to approximate the given numbers correct to four decimal places.

1. **a.** $2^{\sqrt{2}}$ **b.** 3^{π} **c.** $4^{-\sqrt{3}}$ **d.** e^2 **e.** e^{-1}
2. **a.** $(\sqrt{5})^{\sqrt{7}}$ **b.** e^{π} **c.** π^2 **d.** $2^{2/3}$ **e.** $e^{-1/2}$

In Problems 3–20 make a table of values and draw the graph.

3. $y = 4^x$ 4. $y = 4^{-x}$
5. $y = e^x$ 6. $y = e^{-x}$
7. $y = (\tfrac{2}{3})^x$ 8. $f(x) = 2^{x/2}$
9. $F(x) = 2^{x-1}$ 10. $g(x) = (\sqrt{3})^{-x}$ 11. $h(x) = 3^{(1-x)/2}$
12. $y = 2^{x^2}$ 13. $y = 1 - e^{-x}$ 14. $f(x) = 1 - 2^{-x}$
15. $g(x) = 2^{1-x^2}$ 16. $h(x) = 2^{|x|}$ 17. $f(x) = (\tfrac{3}{4})^{x-1}$
18. $F(x) = (\tfrac{3}{2})^{x/2}$ 19. $G(x) = (\tfrac{1}{2})^{2-x}$ 20. $y = 3^{|x-1|}$

21. The sum of \$2,000 is placed in a savings account at $5\tfrac{1}{2}\%$ annual interest. Find the amount at the end of 4 years if interest is compounded:
    a. Annually   **b.** Quarterly   **c.** Continuously
22. A culture of bacteria originally numbers 500. After 2 hours there are 1,500 bacteria. Assuming exponential growth, find how many are present after 6 hours.
23. A radioactive substance has a half-life of 64 hours. If 200 grams of the substance are initially present, how much will remain after 4 days?
24. A culture of 100 bacteria doubles after 2 hours. How long will it take the number of bacteria to reach 3,200?
25. How long will it take 100 grams of a radioactive substance having a half-life of 40 years to be reduced to 12.5 grams?
26. One hundred kilograms of a certain radioactive substance decay to 40 kilograms after 10 years. Find how much will remain after 20 years.

27. In the initial stages a bacteria culture grows approximately exponentially. If the number doubles after 3 hours, what proportion of the original number will be present after 6 hours? After 12 hours?

28. Strontium-90 has a half-life of 25 years. If 200 kilograms were present originally, how much will remain after 10 years?

29. One bank offers 6% interest compounded quarterly. Another offers 6% compounded continuously. How much more income would result from depositing $1,000 in the second account for 5 years than in the first?

30. Determine which of the following is the better way to invest $500 for 2 years:
    a. An account paying $7\frac{1}{2}\%$ compounded annually
    b. An account paying $7\frac{1}{4}\%$ compounded continuously
    If in part **a** interest were compounded quarterly, compare the result with part **b**.

31. The number N of items of a certain type of merchandise sold on a given day diminishes with time according to the formula

$$N = N_0 e^{-k(t-1)}$$

where N_0 is the number sold on the first day. If 20 of these items are sold on the first day and 10 on the fifth day, how many can be expected to be sold on the ninth day?

B   In Problems 32–35 make a table of values and draw the graph.

32. $y = xe^{-x}$

33. $f(x) = \dfrac{e^x + e^{-x}}{2}$

34. $g(x) = \dfrac{e^x - e^{-x}}{2}$

35. $h(x) = \dfrac{e^x - e^{-x}}{e^x + e^{-x}}$

Note. The functions in Problems 33, 34, and 35 are called, respectively, **the hyperbolic cosine, the hyperbolic sine, and the hyperbolic tangent, written cosh x, sinh x, and tanh x.**

36. According to Newton's law of cooling, the rate at which a hot body cools is proportional to the difference in temperature between it and its surroundings. By calculus it can be shown that this results in the following formula for the temperature T of the body after time t:

$$T = T_0 + Ce^{-kt}$$

where T_0 is the temperature of the surrounding medium, and C and k are positive constants. A body is initially at 120°C and is placed in air at 20°C. After $\frac{1}{2}$ hour it has cooled to 80°C. Find its temperature after 1 hour

37. A thermometer registering 20°C is placed in a freezer in which the temperature is -10°C. After 10 minutes the thermometer registers 5°C. What will it register after 30 minutes? (See Problem 36.)

38. A piece of metal is heated to 80°C and is then placed in the outside air at 20°C. After 15 minutes the temperature of the metal is 65°C. What will be its temperature after 15 more minutes? (See Problem 36.)

39. In 1930 the world population was approximately 2 billion and in 1960 approximately 3 billion. A crude approximation to the growth rate of the population is to assume it is exponential, that is, $y = Ce^{kt}$, where y represents the population t years after a given time. Using these data estimate the world population in the year 2000.

40. The air pressure p at an altitude h above the ground is approximately

$$p = p_0 e^{-kh}$$

where p_0 is the pressure at ground level. If the pressure at ground level is 15 pounds per square inch and at height 10,000 feet it is 10 pounds per square inch, find the approximate pressure at 20,000 feet.

41. The atmospheric pressure at sea level is approximately 15 pounds per square inch, and at Denver, which is 1 mile high, the pressure is approximately 12 pounds per square inch. What will be the approximate atmospheric pressure at the top of Vail Pass, which is 2 miles high? (See Problem 40.)

42. The intensity of light passing through a layer of translucent material decreases at a rate approximately proportional to the thickness of the material. It is shown in calculus that this results in the formula

$$I = I_0 e^{-kx}$$

where I_0 is the intensity with which the light first strikes the material and I is the intensity x units inside the material. If sunlight striking water is reduced to half of its original intensity at a depth of 10 feet, what will be the intensity (as a fractional part of the original intensity) at a depth of 30 feet?

---

2 Inverses of Exponential Functions

It is evident from its graph that the exponential function

$$f(x) = a^x \qquad (a > 0, \quad a \neq 1)$$

is one-to-one, since each horizontal line intersects the curve at most once. Thus, an inverse exists for this function. For historical reasons the name given to the inverse is the **logarithm function,** and its value is symbolized by $\log_a x$. This is read "log to the base a of x." So if $f(x) = a^x$, then

$$f^{-1}(x) = \log_a x$$

It is unfortunate that the name and symbol used here do not in any way suggest the relationship of the logarithm function to the exponential; this relationship simply must be learned.

Since for any function f having an inverse f^{-1} it is true that

$$f(f^{-1}(x)) = x \qquad \text{and} \qquad f^{-1}(f(x)) = x$$

we have that

$$a^{\log_a x} = x \tag{7}$$

and

$$\log_a a^x = x \tag{8}$$

Also, we know that a point (x_0, y_0) satisfies $y = f^{-1}(x)$ if and only if the point (y_0, x_0) satisfies $y = f(x)$; that is,

$$y_0 = f^{-1}(x_0)$$

if and only if

$$x_0 = f(y_0)$$

In terms of the logarithmic and exponential functions, this becomes (omitting the subscript)

$$y = \log_a x \qquad \text{if and only if} \qquad x = a^y \tag{9}$$

This is of fundamental importance and should be memorized. We refer to the left-hand equation in (9) as the **logarithmic form** and the right-hand equation as the **exponential form.** We can often deduce facts about logarithms by using an equivalent exponential form. For example, suppose we wish to obtain the value of $\log_2 \frac{1}{16}$. Let us denote this unknown value by y. Then

$$y = \log_2 \tfrac{1}{16}$$

and by (9) the equivalent exponential form is

$$\tfrac{1}{16} = 2^y$$

Since $\frac{1}{16} = (\frac{1}{2})^4 = 2^{-4}$, we have $2^{-4} = 2^y$, from which it follows that $y = -4$. Here are some other examples of this type.

EXAMPLE 5   Find the value of x if $x = \log_3 27$.

Solution   The exponential form is $3^x = 27$, and since $27 = 3^3$, we have $3^x = 3^3$, so that $x = 3$.

EXAMPLE 6   Find y if $6 = \log_2 y$.

Solution   In exponential form this is $2^6 = y$. So $y = 64$.

EXAMPLE 7   Solve for x: $3 = \log_x 125$

Solution   We have $x^3 = 125$, so that $x = \sqrt[3]{125} = 5$.

It helps in changing from logarithmic to exponential form to observe that the base in each case is the same. In the logarithmic form this appears as the subscript:

$$y = \log_{@} x$$
$$\text{Base}$$

and in the exponential form it is the number that is raised to a power:

$$x = @^y$$
$$\text{Base}$$

Also, note that the exponent in the exponential form is the number y, that is, it is the value that the logarithm equals in the logarithmic form. This latter can be stated as follows:

The logarithm to the base a of a number x is the exponent y of the power to which a must be raised to yield that number.

Remark.   The base e is the most important base for logarithms, and logarithms with this base are called natural logarithms. They also are sometimes called **Napierian** (after John Napier, a Scot who invented logarithms in the early seventeenth century). The symbol **ln** is often used instead of the more cumbersome $\log_e$. So

$$\log_e x = \ln x$$

It is also common practice to use "log" to mean "$\log_{10}$," and this is called the **common logarithm.** Historically, common logarithms have been most used in computational work. Now, however, with the advent of hand calculators, they are seldom needed.

The graph of a function involving logarithms can be obtained by changing to exponential form, as the next example shows.

EXAMPLE 8   Draw the graph of the function defined by

$$y = \log_3(4 - x)$$

Solution   The equivalent exponential form is

$$4 - x = 3^y$$

Solving for x we get

$$x = 4 - 3^y$$

Now we make a table of values in which we assign values to y and determine x:

x	3	1	-5	-23	$\frac{11}{3} \approx 3.7$	$\frac{35}{9} \approx 3.9$
y	0	1	2	3	-1	-2

Observe that for y negative but large in absolute value, x is close to 4. The line $x = 4$ is a vertical asymptote. The graph is shown in Figure 4.

Figure 4

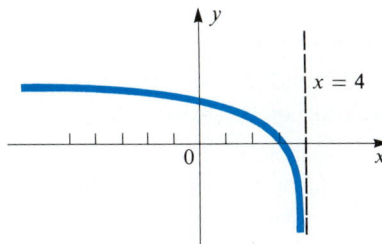

EXAMPLE 9   The formula for the amount y in grams present at time t in years of a radioactive substance is given by

$$y = Q_0 e^{-0.2t}$$

where Q_0 is the amount initially. Find how long it will be until only 10% of the original quantity is left.

Solution   We want to know the value of t for which $y = (0.1)Q_0$. Substituting this for y yields

$$(0.1)Q_0 = Q_0 e^{-0.2t}$$
$$0.1 = e^{-0.2t}$$

To solve for t we write this in logarithmic form:

$$\ln(0.1) = -0.2t$$

So,

$$t = -\frac{\ln(0.1)}{0.2} \approx -\frac{-2.30285}{0.2} \approx 11.513 \text{ years}$$

By calculator:

$$.1 \;\boxed{\ln x}\; \boxed{+/-}\; \boxed{\div}\; .2 \;\boxed{=}\; 11.5129$$

EXAMPLE 10   A man deposits a sum of money in a savings account paying 5% interest compounded continuously. How long will it take for him to double his money?

Solution   Let P be the initial amount. Then, as we found in the previous section,

$$A = Pe^{0.05t}$$

is the formula for the amount after t years. We want to know t when $A = 2P$.

$$2P = Pe^{0.05t}$$
$$2 = e^{0.05t}$$

In logarithmic form this is

$$\ln 2 = 0.05t$$

So,

$$t = \frac{\ln 2}{0.05} \approx \frac{0.6931}{0.05} \approx 13.86 \text{ years}$$

EXAMPLE 11   It is found that in 2 years 10% of a radioactive substance disappears. Find the half-life of the substance.

Solution   Let Q_0 be the amount present initially. If y denotes the amount present at time t years later,

$$y = Ce^{-kt}$$

Substituting $y = Q_0$ when $t = 0$ yields $C = Q_0$. So

$$y = Q_0 e^{-kt}$$

We know that when $t = 2$, $y = (0.9)Q_0$. Thus,

$$(0.9)Q_0 = Q_0 e^{-k2}$$
$$0.9 = e^{-2k}$$

This time we will solve for k (rather than e^{-k}), using the logarithmic form:

$$\ln 0.9 = -2k$$

$$k = -\tfrac{1}{2}\ln 0.9 \approx -\tfrac{1}{2}(-0.10536) = 0.05268$$

So our formula for y becomes

$$y = Q_0 e^{-0.05268t}$$

Finally, we wish to determine the half-life, that is, the value of t when $y = Q_0/2 = 0.5Q_0$:

$$0.5Q_0 = Q_0 e^{-0.05268t}$$

After dividing both sides by Q_0, this can be written as

$$e^{-0.05268t} = 0.5$$

Again, we use the logarithmic form:

$$\ln 0.5 = -0.05268t$$

So,

$$t = \frac{\ln 0.5}{-0.05268} \approx \frac{-0.69315}{-0.05268} \approx 13.158 \text{ years}$$

By calculator:

$$.5 \;\boxed{\ln x}\; \boxed{\div}\; .05268 \;\boxed{=}\; \boxed{+/-}\; 13.157691$$

EXAMPLE 12 The human ear can accommodate an enormous range of sound wave intensities, ranging from about 10^{-12} watt per square meter, taken to be the threshold of hearing, to about 1 watt per square meter, the threshold of pain for most people. Since the range is so great, it is customary to use a logarithmic scale to describe the relative loudness of a sound. The formula

$$\beta = 10 \log_{10} \frac{I}{I_0}$$

is used, where I_0 is the intensity of the threshold of hearing (10^{-12} watt per square meter) and I is the intensity of the sound in question. The number β is said to be the number of **decibels** of the sound. Find the decibel intensity of the noise of a heavy truck passing a pedestrian at the side of a road if the sound wave intensity I of the truck is 10^{-3} watt per square meter.

Solution Since $I_0 = 10^{-12}$ and $I = 10^{-3}$, we have

$$\beta = 10 \log_{10} \frac{I}{I_0} = 10 \log_{10} \frac{10^{-3}}{10^{-12}}$$

$$= 10 \log_{10} 10^9$$

$$= 10(9) = 90$$

So the intensity is 90 decibels.

EXERCISE SET 2

A   Evaluate the expressions in Problems 1–11.

1. **a.** $\log_2 2^3$ **b.** $2^{\log_2 3}$
2. **a.** $\log_3 3^{10}$ **b.** $5^{\log_5 7}$
3. **a.** $\log_b b^x$ **b.** $b^{\log_b x}$
4. **a.** $\log_2 8$ **b.** $\log_3 \frac{1}{9}$
5. **a.** $\log_{10} 10{,}000$ **b.** $\log_{10} 0.001$
6. **a.** $\log_4 2$ **b.** $\log_2 0.125$
7. **a.** $\log_4 64$ **b.** $\log_2 \frac{1}{16}$
8. **a.** $\log_{10} 0.1$ **b.** $\log_3 81$
9. **a.** $\log_{10} 100$ **b.** $\log_e(1/e^2)$
10. **a.** $e^{\log_e 4}$ **b.** $10^{\log_{10} 7}$
11. **a.** $\log_9 9^5$ **b.** $\log_6 6^{-5}$

Find the unknown in Problems 12–24.

12. **a.** $\log_4 x = 2$ **b.** $\log_x 16 = 4$
13. **a.** $\log_2 8 = y$ **b.** $\log_y 3 = -\frac{1}{2}$
14. **a.** $t = \log_2 \frac{1}{8}$ **b.** $\log_{10} x = -2$
15. **a.** $\log_{10} 1{,}000 = x$ **b.** $\log_{10} x = -3$
16. **a.** $\log_u 3 = \frac{1}{2}$ **b.** $\log_{1/2} u = -4$
17. **a.** $\log_4 1 = v$ **b.** $\log_v \frac{4}{9} = -\frac{2}{3}$
18. **a.** $\log_2 y = 6$ **b.** $\log_x 125 = 3$
19. **a.** $\log_4 0.25 = t$ **b.** $\log_4 x = \frac{1}{2}$
20. **a.** $\log_e 1 = y$ **b.** $\log_z 0.01 = -2$
21. **a.** $\log_9 u = -\frac{3}{2}$ **b.** $\log_8 4 = v$
22. **a.** $\log_x 16 = \frac{4}{3}$ **b.** $\log_{4/9} t = -\frac{3}{2}$
23. **a.** $\log_3(x - 1) = 2$ **b.** $\log_2 0.125 = y$
24. **a.** $w = \log_e(1/e)$ **b.** $\log_2 |w| = 3$

In Problems 25–28 write in logarithmic form.

25. **a.** $4^3 = 64$ **b.** $3^{-2} = \frac{1}{9}$
26. **a.** $10^4 = 10{,}000$ **b.** $10^{-3} = 0.001$
27. **a.** $2^8 = 256$ **b.** $2^{-3} = 0.125$
28. **a.** $r^s = t$ **b.** $z^x = m$

In Problems 29–32 write in exponential form.

29. **a.** $\log_2 16 = 4$ **b.** $\log_{10} 100 = 2$
30. **a.** $\log_e 1 = 0$ **b.** $\log_3 \frac{1}{9} = -2$
31. **a.** $\log_5 0.2 = -1$ **b.** $\log_8 4 = \frac{2}{3}$
32. **a.** $\log_a x = y$ **b.** $\log_x z = t$

In Problems 33–41 draw the graph of each function by first writing an equivalent exponential form and then making a table of values.

33. $y = \log_2 x$ 34. $y = \log_3 x$
35. $y = \log_2(x + 1)$ 36. $y = \log_3(1 - x)$
37. $y = \log_4(2x - 3)$ 38. $y = \log_2(1 - 3x)$

39. $y = \log_2 x^2$ **40.** $y = \log_3 |x|$

41. $y = \log_e(-x)$ **42.** $y = 1 - \log_2 x$

43. If \$10,000 is invested at 6% interest compounded continuously, in approximately how many years will the amount have grown to \$15,000?

44. In the early stages a bacterial culture grows approximately exponentially. Assuming this holds true for the time periods in question, if the quantity doubles in 2 hours, how long will it take to triple?

45. If \$5,000 is invested at $5\frac{1}{2}\%$ compounded continuously, approximately how long will it take for the amount to double?

46. A woman has \$10,000 invested at 6% and her brother has \$9,000 invested at 7%. If in each account interest is compounded continuously, find how long it will take for the amount in the brother's account to equal the amount in his sister's.

47. If 100 grams of a radioactive material diminish to 80 grams in 2 years, find the half-life of the substance.

48. Use the information given in Example 12 to find the decibel level of sound at:
    a. The threshold of hearing   **b.** The threshold of pain

49. At a distance of 10 meters from a rock band the intensity of sound is approximately 0.1 watt per square meter. Find the intensity in decibels.

50. At a distance of $\frac{1}{2}$ mile from the runway the noise level of a supersonic transport plane at takeoff is approximately 150 decibels. What is the sound wave intensity in watts per square meter?

51. Find the half-life of a radioactive substance that is reduced by 30% in 20 hours.

B **52.** In a chemical reaction a substance is converted according to the formula

$$y = Ce^{-0.3t}$$

where y is the amount of the unconverted substance at time t minutes after the reaction began. If there are 20 grams of the substance initially, find how long it will take for only 4 grams of it to remain unconverted.

53. A body heated to 120°F is brought into a room in which the temperature is 70°F. After 15 minutes the temperature of the body is 100°F. How long will it take the temperature of the body to drop to 80°F? (See Problem 36, Exercise Set 1.)

54. If a body is brought into a warmer medium than the temperature of the body, a formula analogous to Newton's law of cooling holds true (see Problem 36, Exercise Set 1), namely,

$$T = T_0 - Ce^{-kt}$$

where T_0 is the temperature of the surrounding medium and T is the temperature of the body after time t. An outside thermometer registers 5°C and is brought into a room where the temperature is 20°C. After 10 minutes the thermometer registers 12°C. How long will it take for it to register 18°C?

55. Use the data given in Problem 42, Exercise Set 1, to find at what depth the intensity of illumination will be only $\frac{1}{10}$ the original.

56. A thermometer registers -15°C in a freezer and is brought into a room in which the temperature is 25°C. After 5 minutes the thermometer registers 5°C. Find how long it will take for it to register 24°C. (See Problem 54.)

---

3 Properties of Logarithms

The domain of the exponential function

$$f(x) = a^x \qquad (a > 0)$$

consists of all real numbers, and its range is the set of all positive real numbers. It follows that for the inverse

$$f^{-1}(x) = \log_a x$$

the domain and range are interchanged:

Domain of $\log_a x$ = Set of all positive real numbers

Range of $\log_a x$ = Set of all real numbers

It should be emphasized that the logarithm function is defined *only for positive numbers.* This is also evident from the graph of $y = \log_a x$ (Figure 5), which is obtained by reflecting the graph of $y = a^x$ in the line $y = x$. (Alternately, one can obtain the graph of $y = \log_a x$ by plotting the graph of the equivalent equation $x = a^y$.)

The relations (7) and (8) of Section 2 enable us to exploit the properties of the exponential function to obtain corresponding properties of the logarithm function. In what follows we will repeatedly use the fact that if $a^x = a^y$, then $x = y$, which is a consequence of the fact that the exponential function is one-to-one.

By equation (7) we have that for any $x > 0$ and $y > 0$,

$$x = a^{\log_a x} \qquad \text{and} \qquad y = a^{\log_a y}$$

Figure 5

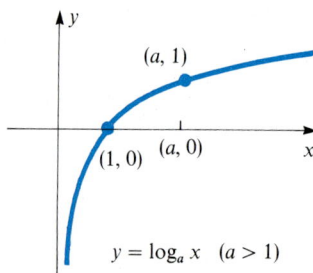

$$y = \log_a x \quad (a > 1)$$

Similarly,

$$xy = a^{\log_a xy}$$

Thus, we have the equality

$$a^{\log_a xy} = a^{\log_a x} \cdot a^{\log_a y}$$

But by the law of exponents for multiplication we can add the exponents on the right, and so obtain:

$$a^{\log_a xy} = a^{\log_a x + \log_a y}$$

The exponents must therefore be equal:

$$\log_a xy = \log_a x + \log_a y \qquad (10)$$

Next consider the following two representations of x^p. By equation (7),

$$x^p = a^{\log_a x^p}$$

but also,

$$x^p = (a^{\log_a x})^p = a^{p \log_a x}$$

where the last equality is a consequence of one of the laws of exponents. The two expressions for x^p must be equal:

$$a^{\log_a x^p} = a^{p \log_a x}$$

which yields:

$$\log_a x^p = p \log_a x \tag{11}$$

Equations (10) and (11) can be used now to obtain a formula for the logarithm of a quotient. We have

$$\log_a \frac{x}{y} = \log_a \left(x \cdot \frac{1}{y} \right) = \log_a x + \log_a \frac{1}{y}$$

by equation (10). And by (11), with $p = -1$,

$$\log_a \frac{1}{y} = \log_a y^{-1} = -\log_a y$$

So finally,

$$\log_a \frac{x}{y} = \log_a x - \log_a y \tag{12}$$

The properties (10), (11), and (12) are basic and account for much of the utility of the logarithm function. These results are summarized in the box, where it is understood that $x > 0$ and $y > 0$.

Properties of Logarithms

1. $\log_a xy = \log_a x + \log_a y$

2. $\log_a \dfrac{x}{y} = \log_a x - \log_a y$

3. $\log_a x^p = p \log_a x$

In the exercises that follow we will often use "log" without explicitly indicating a base, since the results are valid regardless of what (admissible) base is being used. The properties of logarithms are used repeatedly. The following examples are illustrative. When no restriction on x is stated, we will understand that only values for which the logarithm is defined are allowed. In Examples 13–16 we use the properties of logarithms to write the expression in a form that is free of logarithms of products, quotients, and powers.

EXAMPLE 13

$$\log x^2 = 2 \log x \qquad (x > 0)$$

If $x < 0$, we can write

$$\log x^2 = \log|x|^2 = 2 \log|x|$$

EXAMPLE 14

$$\log \frac{2x}{3x^2 + 1} = \log 2x - \log(3x^2 + 1)$$

$$= \log 2 + \log x - \log(3x^2 + 1)$$

A Word of Caution. The properties of logarithms enable us to simplify logarithms of products, quotients, and powers (and roots, since these can be treated as powers), but there is no way to simplify logarithms of sums or differences. Thus, $\log(x + y)$ *cannot* be changed to $\log x + \log y$, however tempting this might be. In fact, we know that $\log x + \log y$ is the same as $\log xy$, not $\log(x + y)$.

EXAMPLE 15

$$\log \sqrt{\frac{1 - x}{1 + x}} = \log \left(\frac{1 - x}{1 + x}\right)^{1/2}$$

$$= \frac{1}{2} \log \frac{1 - x}{1 + x} = \frac{1}{2}[\log(1 - x) - \log(1 + x)]$$

EXAMPLE 16

$$\log \frac{x^3 \sqrt{1 - x^2}}{(2x + 1)^{3/2}(x^4 + 1)} = \log x^3 \sqrt{1 - x^2} - \log(2x + 1)^{3/2}(x^4 + 1)$$

$$= \log x^3 + \log \sqrt{1 - x^2} - [\log(2x + 1)^{3/2} + \log(x^4 + 1)]$$

$$= 3 \log x + \tfrac{1}{2} \log(1 - x^2) - \tfrac{3}{2} \log(2x + 1) - \log(x^4 + 1)$$

We first treated this as a quotient. Then we worked with the products, and finally with the powers. Notice that in the second step we bracketed the two terms preceded by a minus sign. This procedure is highly recommended, for a common pitfall is to apply the minus to one term and not the other.

EXAMPLE 17   Solve for x: $\log x - \log(x - 2) = 2 \log 2$

Solution   By the properties of logarithms this can be written in the form

$$\log \frac{x}{x - 2} = \log 2^2$$

Since the logarithms are equal, so are the numbers (since the logarithm function is 1–1). Thus,

$$\frac{x}{x - 2} = 4$$

$$x = 4(x - 2)$$

$$x = 4x - 8$$

$$3x = 8$$

$$x = \tfrac{8}{3}$$

EXAMPLE 18   Solve for x: $\log_3(x + 1) + \log_3(x + 3) = 1$

Solution   We write the left-hand side as the logarithm of a product,

$$\log_3(x + 1)(x + 3) = 1$$

and then write the result in exponential form.

$$(x + 1)(x + 3) = 3^1$$
$$x^2 + 4x + 3 = 3$$
$$x^2 + 4x = 0$$
$$x(x + 4) = 0$$
$$x = 0 \quad | \quad x = -4$$

Upon checking in the original equation, we find that $x = 0$ works, since

$$\log_3(0 + 1) + \log_3(0 + 3) = \log_3 1 + \log_3 3 = 0 + 1 = 1$$

but $x = -4$ is not permissible, because this would lead to logarithms of negative numbers. The trouble was introduced when we wrote

$$\log_3(x + 1) + \log_3(x + 3) = \log_3(x + 1)(x + 3)$$

When $x = -4$, the left-hand side is not defined, but the product of the two negative numbers on the right is positive, so that the right-hand side is defined for $x = -4$.

EXAMPLE 19   Find the value of x in each of the following in terms of natural logarithms:
a. $2^x = 3$ **b.** $4^{1-x} = 3 \cdot 5^x$

Solution   **a.**   We take the natural logarithm of both sides, and make use of the properties of logarithms:

$$\ln 2^x = \ln 3$$
$$x \ln 2 = \ln 3$$
$$x = \frac{\ln 3}{\ln 2}$$

A Word of Caution.   Do not confuse $\ln 3/\ln 2$ with $\ln \frac{3}{2}$, which is equal to $\ln 3 - \ln 2$.

b.   Again, we equate the natural logarithm of the left side to that of the right:

$$\ln 4^{1-x} = \ln(3 \cdot 5^x)$$
$$(1 - x) \ln 4 = \ln 3 + \ln 5^x$$
$$\ln 4 - x \ln 4 = \ln 3 + x \ln 5$$
$$\ln 4 - \ln 3 = x(\ln 4 + \ln 5)$$
$$\ln \tfrac{4}{3} = x \ln(4 \cdot 5)$$
$$x = \frac{\ln \frac{4}{3}}{\ln 20}$$

Sometimes it is useful to change from one base for logarithms to another. Suppose we are given $\log_a x$ and want to find the value of this same expression involving logarithms to the base b. Let

$$y = \log_a x$$

We write this in exponential form and take the logarithm to the base b of both sides, making use of equation (11):

$$a^y = x$$
$$\log_b a^y = \log_b x$$
$$y \log_b a = \log_b x$$
$$y = \frac{\log_b x}{\log_b a}$$

Therefore, we have the change of base formula

$$\log_a x = \frac{\log_b x}{\log_b a} \tag{13}$$

If we put $x = b$, we obtain the interesting result

$$\log_a b = \frac{1}{\log_b a}$$

which can be used to give the following alternate form of equation (13):

$$\log_a x = (\log_a b)(\log_b x) \tag{14}$$

Another formula which is essentially a change of base formula for exponentials can be obtained as follows. By equation (7),

$$a^x = b^{\log_b a^x}$$

and since $\log_b a^x = x \log_b a$, this gives

$$a^x = b^{x \log_b a} \tag{15}$$

This formula is especially important in calculus when b is taken as e. Then we have

$$a^x = e^{x \ln a} \tag{16}$$

This shows that every exponential can be expressed as an exponential with base e.

EXERCISE SET 3

A In Problems 1–26 use the properties of logarithms to write the expressions in a form that is free of logarithms of products, quotients, and powers.

1. **a.** $\log(x + 1)(x - 2)$ **b.** $\log \dfrac{x + 1}{x - 2}$

2. **a.** $\log(x + 4)^3$ **b.** $\log \sqrt{2x + 3}$

3. **a.** $\log(x - 2)^4$ **b.** $\log(2x + 1)^{3/2}$

4. **a.** $\log(x^2 + 2x)$ **b.** $\log \dfrac{x}{x+1}$

5. **a.** $\log(x^2 - 2x - 3)$ **b.** $\log \dfrac{x^2 - 4}{x - 3}$

6. **a.** $\log \dfrac{x^3}{3x+1}$ **b.** $\log \dfrac{x(x+2)}{(x+3)^2}$

7. **a.** $\log \sqrt[3]{(x+1)^2}$ **b.** $\log \dfrac{1}{\sqrt{3x-4}}$

8. **a.** $\log x^3 \sqrt{x+1}$ **b.** $\log \dfrac{2x^2}{(x-1)^3}$

9. **a.** $\log \sqrt{x^2 + y^2}$ **b.** $\log \sqrt{x^2 - y^2}$

10. $\log \dfrac{x^2}{(x-1)(2x+3)}$ 11. $\log \dfrac{\sqrt[3]{1-2x}}{(x+3)^2}$

12. $\log \dfrac{\sqrt{x+2}}{x^2 - 2x}$ 13. $\log \dfrac{(2x-5)(3x+4)}{(x+2)(x-1)}$

14. $\log \dfrac{x^2 - x - 6}{x^2 - 1}$ 15. $\log \sqrt{\dfrac{(x-1)^3}{x+2}}$

16. $\log \dfrac{2x \sqrt[3]{x-2}}{x^2}$ 17. $\log \dfrac{3x^4}{\sqrt{(2x+1)^3}}$

18. $\log \sqrt{\dfrac{3x-7}{x^3}}$ 19. $\log \dfrac{x^2 \sqrt{1-3x}}{1+2x}$

20. $\log \dfrac{\sqrt{x^2 - 1}}{x^3 + 2x^2}$ 21. $\log \dfrac{(2x+3)^{3/2}(x+1)^4}{3x\sqrt{1-x}}$

22. $\log \left(\dfrac{x^2 - 9}{x^2 - 2x - 5} \right)^{1/3}$ 23. $\log \dfrac{3x(x^2+4)^2}{(x+2)\sqrt{2x+3}}$

24. $\log \dfrac{5x^4}{(x+3)^{2/3}(x-2)^3}$ 25. $\log \dfrac{1}{\sqrt{2x^2 - x - 3}}$

26. $\log \dfrac{3x^2 \sqrt{1-x}}{5(x+2)^3 \cdot \sqrt{2x+1}}$

Find the values of the expressions in Problems 27–30.

27. **a.** $2^{4 \log_2 3}$ **b.** $10^{2 \log_{10} 5}$
28. **a.** $e^{5 \ln 2}$ **b.** $e^{b \ln a}$
29. **a.** $\log_2 \dfrac{\sqrt[3]{4}}{16}$ **b.** $\log_3 \dfrac{(81)^2}{\sqrt{27}}$

30. **a.** $\ln \dfrac{e^{3/2}}{\sqrt[3]{e}}$ **b.** $\log_4 \dfrac{\sqrt{8}}{32}$

In Problems 31–36 use the properties of logarithms to combine each expression into a single term.

31. **a.** $\log x - \log y$ **b.** $2 \log x + 3 \log(x+1)$
32. **a.** $3 \log x - 2 \log y$ **b.** $\log 2 + \log x + \frac{1}{2} \log(x+1)$

33. a. $\frac{1}{2} \log(x - 1) + \log 2 - 3 \log(x + 2)$
    b. $3 \log(x + 2) - \frac{1}{2} \log x - \frac{1}{2} \log(1 - x)$

34. a. $\log 3 + \frac{2}{3} \log(x^2 + 4) - 2 \log(2x - 3)$
    b. $2 \log(x + 1) - 3 \log(x - 1) - \frac{1}{2} \log(1 - 2x)$

35. a. $\frac{1}{2} \log(5x + 3) - [2 \log(x + 2) + \log(3x + 1)]$
    b. $\log 2 + \log x - \frac{1}{2} \log(x + 1) + \log C$

36. a. $\log(x^2 + 1) + \frac{2}{3} \log(x - 3) - \log 2 - \frac{1}{2} \log(3x - 4) + \log C$
    b. $\log 5 + 2 \log(6x + 5) - \frac{1}{2}[\log(2x + 1) + 3 \log(x - 2)]$

In Problem 37–39 find x in terms of natural logarithms. (See Example 19.)

37. a. $4^x = 3$ **b.** $3^x = 5^{x-1}$

38. a. $2 \cdot 3^{-x} = 6^{2x}$ **b.** $3^{x+1} = e^{x/2}$

39. a. $e^{-x} = 2^{x-3}$ **b.** $3 \cdot 4^{2x} = 2 \cdot 3^{-x}$

In Problems 40–52 solve for x, and check your answers.

40. $\log 2 + \log x = \log 3 + \log(x - 1)$

41. $2 \log x = \log 2 + \log(x + 4)$

42. $2 \log x = \log(x + 10) - \log 3$

43. $\log x + \log(2x - 5) = \log 3$

44. $\log 3 + \log(x + 2) = \log 2 + \log(3x - 1)$

45. $\log x + \log(x - 4) = \log(x + 2) + \log(x - 5)$

46. $2 \log(x + 1) - \log(x + 4) = \log(x - 1)$

47. $\log(x - 1) - \log(x + 6) = \log(x - 2) - \log(x + 3)$

48. $\log x + \log(x - 2) = \log(x + 4)$

49. $\log_2(-x) + \log_2(3 - x) = 2$

50. $\log_2(x - 1) + \log_2(x - 2) = 1$

51. $\log_3 x + \log_3(x + 8) = 2$

52. $\log_9(2 - x) + \log_9(-x) = \frac{1}{2}$

53. This problem is taken from an ARCO study guide for the Medical College Admission Test (MCAT):*

Which of the following equations is best represented by the graph?
(A) $x + y = a^b$ (B) $x - y = e^2$ (C) $ax^2 + by^2 = 0$
(D) $x + y = ab$ (E) $y = ax^b$

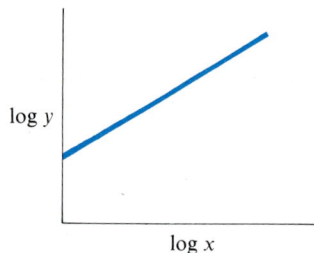

In Problems 54–60 find y as a function of x.

54. $\log y = \log x - \log(x - 1) + \log C$

55. $2 \log y - 3 \log x = \log 4$

---

* David R. Turner, *Medical College Admission Test*, 6th ed. (New York: ARCO Publishing, Inc., 1977), p. 242. Reprinted by permission.

56. $\log y = 2 \log(x + 1) - \log x + \log C$

57. $\log y = 3 \log x + \log(2x - 3) - \frac{1}{2} \log(x + 2) + \log C$

58. $\ln y = x + \ln C$

59. $\ln(2y - 3) = 2 \ln(x - 1) + \ln C$

60. $\ln(y - 1) = 2x + \ln C$

61. Let $f(x) = \log_a x$ and $g(x) = \log_b x$. Verify each of the following:

  a. $f(x) = \dfrac{g(x)}{g(a)}$ **b.** $g(x) = \dfrac{f(x)}{f(b)}$ **c.** $f(b) \cdot g(a) = 1$

62. Explain the differences in meaning among the following:
  a. $\log x^2$ **b.** $(\log x)^2$ **c.** $\log(\log x)$
  Show by means of an example that these expressions yield different results.

In Problems 63–67 use a calculator to approximate the value of x to four significant figures.

63. **a.** $4^x = 3$ **b.** $3^{1-x} = 7$

64. **a.** $3^x = 2^{3/2}$ **b.** $5^{x/2} = 3^5$

65. **a.** $4 \cdot 2^{-x} = 3^{x+1}$ **b.** $2 \cdot 5^x = 3^{2x-4}$

66. **a.** $(2.034)^x = 12.06$ **b.** $(0.6305)^{-x} = 3.125$

67. **a.** $x = \log_2(3.104)$ **b.** $x = \dfrac{1}{\log_3 15.24}$

B In Problems 68–73 solve for x and check your answers.

68. $2 \log_3(x - 2) - \log_3(x + 4) = 1$

69. $\log_e(2x - 1) + \log_e(x - 1) = 0$

70. $\log_4(x - 3) - \log_4(2x + 1) = -1$

71. $\log_{10} x + \log_{10} 2 = 1 - \log_{10}(x + 4)$

72. $\log_2 x + \log_2(x^2 - 3) = 1$

73. $\log_2(x + 3) - \log_2 3 = \log_2(3x + 4)$ $③ = \log_2 2^3 = 3\log_2 2 = (3)(1) = 3$

74. Show that $-\log(x - \sqrt{x^2 - 1}) = \log(x + \sqrt{x^2 - 1})$.

75. Show that $\log \dfrac{1}{\sqrt{x} - \sqrt{x - 1}} = \log(\sqrt{x} + \sqrt{x - 1})$.

In Problems 76–78 give the graphical solution of each system of inequalities.

76. $\begin{cases} x > 0 \\ y \le \ln x \\ x - y < 4 \end{cases}$ **77.** $\begin{cases} x < 1 \\ y + \ln(1 - x) \ge 0 \\ y - 2x \le 4 \end{cases}$ **78.** $\begin{cases} y \ge 1 + e^{-x} \\ y \le 1 + \ln x \\ 2x + 3y \le 12 \end{cases}$

79. Solve for x:

$$\frac{e^x - e^{-x}}{2} = 2$$

Hint. By clearing of fractions and negative exponents, obtain the equation in the form $e^{2x} - 4e^x - 1 = 0$, and observe that this is quadratic in e^x.

80. Solve for x:

$$\frac{e^x + e^{-x}}{2} = 3$$

(See hint for Problem 79.)

81. Solve for x:

$$x^{\log_2 x} = \frac{x^4}{8}$$

Hint.   Take logarithm to base 2 of both sides.

Review Exercise Set

A   In Problems 1 and 2 make a table of values and draw the graph of each function.

1.   **a.** $y = (3/2)^x$ **b.** $y = 1 - 2^{-x}$
       c. $y = \log_2 x$ **d.** $y = \ln(1 - x)$
2.   **a.** $f(x) = 2^{x/2} - 1$ **b.** $g(x) = \log_2(1 - 2x)$
       c. $h(x) = 3^{(x-1)/2}$ **d.** $F(x) = 2 - \log_e(x - 2)$

3.   Write in exponential form:
       a. $\log_3 9 = 2$ **b.** $\log_{10} 0.001 = -3$ **c.** $\log_2 256 = 8$
       d. $v = \log_k y$ **e.** $z = \log_r s$
4.   Write in logarithmic form:
       a. $4^{3/2} = 8$ **b.** $27^{-2/3} = \frac{1}{9}$ **c.** $10^3 = 1,000$
       d. $p = q^s$ **e.** $n = a^t$

In Problems 5–7 find the unknown.

5.   **a.** $\log_2 x = 4$ **b.** $\log_y 16 = -2$ **c.** $\log_3 81 = z$
6.   **a.** $y = \log_3 27$ **b.** $\log_x 0.0001 = -4$ **c.** $\log_4 z = -3$
7.   **a.** $x = e^{\ln 3}$ **b.** $y = \log_5 5^2$ **c.** $\log_2(1 - x) = 3$

In Problems 8–10 write in a form that is free of logarithms of powers, roots, products, and quotients.

8.   **a.** $\log \dfrac{2x^3}{\sqrt{x - 1}}$ **b.** $\log \dfrac{x(x - 2)}{2(x^2 + 1)^3}$

9.   **a.** $\log \dfrac{x - 1}{(x + 2)^3}$ **b.** $\log \sqrt{\dfrac{2x - 1}{3x}}$

10.   **a.** $\log \dfrac{x^2 - 9}{x^2 - 4x + 4}$ **b.** $\log \dfrac{4x^2\sqrt{2x - 1}}{(x - 2)(x + 4)^{3/2}}$

Combine the expressions in Problems 11–13 into a single term.

11.   **a.** $\frac{1}{2}\log(2x - 3) + \log x - 3\log 2 + \log C$
        b. $4\log x - \frac{1}{2}\log(x + 2) - \log(x - 1)$
12.   **a.** $\log(3x + 4) - 2\log x - \log(x + 2)$
        b. $3\log(x + 2) + \frac{1}{2}\log(2x - 1) - \frac{3}{2}\log(2 - x)$
13.   **a.** $\log 2 + 3\log x - \frac{1}{3}[\log(x - 1) + \log(x + 2)]$
        b. $\frac{3}{2}\log(2x + 3) - \log 2 - 3\log(x + 4)$

Evaluate the expressions in Problems 14 and 15.

14.   **a.** $\log_{10} 10^{-12}$ **b.** $e^{\ln 5}$
        c. $2^{3\log_2 5}$ **d.** $10^{2\log_{10} 4}$

15. **a.** $\log_4 8$ **b.** $\log_2 0.125$

     c. $\log_3 \frac{1}{81}$ **d.** $\log_{10} 0.00001$

16. Solve for x in terms of natural logarithms.

     a. $3^x = 7$ **b.** $2^{x+1} = 3^{2x}$

     c. $4 \cdot 5^x = 3^{x-2}$ **d.** $3^x \cdot 2^{x+3} = 5^{2x}$

17. Solve the formula $y = C(1 - e^{-kt})$ for k.

In Problems 18–25 solve for x and check your answer.

18. $\log(3x + 2) - \log(2x - 1) = \log 2$

19. $\log x + \log(x - 2) = \log 3$

20. $\log x + \log(2x - 1) = \log 3$

21. $\log(x + 2) - \log(3x - 1) = \log(x - 1) - \log(x + 3)$

22. $\log_2(1 - x) + \log_2(4x + 1) = 0$

23. $\log_5(3x + 1) + \log_5(x + 1) = 1$

24. $\log_2(2x + 1) - \log_2(x - 1) = 2$

25. $\log_4(x - 3) + \log_4(2x + 1) = 1$

26. Solve for y as a function of x.

     a. $\ln(2y - 1) = 3x + \ln C$

     b. $\log y = 2 \log(x - 1) - \log(x + 1) + \log C$

27. A radioactive substance has a half-life of 6 years. If 20 pounds are present initially, how much will remain after 2 years?

28. A culture of bacteria increases from 1,000 to 5,000 in 8 hours. Assuming the law of exponential growth applies, how many will be present after 20 hours?

29. The population of a certain city in Florida increased by 40% between 1970 and 1978. If the population in 1978 was 210,000, what will be the population in the year 2000? (Assume the law of exponential growth holds.)

30. An object cools from 140°F to 120°F in 5 minutes when placed in outside air at 40°F. After how many more minutes will the temperature of the object be 70°F? (See Problem 36, Exercise Set 1.)

31. The sum of $5,000 is placed in a savings account paying 6% annual interest.

     a. How much money will there be after 5 years if interest is compounded quarterly? Continuously?

     b. If interest is compounded continuously, how long will it take for the amount to double?

32. At a distance of 1 meter the intensity of sound of normal conversation is about 10^{-6} watt per square meter. What is the intensity in decibels? (See Example 12.)

33. If atmospheric pressure at sea level is 14.7 pounds per square inch and at a height of 18,000 feet the pressure is half as great, find the pressure at a height of 10,000 feet, assuming pressure p obeys the law

$$p = p_0 e^{-kh}$$

where p_0 is the pressure at sea level and h is the height above sea level.

34. Find how many years are required for a principal of $10,000 to grow to $15,000 if it is invested at 6% compounded annually.

35. At what interest rate would an amount of money have to be invested in order to double after 10 years if interest is compounded continuously?

In Problems 36 and 37 use a calculator to approximate the unknown to four significant figures.

36. **a.** $5^{x-1} = 3$ **b.** $2^t = 3^{1-t}$

37. **a.** $4 \cdot 6^y = 7 \cdot 5^{y/2}$ **b.** $(3.025)^{2x-1} = (0.7134)^{-x}$

B   In Problems 38 and 39 solve the systems of inequalities graphically.

38.
$$\begin{cases} x > 1 \\ y < \log_2(2x - 1) \\ 2x - 3y < 6 \end{cases}$$

39.
$$\begin{cases} y - 1 \le \ln(x + 1) \\ y + 1 \ge e^{x-1} \end{cases}$$

40.   Solve for x:

$$\frac{e^x - e^{-x}}{e^x + e^{-x}} = \frac{1}{2}$$

(See Problem 79, Exercise Set 3.)

41.   If sugar is placed in water, the amount undissolved after t seconds is given by the formula $A = Ce^{-kt}$. If 30 grams of sugar are placed in water and it takes 10 seconds for half of it to dissolve, how long will it take for all but 3 grams to dissolve?

42.   If a body falls through the air and air resistance is taken into consideration, then by calculus it can be shown that the velocity after t seconds is given by

$$v = \frac{mg}{k} + \left(v_0 - \frac{mg}{k}\right)e^{-kt/m}$$

where m is the mass of the body, g is the acceleration due to gravity, v_0 is the initial velocity, and k is a positive constant. If $v_0 = 30$, $m = 2$, $g = 32$, and $k = 0.2$, find how long it will take to attain a velocity of 200.

43.   When limitations on size are considered for the growth of a colony of bacteria (due to physical limitations or limitations on nutrients, for example) the growth is described reasonably accurately by what is known as the **law of logistic growth:**

$$Q = \frac{mQ_0}{Q_0 + (m - Q_0)e^{-kmt}}$$

where Q_0 is the initial quantity present, m is the maximum size, and k is a positive constant. If $Q_0 = 200$, $m = 1{,}000$, and $Q = 400$ when $t = \frac{1}{2}$, find k.

44.   The so-called **learning curve** in educational psychology has an equation of the form $f(t) = C(1 - e^{-kt})$, where C and k are positive constants and t represents time. The value of $f(t)$ can be interpreted as the amount learned at time t. This also has applications in industry.
   a.   Draw the graph of f for $C = 10$ and $k = 0.1$.
   b.   Suppose that learning vocabulary in a foreign language follows the learning curve, and that for an average first-year college student $C = 20$, with time t measured in days. Suppose also that on the tenth day of study it has been found that first-year students can be expected to learn 15 new words. Find how many words a student would be expected to learn on the fifth day.

Cumulative Review Exercise Set II (Chapters 4–7)

1. Find the domain of each of the functions.

    a. $f(x) = \sqrt{\dfrac{2x-1}{x^2-4}}$ 　　**b.** $g(x) = \sqrt{3x^3 - 5x^2 - 38x + 40}$

2. Find all zeros of the polynomial $P(x) = 6x^3 - 19x^2 - 26x + 24$. Factor the polynomial with integer coefficients.

3. Let

$$f(x) = \begin{cases} x^2 - 16 & \text{if} & x > 4 \\ \sqrt{x} & \text{if} & 0 < x \le 4 \\ -1 & \text{if} & x \le 0 \end{cases}$$

    Draw the graph of f. Find:
    a. $f(4)$ 　　**b.** $f(0)$ 　　**c.** $f(1)$ 　　**d.** $f(5)$ 　　**e.** $f(-1)$

4. **a.** Solve for x in terms of natural logarithms:

$$2^{(3-x)/2} = 4 \cdot 3^x$$

    b. Solve for x:

$$e^{3 \ln(x-1)} = \ln e^{(3-x)}$$

5. A piece of machinery valued at \$32,000 is estimated to have a residual value of \$2,000 after 20 years. If it is depreciated linearly, express its value after t years as a function of t. What will be its value after 16 years?

6. Let $g(x) = \frac{1}{2}(x^2 - 4x + 6)$. Draw the graph of g, and identify the curve. Is g 1–1 on R? If not, give a restriction on the domain so that on the restricted domain g is 1–1, and find g^{-1}. What are the domain and range of g^{-1}?

7. Let $f(x) = 1 + e^{2x}$ and $g(x) = \ln(x - 1)$. Find $f \circ g$ and $g \circ f$, and draw their graphs. Give the domain of each.

8. **a.** Show that the function

$$f(x) = \frac{1 - 2x}{3}$$

    is 1–1 on R, and find f^{-1}.
    b. Prove that the function $g(x) = \sqrt{x-1}$ is 1–1 from the set $A = \{x: \ x \ge 1\}$ onto the set R^+.

9. Use graphical means to solve the inequalities.
    a. $x(4 - x) \ge -12$ 　　**b.** $x^3 - 12x + 16 > 0$

10. Find x and y intercepts, vertical and horizontal asymptotes, and sketch.

    a. $y = \dfrac{9 - x^2}{x^2 + 2x - 8}$ 　　**b.** $y = \dfrac{x + 4}{x^2 - 4}$

11. A right circular cone has base radius r and altitude h. Express the area of a cross-section taken x units above the base as a function of x.

12. Sketch the graph of the polynomial function

$$y = (x - 2)(x + 1)^2(x - 5)^3(x + 4)$$

13. Let $f(x) = 1 + |x - 1|$. Give the domain and range of f, and draw its graph. Is f 1–1? Explain why or why not.

14. A certain radioactive substance has a half-life of 8 years. If 200 grams are present initially, how much will remain at the end of 12 years? How long will it be until only 10% of the original amount remains?

15. Let $f(t) = \sqrt{t - 1}$ and $g(t) = t^2 - 3$. Find $f \circ g$ and $g \circ f$, give the domain and range of each, and draw their graphs.

16. Find all roots of the equation

$$4x^4 - 16x^3 + 9x^2 + 5x + 25 = 0$$

Make a table of values using synthetic division, and draw the graph of the given polynomial.

17. Solve for x and check:

$$2 \log_2|x - 1| = 2 - \log_2(x + 2)$$

18. By calculus it can be shown that the slope of the tangent line to the curve $x^2 - y^2 = 9$ at any point (x, y) on the curve is given by $m = x/y$. Find the equations of the tangent and normal lines at each point on the curve with abscissa 5. Draw the curve, showing these tangent and normal lines.

19. Let $f(x) = 1/\sqrt{x}$. Find

$$\frac{f(x + h) - f(x)}{h}$$

and express the answer with a rational numerator.

20. **a.** Show that by taking logarithms of both sides of the equation $y = a^x$ and making the substitution $Y = \log y$, Y is a linear function of x.
   b. Similarly, in $y = x^a$ take logarithms, and let $X = \log x$ as well as $Y = \log y$, and show that Y is a linear function of X.
   c. For $y = 2^x$ graph $\log y$ versus x, and for $y = x^2$ graph $\log y$ versus $\log x$.

21. The formula $T = T_0 + Ce^{-kt}$ gives the temperature T of a body t units of time after being placed in a medium of temperature T_0. A body initially at $80°C$ is placed in outside air at $25°C$, and after 15 minutes it has cooled to $60°C$. What will its temperature be after 1 hour? How long will it take to reach a temperature of $30°C$?

22. The volume of oil that flows through a pipeline per day is jointly proportional to the velocity of flow and the square of the diameter of the pipe. If approximately 3 million barrels of oil per day flow through a pipe which is 3 feet in diameter when the velocity is 10 feet per second, how many barrels would flow per day through a pipe 2 feet in diameter if the velocity is 15 feet per second?

23. A manufacturer of solar energy cells finds that the cost, in dollars, of producing x units of a certain type per month is given by $30x + 1{,}500$, and he sets the selling price per unit, depending on the number of units sold, as $120 - 0.1x$. How many units should be manufactured and sold per month to maximize profit? What is the maximum profit?

24. Sketch the graph of each of the following. Identify the graph in each case, and state whether the graph is that of a function of x.
   a. $y^2 + 2x - 4y = 0$ **b.** $y = -\sqrt{9 - x^2}$
   c. $x^2 + 2y^2 = 4$ **d.** $4x^2 - 9y^2 + 36 = 0$
   e. $y = 2x^2 - 3x - 5$

25. The illumination given by a light varies directly as the candlepower of the light and inversely as the square of the distance from the source. Two lights are placed 15 meters apart. One has four times as much candlepower as the other. An object is to be placed on the line between the lights in such a way that it receives equal illumination from the two lights. How far from the stronger light should it be placed?

26. Prove that the points $(3, 2)$, $(-1, -1)$, and $(6, -2)$ are vertices of an isosceles right triangle. Find the equation of the altitude drawn from the right angle vertex to the hypotenuse.

27. The cost in hundreds of dollars for a company to produce x tons of a certain type of fertilizer per day is given by $C = 4x^2 - 20x + 29$. Find the number of tons that should be produced each day to minimize cost. What is the minimum cost?

28. Find the equation of the tangent line to the circle $x^2 + y^2 - 4x + 2y - 15 = 0$ at the point $(4, 3)$.

29. Draw the graph of each of the following:
   a. $f(x) = \ln(1 + x^2)$ **b.** $g(x) = 1 - e^{-|x|}$
   c. $y = 2^{(x-1)/2}$ **d.** $y = 1 + \log_2|x - 1|$
30. Let $f(x) = \ln(x^2 - x) - \ln(x^2 + 3) + \ln 2$.
   a. Find the domain of f.
   b. Find the zeros of f.
   c. Find all vertical asymptotes to the graph of f.
   d. Discuss the behavior of f as x gets large in absolute value. What can you conclude concerning horizontal asymptotes?
   e. Sketch the graph of f.

8 Introduction to Trigonometric Functions

While trigonometry has long been an important tool in the study of physics and chemistry, it sometimes has uses in the social sciences also, as the following excerpt from a psychology textbook shows.*

If the subject is looking directly at a point in space, then this fixation point is arriving at the center of the subject's eye. Figure 5 presents a top view of one eye of a subject looking at a fixation point. . . .

Figure 5

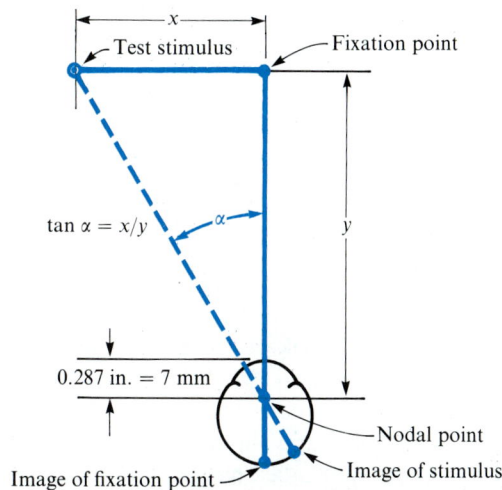

Using trigonometry, we can compute the angle α for any test stimulus if we know the distance between the eye and the fixation point and the separation between the fixation point and the test stimulus. The value of α for the test stimulus in Figure 5 can be determined by determining the angle whose tangent is x/y.

This example illustrates the use of right triangle trigonometry. The tangent function, employed here, is one of the six trigonometric functions you will study in this chapter and the next.

* Dominic W. Massaro, *Experimental Psychology and Information Processing*, pp. 149, 150. Copyright © 1975 by Rand McNally College Publishing Company. Reprinted by permission.

1 Introduction

The introduction of trigonometry as a separate area of study is generally believed to have been due to the Greek Hipparchus in the second century BC, but his works are lost. The first exposition of the subject still in existence comes from the work of Ptolemy, the Greek astronomer who lived in the second century AD. Rudiments of the subject are much older, however, and can be traced to Babylon and ancient Egypt. The principal use of trigonometry up until the fifteenth century was in astronomy, because it afforded a means of making indirect measurements. The name *trigonometry* was first used by Pitiscus (a German) in 1595 as the title of his book. The name is a combination of three Greek words meaning "three-angle measurement," or triangle measurement.

As the name implies, trigonometry originally meant a study of triangles, or more generally of angles of triangles, and its primary utility lay in the fact that by means of the trigonometric functions inaccessible quantities could be measured. In more modern times, while trigonometry still is of value for this purpose, it is the analytical aspects of the subject that make it indispensable in the study of many physical phenomena. We will indicate how it is useful in indirect measurement, but our emphasis will be on the analytical properties, since these are more important in calculus.

2 The Measurement of Angles

When two rays emanate from the same point, as in Figure 1, we say they form an angle. The common point is called the vertex. In trigonometry it is useful to think of the angle as having been formed by having the rays initially coincident and then rotating one of them. We indicate the direction of rotation by a small circular arc with an arrowhead. The fixed ray is called the **initial side** and the rotated ray is called the **terminal side.** A counterclockwise rotation is called **positive;** a clockwise rotation is called **negative.** These ideas are illustrated in Figure 2.

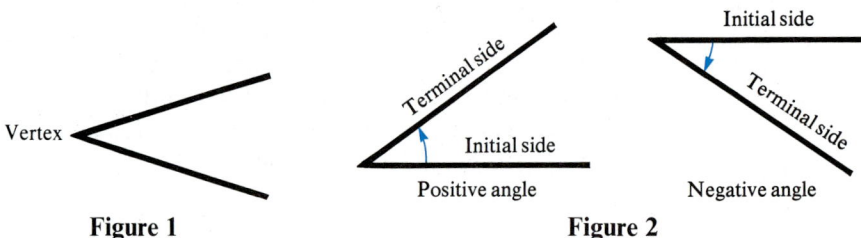

Figure 1   **Figure 2**

When two angles are generated by different rotations but have the same initial and terminal sides, they are said to be **coterminal.** Two coterminal angles are illustrated in Figure 3.

Figure 3

Coterminal angles

The most familiar way of measuring the size of angles is by means of the degree.* If a circle is divided into 360 equal parts, then an angle formed by two rays from the center passing through two consecutive points on the circle is said to have a measure of one **degree,** indicated $1°$. Degrees are divided into 60 equal parts called **minutes,** and minutes are further divided into **seconds,** with 60 seconds equalling one minute. One minute is designated $1'$ and one second $1''$. If we write, for example, $A = 25°32'15''$, we mean that A is an angle whose measure is 25 degrees, 32 minutes, and 15 seconds. In our work we will seldom use seconds. An alternate way of indicating fractions of a degree is to use decimal notation. For example, we might have $B = 47.3°$. This form is especially useful with scientific hand calculators, since most of these require angles to be written in decimal form. It is important to be able to go from one form to the other. For example, since $1° = 60'$, we see that $0.3° = (0.3)(60') = 18'$. So $47.3° = 47°18'$. Also, to change minutes to decimal parts of degrees, divide the number of minutes by 60. This is illustrated by

$$35°15' = \left(35\frac{15}{60}\right)° = 35.25°$$

While the measurement of angles by degrees has the weight of history and the advantage of familiarity on its side, there is another method of measurement that for many purposes is more useful, especially in the study of calculus and its applications. This is the **radian.** To define it we consider a given angle and construct any circle with its center at the vertex of the angle, as in Figure 4. Designate the angle by θ and let s be the length of the arc on the circle subtended by θ. If r is the length of the radius, then we define the **radian measure** of θ to be the ratio s/r. It might appear that this definition is dependent on which circle we use, but this is not the case. For if we take another circle of radius r' and subtended arc s', as in Figure 4, then the two circular sectors are similar (just as if they were triangles), and so $s/r = s'/r'$. Thus we get the same number for the radian measure of θ regardless of which circle is used. As with degree measure, we often use the same symbol for the name of an angle and for its measure. So we can write

$$\theta = \frac{s}{r} \qquad (1)$$

---

* No one knows for sure the origin of degree measurement, but it can be traced back to the ancient Sumerians (4000–2000 B.C.). One theory is that 360 was used because of their erroneous calculation of 360 days in a year. They and the Babylonians (2000–600 B.C.) used 60 as a base in their arithmetic.

Figure 4

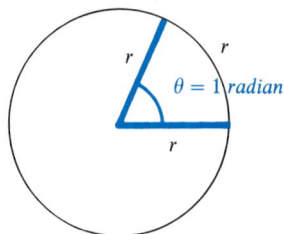

Figure 5

As a practical matter, it is useful to write this in the equivalent form

$$s = r\theta \tag{2}$$

since we can measure angles and straight lines more easily than arcs of circles. Equation (2) says that the length of arc subtended on a circle of radius r by an angle of θ *radians* (not degrees) equals the product $r \cdot \theta$. This is an important result and should be remembered.

Another observation is that according to Equation (1) the radian measure of θ is the ratio of two lengths, and hence the radian is dimensionless. In analyzing the dimensional properties of an expression, then, if an angle in radians appears in the expression, the dimensionality is not affected.

According to equation (1), an angle of one radian subtends, on any circle with its center at the vertex, an arc equal in length to the radius (Figure 5). This helps us to visualize the relative size of a radian. We know that the circumference of a circle is $2\pi r$. That is, we could mark off 2π arcs on the circle each equal in length to the radius (since $\pi \approx 3.1416$, we could mark off 6 full arcs equal to the radius and have a little more than a quarter of a radius left over). But for each arc on the circle of length r, there is an angle of one radian at the center. It follows then that there are 2π radians in one revolution. Since there are also $360°$ in one revolution, we have the relationships:

$$2\pi \text{ radians} = 360°$$
$$\pi \text{ radians} = 180°$$
$$1 \text{ radian} = \frac{180°}{\pi} \approx 57.3° \tag{3}$$
$$1 \text{ degree} = \frac{\pi}{180} \text{ radians}$$

Probably the easiest of these to remember is the second

$$\pi \text{ radians} = 180°$$

and the others can be obtained from it. In the future, unless the degree symbol is used in speaking of the measure of an angle, we will automatically mean radian measure. Thus, if we write $\theta = \pi$, $\pi/6$, or $\theta = 2$, we will mean the measure of θ is π radians, $\pi/6$ radians, or 2 radians, respectively.

The relationships (3) enable us to find the radian measure of an angle whose degree measure is known, and vice versa. The following example illustrates this.

EXAMPLE 1   Convert the degree measures in parts **a** and **b** to radians, and convert the radian measures in parts **c** and **d** to degrees.

a. 120°   **b.** 540°   **c.** $\dfrac{7\pi}{6}$ **d.** $\dfrac{2}{3}$

Solution   **a.**   Since $1° = \pi/180$ radians, we multiply 120 by $\pi/180$.

$$120 \cdot \frac{\pi}{180} = \frac{2\pi}{3} \text{ radians}$$

b.
$$540 \cdot \frac{\pi}{180} = 3\pi \text{ radians}$$

c.   Since 1 radian $= 180/\pi$ degrees, we multiply $7\pi/6$ by $180°/\pi$.

$$\frac{7\pi}{6} \cdot \frac{180°}{\pi} = 210°$$

d.
$$\frac{2}{3} \cdot \frac{180°}{\pi} = \left(\frac{120}{\pi}\right)° \approx 38.2°$$

Note.   We will often leave the radian measure of an angle as a multiple of π, as in parts **a** and **b,** rather than give the decimal equivalent.

The next two examples illustrate uses of equations (1) and (2).

EXAMPLE 2   A central angle in a circle of diameter 8 centimeters subtends an arc of 3 centimeters. Find the degree measure of the angle.

Solution   Since the diameter is 8, the radius is 4. Since $s = 3$, we have by (1)

$$\theta = \frac{s}{r} = \frac{3}{4} \text{ radians}$$

To convert to degrees, we multiply by $180°/\pi$.

$$\theta = \frac{3}{4} \cdot \frac{180°}{\pi} = \left(\frac{135}{\pi}\right)° \approx 42.97°$$

EXAMPLE 3   Find the arc length on a circle of radius 7 feet subtended by a central angle of 60°.

Solution   We use $s = r\theta$, but first we must find θ in radians.

$$\theta = 60° \cdot \frac{\pi}{180°} = \frac{\pi}{3}$$

So

$$s = 7 \cdot \frac{\pi}{3} = \frac{7\pi}{3} \text{ feet} \approx 7.33 \text{ feet}$$

Suppose now that an object is traveling in a circular path at a constant rate. Its **linear velocity** v is the distance along the circular arc covered per unit of time. Thus, if in time t it covers a distance of s units of arc, then

$$v = \frac{s}{t}$$

There is also an **angular velocity,** which we designate by ω, associated with the moving object. This is the number of radians turned through per unit of time. Thus, if in time t a central angle of θ radians has been turned through, then

$$\omega = \frac{\theta}{t}$$

Since $s = r\theta$, we have

$$\frac{s}{t} = r \cdot \frac{\theta}{t}$$

or

$$v = r\omega \tag{4}$$

EXAMPLE 4   A point on a flywheel of radius 2 feet is turning at an angular velocity of 300 radians per second. What is the linear velocity of the point?

Solution $$v = r\omega = 2 \cdot 300 = 600 \text{ feet per second}$$

EXAMPLE 5   A wheel of diameter 4 feet is rotating at the rate of 1,200 revolutions per minute. Find the linear velocity of a point on the rim in feet per second.

Solution   In order to find the angular velocity ω in radians per second, we note that each revolution contains 2π radians, and since there are 1,200 revolutions each minute, which is equivalent to 20 revolutions each second, we have

$$\omega = 2\pi(20) = 40\pi \text{ radians per second}$$

Thus,

$$v = r\omega = 2(40\pi) = 80\pi \text{ feet per second}$$
$$\approx 251.33 \text{ feet per second}$$

EXERCISE SET 2

A In Problems 1–10 find the radian measure of the angles whose degree measures are given. Leave answers in terms of π.

1. a. $30°$ **b.** $45°$ **2. a.** $60°$ **b.** $90°$
3. a. $120°$ **b.** $135°$ **4. a.** $150°$ **b.** $225°$
5. a. $240°$ **b.** $270°$ **6. a.** $300°$ **b.** $315°$
7. a. $330°$ **b.** $15°$ **8. a.** $-50°$ **b.** $72°$
9. a. $600°$ **b.** $-144°$ **10. a.** $36°$ **b.** $-80°$

In Problems 11–20 give the degree measure of the angles having the given radian measures.

11. a. $\dfrac{3\pi}{4}$ **b.** $\dfrac{5\pi}{3}$ **12. a.** 4π **b.** $\dfrac{5\pi}{2}$

13. a. $\dfrac{5\pi}{6}$ **b.** $\dfrac{-4\pi}{3}$ **14. a.** $\dfrac{-7\pi}{2}$ **b.** $\dfrac{3\pi}{10}$

15. a. $\dfrac{5\pi}{9}$ **b.** 2 **16. a.** $\dfrac{3\pi}{2}$ **b.** $\dfrac{5\pi}{4}$

17. a. 3 **b.** $\dfrac{\pi}{12}$ **18. a.** $\dfrac{7\pi}{12}$ **b.** $\dfrac{\pi}{5}$

19. a. -4 **b.** $\dfrac{11\pi}{6}$ **20. a.** $\dfrac{9\pi}{4}$ **b.** $\dfrac{13\pi}{3}$

In Problems 21–23 use a calculator to convert to decimal degrees. Express answer to nearest hundredth of a degree.

21. a. $32°51'$ **b.** $102°35'$
22. a. $18°03'$ **b.** $321°48'$
23. a. $27°13'24''$ **b.** $-56°19'12''$

In Problems 24–27 use a calculator to convert to degrees and minutes, to the nearest minute.

24. a. $86.32°$ **b.** $29.78°$
25. a. $-13.05°$ **b.** $153.41°$
26. a. $\dfrac{\pi}{13}$ radians **b.** 2.563 radians
27. a. 3 radians **b.** 7.092 radians

In Problems 28–30 convert to radians, to the nearest thousandth of a radian.

28. a. $25.426°$ **b.** $115.750°$
29. a. $13°22'31''$ **b.** $290°12'24''$
30. a. $30°$ **b.** $-46.023°$

In Problems 31–34, θ is a central angle on a circle of radius r, and s is the arc on the circle subtended by θ. Find the value (s, r, or θ) which is not given.

31. a. $r = 3, \theta = 2$ **b.** $s = 4, \theta = 3$

32. a. $r = 5, s = 12$ **b.** $r = 2, \theta = 30°$

33. a. $s = 8, \theta = 45°$ **b.** $s = 4, r = 6$

34. a. $\theta = \dfrac{\pi}{3}, \ s = 6$ **b.** $\theta = \dfrac{3\pi}{4}, \ r = 4$

35. Find the arc length on the equator (in miles) subtended by an angle of $1°$ at the center of the earth. Assume the radius of the earth is 3,960 miles.

36. What is the length of the arc swept out by the tip of the minute hand of a clock during the time interval from 6:00 to 6:20 if the minute hand is 4 inches long?

37. The diameter of the steering wheel of a car is 15 inches, and it has 3 equally spaced spokes. Find the distance on the steering wheel between consecutive spokes.

38. A wheel is revolving at an angular velocity of $5\pi/3$ radians per second. Find the number of revolutions per minute (rpm) through which the wheel is turning.

39. A flywheel is turning at 1,800 rpm. Through how many radians per second is it turning?

B 40. The earth completes one revolution about its axis in 24 hours. Find the velocity in miles per hour of a point on the equator (take $r = 3,960$ miles). What is the velocity in feet per second?

41. A train is traveling on a circular curve of $\frac{1}{2}$ mile radius at the rate of 30 miles per hour. Through what angle (in radians) will the train turn in 45 seconds? What is the angle in degrees?

42. A flywheel 4 feet in diameter is revolving at the rate of 50 rpm. Find the speed of a point on the rim in feet per second.

43. Assume the earth moves around the sun in a circular orbit with radius 93,000,000 miles. A complete revolution takes approximately 365 days. Find the approximate speed of the earth in its orbit in miles per hour.

44. An automobile tire is 28 inches in diameter. If the car is traveling 30 miles per hour, through how many revolutions per minute is the wheel turning?

The following two problems are taken from an engineering textbook.*

45. Two points B and C lie on a radial line of a rotating disk. The points are 2 in. apart. $v_B = 700$ fpm [feet per minute] and $v_C = 880$ fpm. Find the radius of rotation for each of these points.

46. The tire of an automobile has an outside diameter of 27 in. If the rpm of the wheel is 700, determine the speed of the automobile (a) in miles per hour, (b) in feet per second, and (c) the angular speed of the wheel in radians per second.

---

3 Some Special Angles

An angle of $90°$ is called a **right angle,** and an angle of $180°$ is called a **straight angle.** An **acute angle** is an angle between $0°$ and $90°$, and an **obtuse angle** is one between $90°$ and $180°$. A triangle in which one angle is a right angle is called

---

* George H. Martin, *Kinematics and Dynamics of Machines*, rev. printing (New York: McGraw-Hill Book Company, 1969), p. 43. Reprinted by permission.

a **right triangle,** and the side opposite the 90° angle is called the **hypotenuse.** The other two sides are often referred to as the **legs** of the triangle. A triangle which is not a right triangle is said to be an **oblique** triangle. The following fundamental result about right triangles is proved in plane geometry. (A proof is outlined in Problem 34 at the end of this section.)

THE PYTHAGOREAN THEOREM **The sum of the squares of the lengths of the legs of a right triangle equals the square of the length of the hypotenuse.**

In Figure 6 we have labeled a right triangle with angles named by capital letters and sides opposite the angles named with the corresponding lowercase letters. This is a standard notation, and we will understand all right triangles to be designated this way unless specific instructions are given otherwise. The right angle is at C. We will follow the common practice of using these capital letters both to name the angles and to designate their measure. Similarly, we will use the lowercase letters as names of the sides as well as to designate their lengths. For example, we might say $A = 30°$, rather than "the degree measure of angle A is 30," and we might write $a = 2$ to mean "the length of side a is 2." This dual interpretation should not cause any difficulty. With this notation the Pythagorean theorem states that

$$a^2 + b^2 = c^2$$

The converse of this theorem is also true, and we call for a proof of this in Problem 35 at the end of this section. That is, if for a triangle with sides a, b, and c it is true that $a^2 + b^2 = c^2$, then the triangle is a right triangle, with the 90° angle opposite side c.

Figure 6

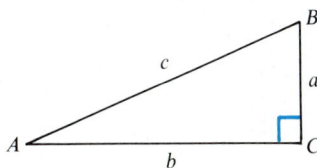

Another fundamental property of triangles proved in plane geometry is that the sum of the three angles in *any* triangle (not just a right triangle) is 180°. In particular, if the triangle is a right triangle, so that one of the angles is 90°, the sum of the two acute angles is 90°. Such angles are said to be **complementary,** and each is said to be the **complement** of the other. In Figure 6, angles A and B are complementary.

There are two right triangles that we single out for special attention. The first of these is referred to as a **30°–60° right triangle** because the acute angles are 30° and 60°, respectively. Let ABC be a 30°–60° right triangle with $A = 30°$, and $B = 60°$. If we flip the triangle over with side AC as an axis, as in Figure 7, we obtain a triangle ABB' in which all angles are 60°. Thus, this triangle is

Figure 7

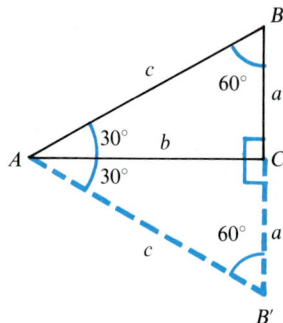

equiangular (all angles equal), and hence also **equilateral** (all sides equal). So $2a = c$, or $a = c/2$. This is the result we wish to emphasize.

In a **30°–60° right triangle,** the side opposite the 30° angle is one-half the hypotenuse.

As a special case, consider a right triangle ABC with $A = 30°$, $B = 60°$, and $c = 2$. Then by what we have just shown, we know that $a = 1$. We use the Pythagorean theorem to find b.

$$b^2 = c^2 - a^2 = 4 - 1 = 3$$
$$b = \sqrt{3}$$

Figure 8 illustrates the result, and it is useful to commit this to memory. All other 30°–60° right triangles are similar to this one, and so the sides are proportional to the corresponding sides of this triangle.

The second special type of right triangle we want to consider is the **isosceles right triangle,** that is, one in which the two legs are equal. It follows that the two acute angles are also equal, and hence each is 45°. If we let each leg be 1 unit, we find by the Pythagorean theorem that the hypotenuse is $\sqrt{1^2 + 1^2} = \sqrt{2}$. The situation is shown in Figure 9, which again should be committed to memory.

Figure 8

Figure 9

Example 6 illustrates how the concepts discussed in this section can be used to find unknown sides of certain right triangles.

EXAMPLE 6   In a right triangle ABC, with right angle at C, find the unknown sides from the given information.

a. $a = 3, \quad c = 5$ b. $A = 30°, \quad c = 10$
c. $B = 45°, \quad a = 8$ d. $A = 60°, \quad b = 12$

Solution   a.   In Figure 10, by the Pythagorean theorem

$$b^2 = c^2 - a^2 = 25 - 9 = 16$$
$$b = 4$$

Note.   This is known as a **3–4–5 right triangle,** and it is useful to remember that a triangle with sides 3, 4, and 5, or with sides respectively proportional to 3, 4, and 5, is a right triangle.

Figure 10

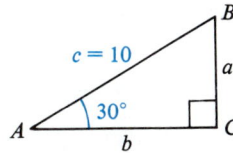

Figure 11

b.   Since $c = 10$, we know that $a = 5$. Using proportionality and Figure 8, we see that in Figure 11 $b = 5\sqrt{3}$. Alternatively, we could use the Pythagorean theorem to find b:

$$b = \sqrt{c^2 - a^2} = \sqrt{100 - 25} = \sqrt{75} = 5\sqrt{3}$$

c.   Since $B = 45°$, the triangle is isosceles. So $b = 8$, and from Figure 9 and proportionality we determine in Figure 12 that $c = 8\sqrt{2}$. Again, we could also find c by the Pythagorean theorem:

$$c = \sqrt{a^2 + b^2} = \sqrt{64 + 64} = \sqrt{(64) \cdot 2} = 8\sqrt{2}$$

d.   In Figure 13, angle $B = 90° - A = 30°$, and since the side opposite the 30° angle is half the hypotenuse, it follows that $c = 24$. Comparison with the basic 30°–60° right triangle of Figure 8, or use of the Pythagorean theorem, gives $a = 12\sqrt{3}$.

Figure 12

Figure 13

EXERCISE SET 3

A   In Problems 1–20 ABC is a right triangle with right angle at C. In each problem find the unknown sides.

1. $A = 30°, \quad c = 5$ **2.** $B = 60°, \quad a = 3$

3. $A = 60°, \quad b = 10$ **4.** $A = 30°, \quad b = 4\sqrt{3}$

5. $A = 30°, \quad b = 6$ **6.** $B = 30°, \quad a = 12$

7. $B = 45°, \quad c = 4\sqrt{2}$ **8.** $A = 45°, \quad c = 4$

9. $A = 60°, \quad c = 5$ **10.** $B = 60°, \quad b = 3$

11. $B = 45°, \quad a = 3$ **12.** $A = 60°, \quad a = 8$

13. $a = 2, \quad b = 3$ **14.** $a = 5, \quad c = 7$

15. $a = 7, \quad c = 25$ **16.** $b = 12, \quad c = 13$

17. $a = 14, \quad c = 50$ **18.** $a = 3, \quad b = \sqrt{3}$
                                          Also find angles A and B.

19. $a = 1, \quad b = 2\sqrt{2}$ **20.** $a = 8, \quad c = 17$

In Problems 21–26 two angles of a triangle are given. Find the third angle.

21. $23°17', \quad 75°34'$ **22.** $43.21°, \quad 68.35°$

23. $52.76°, \quad 103.42°$ **24.** $92°47', \quad 21°54'$

25. $\dfrac{\pi}{4}$ radians, $\dfrac{\pi}{3}$ radians   **26.** 1.25 radians, 0.78 radians

27. If a, b, and c are positive integers for which $a^2 + b^2 = c^2$, the numbers are said to form a **Pythagorean triple,** and we know that a triangle having sides of lengths a, b, and c, respectively, is a right triangle. Show that the following are Pythagorean triples.
  a. 6, 8, 10   **b.** 5, 12, 13   **c.** 8, 15, 17   **d.** 7, 24, 25   **e.** 9, 40, 41

B   **28.** It is proved in more advanced mathematics that all Pythagorean triples (see Problem 27) are of the form $a = m^2 - n^2$, $b = 2mn$, and $c = m^2 + n^2$, where m and n are positive integers, with $m > n$.
  a. Verify that all such numbers do form a Pythagorean triple.
  b. Find the values of m and n which produce each triple in Problem 27.
  c. Determine two additional Pythagorean triples not proportional to any of those in Problem 27.

29. In the accompanying figure the 45° right triangle is constructed so that one of its legs is the hypotenuse of the 30°–60° right triangle. Find
  a. the hypotenuse of the 45° triangle
  b. the combined areas of the two triangles.

30. Find a formula for the area of an equilateral triangle with side of length a.

31. Prove that in a triangle ABC with $A = 30°$ and $C = 90°$, the median drawn from C has length a. (A **median** is the line segment from a vertex to the midpoint of the opposite side.)

32. Find a formula for the area of the inscribed circle in an equilateral triangle with side of length a.

   Hint. The angle bisectors, which in an equilateral triangle coincide with the medians and the altitudes, intersect at the center of the inscribed circle.

33. Find the area of the circumscribed circle to an equilateral triangle with side of length a. (See hint to Problem 32. The inscribed circle and circumscribed circle are concentric.)

34. By the following steps prove the Pythagorean theorem.
   a. Consider a right triangle with legs of lengths a and b and hypotenuse of length c. Construct a square of side $a + b$ as shown, and draw four replicas (I, II, III, and IV) of the given triangle inside the square as shown.
   b. Show that the quadrilateral V is a square. (Work with angles.)
   c. Write the equation that puts into mathematical form the fact that the sum of the areas I, II, III, IV, and V equals the area of the large square.
   d. By simplifying the equation in **c**, draw the desired conclusion.

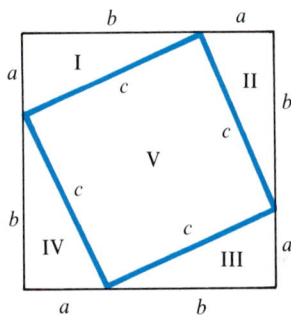

35. Follow the steps given to prove the converse of the Pythagorean theorem.
   a. Let ABC be a triangle in which $c^2 = a^2 + b^2$.

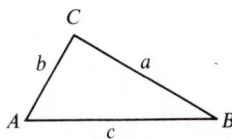

   b. Construct a right triangle $A'B'C'$ having legs a and b. Let the hypotenuse be of length c'. Use the Pythagorean theorem to express c' in terms of a and b.

   c. How can you conclude that $c' = c$?
   d. What does this say about triangle ABC compared with triangle $A'B'C'$?
   e. What do you conclude about angle C?

4 Right Triangle Trigonometry

We next introduce the trigonometric functions of an acute angle θ. These functions form the basis for the study of what is called *right triangle trigonometry*. The definitions will be extended to arbitrary angles in Section 6.

Let θ denote any acute angle, and consider any right triangle having θ as one of its angles. As shown in Figure 14 we label the legs opposite to θ and adjacent to θ. In the following definition we use *opposite*, *adjacent*, and *hypotenuse* to mean the *lengths* of these sides.

Figure 14

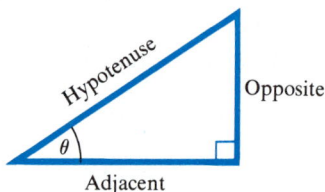

DEFINITION 1

Name	Abbreviation	Value
sine of θ	$\sin \theta$	$\dfrac{\text{opposite}}{\text{hypotenuse}}$
cosine of θ	$\cos \theta$	$\dfrac{\text{adjacent}}{\text{hypotenuse}}$
tangent of θ	$\tan \theta$	$\dfrac{\text{opposite}}{\text{adjacent}}$
cotangent of θ	$\cot \theta$	$\dfrac{\text{adjacent}}{\text{opposite}}$
secant of θ	$\sec \theta$	$\dfrac{\text{hypotenuse}}{\text{adjacent}}$
cosecant of θ	$\csc \theta$	$\dfrac{\text{hypotenuse}}{\text{opposite}}$

Note.   The domain of each function is the set of all acute angles, while the range is a subset of R.

Although the definition makes use of a right triangle, it is important to realize that the values of the functions depend only on θ and not on which right triangle having θ as one of its acute angles is used. To see this, consider any two such right triangles, as in Figure 15. Since $A = A'$ and $C = C'$ (both 90°), it follows that $B = B'$, so that the triangles are similar. Thus corresponding sides are proportional. In particular,

$$\frac{a}{c} = \frac{a'}{c'} \qquad \frac{b}{c} = \frac{b'}{c'} \qquad \frac{a}{b} = \frac{a'}{b'}$$

Figure 15

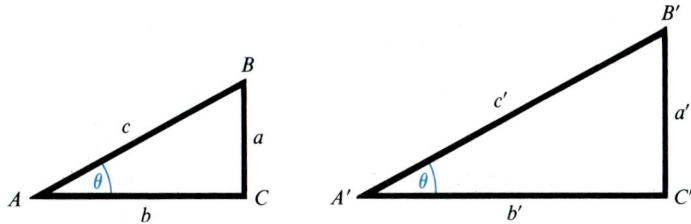

and so on. That is, we get the same values for sin θ, cos θ, tan θ, and the other functions regardless of which of the two triangles we use.

In Figure 16 we have labeled the angles and sides of a right triangle in standard notation. Observe that side a is opposite to angle A but is adjacent to angle B. Similarly, side b is adjacent to angle A but is opposite to angle B. So we have

$$\sin A = \frac{a}{c} = \cos B$$

$$\cos A = \frac{b}{c} = \sin B$$

$$\tan A = \frac{a}{b} = \cot B$$

$$\sec A = \frac{c}{b} = \csc B$$

$$\csc A = \frac{c}{a} = \sec B$$

Figure 16

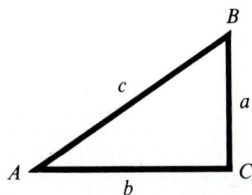

We call the sine and cosine **cofunctions** of one another. Similarly, the tangent and cotangent are cofunctions, as are the secant and cosecant. Since angles A and B are complementary, we have therefore shown the following:

Any trigonometric function of an acute angle equals the corresponding cofunction of its complement.

It is important that the trigonometric functions be learned in terms of *opposite*, *adjacent*, and *hypotenuse*, rather than a set of letters such as those used above, because we will not always be using standard notation.

By using the special 30°–60° and 45° right triangles, we can now determine the values of the trigonometric functions of 30°, 45°, and 60°. For other angles we rely either on a calculator or on tables (such as those in the back of this book) which are based on techniques studied in calculus. Hand calculators are both faster and more accurate to use than tables, and we have used a calculator in the examples throughout the remainder of this chapter involving numerical calculations. It is a good idea for you to become familiar with the use of tables, however. Most of our calculations involve approximate values, and we round answers accordingly. For simplicity, we will use equals signs throughout, even when the answers are only approximate.

EXAMPLE 7

Solve the right triangle *ABC* in which $A = 37°30'$ and $b = 17.3$ (Figure 17).

Note.   To "solve a triangle" means to find all unknown sides and angles.

Figure 17

Solution   Since *A* and *B* are complementary, $B = 90° - 37°30' = 52°30'$. Using the tangent of angle *A* we get

$$\tan A = \frac{a}{b}$$

$$a = b \tan A = 17.3 \tan 37°30' = 13.3$$

By calculator:
$$17.3 \boxed{\times} 37.5 \boxed{\text{TAN}} \boxed{=} 13.274757$$

To find *c* we use the cosine of *A*:

$$\cos A = \frac{b}{c}$$

$$c = \frac{b}{\cos A} = \frac{17.3}{\cos 37°30'} = 21.8$$

By calculator:
$$17.3 \boxed{\div} 37.5 \boxed{\text{COS}} \boxed{=} 21.806173$$

One of the chief applications of right triangle trigonometry is the calculation of inaccessible distances. An illustration is given in the next example.

EXAMPLE 8   Figure 18 illustrates a river and two points P and Q on opposite sides. By means of a transit at P, a line of sight perpendicular to PQ is determined, and a distance of 100 feet (to the nearest foot) along this line from P to R is measured. At R the transit is again set up and the angle from RP to RQ is measured and found to be 32.3°. It is desired to find the distance from P to Q.

Figure 18

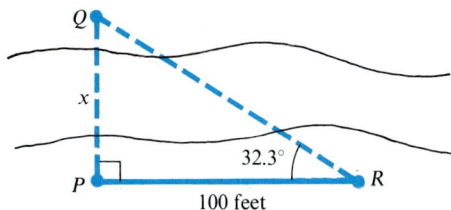

Solution   Let the distance from P to Q be denoted by x. Then

$$\tan 32.3° = \frac{x}{100}$$

$$x = 100 \tan 32.3° = 63.2 \text{ feet}$$

The following terminology will be employed in certain applications.

Angle of Elevation.   Angle from the horizontal upward to the line of sight of the observer.

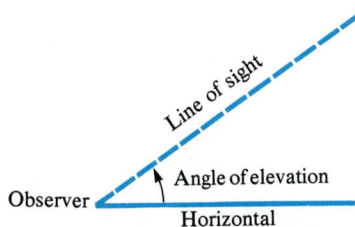

Angle of Depression.   Angle from the horizontal downward to the line of sight of the observer.

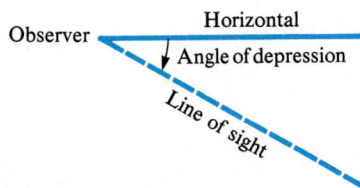

Bearing.   A means of giving the direction of a path by using either North or South as a base line and then indicating an acute angle either East or West of the base line. For example, N 30° E means a path in a direction 30° to the

East of North. Similarly, S 60° W means a direction which is 60° West of South.

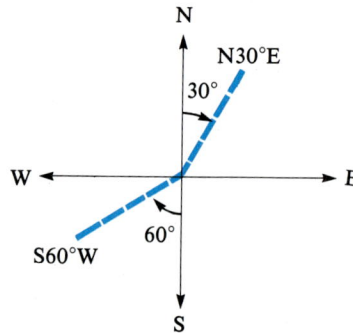

Heading. An alternate means of indicating direction in which an angle between 0° and 360° measured clockwise from North is given. The figure shows a heading of 225°. This means of indicating direction is widely employed, especially in air navigation.

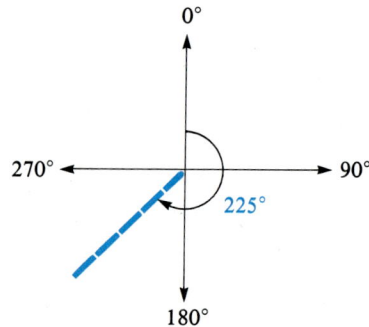

EXAMPLE 9   The angle of elevation of the top of a mountain from point A is 36.2°, and the angle of elevation of the top from point B, 1,000 feet (to the nearest foot) nearer the base of the mountain and on the same level as A, is 41.7° (see Figure 19). Find the height of the mountain.

Figure 19

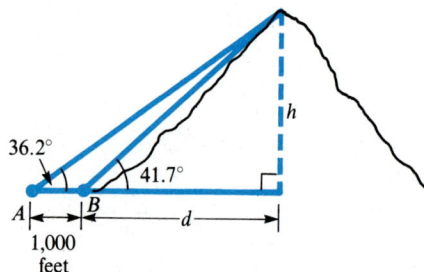

Solution We introduce the auxiliary unknown d in the figure, since it will be involved in the functions we use. There are two right triangles, each involving the unknown height h. In each triangle, h is the side opposite the known angle, and the adjacent side is the other about which we have at least some information. We could therefore use either the tangent or the cotangent. Either one would involve both h and d. By using both triangles we will get two equations in these two unknowns. Our object will be to eliminate d between the two equations, thereby obtaining an equation in h alone. We choose the cotangent function, since this facilitates the elimination of d.

$$\cot 36.2° = \frac{1{,}000 + d}{h}$$

$$1{,}000 + d = h \cot 36.2°$$

$$\cot 41.7° = \frac{d}{h}$$

$$d = h \cot 41.7°$$

Now we substitute for d from the last equation into the second, and then solve for h.

$$1{,}000 + h \cot 41.7° = h \cot 36.2°$$

$$h(\cot 36.2° - \cot 41.7°) = 1{,}000$$

$$h = \frac{1{,}000}{\cot 36.2° - \cot 41.7°}$$

$$= 4{,}099$$

By calculator:

1000 ÷ (36.2 TAN 1/x − 41.7

TAN 1/x) = 4099.1782

So the mountain is approximately 4,100 feet above the surrounding countryside. If the elevation of points A and B above sea level is known, this can be added to 4,100 to give the height of the mountain above sea level.

EXAMPLE 10 Ships A and B leave port at the same time, ship A traveling in the direction N 39°24′ E at an average speed of 25 miles per hour, and ship B traveling in the direction S 50°36′ E at an average speed of 15 miles per hour. Find how far apart the ships are after two hours and the bearing of ship B from ship A.

Solution Since $39°24′ + 50°36′ = 90°$, we see that the paths of the two ships are at right angles to each other, as shown in Figure 20. After two hours ship A has gone 50 miles and ship B 30 miles. Let d denote the distance between the ships at that time. Then, by the Pythagorean theorem

$$d^2 = (50)^2 + (30)^2 = 2{,}500 + 900 = 3{,}400$$

$$d = 58.3 \text{ miles}$$

Figure 20

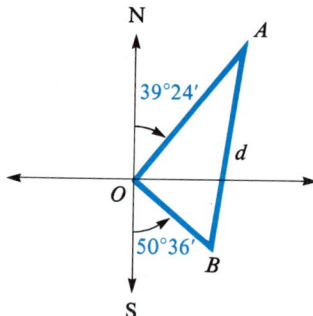

To find the bearing of B from A, first we find the angle at A in triangle AOB. We have

$$\tan A = \tfrac{30}{50} = 0.6000$$

$$A = 30°58'$$

Now, if we draw a line from A in the south direction (see Figure 21), we see by geometry that the angle from this line to OA is $39°24'$. So the angle from this line to AB is

$$39°24' - 30°58' = 8°26'$$

The bearing of B from A is therefore S $8°26'$ W.

Figure 21

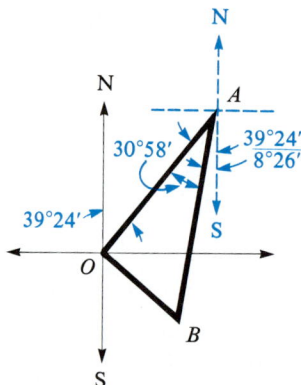

EXERCISE SET 4

A In Problems 1–16 triangle ABC is a right triangle with right angle at C. Solve the triangle.

1. $A = 57.4°$, $b = 15.2$	**2.** $a = 32.5$, $b = 12.7$
3. $B = 67.3°$, $b = 13.5$	**4.** $A = 33°20'$, $c = 120$
5. $A = 49.7°$, $c = 24.6$	**6.** $B = 37°40'$, $c = 14.2$
7. $A = 32.5°$, $a = 24.7$	**8.** $B = 64.3°$, $a = 205$
9. $a = 15.35$, $c = 32.14$	**10.** $B = 62°15'$, $c = 104.3$
11. $B = 22°40'$, $b = 2.56$	**12.** $A = 43°20'$, $b = 10.5$
13. $A = 35.57°$, $a = 3.462$	**14.** $a = 32.51$, $b = 21.28$
15. $b = 25.4$, $c = 38.2$	**16.** $a = 5.136$, $c = 8.423$

17. From a point on the ground 150 feet from the base of a building, the angle of elevation of the top of the building is 68.5°. How high is the building?

18. A rectangle is 14.3 inches long and 8.72 inches high. Find the angle between a diagonal and the base. What is the length of the diagonal?

19. From the top of a lighthouse the angle of depression of a boat is 32.4°. If the lighthouse is 80.5 feet high, how far is the boat from the base of the lighthouse?

20. A tower 102.6 feet high is on the bank of a river. From the top of the tower the angle of depression of a point on the opposite side of the river is 28°14′. How long a cable would be required to reach from the top of the tower to the point on the opposite bank?

21. A guy wire for a telephone pole is anchored to the ground at a point 21.3 feet from the base of the pole, and it makes an angle of 64.7° with the horizontal. Find the height of the point where the guy wire is attached to the pole and the length of the guy wire.

22. A surveyor wants to find the distance between points A and B on opposite sides of a pond. With her transit at point A, she determines a line of sight at right angles to AB and establishes point C along this line 150 feet from A. Then she measures the angle at C from CA to CB and finds it to be 62°10′. How far is it from A to B?

23. Town A is 12.0 miles due west of town B, and town C is 15.0 miles due south of town B. How far is it from town A to town C? Assuming straight roads connect the three towns, what is the angle at A between the roads leading to B and C?

24. A bar with a regular pentagonal (five-sided) cross-section is to be milled from round stock. What diameter should the stock be if the dimension of each flat section is to be 2.50 centimeters? (See figure.)

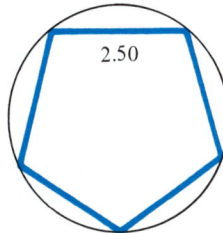

25. Points A and B are situated on the coast, with B 1,250 meters due south of A. From A the bearing of a lighthouse on an island is S 42.2° E, and from B the bearing of the lighthouse is N 47.8° E. Find the distance of the lighthouse from each of the points A and B.

26. An oil drilling platform is located in the Gulf of Mexico 3.25 miles from the nearest point, A, on shore. From a point B on the shore due east of A the bearing of the platform is S 51.2° W. How far is it from B to the platform?

27. Two forest ranger towers are 10.35 miles apart. Smoke is sighted from the first tower at a bearing of N 36°24′ W, and simultaneously it is spotted from the second tower at a bearing of N53°36′ E. If the first tower is due east of the second, find the distance from each tower to the source of the smoke.

28. A jetliner travels at a heading of 312° for 45 minutes at an average speed of 480 miles per hour. Then the course is changed to a heading of 42°. After flying at this new heading for 25 minutes, maintaining the same average speed as before, what is the distance of the jetliner from the starting point? (Neglect the effect of the wind.)

29. An airplane flies in a straight path in a southwesterly direction. After one hour the plane is 205 miles west and 78 miles south of its starting point. If the velocity of the wind was negligible, determine the heading of the airplane. What was its average speed?

B 30. The accompanying figure shows the angles of elevation of a balloon at a certain instant from points A and B 1,200 meters apart. Find the height of the balloon at that instant.

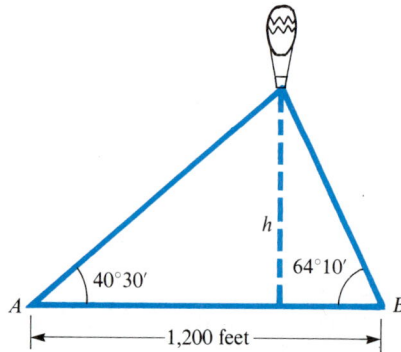

31. From a lighthouse 120 feet high, the angles of depression of two boats directly in line with and on the same side of the lighthouse are found to be 34°30′ and 27°40′. How far apart are the boats?

32. At a point 250 feet from the base of a building the angle of elevation of the top of the building is 27.5°, and the angle of elevation of the top of a statue on the top edge of the building is 30.2°. How high is the statue?

33. Find the length of 1° of longitude on the circle of latitude through Chicago, 41°50′ north. (Assume the radius of the earth is 3,960 miles.)

34. Ship A leaves port at 2:00 P.M. and travels in the direction S 34° E at an average speed of 15 knots (nautical miles per hour). At 2:45 P.M. ship B leaves the same port and travels in the direction N 56° E at an average speed of 20 knots. Find:
    a. the distance between the ships at 4:00 P.M., and
    b. the bearing of ship B from ship A at 4:00 P.M.

35. From a ship, the bearings of two landmarks on shore are found to be S 37.2° W and S 21.7° W, respectively. If the landmarks are known to be 5 kilometers apart, find how far the ship is from the nearest point on shore.

36. A pilot leaves point A and flies for 35 minutes at a heading of 142°20′ and arrives at point B. The pilot then flies at a heading of 232°20′ for 1 hour and 12 minutes, arriving at point C. The average speed on each leg of the trip was 180 miles per hour, and wind velocity was negligible. How far is it from A to C? If the pilot wanted to fly directly from A to C, what would be the heading?

5 Vectors

Certain physical quantities have both *magnitude* and *direction*. Examples are force, velocity, and acceleration. Such quantities can be represented geometrically by means of a line segment with an arrowhead indicating direction. The length of the segment represents the magnitude of the quantity, and the direction of the segment as measured by an angle from some base line (such as the x axis) represents the direction of the physical quantity. Such a directed line segment is called a **vector** (see Figure 22). The endpoint of the segment with the arrowhead is called the terminal point (or tip) of the vector, and the other endpoint is called the initial point (or tail).

A vector

Figure 22

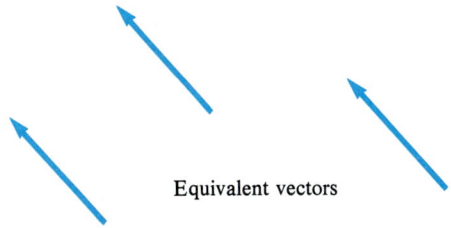

Equivalent vectors

Figure 23

There are various means of designating vectors. Frequently a single boldface letter, such as **V**, is used. Alternately, the symbol $\vec{V}$ is employed (this is especially useful in written work, where boldface letters are not easily made). If the endpoints of a vector are named by letters, the vector can also be indicated by using the two letters. For example, the vector from point A to point B could be designated either by **AB** or by $\vec{AB}$. The magnitude of a vector **V** is designated by $|\mathbf{V}|$. Similarly, using the other notations, the magnitude is designated by $|\vec{V}|$, $|\mathbf{AB}|$, or $|\vec{AB}|$.

Two vectors are said to be **equivalent** if they have the same magnitude and direction. Figure 23 shows three equivalent vectors. If **V** and **W** are equivalent, we write **V** = **W**, and we may treat them as if they were the same vector. A consequence of this is that a vector can be moved from one place to another, without changing its effect, so long as it remains parallel to its original direction.

Two vectors having different directions are *added* as follows. Place the vectors so that their initial points coincide. Then construct a parallelogram with the two vectors as adjacent sides. The diagonal from the common initial point is then the sum of the two vectors. This is illustrated in Figure 24. It should be clear that **V** + **W** = **W** + **V**. That is, vector addition is commutative. When **V** and **W** are in the same direction, their sum is a vector in that direction with magnitude $|\mathbf{V}| + |\mathbf{W}|$. When **V** and **W** are in opposite directions, their sum is in the direction of the vector with the greater magnitude, and the magnitude of the sum vector is the magnitude of the larger minus the magnitude of the smaller vector. In case they are equal in magnitude and opposite in direction, their sum is the zero vector, denoted by **0**. No direction is assigned to the zero vector.

Figure 24

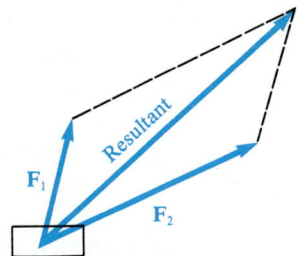

Figure 25

The sum of two vectors is often called their **resultant.** This name comes from the physical problem of the application of two forces to a body, as in Figure 25. The net result, or resultant, of the two forces is in the direction of the diagonal and has magnitude given by the length of the diagonal. That is, the resultant force is the sum $\mathbf{F}_1 + \mathbf{F}_2$. The two forces could be replaced by the single force represented by the resultant vector.

An alternate way of viewing the sum of two vectors $\mathbf{V}$ and $\mathbf{W}$ is to place the initial point of $\mathbf{W}$ at the terminal point of $\mathbf{V}$ and complete the triangle from the initial point of $\mathbf{V}$ to the terminal point of $\mathbf{W}$, as in Figure 26. You can convince yourself that this definition of $\mathbf{V} + \mathbf{W}$ is equivalent to the one previously given.

Figure 26

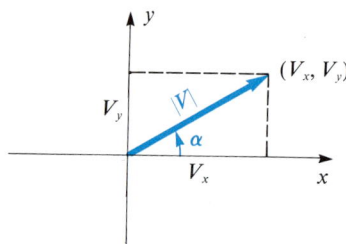

Figure 27

It is frequently convenient to introduce a rectangular coordinate system when working with vectors. Let the initial point of a non-zero vector $\mathbf{V}$ be placed at the origin, (we say the vector is then in **standard position**), and denote the coordinates of the terminal point of $\mathbf{V}$ by (V_x, V_y), as in Figure 27. These coordinates are called the **horizontal component** and the **vertical component,** respectively, of the vector $\mathbf{V}$. If α denotes the angle in standard position from the positive x axis to $\mathbf{V}$, we see that

$$\cos \alpha = \frac{V_x}{|\mathbf{V}|} \quad \text{and} \quad \sin \alpha = \frac{V_y}{|\mathbf{V}|}$$

or

$$V_x = |\mathbf{V}| \cos \alpha \quad \text{and} \quad V_y = |\mathbf{V}| \sin \alpha$$

Also, by the Pythagorean theorem

$$|\mathbf{V}| = \sqrt{V_x^2 + V_y^2}$$

Remark. As defined above, V_x and V_y are *numbers* and not vectors. However, it is also sometimes convenient to speak of **vector components** of $\mathbf{V}$. The horizontal *vector* component, $\mathbf{V}_x$, of $\mathbf{V}$ is the vector with initial point at the origin and terminal point at $(V_x, 0)$ on the x axis. The vertical *vector* component, $\mathbf{V}_y$, is the vector from the origin to the point $(0, V_y)$ on the y axis. Note that $|\mathbf{V}_x| = V_x$, $|\mathbf{V}_y| = V_y$, and $\mathbf{V}_x + \mathbf{V}_y = \mathbf{V}$. More generally, if $\mathbf{V} = \mathbf{U} + \mathbf{W}$, then $\mathbf{U}$ and $\mathbf{W}$ are vector components of $\mathbf{V}$. We sometimes wish to find particular vector components of a vector $\mathbf{V}$, and when this is done, we say we have *resolved* $\mathbf{V}$ *into its vector components.* Resolving a vector into horizontal and vertical vector components is particularly common.

A vector $\mathbf{V}$ in standard position is completely determined by specifying its horizontal and vertical components V_x and V_y. Conversely, from $\mathbf{V}$, we can find V_x and V_y. For this reason we sometimes write

$$\mathbf{V} = (V_x, V_y)$$

For example, when we write $\mathbf{V} = (2, 3)$ we mean $\mathbf{V}$ is the vector whose horizontal component is 2 and whose vertical component is 3 (see Figure 28).

Figure 28

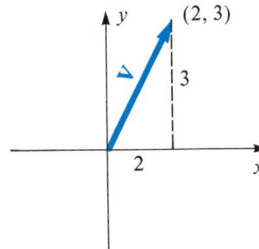

(2, 3)

EXAMPLE 11

In a rectangular coordinate system a vector is drawn from $A(3, -4)$ to $B(-5, 2)$, as shown in Figure 29. Find the horizontal and vertical components of $\overrightarrow{AB}$.

Figure 29

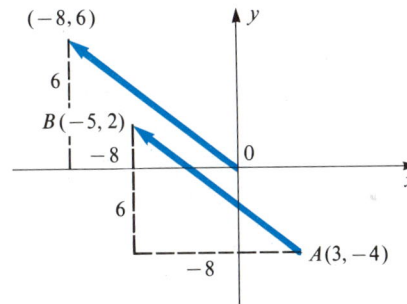

Solution

The horizontal displacement from A to B is $-5 - 3 = -8$, and the vertical displacement is $2 - (-4) = 6$. So $\overrightarrow{AB}$ is equivalent to a vector drawn from the origin, with terminal point $(-8, 6)$. Therefore, the horizontal component of $\overrightarrow{AB}$ is -8, and the vertical component is 6.

EXAMPLE 12

A force of 225 pounds is acting horizontally to the right on an object, and a force of 175 pounds is acting vertically upward on the object. Find the magnitude and direction of the resultant force.

Solution

We represent the two forces by vectors as shown in Figure 30. Let $\mathbf{R}$ be the resultant force. Then

$$|\mathbf{R}| = \sqrt{(225)^2 + (175)^2} = 285 \text{ pounds}$$

$$\tan \theta = \frac{175}{225} = 0.7778$$

$$\theta = 37.9°$$

Figure 30

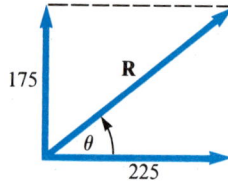

EXAMPLE 13   An airplane is flying at a heading of 126° with an indicated airspeed of 225 miles per hour. The wind velocity is 90 miles per hour from 216°. Find the actual course of the airplane and its actual speed, relative to the ground.

Solution   We represent the velocity of the airplane and the wind velocity by vectors, as shown in Figure 31. Since the wind is blowing from 216°, it is blowing in the direction 180° from this, or 36°. The angle between the vectors is therefore 90°. If we designate by θ the angle between the resultant and the velocity vector of the airplane, we have

$$\tan \theta = \frac{90}{225} = 0.4000$$

$$\theta = 21°50'$$

Thus, the true course of the airplane relative to the ground is $126° - 21°48' = 104°10'$. The true speed is the magnitude of the resultant,

$$|\mathbf{R}| = \sqrt{(225)^2 + (90)^2} = \sqrt{58,725} = 242 \text{ miles per hour}$$

Figure 31

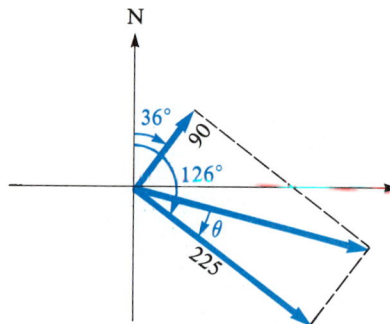

EXAMPLE 14   A 1,000 pound weight is resting on an inclined plane which makes an angle of 30° with the horizontal. Find the components of the weight parallel to and perpendicular to the plane.

Solution   We represent the weight by a vector $\mathbf{F}$, as shown in Figure 32. Its vector components $\mathbf{F}_x$ and $\mathbf{F}_y$ parallel and perpendicular to the inclined plane are also shown. By similar triangles we see that the angle between $\mathbf{F}$ and $\mathbf{F}_y$ is also 30°.

Figure 32

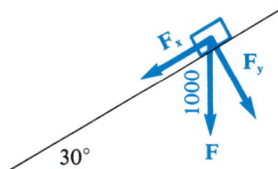

The magnitudes of $\mathbf{F}_x$ and $\mathbf{F}_y$ are therefore

$$|\mathbf{F}_x| = 1{,}000 \sin 30° = 500 \text{ pounds}$$
$$|\mathbf{F}_y| = 1{,}000 \cos 30° = 866 \text{ pounds}$$

EXERCISE SET 5

A   In Problems 1–4 the horizontal and vertical components of a vector $\mathbf{V}$, with initial point at the origin, are given. Find the magnitude of $\mathbf{V}$ and the angle α from the positive x axis to $\mathbf{V}$.

1. $V_x = 7, \quad V_y = 3$
3. $V_x = -2.10, \quad V_y = -3.70$

2. $V_x = -5, \quad V_y = 2$
4. $V_x = 30.4, \quad V_y = -57.8$

In Problems 5–8 the magnitude of a vector $\mathbf{V}$ in standard position and its angle α from the positive x axis are given. Find V_x and V_y.

5. $|\mathbf{V}| = 25, \quad \alpha = 32°$
7. $|\mathbf{V}| = 2.03, \quad \alpha = 342°12'$

6. $|\mathbf{V}| = 18.3, \quad \alpha = 162.3°$
8. $|\mathbf{V}| = 102.6, \quad \alpha = 212.53°$

In Problems 9–12 the coordinates of the initial point A and the terminal point B of a vector $\overrightarrow{AB}$ are given. Find the horizontal and vertical components of $\overrightarrow{AB}$.

9. $A = (3, 4), \quad B = (6, 1)$
11. $A = (5, -2), \quad B = (-7, -3)$

10. $A = (-2, 5), \quad B = (0, 3)$
12. $A = (-4, -8), \quad B = (-1, 3)$

In Problems 13–18 the terminal points of two vectors are given, and the initial point of each vector is the origin. Using graph paper draw the two vectors, and find the sum geometrically.

13. $(5, 1), \quad (-2, 3)$
15. $(-8, -3), \quad (-6, 4)$
17. $(3, 2), \quad (6, 4)$

14. $(3, -2), \quad (-1, -4)$
16. $(6, -5), \quad (-2, 4)$
18. $(2, -1), \quad (-4, 2)$

19. A force of 150 pounds is being exerted on a body acting horizontally to the right. A second force of 68 pounds exerted on the body is acting vertically upward. Find the magnitude and direction of the resultant force.

20. A pilot sets his heading at 120° and flies at an indicated airspeed of 195 miles per hour. There is a wind blowing from 210° at 62 miles per hour. What are the true course and speed of the airplane relative to the ground?

21. A pilot flew to a destination due south of her starting point. If the wind was from 300° at 80 miles per hour and her actual ground speed averaged 160 miles per hour, find her indicated heading and airspeed.

22. A boy can row 5 miles per hour in still water. He heads directly across a stream which has a current of 2 miles per hour. Find the resultant velocity of the boat, giving both magnitude and direction. If the river is 300 feet wide, how long will it take him to get across?

23. A 1,000 newton weight is resting on a plane making an angle of 28° with the horizontal. Find the components of the weight parallel to and perpendicular to the plane.

24. A hot-air balloon is rising vertically at the rate of 70 feet per second. If the wind is blowing horizontally at the rate of 30 miles per hour, find the actual path of the balloon and its speed along that path.

25. The pilot of a small plane plans a trip from town A to town B, 400 miles due south of A. He will cruise at an indicated airspeed of 180 miles per hour. The wind is from the west at 40 miles per hour. What should his heading be in order to compensate for the wind? How long will it take to make the trip?

B 26. If **V** is a non-zero vector and c is a non-zero real number, then c**V** is a vector with magnitude $|c|\,|\mathbf{V}|$, directed in the same direction as **V** if $c > 0$ and in the opposite direction if $c < 0$. If $c = 0$, then c**V** is the zero vector. Let **V** and **W** be vectors in standard position, with terminal points $(3, -2)$ and $(2, 1)$, respectively. Find each of the following geometrically.
    a. 2**V**   **b.** -3**W**   **c.** 3**V** + 2**W**   **d.** 2**V** $-$ 3**W**

27. Let **U**, **V**, and **W** be in standard position, with terminal points $(-1, 2)$, $(4, 5)$, and $(3, 1)$, respectively. By a geometric construction show that there are numbers a and b such that $\mathbf{U} = a\mathbf{V} + b\mathbf{W}$. (See Problem 26.)

28. Repeat Problem 32 if the terminal points of **U**, **V**, and **W** are $(-3, -2)$, $(7, 2)$, and $(-2, 1)$, respectively.

29. If **U** and **V** are vectors, $\mathbf{U} - \mathbf{V}$ is defined as $\mathbf{U} + (-\mathbf{V})$, where $-\mathbf{V} = (-1)\mathbf{V}$. (See Problem 26.) Show how $\mathbf{U} - \mathbf{V}$ can be described in terms of the parallelogram having **U** and **V** as adjacent sides.

30. For any vector $\mathbf{V} = (V_x, V_y)$ and any real number c, prove that $c\mathbf{V} = (cV_x, cV_y)$. (See Problem 26.)

31. Prove that if $\mathbf{V} = (V_x, V_y)$ and $\mathbf{W} = (W_x, W_y)$, then $\mathbf{V} + \mathbf{W} = (V_x + W_x, V_y + W_y)$.

32. Points A and B are on opposite sides of a lake, 1.5 kilometers apart, and the bearing of B from A is N 23° W. A swimmer wishes to swim from A to B, and she can swim at an average speed of 6 kilometers per hour. The predominant current is in the direction S 67° W at 3 kilometers per hour. In what direction should she swim in order to actually go in a straight line from A to B? How long will it take her?

33. A weight of 1,500 pounds is being held in place on an inclined plane by a cable extending over a pulley as shown. What is the force **F** on the cable necessary to keep the weight from sliding? (Neglect friction.)

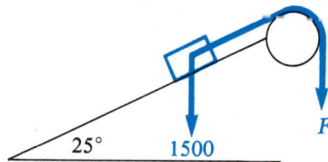

25°   1500   *F*

---

6 Trigonometric Functions of General Angles

Right triangle methods can also be used to solve oblique triangles, but before illustrating the techniques involved, it will be necessary to extend our definitions of the trigonometric functions to arbitrary angles, not just those between 0° and 90°. To do this, we let θ denote any angle, and we orient it so that its vertex is at the origin and its initial side coincides with the x axis as in Figure

33. An angle placed this way is said to be in **standard position.** Choose any point (x, y) other than the origin on the terminal side of θ, and denote by r the distance from $(0, 0)$ to (x, y).

Figure 33

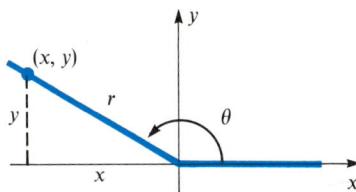

DEFINITION 2

$$\sin \theta = \frac{y}{r} \qquad \cos \theta = \frac{x}{r} \qquad \tan \theta = \frac{y}{x} \ (x \neq 0)$$

$$\csc \theta = \frac{r}{y} \ (y \neq 0) \qquad \sec \theta = \frac{r}{x} \ (x \neq 0) \qquad \cot \theta = \frac{x}{y} \ (y \neq 0)$$

The choice of the particular point (x, y) on the terminal side of θ is immaterial since, by similar triangles, the ratios would be the same if any other point were used (except the origin, which we exclude).

We note that if θ is acute, this definition is consistent with Definition 1, as can be seen by considering the right triangle having hypotenuse r, adjacent side x, and opposite side y.

Since r is always positive, the sine and cosine are defined for all angles θ. But there are certain values of θ excluded from the domain of each of the other functions, namely those angles which cause the denominator in the fraction defining the function to be zero. In particular, $\tan \theta$ and $\sec \theta$ are undefined when $x = 0$, and $\cot \theta$ and $\csc \theta$ are undefined when $y = 0$. Thus $\theta = 90°$, $270°$, and all angles coterminal with these are excluded from the domains of the tangent and secant. Similarly, $\theta = 0°$, $180°$, and all angles coterminal with these are excluded from the domains of the cotangent and cosecant.

We name the positive acute angle between the terminal side of θ and the x axis the **reference angle** for θ (Figure 34). For example, the reference angle of $150°$ is $30°$, and the reference angle of $315°$ is $45°$. There is a close relationship between the functions of an angle θ and of its reference angle. When θ is in standard position and we have chosen a point (x, y) on its terminal side, if we superimpose a right triangle with hypotenuse r so that the reference

Figure 34

Reference angle

angle for θ is one of the angles of the triangle, then the legs of the triangle have lengths equal in absolute value to x and y respectively (Figure 33). But whereas x and y may be either positive or negative, the lengths of the sides of a triangle are positive. We conclude that *any trigonometric function of θ is equal in absolute value to the same function of its reference angle.* The correct sign must be affixed according to the function and the signs of x and y in the quadrant in which the terminal side lies. We can illustrate this with several examples.

EXAMPLE 15   Find all six trigonometric functions of 225°.

Solution   The terminal side lies in quadrant III, and the reference angle is 45°, as shown in Figure 35. A convenient point to choose on the terminal side is $(-1, -1)$, and then $r = \sqrt{2}$. So we have

$$\sin 225° = -\frac{1}{\sqrt{2}} \quad \cos 225° = -\frac{1}{\sqrt{2}} \quad \tan 225° = 1$$

$$\csc 225° = -\sqrt{2} \quad \sec 225° = -\sqrt{2} \quad \cot 225° = 1$$

Figure 35

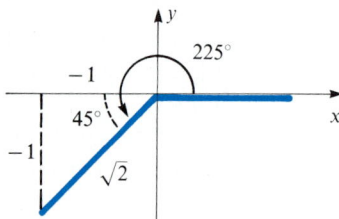

EXAMPLE 16   Find all six trigonometric functions of $5\pi/3$.

Solution   This time the angle is given in radians. With practice you will find it as convenient to work with radians as with degrees, but at this stage you may prefer to convert to degrees.

$$\frac{5\pi}{3} \text{ radians} = \frac{5\pi}{3} \cdot \frac{180°}{\pi} = 300°$$

The terminal side is in the fourth quadrant, and the reference angle is 60° (Figure 36). So we have a 30°–60° right triangle as shown and choose $r = 2$, $x = 1$, $y = -\sqrt{3}$. Thus we have,

$$\sin \frac{5\pi}{3} = -\frac{\sqrt{3}}{2} \quad \csc \frac{5\pi}{3} = -\frac{2}{\sqrt{3}}$$

$$\cos \frac{5\pi}{3} = \frac{1}{2} \quad \sec \frac{5\pi}{3} = 2$$

$$\tan \frac{5\pi}{3} = -\sqrt{3} \quad \cot \frac{5\pi}{3} = -\frac{1}{\sqrt{3}}$$

Figure 36

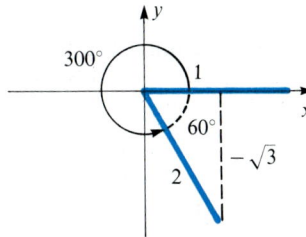

EXAMPLE 17   Find all six trigonometric functions of $510°$.

Solution   The first thing to do is observe that $510°$ is coterminal with $150°$ (Figure 37). Thus, the values of the trigonometric functions of $510°$ are the same as those of $150°$. The angle $150°$ lies in the second quadrant and has a reference angle of $30°$. Placing our standard $30°$–$60°$ triangle as shown in the figure, we read the following function values.

$$\sin 510° = \frac{1}{2} \qquad \csc 510° = 2$$

$$\cos 510° = -\frac{\sqrt{3}}{2} \qquad \sec 510° = -\frac{2}{\sqrt{3}}$$

$$\tan 510° = \frac{1}{\sqrt{3}} \qquad \cot 510° = -\sqrt{3}$$

Figure 37

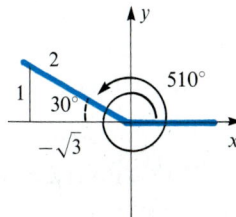

These examples illustrate how we can find exact values of all angles having as reference angles $30°$, $45°$, or $60°$. In particular, we can find the functions of $30°$, $45°$, $60°$, $120°$, $135°$, $150°$, $210°$, $225°$, $240°$, $300°$, $315°$, and $330°$, as well as angles coterminal with any of these.

The angles $0°$, $90°$, $180°$, $270°$, and all angles coterminal with these are called **quadrantal angles.** Using Definition 2 we can find the values of the trigonometric functions of all such angles. We illustrate how to do this for $0°$ and $90°$.

EXAMPLE 18   Find the six trigonometric functions of $0°$.

Solution   In applying Definition 2 we may choose any point on the terminal side of the angle. For simplicity we choose $(1, 0)$ in this case (Figure 38). Thus $x = 1$, $y = 0$, and $r = 1$. So we have

$$\sin 0° = \frac{0}{1} = 0 \qquad \csc 0° = \frac{1}{0} \quad \text{undefined}$$

$$\cos 0° = \frac{1}{1} = 1 \qquad \sec 0° = \frac{1}{1} = 1$$

$$\tan 0° = \frac{0}{1} = 0 \qquad \cot 0° = \frac{1}{0} \quad \text{undefined}$$

Remark.   In working with quadrantal angles it will be typical that two of the functions will be undefined. The thing to remember is that *division by 0 is not defined.*

Figure 38

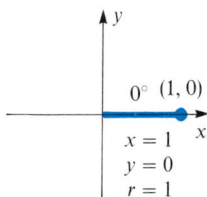

EXAMPLE 19   Find the six trigonometric functions of $90°$.

Solution   We select the point $(0, 1)$ on the terminal side, so that $x = 0$, $y = 1$, and $r = 1$ (Figure 39). Definition 2 gives the following.

$$\sin 90° = \frac{1}{1} = 1 \qquad \csc 90° = \frac{1}{1} = 1$$

$$\cos 90° = \frac{0}{1} = 0 \qquad \sec 90° = \frac{1}{0} \quad \text{undefined}$$

$$\tan 90° = \frac{1}{0} \quad \text{undefined} \qquad \cot 90° = \frac{0}{1} = 0$$

Figure 39

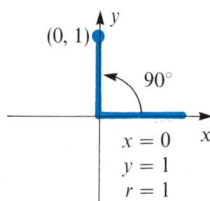

EXERCISE SET 6

Do all problems without using tables or a calculator.

A   In Problems 1–15 find exact values of the six trigonometric functions of the given angle.

1. $150°$ **2.** $135°$ **3.** $330°$ **4.** $240°$ **5.** $120°$

6. $180°$ **7.** $270°$ **8.** $\dfrac{5\pi}{6}$ **9.** $\dfrac{7\pi}{4}$ **10.** $\dfrac{7\pi}{6}$

11. $-\dfrac{\pi}{6}$ **12.** $-\dfrac{2\pi}{3}$ **13.** $480°$ **14.** $600°$ **15.** 3π

In Problems 16–21 evaluate each function.

16. **a.** $\sin 120°$ **b.** $\cos 315°$ **c.** $\tan 210°$ **d.** $\sec 240°$ **e.** $\csc 330°$

17. **a.** $\cos \dfrac{3\pi}{4}$ **b.** $\tan \dfrac{2\pi}{3}$ **c.** $\csc \dfrac{5\pi}{6}$ **d.** $\sin \dfrac{5\pi}{4}$ **e.** $\cot \dfrac{7\pi}{6}$

18. **a.** $\tan 480°$ **b.** $\sec 900°$ **c.** $\sin(-270°)$ **d.** $\cos \dfrac{10\pi}{3}$ **e.** $\cot \dfrac{3\pi}{2}$

19. **a.** $\sin \dfrac{7\pi}{6}$ **b.** $\cos 330°$ **c.** $\tan \dfrac{7\pi}{4}$ **d.** $\sec 135°$ **e.** $\cot \dfrac{3\pi}{4}$

20. **a.** $\csc \dfrac{11\pi}{6}$ **b.** $\tan 600°$ **c.** $\sin \dfrac{4\pi}{3}$ **d.** $\cos 225°$ **e.** $\sec \dfrac{7\pi}{6}$

21. **a.** $\cot(-300°)$ **b.** $\sec \dfrac{9\pi}{4}$ **c.** $\tan\left(-\dfrac{17\pi}{6}\right)$ **d.** $\cos 660°$ **e.** $\csc(-240°)$

In Problems 22–25 give an equivalent expression as a function of an acute angle.

22. **a.** $\sin 250°$ **b.** $\cos 132°$ **c.** $\tan 97°$
  d. $\sec 280°$ **e.** $\csc 310°$

23. **a.** $\cot 212°$ **b.** $\sin 562°$ **c.** $\tan 620°$
  d. $\cos(-430°)$ **e.** $\csc(-491°)$

24. **a.** $\cos 123°40'$ **b.** $\tan 312°15'$ **c.** $\csc(-240°38')$
  d. $\cot 263°24'$ **e.** $\sin(-158°13')$

25. **a.** $\tan \dfrac{7\pi}{12}$ **b.** $\sec \dfrac{7\pi}{8}$ **c.** $\sin \dfrac{9\pi}{5}$

  d. $\csc \dfrac{8\pi}{9}$ **e.** $\cos \dfrac{13\pi}{12}$

In Problems 26–31 a point on the terminal side of an angle θ in standard position is given. Find all six trigonometric functions of θ.

26. $(-3, 4)$ **27.** $(5, -12)$ **28.** $(-15, -8)$
29. $(2, -3)$ **30.** $(-1, 2)$ **31.** $(-7, -24)$

32.   Evaluate the expression

$$\frac{\sin \theta + \cos 2\theta}{\tan \theta \cot 2\theta}$$

when $\theta = 5\pi/6$.

33. Evaluate the expression

$$\left(\sec\theta - \csc\frac{\theta}{4}\right)(1 + \cos 3\theta)$$

when $\theta = 2\pi/3$.

B   In Problems 34–39 draw the angle θ in standard position for which $0 \le \theta < 2\pi$ and find the other five trigonometric functions of θ.

34. $\sin\theta = -\frac{4}{5}$, θ in quadrant III   **35.** $\cos\theta = \frac{5}{13}$, θ in quadrant IV
36. $\sec\theta = -\frac{3}{2}$, $\tan\theta > 0$ **37.** $\csc\theta = 3$, $\cos\theta < 0$
38. $\tan\theta = \frac{1}{2}$, $\csc\theta < 0$ **39.** $\cot\theta = -\frac{1}{3}$, $\sin\theta > 0$

40. If $\sin\theta = y > 0$, find expressions for the other five trigonometric functions in terms of y. (Two solutions.)

41. If $\tan\theta = t > 0$, find expressions for the other five trigonometric functions of θ in terms of t. (Two solutions.)

42. If $\sec\theta = r > 0$, find expressions for the other five trigonometric functions in terms of r. (Two solutions.)

43. For $0 < \theta < \pi/2$, express all six trigonometric functions of each of the following in terms of θ alone.

   a. $\pi - \theta$ **b.** $\pi + \theta$ **c.** $\dfrac{\pi}{2} + \theta$ **d.** $\dfrac{3\pi}{2} - \theta$ **e.** $2\pi - \theta$

   Hint.   Find the reference angle in each case.

44. Prove that $\cos n\pi = (-1)^n$, where n is any integer.

45. Prove that $\sin\dfrac{(2n+1)\pi}{2} = (-1)^n$, where n is any integer.

46. Prove that for all integers k,

$$\cos\frac{\pi}{3}(1 + 3k) = \frac{(-1)^k}{2}$$

47. Prove that for all integers k,

$$\tan\frac{\pi}{4}(1 + 2k) = (-1)^k$$

48. Using distances, prove that the points $A(8, 3)$, $B(7, -5)$, and $C(4, -3)$ are vertices of a right triangle. Find the six trigonometric functions of angle A.

---

7   The Law of Sines

Consider an oblique triangle ABC, as shown in Figure 40. The altitude from C divides the triangle into two right triangles, as shown. From triangle ADC

Figure 40

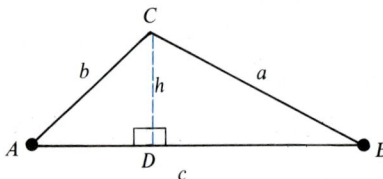

we obtain

$$\sin A = \frac{h}{b}$$

so that $h = b \sin A$. Similarly, from triangle BDC,

$$\sin B = \frac{h}{a}$$

so that $h = a \sin B$. The two expressions for h must be the same, giving $a \sin B = b \sin A$, or equivalently,

$$\frac{a}{\sin A} = \frac{b}{\sin B} \tag{5}$$

Next we orient the original triangle ABC with respect to a rectangular coordinate system so that C coincides with the origin and vertex A is on the positive x axis, as in Figure 41. Let the ordinate of B be designated by y.

Figure 41

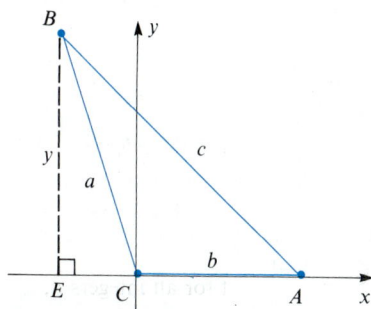

Then, since angle C is in standard position, we have that

$$\sin C = \frac{y}{a}$$

or $y = a \sin C$. If E is the foot of the perpendicular from B to the x axis, we can use the right triangle ABE to get

$$\sin A = \frac{y}{c}$$

so that $y = c \sin A$. Equating the two values of y gives $a \sin C = c \sin A$, or equivalently,

$$\frac{a}{\sin A} = \frac{c}{\sin C} \tag{6}$$

Finally, combining equations (5) and (6), we get the **law of sines:**

The Law of Sines

$$\frac{a}{\sin A} = \frac{b}{\sin B} = \frac{c}{\sin C}$$

Although the triangle we used to derive this result had an obtuse angle (C), the derivation is valid also when all three angles are acute.

The law of sines can be employed to find the missing parts of a triangle in either of the following cases:

1. Two angles and one side are given
2. Two sides and the angle opposite one of them are given

In either case, an equation having only one unknown can be obtained from the law of sines. After solving for the unknown in the equation, all remaining unknowns can be found. The following examples illustrate typical situations.

EXAMPLE 20   In triangle ABC, $A = 22°$, $B = 110°$, and $c = 13.4$. Find sides a and b and angle C.

Solution   Since the sum of the angles must be 180°, we find that $C = 180° - 132° = 48°$. From the law of sines, we select $a/\sin A = c/\sin C$. Substituting known values, we obtain

$$\frac{a}{\sin 22°} = \frac{13.4}{\sin 48°}$$

so that

$$a = \frac{(13.4)(\sin 22°)}{\sin 48°} = 6.75$$

By calculator:

$$13.4 \boxed{\times} \ 22 \ \boxed{\text{SIN}} \ \boxed{\div} \ 48 \ \boxed{\text{SIN}} \ \boxed{=} \ 6.7547108$$

To find b we employ $b/\sin B = c/\sin C$.

$$\frac{b}{\sin 110°} = \frac{13.4}{\sin 48°}$$

$$b = \frac{(13.4)(\sin 110°)}{\sin 48°} = 16.9$$

The triangle is now solved.

Before proceeding to other examples, let us analyze what the possibilities are in case 2, in which we are given two sides and the angle opposite one of them. Suppose we are given a, b, and A. First, draw angle A with side b adjacent, thus determining vertex C (Figure 42). Now side a extends from C until it strikes the base. But it is quite evident that several possibilities exist, depending on the length of side a. A compass set at C with radius a clearly shows what can happen. If a exceeds the altitude from C but is shorter than b, then there are two distinct solutions, as Figure 43 shows. If a exceeds the altitude from C and also exceeds b, only one solution exists, as Figure 44 shows. If a equals the altitude from C, the triangle is a right triangle, and

Figure 42

Figure 43

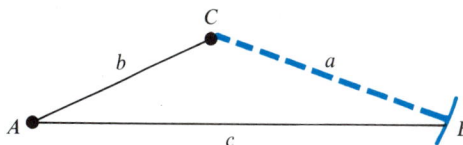

Figure 44

there is again just one solution, as shown in Figure 45. It should be noted that while this is a theoretical possibility, in actual practice it is extremely unlikely that this case will occur. Finally, if a is less than the altitude from C, there is no triangle at all, as shown in Figure 46.

Figure 45

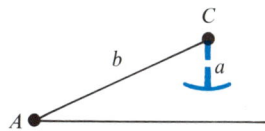

Figure 46

For obvious reasons, case 2 is known as the **ambiguous case.** Fortunately, it is not necessary to determine in advance which situation exists; after the law of sines is employed, the situation will become clear. It is necessary, however, to be alert and to interpret from the result whether one, two, or no solutions exist.

EXAMPLE 21   Solve the triangle for which $a = 125$, $b = 150$, and $A = 54.0°$.

Solution   From $a/\sin A = b/\sin B$ we get

$$\frac{125}{\sin 54°} = \frac{150}{\sin B}$$

so that

$$\sin B = \frac{(150)(\sin 54°)}{125} = 0.9708$$

By calculator:

$$150 \quad \boxed{\times} \quad 54 \quad \boxed{\text{SIN}} \quad \boxed{\div} \quad 125 \quad \boxed{=} \quad \boxed{\text{INV}} \quad \boxed{\text{SIN}} \quad 76.124805$$

So B is approximately $76.1°$. But the supplement of this angle is also a possibility. We must therefore consider an alternative value of B, $180° - 76.1° = 103.9°$, and then calculate the third angle in order to find out whether the second value of B is feasible. We have

$$C = 180° - (A + B) = 180° - (54° + 103.9°) = 22.1°$$

Thus, two distinct solutions exist. Let us designate by B_1 the value $76.1°$ and by B_2 the value $103.9°$. Corresponding subscripts will be used for angle C and side c. Thus,

$$C_1 = 180° - (A + B_1) = 180° - (54° + 76.1°) = 49.9°$$

and $C_2 = 22.1°$, as we have already calculated.

We use $a/\sin A = c/\sin C$ to calculate side c for each case. So we have

$$\frac{125}{\sin 54°} = \frac{c_1}{\sin 49.9°} \quad \text{and} \quad \frac{125}{\sin 54°} = \frac{c_2}{\sin 22.1°}$$

These yield

$$c_1 = \frac{(125)(\sin 49.9°)}{\sin 54°} = 118$$

$$c_2 = \frac{(125)(\sin 22.1°)}{\sin 54°} = 58.1$$

The two solutions can be summarized as shown in Figure 47.

Figure 47

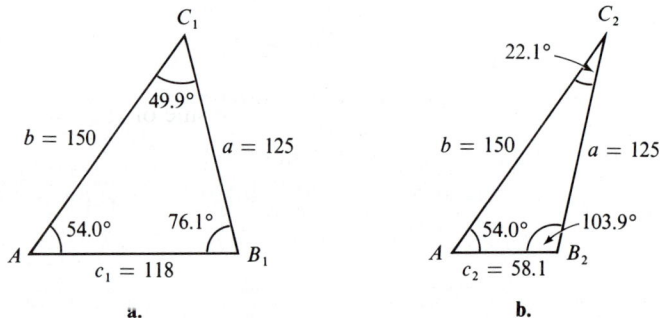

a.

b.

EXAMPLE 22   Solve the triangle ABC in which $b = 13.2$, $c = 10.5$, and $B = 42.0°$.

Solution   From $b/\sin B = c/\sin C$, we find that

$$\sin C = \frac{c \sin B}{b} = \frac{(10.5)(\sin 42°)}{13.2} = 0.5323$$

so that C is either $32.2°$ or its supplement, $147.8°$. But if $C = 147.8°$, then $B + C = 189.8°$, which is impossible since the sum of two angles of a triangle must be less than $180°$. Thus, only one solution exists. Using $C = 32.2°$, we get

$$A = 180° - (B + C) = 180° - (42° + 32.2°) = 105.8°$$

Finally, we use $a/\sin A = b/\sin B$ to find side a.

$$a = \frac{b\sin A}{\sin B} = \frac{(13.2)(\sin 105.8°)}{\sin 42°} = 19.0$$

The solution is shown in Figure 48.

Figure 48

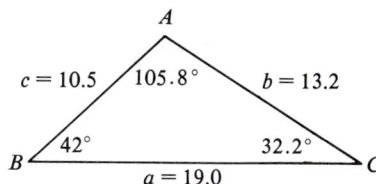

EXAMPLE 23   Solve the triangle ABC for which $a = 23.5$, $c = 12.0$, and $C = 35°$.

Solution   From $a/\sin A = c/\sin C$, we get

$$\sin A = \frac{a\sin C}{c} = \frac{(23.5)(\sin 35°)}{12.0} = 1.123$$

But this is impossible, since it is clear from the definition that the sine never exceeds 1. So there is no solution; that is, there is no triangle having a, c, and C as given.

A Word of Caution.   If the sine of the angle found in the first step of solving a Case 2 problem is less than 1, you *must* consider as possible solutions both the acute angle found from tables or a calculator *and* its supplement. The supplement will be a solution provided that it, together with the given angle, add up to an angle less than 180° (as in Example 21).

EXERCISE SET 7

A   In Problems 1–15 use the law of sines to solve the triangle.

1. $a = 5.0$, $A = 40°$, $B = 20°$
2. $b = 37.4$, $A = 64.2°$, $C = 37.6°$
3. $b = 125$, $c = 85.0$, $C = 36°30'$
4. $a = 10.5$, $c = 12.8$, $A = 68.0°$
5. $A = 28.5°$, $a = 21.8$, $b = 10.2$
6. $C = 30.0°$, $b = 15.2$, $c = 7.60$
7. $B = 47.2°$, $C = 25.8°$, $c = 7.34$
8. $A = 63.9°$, $C = 72.4°$, $a = 102$
9. $A = 37°25'$, $B = 64°37'$, $b = 14.72$
10. $c = 3.504$, $B = 102°24'$, $C = 23°42'$
11. $B = 43.25°$, $b = 17.52$, $c = 10.27$
12. $C = 23.48°$, $a = 21.83$, $c = 15.27$
13. $B = 108°32'$, $b = 112.6$, $c = 73.43$
14. $A = 65.26°$, $a = 33.24$, $b = 68.73$
15. $C = 22°30'$, $a = 6.432$, $c = 3.871$

16. The angle between two vectors $\mathbf{V}$ and $\mathbf{W}$ is 37.0° and the angle between $\mathbf{V}$ and $\mathbf{V} + \mathbf{W}$ is 15.0°. If $|\mathbf{V}| = 12.8$, find $|\mathbf{W}|$ and $|\mathbf{V} + \mathbf{W}|$.

17. The magnitude of the resultant $\mathbf{R}$ of two forces $\mathbf{F}_1$ and $\mathbf{F}_2$ acting on an object is $|\mathbf{R}| = 223.4$ pounds, and $|\mathbf{F}_2| = 111.5$ pounds. If the angle between $\mathbf{F}_1$ and $\mathbf{R}$ is $27°34'$, and the angle between $\mathbf{F}_1$ and $\mathbf{F}_2$ is acute, find $|\mathbf{F}_1|$ and the angle between $\mathbf{F}_1$ and $\mathbf{F}_2$.

18. Points A and B are on opposite sides of a river, and it is desired to find the distance between them. Point C, on the same side of the river as A, is 35.0 feet from A. In the triangle ABC, the angle at C is found to be $42°30'$ and the angle at A to be $103°24'$. How far is it from A to B?

19. The distance x across a gorge is to be determined in order that a cable car traversing it can be constructed. One side of the gorge has only a moderate slope so that a distance along it can be measured, as shown in the figure. The angles shown are also determined. Find the distance x.

20. Points A and B are on opposite sides of a swampy area. To find the distance between them, a point C is located 254 feet from B and 197 feet from A. The angle at A from AB to AC is found to be $47.2°$. Find the distance from A to B.

B 21. A boat leaves point A and travels in the direction S 48° E at an average speed of 15 knots (nautical miles per hour). A coast guard cutter at point B, 21 nautical miles due east of A, wishes to intercept the boat. If the cutter can average 25 knots, what should its direction be (assuming the cutter leaves at the same time as the boat)? When will the interception be made?

22. The pilot of a light airplane plans to fly from town A to town B, a distance of 650 miles. The bearing of town B from town A is S 48° 32′ E. The pilot will fly at an average airspeed of 175 miles per hour. If a constant wind is blowing from the northeast at 35 miles per hour, what should the pilot's heading be? How long will it take to make the trip?

23. Point B is on the coast 5 miles due south of A. From A the bearing of a ship is S 32.4° E, and from B the bearing of the ship is N 42.7° E. How far is it from each of the points A and B to the ship? How far is it from the ship to the nearest point on shore?

24. A pilot is planning to make a trip from A to B, 350 miles due north of A, and then back to A. There is a wind blowing from 310° at 55 miles per hour. If the average airspeed of the plane is 210 miles per hour, find the heading the pilot should take on each part of the trip. What will be the total flying time?

8 The Law of Cosines

When we are given two sides of an oblique triangle and the angle between them, or when we are given all three sides, the law of sines cannot be used, because there will always be two unknowns in any of the equations. In this section we derive a formula that will handle these situations.

Figure 49

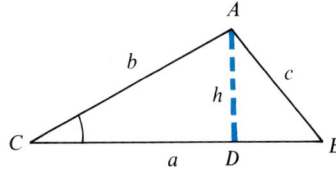

Consider first a triangle as shown in Figure 49, with angle C acute. Construct the altitude AD and designate its length by h. Then, from triangle ADB and the Pythagorean theorem,

$$c^2 = h^2 + \overline{BD}^2 \tag{7}$$

From triangle ADC we have

$$b^2 = h^2 + \overline{CD}^2 \tag{8}$$

and since

$$\cos C = \frac{\overline{CD}}{b}$$

we obtain $\overline{CD} = b \cos C$. Since $\overline{BD} = a - \overline{CD}$, we can replace $\overline{BD}$ in equation (7) by $a - b \cos C$. Also, from equation (8), $h^2 = b^2 - \overline{CD}^2 = b^2 - (b \cos C)^2$. Making these substitutions in equation (7), we obtain

$$c^2 = b^2 - b^2 \cos^2 C + (a - b \cos C)^2$$
$$= b^2 - b^2 \cos^2 C + a^2 - 2ab \cos C + b^2 \cos^2 C$$
$$= a^2 + b^2 - 2ab \cos C$$

Figure 50

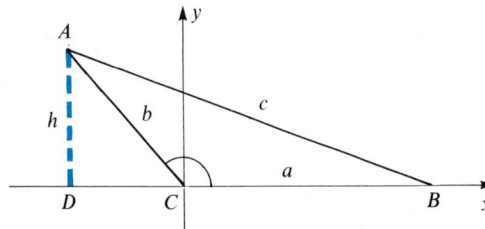

If C is obtuse, we introduce a coordinate system as in Figure 50, with C in standard position. As before, we have

$$c^2 = h^2 + \overline{BD}^2 \tag{9}$$

and

$$b^2 = h^2 + \overline{CD}^2 \tag{10}$$

Since the abscissa of A is negative, we have

$$\cos C = \frac{-\overline{CD}}{b}$$

or $\overline{CD} = -b \cos C$. Also,

$$\overline{BD} = a + \overline{CD} = a - b \cos C$$

Substituting these results into equations (9) and (10) and combining yields

$$c^2 = b^2 - (-b \cos C)^2 + (a - b \cos C)^2$$
$$= b^2 - b^2 \cos^2 C + a^2 - 2ab \cos C + b^2 \cos^2 C$$
$$= a^2 + b^2 - 2ab \cos C$$

which is the same as before.

By working from the other two vertices, in turn, analogous formulas are obtained. We have, then, the following three formulas:

$$a^2 = b^2 + c^2 - 2bc \cos A$$
$$b^2 = a^2 + c^2 - 2ac \cos B$$
$$c^2 = a^2 + b^2 - 2ab \cos C$$

These formulas are expressions of the **law of cosines.**

The Law of Cosines

The square of any side of a triangle equals the sum of the squares of the other two sides, minus twice the product of these two sides and the cosine of the angle between them.

If two sides and the angle between them are given, we select the form of the law of cosines that involves the given angle. Then the side opposite the angle can be calculated. To complete the solution of the triangle the law of sines is employed. For example, if a, c, and angle B are given, the formula

$$b^2 = a^2 + c^2 - 2ac \cos B$$

is employed to calculate b. Then either angle A or angle C can be found using the law of sines.

If all three sides of a triangle are given, any one of the forms of the law of cosines can be used to calculate one of the angles. Then another angle can be found either by another form of the law of cosines or by the law of sines. For example, suppose a, b, and c are given. Then we may use

$$a^2 = b^2 + c^2 - 2bc \cos A$$

to solve first for $\cos A$,

$$\cos A = \frac{b^2 + c^2 - a^2}{2bc}$$

and then find A from tables or a calculator.

EXAMPLE 24   In a triangle one angle is 120° and the two sides adjacent to this angle have lengths 3 and 5. Find all other parts of the triangle.

Solution   Let the given sides be $a = 3$, $b = 5$. Then $C = 120°$.

$$c^2 = a^2 + b^2 - 2ab \cos C$$
$$= 9 + 25 - 2(3)(5)(-\tfrac{1}{2})$$
$$= 9 + 25 + 15 = 49$$

so $c = 7$.

From the law of sines, $a/\sin A = c/\sin C$, we get

$$\sin A = \frac{a \sin C}{c} = \frac{3(\sqrt{3}/2)}{7} = \frac{3\sqrt{3}}{14} = 0.3712$$

$$A = 21.8°$$

Finally,

$$B = 180° - (A + C) = 180° - 141.8° = 38.2°$$

EXAMPLE 25   Find the angles in triangle ABC for which $a = 13$, $b = 21$, $c = 15$ (exact values).

Solution   We have

$$\cos A = \frac{b^2 + c^2 - a^2}{2bc} = \frac{441 + 225 - 169}{2(21)(15)} = 0.7889$$

By calculator:

21 $\boxed{x^2}$ $\boxed{+}$ 15 $\boxed{x^2}$ $\boxed{-}$ 13 $\boxed{x^2}$ $\boxed{=}$ $\boxed{\div}$ $\boxed{(}$ 2 $\boxed{\times}$ 21 $\boxed{\times}$

15 $\boxed{)}$ $\boxed{=}$ $\boxed{INV}$ $\boxed{COS}$ 37.918203

So $A = 37.9°$.

$$\cos B = \frac{a^2 + c^2 - b^2}{2ac} = \frac{169 + 225 - 441}{2(13)(15)} = -0.1205$$

and $B = 96.9°$. Thus, $C = 180° - (A + B) = 180° - 134.8° = 45.2°$.

EXAMPLE 26   Find the magnitude and direction of the resultant of the two forces $\mathbf{F}_1$ and $\mathbf{F}_2$ shown in Figure 51 if $|\mathbf{F}_1| = 87.2$ pounds and $|\mathbf{F}_2| = 53.8$ pounds.

Solution   We complete the parallelogram, as shown in Figure 52. The angle θ is the supplement of $39.7°$:

$$\theta = 180° - 39.7° = 140.3°$$

Figure 51

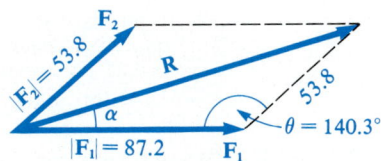

Figure 52

By the law of cosines,

$$|\mathbf{R}|^2 = |\mathbf{F}_1|^2 + |\mathbf{F}_2|^2 - 2|\mathbf{F}_1||\mathbf{F}_2| \cos \theta$$
$$= (87.2)^2 + (53.8)^2 - 2(87.2)(53.8) \cos 140.3°$$
$$= 17,717.34$$

so $|\mathbf{R}| = 133.1$ pounds. We indicate the direction of $\mathbf{R}$ by finding the angle α by the law of sines.

$$\frac{|\mathbf{F}_2|}{\sin \alpha} = \frac{|\mathbf{R}|}{\sin \theta}$$

$$\sin \alpha = \frac{|\mathbf{F}_2| \sin \theta}{|\mathbf{R}|} = \frac{(53.8) \sin 140.3°}{57.3} = 0.2582$$

Thus, $\alpha = 15.0°$.

EXERCISE SET 8

A   Solve the triangles in Problems 1–12. Assume exact values in Problems 1, 4, and 5.

1. $A = 60°$, $b = 15$, $c = 10$
2. $B = 150°$, $a = 2.3$, $c = 1.2$
3. $C = 97°20'$, $a = 5.1$, $b = 11.6$
4. $a = 3$, $b = 4$, $c = 2$
5. $a = 12$, $b = 8$, $c = 15$
6. $A = 32.4°$, $b = 12.3$, $c = 15.8$
7. $B = 103.5°$, $a = 234$, $c = 160$
8. $C = 67°42'$, $a = 35.2$, $b = 42.3$
9. $a = 3.61$, $b = 4.72$, $c = 2.85$
10. $a = 21.5$, $b = 32.6$, $c = 50.7$
11. $b = 30.75$, $c = 25.02$, $A = 84°23'$
12. $a = 0.231$, $c = 0.415$, $B = 102.4°$

13. Two sides of a parallelogram are 8 centimeters and 10 centimeters, respectively, and the shorter diagonal is 12 centimeters (exact values). Find the length of the longer diagonal.

14. Two cars leave simultaneously from the same point, one going east at an average speed of 60 kilometers per hour and the other going southwest at an average speed of 80 kilometers per hour. How far apart are they after two hours?

15. Find the magnitude and direction of the resultant of two forces of 25 pounds and 30 pounds, respectively, acting on an object, if the angle between the forces is 23°.

16. If the angle between the vectors $\mathbf{V}$ and $\mathbf{W}$ is 47.2°, and $|\mathbf{V}| = 21.5$, $|\mathbf{W}| = 37.2$, find $|\mathbf{V} + \mathbf{W}|$ and the angle from $\mathbf{V}$ to $\mathbf{V} + \mathbf{W}$.

17. A river that flows north to south has a current of 8 miles per hour. A motorboat leaves the west bank and heads in the direction S 75° E at an indicated speed of 20 miles per hour. Find the actual speed and direction of the boat.

18. A light airplane is heading in the direction 175° at an indicated airspeed of 160 miles per hour. If a wind of 43 miles per hour is blowing from 200°, find the true course and speed of the airplane.

19. A surveyor wishes to find the distance from point A to point B but cannot do so directly because there is a swamp between them. He sets up a transit at C and makes the following measurements: Angle $C = 27°32'$, $\overline{CA} = 125.3$ feet, $\overline{CB} = 117.5$ feet. Find $\overline{AB}$.

B   20. A regular pentagon is inscribed in a circle of radius 4 centimeters. Make use of the law of cosines to find the perimeter of the pentagon.

21. Airplane A leaves Chicago at 1:00 P.M. and flies at a heading of 203° at an average speed of 350 miles per hour. Airplane B leaves the same airport at 1:30 P.M. and flies at a heading of 85° at an average speed of 400 miles per hour. How far apart are the planes at 2:00 P.M.? (Neglect wind velocity.)

22. Let V_1 and V_2 be vectors in standard position having terminal points (x_1, y_1) and (x_2, y_2), respectively. The *dot product* of V_1 and V_2, denoted by $V_1 \cdot V_2$, is defined by $V_1 \cdot V_2 = x_1 x_2 + y_1 y_2$. Use the law of cosines to prove that if θ is the angle between V_1 and V_2, then

$$\cos \theta = \frac{V_1 \cdot V_2}{|V_1||V_2|}$$

23. Let $V_1 = (5, 3)$ and $V_2 = (-2, 7)$. Use the result of Problem 22 to find the angle between V_1 and V_2.

24. Repeat Problem 22 with $V_1 = (-3, 5)$ and $V_2 = (-1, -4)$.

25. Three forces of magnitude $|F_1| = 30$ pounds, $|F_2| = 45$ pounds, and $|F_3| = 56$ pounds are acting on an object as shown. Find the magnitude of the resultant, and give its angle from F_1.

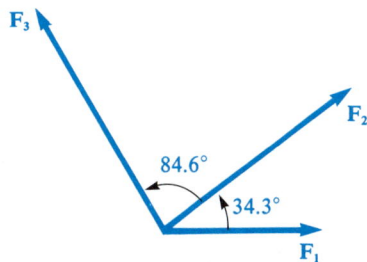

26. The heading of a jetliner flying at an indicated airspeed of 465 miles per hour is 220°. If a wind of 90 miles per hour is blowing from 300°, find the ground speed of the plane and its actual course.

27. A boat traveling at 23 miles per hour heads in the direction N 42.5° W for 45 minutes and then changes to the direction N 36.8° E and goes on this course for 1 hour and 15 minutes. How far is the boat from its starting point?

28. In order to determine the distance between two inaccessible points A and B on the opposite side of a river from an observer, two points C and D are established 50 feet apart, and angles are determined as shown. Find the distance between A and B.

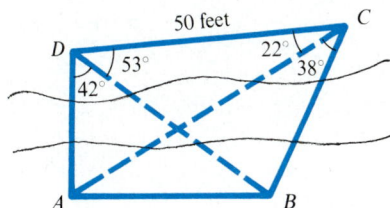

9 Areas of Triangles

The basic formula for the area of a triangle is well-known: Area $= \frac{1}{2}bh$, where b designates the base, and h is the altitude drawn from that base. When the triangle is a right triangle, either leg can be taken as the base and the other

Figure 53

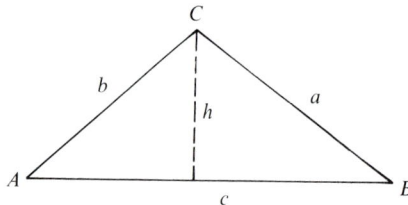

leg is then the altitude. For oblique triangles, the complication arises of how to find the altitude. The method of deriving the law of sines gives a clue as to how this can be done.

Suppose a triangle is oriented as shown in Figure 53. Since $\sin A = h/b$, we have $h = b \sin A$. Since the base corresponding to this altitude is c,

$$\text{Area} = \tfrac{1}{2}bc \sin A \tag{11}$$

Notice that the formula involves two sides and the angle between them. By working from one of the other vertices, we obtain

$$\text{Area} = \tfrac{1}{2}ab \sin C = \tfrac{1}{2}ac \sin B$$

If enough information to solve the triangle is given, then the area can always be found in this way.

EXAMPLE 27   Find the area of triangle ABC for which $a = 10$, $b = 7$, and $C = 60°$.

Solution
$$\text{Area} = \frac{1}{2} ab \sin C = \frac{1}{2}(\overset{5}{10})(7)\left(\frac{\sqrt{3}}{2}\right) = \frac{35\sqrt{3}}{2} = 30.31$$

EXAMPLE 28   Find the area of a triangle having sides 5, 7, and 3.

Solution   Let $a = 5$, $b = 7$, and $c = 3$. We could work with any angle, but we choose B. (A little scratch work will show this is the easiest one to find.) By the law of cosines,

$$\cos B = \frac{a^2 + c^2 - b^2}{2ac} = \frac{25 + 9 - 49}{2(15)} = \frac{-15}{30} = -\frac{1}{2}$$

So $B = 120°$. (Why?) The area now can be found:

$$\text{Area} = \tfrac{1}{2}ac \sin B = \tfrac{1}{2}(5)(3) \sin 120°$$
$$= \tfrac{1}{2}(15)\left(\frac{\sqrt{3}}{2}\right) = \frac{15\sqrt{3}}{4} = 6.50$$

EXERCISE SET 9

A   Find the area of triangle ABC in Problem 1–14.

1. $A = 30°$, $b = 36$, $c = 24$
2. $C = 23°$, $a = 7$, $b = 9$
3. $B = 112°$, $a = 14$, $c = 10$
4. $a = 1.2$, $b = 2.1$, $c = 2.8$

5. $A = 65.2°$, $b = 3.5$, $c = 2.8$
7. $a = 10$, $b = 6$, $c = 14$
9. $A = 30°$, $a = 12$, $b = 10$
11. $A = 69.5°$, $C = 41.7°$, $b = 54.6$
13. $a = 1.023$, $b = 2.142$, $c = 1.597$

6. $C = 93°20'$, $a = 12.3$, $b = 18.2$
8. $C = 102.5°$, $a = 24$, $b = 13$
10. $B = 98°33'$, $b = 4.03$, $c = 2.52$
12. $B = 36.8°$, $C = 101.3°$, $a = 14.9$
14. $C = 43°15'$, $b = 25.1$, $c = 32.3$

B
15. Show that equation (11) continues to hold true when A is an obtuse angle.
16. Derive the following formula for the area of triangle ABC.

$$\text{Area} = \frac{b^2 \sin A \sin C}{2 \sin B}$$

Hint. Use equation (11) and the law of sines.
17. Use the result of Problem 16 to find the area of the triangle ABC in which $b = 8$, $B = 32°$, $C = 54°$.
18. Rework Problem 11 using the result of Problem 16.
19. Rework Problem 12 using a formula analogous to the one derived in Problem 16.
20. Find the area of the triangle whose vertices in a rectangular coordinate system are $(2, 1)$, $(-4, -7)$, and $(-1, 5)$.
21. Let the lengths of the two diagonals of an arbitrary quadrilateral be d_1 and d_2, and let α be their angle of intersection (either of the two angles). Prove that the area of the quadrilateral is given by $\frac{1}{2}d_1 d_2 \sin \alpha$.

REVIEW EXERCISE SET

A In Problems 1–14 solve the right triangles. Whenever possible solve without the use of a calculator or tables. The right angle is always at C.

1. $A = 60°$, $b = 5$
3. $B = 60°$, $a = 4$
5. $B = 45°$, $c = 10$
7. $a = 7$, $c = 14$
9. $A = 33°$, $c = 13$
11. $b = 102$, $c = 151$
13. $B = 26.2°$, $c = 33.5$

2. $B = 30°$, $c = 9$
4. $A = 45°$, $a = 12$
6. $A = 30°$, $c = 5$
8. $a = 8$, $b = 15$
10. $a = 4$, $b = 7$
12. $A = 67°$, $a = 12.6$
14. $B = 62.3°$, $a = 2.53$

15. Give the measure of the angle in radians:
    a. $240°$ b. $315°$ c. $15°$ d. $540°$ e. $160°$
16. Give the measure of the angle in degrees:
    a. $5\pi/6$ b. $2\pi/9$ c. 3π d. 5 e. $7\pi/4$
17. a. What is the length of an arc on a circle of radius 20 subtended by a central angle of $36°$?
    b. An arc of 8 feet is subtended by a central angle θ on a circle of radius 6 feet. Find θ in degrees.
18. A wheel 18 inches in diameter is turning at the rate of 600 rpm. What is the velocity in feet per second of a point on the extremity of the wheel?

In Problems 19 and 20 evaluate the function without using tables or a calculator.

19. a. $\cos(5\pi/3)$ b. $\sin 210°$ c. $\tan(-5\pi/6)$ d. $\cot 270°$
    e. $\sec(3\pi/4)$ f. $\csc 390°$ g. $\tan(5\pi/4)$ h. $\sin(-90°)$
    i. $\sec 480°$ j. $\cos(-7\pi/6)$
20. a. $\sin(3\pi/2)$ b. $\cos(11\pi/6)$ c. $\tan 225°$ d. $\sec(-3\pi)$

    e. $\cot(5\pi/3)$ **f.** $\sin 390°$ **g.** $\cos(4\pi/3)$ **h.** $\tan(-315°)$
    i. $\sec(5\pi/4)$ **j.** $\csc(7\pi/6)$

In Problems 21–31 solve the triangles.

21. $A = 34.3°$, $B = 26.8°$, $a = 13.4$

22. $B = 54°30'$, $C = 48°20'$, $a = 102.5$

23. $C = 32°$, $b = 15$, $c = 8$ **24.** $a = 4$, $b = 7$, $C = 110°$

25. $a = 22.3$, $b = 17.9$, $c = 10.5$ **26.** $A = 110°$, $C = 28°$, $c = 12$

27. $A = 63.2°$, $a = 14.3$, $b = 25.2$ **28.** $B = 36°20'$, $b = 34.5$, $c = 12.7$

29. $a = 8$, $b = 9$, $c = 13$ **30.** $a = 2.05$, $c = 3.72$, $B = 61°40'$

31. $A = 25.2°$, $c = 27.4$, $a = 15.1$

32. Find the area of each of the following triangles:
    a. $a = 32$, $b = 51$, $C = 25°$ **b.** $b = 1.2$, $c = 3.5$, $C = 102°$

33. A 40 foot high building is at the edge of a river. Directly opposite on the other edge an observer finds that the angle of elevation of the top of the building is $33°10'$. How wide is the river at that point?

34. The sides of a parallelogram are 6 and 10, and the longer diagonal is 14. Find the interior angles of the parallelogram.

35. A lot is in the shape of a triangle in which two sides are 100 feet and 120 feet, and the angle between them is 55°. Find the length of the third side and the area of the lot.

36. A portion of a modern metal sculpture consists of a large triangular plate mounted vertically, with one vertex at the top and with a horizontal base. The length of the base is 12 feet, and the base angles are 30° and 50°, respectively. Find the lengths of the other two sides of the triangle. What is its area?

37. The angle between two vectors $\mathbf{V}_1$ and $\mathbf{V}_2$ is 27.5°, and the angle from $\mathbf{V}_1$ to $\mathbf{V}_1 + \mathbf{V}_2$ is 16.1°. If $|\mathbf{V}_1| = 10.7$, find $|\mathbf{V}_2|$ and $|\mathbf{V}_1 + \mathbf{V}_2|$.

38. Two forces, of magnitudes $|\mathbf{F}_1| = 8.67$ newtons and $|\mathbf{F}_2| = 6.43$ newtons, act on an object. If the angle between $\mathbf{F}_1$ and $\mathbf{F}_2$ is $72°33'$, find the magnitude and direction of the resultant.

39. Two forces, of magnitudes $|\mathbf{F}_1| = 36.5$ pounds and $|\mathbf{F}_2| = 53.4$ pounds, are acting on an object. If the resultant $\mathbf{R}$ makes an angle of $32°15'$ with $\mathbf{F}_1$, find $|\mathbf{R}|$. What is the angle between $\mathbf{F}_1$ and $\mathbf{F}_2$?

B   **40.** Find the area of the triangle whose vertices are the points $(3, -5)$, $(-1, -2)$, and $(8, 7)$.

41. An observer is 100 feet from the base of a building. She finds the angles of elevation to the bottom and top of a flagpole on the roof of the building to be 59.3° and 62.4°, respectively. How high is the flagpole?

42. Points A and B are on opposite sides of a pond, and it is desired to find the distance between them. Point C is located so that $\overline{AC} = 254$ feet and $\overline{BC} = 198$ feet. The angle at A from AB to AC is found to be $47°21'$. Find the distance from A to B.

43. At 4:00 PM an airplane leaves Chicago and heads due south at a cruising speed of 400 miles per hour. At 5:00 PM another plane leaves from the same airport and travels at a heading of 220°, cruising at 500 miles per hour. How far apart are the two planes at 6:00 PM?

44. Two guy wires are attached on opposite sides of a pole. They make angles of 36° and 42° with the horizontal, and the points where they meet the ground are 50 feet apart. Find the length of each wire.

45. A ranger in a lookout tower spots a fire on a line N 40° W. A second ranger at a tower 10 miles to the west of the first tower also sees the fire and finds it to be on a line N 35° E. How far is the fire from each lookout tower?

46. If there were no wind, a pilot would head in the direction 215° to go from city *A* to city *B*. The distance between the cities is 425 miles. If a 40 mile per hour wind is blowing from 290°, and if the average airspeed of the plane is 185 miles per hour, find the heading the pilot should take to go from *A* to *B*. If she also wishes to return to *A*, what should her heading be? What will the total flying time be for the round trip?

47. From the top of a lighthouse 120 feet high the angle of depression of ship *A* is 12.8° and the angle of depression of ship *B* is 14.2°. The bearing of ship *A* from the lighthouse is N 35.7° E and the bearing of *B* is S 64.3° E. Find the distance between the ships and the bearing of ship *B* from ship *A*.

48. A hill slopes at an angle of 23°10′, and a monument is erected on top of the hill, as shown in the figure. From point *A* at the base of the hill the angle of elevation of the top of the monument is 34°37′, and from point *B*, 200 feet up the hill from *A*, the angle of elevation of the top of the monument is 41°06′. How high is the monument?

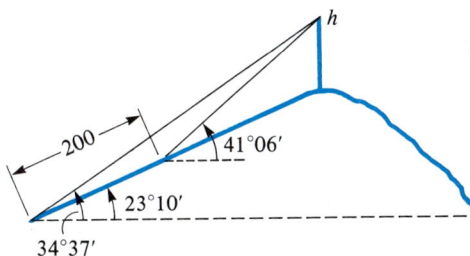

9 Analytical Trigonometry

Relationships between the trigonometric functions, known as **trigonometric identities,** make possible the solution of many calculus problems. The use of such identities appears again and again in the part of calculus called *integration.* The following example from a calculus text illustrates this.*

Evaluate $\displaystyle\int \frac{dx}{(1 + x^2)^2}$.

... We use the substitution $x = \tan \theta$, which gives $dx = \sec^2 \theta \, d\theta$. This leads to

$$\int \frac{dx}{(1 + x^2)^2} = \int \frac{\sec^2 \theta \, d\theta}{(1 + \tan^2 \theta)^2} = \int \frac{\sec^2 \theta \, d\theta}{\sec^4 \theta} = \int \frac{d\theta}{\sec^2 \theta}$$

$$= \int \cos^2 \theta \, d\theta = \tfrac{1}{2} \int (1 + \cos 2\theta) \, d\theta = \tfrac{1}{2}\theta + \tfrac{1}{4} \sin 2\theta + C$$

Now, from the original substitution, we have

$$\theta = \text{Arctan } x$$

and, from the figure or trigonometric identities,

$$\sin \theta = \frac{x}{\sqrt{1 + x^2}} \qquad \text{and} \qquad \cos \theta = \frac{1}{\sqrt{1 + x^2}}$$

Thus

$$\sin 2\theta = 2 \sin \theta \cos \theta = \frac{2x}{1 + x^2}$$

This gives

$$\int \frac{dx}{(1 + x^2)^2} = \tfrac{1}{2}\theta + \tfrac{1}{4}\sin 2\theta + C = \tfrac{1}{2} \text{Arctan } x + \frac{x}{2(1 + x^2)} + C$$

While this contains some mysterious symbols, it is loaded with notions that will be studied in this chapter. For example, the following relationships are employed that will be shown shortly:

$$1 + \tan^2 \theta = \sec^2 \theta \qquad \cos^2 \theta = \tfrac{1}{2}(1 + \cos 2\theta) \qquad \sin 2\theta = 2 \sin \theta \cos \theta$$

Also, the meaning of the notation "Arctan x" will be made clear in this chapter.

---

* Douglas F. Riddle, *Calculus and Analytic Geometry*, 3d ed. (Belmont, Ca.: Wadsworth Publishing Co., 1979), p. 468. Reprinted by permission.

317

1 Trigonometric Functions of Real Numbers

So far our definitions of the trigonometric functions have had as domain the set of all admissible angles. The values depend only on the angle, and not on whether the angle is measured in degrees or radians. The next stage of this course is an important one, although it is somewhat subtle. We wish to give meaning to such expressions as sin x, cos x, and tan x, where x stands for a *real number*.

Toward this end, let us recall that in the definition of the radian measure of an angle, we used an arbitrary circle with its center at the vertex of the angle. We find it useful in the present case to specify a circle of radius 1, with center at the origin, and we refer to this as the **unit circle** (Figure 1). If we are given an angle of θ radians, then the arc length subtended on a circle of radius r is $s = r\theta$, so if $r = 1$, the arc length s equals the angle θ. In other words, the linear measure (using the measurement units of r) of the arc length equals the angular measure of the central angle in radians. This relationship provides us with a way of defining the trigonometric functions of real numbers that is consistent with our previous definition.

Figure 1

Figure 2

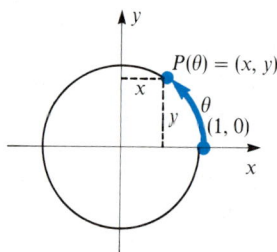

Given any real number θ (not at present to be thought of as the measure of an angle, but just a number), we mark off a distance of θ units on the unit circle, starting from $(1, 0)$ and moving counterclockwise when θ is positive and clockwise when θ is negative. Let $P(\theta)$ be the point arrived at in this manner with coordinates (x, y), as shown in Figure 2.* With this established, we can define the following:

---

* $P(\theta)$ is thus a function of the real variable θ, whose range consists of ordered pairs (x, y) representing points on the circle.

DEFINITION 1

$$\sin \theta = y \qquad\qquad \csc \theta = \frac{1}{y} \quad (y \neq 0)$$

$$\cos \theta = x \qquad\qquad \sec \theta = \frac{1}{x} \quad (x \neq 0)$$

$$\tan \theta = \frac{y}{x} \quad (x \neq 0) \qquad \cot \theta = \frac{x}{y} \quad (y \neq 0)$$

Note that for the tangent and secant, θ cannot be any number for which $x = 0$; and for the cotangent and cosecant, θ cannot be any number for which $y = 0$.

The relationship between the functions defined in terms of numbers and those defined in terms of angles should now be apparent. We simply consider the angle with initial side the positive x axis and terminal side connecting the origin and $P(\theta)$, as shown in Figure 3. Then the radian measure of this angle is precisely θ, the same as the number of units of length of arc. Now by the definitions of the trigonometric functions of the *angle* θ given in Section 4 of Chapter 8, we have:

$$\sin \theta = \frac{y}{r} = \frac{y}{1} = y \qquad \csc \theta = \frac{r}{y} = \frac{1}{y}$$

$$\cos \theta = \frac{x}{r} = \frac{x}{1} = x \qquad \sec \theta = \frac{r}{x} = \frac{1}{x}$$

$$\tan \theta = \frac{y}{x} \qquad\qquad \cot \theta = \frac{x}{y}$$

Comparing these with Definition 1 for the functions of the *number* θ, we see that they are precisely the same.

Suppose, then, that we are given the expression "sin 2." How shall we interpret it? Does it mean the sine of the number 2 or the sine of the angle whose radian measure is 2? The answer is that it does not matter, because the values are the same. Conceptually these are quite different, but sin 2 where 2 is a number has the same value as sin 2 where 2 is the radian measure of an angle. More generally, any trigonometric function of a real number has the same value as the same trigonometric function of the angle of θ radians. Thus, insofar as

Figure 3

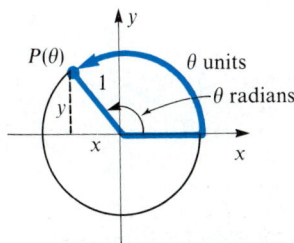

values of the trigonometric functions are concerned, it makes no difference whether we think in terms of an angle measured in radians or in terms of the real number that equals the number of radians in the angle.

EXAMPLE 1   The x coordinate of the point $P(\theta)$ on the unit circle is $-\frac{4}{5}$, and $P(\theta)$ is in the second quadrant. Find the y coordinate of $P(\theta)$ and write all six trigonometric functions of θ.

Solution   By the Pythagorean theorem we have

$$(-\tfrac{4}{5})^2 + y^2 = 1$$
$$y^2 = 1 - \tfrac{16}{25} = \tfrac{9}{25}$$
$$y = \tfrac{3}{5}$$

By Definition 1,

$$\sin \theta = y = \frac{3}{5} \qquad \csc \theta = \frac{1}{y} = \frac{5}{3}$$

$$\cos \theta = x = -\frac{4}{5} \qquad \sec \theta = \frac{1}{x} = -\frac{5}{4}$$

$$\tan \theta = \frac{y}{x} = -\frac{3}{4} \qquad \cot \theta = \frac{x}{y} = -\frac{4}{3}$$

EXAMPLE 2   Determine the value of θ, where $0 \le \theta < 2\pi$.
a. $P(\theta) = (-\sqrt{3}/2, -\frac{1}{2})$ **b.** $P(\theta) = (-1/\sqrt{2}, 1/\sqrt{2})$

Solution   **a.**   We observe that the reference angle of the angle determined by the radius drawn to the given point is 30°, or $\pi/6$ radians. So the angle itself is $7\pi/6$ radians. Therefore $\theta = 7\pi/6$.
b.   The reference angle in this case is 45°, or $\pi/4$ radians, and the angle is therefore $3\pi/4$ radians. So $\theta = 3\pi/4$.

Figure 4

Figure 5

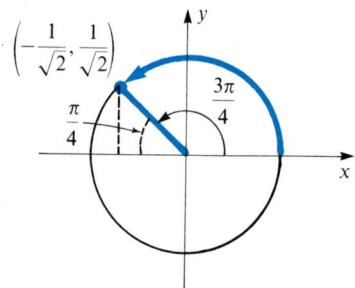

If you are using a calculator, you can find trigonometric functions of real numbers by considering the number as the radian measure of an angle, and this can be done regardless of the size of the number. For example, using a calculator we can read

$$\sin 2 = 0.9093 \qquad \cos 10 = -0.8391 \qquad \tan(-3.5) = -0.3746$$

and so on. However, to read these values from a table such as Table V at the end of this book requires some preliminary steps. This is because the table only gives functions of angles between $0°$ and $90°$, or equivalently, between 0 and $\pi/2$ radians. For larger angles, we make use of reference angles. Since $\pi/2 \approx 1.5708$, we cannot find functions of numbers greater than this directly from the table. To get sin 2, for example, we proceed as follows: As an angle in radians 2 lies in the second quadrant (between $\pi/2 \approx 1.5708$ and $\pi \approx 3.1416$). We show this in Figure 6. The reference angle is therefore $\pi - 2 \approx 1.1416$. Since the sine is positive in the second quadrant, we have that sin 2 is approximately equal to sin 1.1416. Reading from Table V (and interpolating between values found there), we see that this is approximately 0.9093. We could also obtain cos 2 by observing that the cosine is negative in quadrant II. Then, again using the reference angle, we find $\cos 2 \approx -0.4161$. Thus, the coordinates of the point $P(2)$ on the unit circle are approximately $(-0.4161, 0.9093)$.

Figure 6

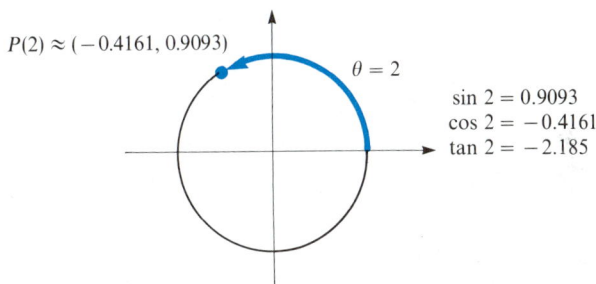

$P(2) \approx (-0.4161, 0.9093)$

$\theta = 2$

$\sin 2 = 0.9093$
$\cos 2 = -0.4161$
$\tan 2 = -2.185$

To find the functions of 10 using Table V, we again must find the reference angle. Since 10 exceeds 2π, the first thing to do is to subtract 2π from 10, in order to obtain an angle in the first revolution that is coterminal with 10. This gives

$$10 - 2\pi \approx 10 - 6.2832 = 3.7168$$

This is seen to be in the third quadrant (Figure 7), and so the reference angle is

$$3.7168 - 3.1416 = 0.5752$$

From the table we can now obtain sin 0.5752 = 0.5440 and cos 0.5752 = 0.8391. Since both sine and cosine are negative in the third quadrant, we have finally that

$$\sin 10 \approx -0.5440 \qquad \text{and} \qquad \cos 10 \approx -0.8391$$

The advantage of a calculator for finding functions of real numbers should be evident.

Figure 7

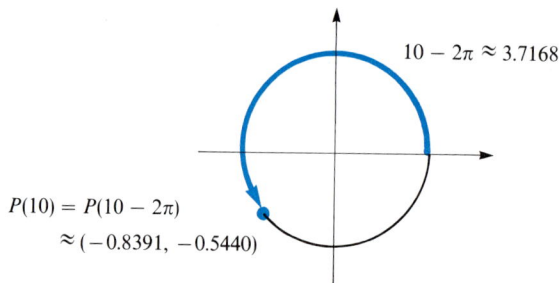

$10 - 2\pi \approx 3.7168$

$P(10) = P(10 - 2\pi)$
$\approx (-0.8391, -0.5440)$

EXERCISE SET 1

A   In Problems 1–10 find all six trigonometric functions of θ.

1. $P(\theta) = (-\frac{1}{3}, -2\sqrt{2}/3)$

2. $P(\theta) = (-2/\sqrt{5}, 1/\sqrt{5})$

3. $P(\theta) = (\frac{5}{13}, -\frac{12}{13})$

4. $P(\theta) = (-0.6, 0.8)$

5.   The x coordinate of $P(\theta)$ is $\frac{1}{4}$, and $P(\theta)$ is in the fourth quadrant.

6.   The y coordinate of $P(\theta)$ is $\frac{4}{5}$, and $\pi/2 \le \theta \le \pi$.

7.   The abscissa of $P(\theta)$ is $-\frac{1}{2}$, and $\pi \le \theta \le 2\pi$. What is the value of θ?

8.   The ordinate of $P(\theta)$ is $\sqrt{3}/2$, and the abscissa of $P(\theta)$ is negative. What is the value of θ?

9.   The abscissa of $P(\theta)$ is $\frac{1}{3}$, and the ordinate is negative.

10.   The ordinate of $P(\theta)$ is $-\frac{5}{13}$, and $3\pi \le \theta \le 4\pi$.

In Problems 11 and 12 give the coordinates of the point $P(\theta)$ for the given values of θ.

11. **a.** $P(\pi/2)$ **b.** $P(\pi)$ **c.** $P(3\pi/2)$
      d. $P(5\pi/6)$ **e.** $P(4\pi/3)$

12. **a.** $P(5\pi/4)$ **b.** $P(8\pi/3)$ **c.** $P(-7\pi/4)$
      d. $P(5\pi)$ **e.** $P(31\pi/6)$

In Problems 13 and 14 indicate the approximate location of $P(\theta)$ on the unit circle for the given value of θ.

13. **a.** $\theta = 0.5$ **b.** $\theta = -2$ **c.** $\theta = 4$ **d.** $\theta = -15$

14. **a.** $\theta = 8.2$ **b.** $\theta = 12.75$ **c.** $\theta = -1.54$ **d.** $\theta = 4.72$

In Problems 15 and 16 give the value of θ if $0 \le \theta < 2\pi$.

15. **a.** $P(\theta) = (\sqrt{3}/2, \frac{1}{2})$ **b.** $P(\theta) = (1/\sqrt{2}, 1/\sqrt{2})$
      c. $P(\theta) = (\frac{1}{2}, \sqrt{3}/2)$ **d.** $P(\theta) = (0, 1)$
      e. $P(\theta) = (1, 0)$

16. **a.** $P(\theta) = (-\frac{1}{2}, -\sqrt{3}/2)$ **b.** $P(\theta) = (0, -1)$
      c. $P(\theta) = (-\sqrt{3}/2, \frac{1}{2})$ **d.** $P(\theta) = (\sqrt{2}/2, -\sqrt{2}/2)$
      e. $P(\theta) = (-1, 0)$

In Problems 17 and 18 find $\sin \theta$, $\cos \theta$, and $\tan \theta$ using either a calculator or tables.

17. **a.** $\theta = 0.3$ **b.** $\theta = 2.718$ **c.** $\theta = 14.03$ **d.** $\theta = -3.625$

18. **a.** $\theta = 7.1432$ **b.** $\theta = 0.2967$ **c.** $\theta = -5.1324$ **d.** $\theta = 10.5146$

19. Find all values of θ such that $0 \leq \theta < 2\pi$ for which:

    a. $\sin \theta = 1$ **b.** $\cos \theta = 1$ **c.** $\tan \theta = 1$

    d. $\sin \theta = 0$ **e.** $\cos \theta = 0$ **f.** $\tan \theta = 0$

    g. $\sin \theta = -1$ **h.** $\cos \theta = -1$ **i.** $\tan \theta = -1$

B   **20.** Use the unit circle to show that:

    a. $\sin(\pi - \theta) = \sin \theta$ **b.** $\cos(\pi - \theta) = -\cos \theta$

    c. $\sin(\pi + \theta) = -\sin \theta$ **d.** $\cos(\pi + \theta) = -\cos \theta$

    e. $\tan(\pi + \theta) = \tan \theta$

21. Show that for all integers n, each of the following is undefined for the stated values of θ:

    a. $\tan \theta$ for $\theta = \dfrac{2n + 1}{2}\pi$ **b.** $\cot \theta$ for $\theta = n\pi$

    c. $\sec \theta$ for $\theta = \dfrac{2n + 1}{2}\pi$ **d.** $\csc \theta$ for $\theta = n\pi$

22. Show that $|\sec \theta| \geq 1$ and $|\csc \theta| \geq 1$ for all θ in the domains of these functions.

23. Prove that the range of $\tan \theta$ is the set of all real numbers.

24. Let

$$S = \left\{ \theta \in R : \quad \theta \neq \frac{(2n + 1)\pi}{2}, n = 0, \pm 1, \pm 2, \ldots \right\}$$

$$T = \{ \theta \in R : \quad \theta \neq n\pi, n = 0, \pm 1, \pm 2, \ldots \}$$

$$U = \{ k \in R : \quad |k| \geq 1 \}$$

Prove that if $f(\theta) = \sec \theta$ and $g(\theta) = \csc \theta$, then:

a. f is a function from S onto U

b. g is a function from T onto U

Is either f or g a 1–1 function? Explain.

2   Some Basic Trigonometric Identities

You may have already noticed the following relationships among the trigonometric functions:

$$\tan \theta = \frac{\sin \theta}{\cos \theta} \qquad \csc \theta = \frac{1}{\sin \theta}$$

$$\cot \theta = \frac{\cos \theta}{\sin \theta} \qquad \cot \theta = \frac{1}{\tan \theta}$$

$$\sec \theta = \frac{1}{\cos \theta}$$

These are seen to be true from Definition 2 of Chapter 8 or Definition 1 of this chapter. They are examples of **trigonometric identities**—so-called because they are true for all admissible values of θ. There are many other identities, and some are so basic that they should be committed to memory. These will be indicated as we proceed.

The Pythagorean theorem is the basis for another important set of identities. Using the theorem, we have, for (x, y) on the unit circle (see Figure 8),

$$x^2 + y^2 = 1$$

Figure 8

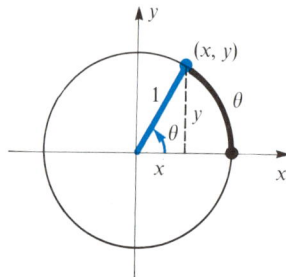

But $x = \cos \theta$ and $y = \sin \theta$. So

$$\sin^2 \theta + \cos^2 \theta = 1$$

If we divide both sides of the first equation by x^2 (assuming $x \neq 0$), we obtain

$$1 + \left(\frac{y}{x}\right)^2 = \left(\frac{1}{x}\right)^2$$

which, according to our definitions, is

$$1 + \tan^2 \theta = \sec^2 \theta$$

However, if we divide the first equation by y^2, we get

$$\left(\frac{x}{y}\right)^2 + 1 = \left(\frac{1}{y}\right)^2$$

or

$$\cot^2 \theta + 1 = \csc^2 \theta$$

We collect these results together:

$$\sin^2 \theta + \cos^2 \theta = 1$$
$$1 + \tan^2 \theta = \sec^2 \theta$$
$$1 + \cot^2 \theta = \csc^2 \theta$$

These are known as the **Pythagorean identities** and should be learned. Notice the similarity between the last two. In applying these, it may be necessary to write them in various equivalent forms, for example, $\cos^2 \theta = 1 - \sin^2 \theta$ or $\sec^2 \theta - 1 = \tan^2 \theta$, but it is probably best to concentrate on learning them in just one form, such as the one given. You can then mentally rewrite them in various ways.

Starting from any point on the unit circle, if we go 2π units along the circle either clockwise or counterclockwise, we wind up at the same point, since the circumference of the unit circle is 2π. Thus, for any θ, $P(\theta) = P(\theta + 2n\pi)$, where n is any integer, positive or negative. Since the values of the trigonometric functions depend only on the coordinates of $P(\theta)$, it follows that

$$\sin(\theta + 2n\pi) = \sin\theta$$
$$\cos(\theta + 2n\pi) = \cos\theta$$

and so on, for the remaining trigonometric functions. These can be expressed briefly by saying that each of the trigonometric functions is **periodic,** with **period 2π.***

Figure 9

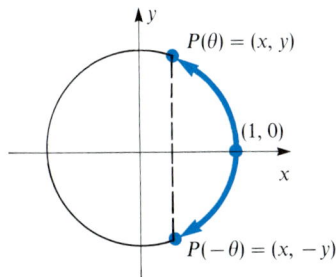

Consider next the relationships between the functions of θ and $-\theta$. By symmetry we see that if the coordinates of $P(\theta)$ are (x, y), then those of $P(-\theta)$ are $(x, -y)$ (Figure 9). The sine of $-\theta$ is by definition the y coordinate of $P(-\theta)$, but this is the negative of the y coordinate of θ. Thus, $\sin(-\theta) = -\sin\theta$. Since the x coordinates of $P(\theta)$ and $P(-\theta)$ are the same, it follows that $\cos(-\theta) = \cos\theta$. Similar relationships for the other functions can now be obtained:

$$\sin(-\theta) = -\sin\theta \qquad \csc(-\theta) = -\csc\theta$$
$$\cos(-\theta) = \cos\theta \qquad \sec(-\theta) = \sec\theta$$
$$\tan(-\theta) = -\tan\theta \qquad \cot(-\theta) = -\cot\theta$$

It is most important to learn the relationships $\sin(-\theta) = -\sin\theta$ and $\cos(-\theta) = \cos\theta$, since they occur more frequently than the others and since the others can be deduced easily from these two.

---

* In general, if $f(x + k) = f(x)$ for all x, then f is said to be *periodic with period k*. The smallest positive k for which this is true is called the **fundamental period.** For the sine, cosine, secant, and cosecant, the fundamental period is 2π, but for the tangent and cotangent, it is π.

EXAMPLE 3   Make use of the basic identities of this section to find the other five trigonometric functions of θ if $\tan \theta = -2$ and $\cos \theta < 0$.

Solution   First we observe that $\cot \theta = 1/\tan \theta = -\frac{1}{2}$. Next, since $\sec^2 \theta = 1 + \tan^2 \theta = 1 + (-2)^2 = 5$, we have $\sec \theta = \pm\sqrt{5}$. But $\cos \theta$ is negative, so that $\sec \theta$, which is $1/\cos \theta$, is also negative. Thus, $\sec \theta = -\sqrt{5}$. Therefore, $\cos \theta = -1/\sqrt{5}$.

Now we use $\sin^2 \theta = 1 - \cos^2 \theta = 1 - \frac{1}{5} = \frac{4}{5}$. Since $\tan \theta$ and $\cos \theta$ are both negative, and $\tan \theta = \sin \theta/\cos \theta$, it follows that $\sin \theta$ is positive. Thus, $\sin \theta = 2/\sqrt{5}$. Finally, $\csc \theta = 1/\sin \theta = \sqrt{5}/2$.

Note.   We could also have determined the signs of each of the functions by observing that for both $\tan \theta$, which is y/x, and $\cos \theta$, which is x, to be negative, we must have y positive, so that the point $P(\theta)$ is in the second quadrant, or equivalently, the angle of θ radians terminates in the second quadrant.

EXAMPLE 4   In each of the following use the basic identities to show that the first expression can be transformed into the second:

a. $\dfrac{\sin \theta}{\tan \theta},\ \cos \theta$ **b.** $\dfrac{\cos \theta}{\tan \theta},\ \csc \theta - \sin \theta$

Solution   **a.**   Since $\tan \theta = \sin \theta/\cos \theta$, we have

$$\frac{\sin \theta}{\tan \theta} = \frac{\sin \theta}{\dfrac{\sin \theta}{\cos \theta}} = \sin \theta \cdot \frac{\cos \theta}{\sin \theta} = \cos \theta$$

b.
$$\frac{\cos \theta}{\tan \theta} = \cos \theta \cdot \frac{\cos \theta}{\sin \theta} = \frac{\cos^2 \theta}{\sin \theta}$$

Now we use the identities $\cos^2 \theta = 1 - \sin^2 \theta$ and $\csc \theta = 1/\sin \theta$ to get

$$\frac{\cos^2 \theta}{\sin \theta} = \frac{1 - \sin^2 \theta}{\sin \theta} = \frac{1}{\sin \theta} - \frac{\sin^2 \theta}{\sin \theta} = \csc \theta - \sin \theta$$

EXERCISE SET 2

A   In Problems 1–8 find the remaining five trigonometric functions of θ, using the basic identities of this section.

1. $\sin \theta = -\frac{3}{5},\ \tan \theta > 0$ **2.** $\sec \theta = \frac{13}{12},\ \csc \theta < 0$

3. $\tan \theta = -\frac{4}{3},\ \pi/2 < \theta < 3\pi/2$ **4.** $\cot \theta = \frac{5}{12},\ \pi < \theta < 2\pi$

5. $\cos \theta = 2/\sqrt{5},\ \cot \theta < 0$ **6.** $\csc \theta = -\frac{17}{5},\ \tan \theta > 0$

7. $\sin \theta = \frac{1}{3},\ 5\pi/2 < \theta < 7\pi/2$ **8.** $\sec \theta = 3,\ 3\pi < \theta < 4\pi$

In Problems 9–18 show that the first expression can be transformed into the second, using basic identities.

9. $\dfrac{\tan \theta}{\sin \theta},\ \sec \theta$ **10.** $\dfrac{\cot \theta}{\csc \theta},\ \cos \theta$

11. $\dfrac{\sin \theta}{\cot \theta}$, $\sec \theta - \cos \theta$

12. $\sec^2 \theta \sin^2 \theta$, $\sec^2 \theta - 1$

13. $\cot \theta \sec \theta$, $\csc \theta$

14. $\tan \theta \csc \theta$, $\sec \theta$

15. $\dfrac{\sec \theta}{\csc \theta}$, $\tan \theta$

16. $1 - \dfrac{\sin \theta}{\csc \theta}$, $\cos^2 \theta$

17. $\dfrac{1}{\sec^2 \theta} + \dfrac{1}{\csc^2 \theta}$, 1

18. $\sec^2 \theta - \sin^2 \theta \sec^2 \theta$, 1

B **19.** By making the substitution $t = \tan \theta$, where $-\pi/2 < \theta < \pi/2$, show that

$$\frac{\sqrt{1 + t^2}}{t} = \csc \theta$$

20. By making the substitution $t = 2 \sin \theta$, where $-\pi/2 < \theta < \pi/2$, show that

$$\frac{t}{\sqrt{4 - t^2}} = \tan \theta$$

21. By making the substitution $t = \frac{3}{2} \sec \theta$, where $0 < \theta < \pi/2$ if $t > 0$ and $\pi < \theta < 3\pi/2$ if $t < 0$, show that

$$\frac{\sqrt{4t^2 - 9}}{t} = 2 \sin \theta$$

22. If $\tan \theta = t$, prove that

$$\sin \theta \cos \theta = \frac{t}{1 + t^2}$$

23. If $\cot \theta = t$, prove that

$$\sec \theta \csc \theta = \frac{1 + t^2}{t}$$

3 Proving Identities

By using the basic identities of the last section, we can prove a multitude of others, but fortunately it is not particularly useful to try to memorize any of the results. By proving an identity, we mean to show that the given equation is true for all admissible values of the variable or variables involved. The general procedure is to work only on one side of the equation, and by use of the basic identities transform it so that in the final stage it is identical to the other side. Often the more complicated side is the better to work with, since it offers more obvious possibilities for alteration, but there are times in calculus when it is better to change a simpler expression into a more complicated one. We illustrate the procedure by means of several examples.

EXAMPLE 5 Prove the identity $\tan \theta + \cot \theta = \sec \theta \csc \theta$.

Solution Perhaps it would be better to word the instructions, "Prove that the following is an identity." For we cannot prove it is true by assuming it is true, and this is an important point of logic often missed. This precludes, for example, working on both sides of the equation, unless we verify that each step is reversible. A proper approach is to begin with the left-hand side and try to obtain the right-hand side:

$$\tan \theta + \cot \theta = \frac{\sin \theta}{\cos \theta} + \frac{\cos \theta}{\sin \theta}$$

$$= \frac{\sin^2 \theta + \cos^2 \theta}{\cos \theta \sin \theta}$$

$$= \frac{1}{\cos \theta \sin \theta}$$

$$= \frac{1}{\cos \theta} \cdot \frac{1}{\sin \theta}$$

$$= \sec \theta \csc \theta$$

and now the given equation is verified. It is true for all admissible values of θ, and in this case this means all values except 0, $\pi/2$, $3\pi/2$, and any angles coterminal with these since, at each of these values, two of the given functions are undefined. Usually we will understand that such exceptions are necessary without mentioning them explicitly.

EXAMPLE 6   Prove the identity

$$\frac{1}{\sec x + 1} = \cot x \csc x - \csc^2 x + 1$$

Solution   It would be possible to transform the right-hand side into the left, and may even be easier, but we choose to work from the left-hand side because in later applications the right-hand side will be seen to be the more desirable final form. We begin with a commonly used trick, that of multiplying numerator and denominator by the same factor.

$$\frac{1}{\sec x + 1} = \frac{1}{\sec x + 1} \cdot \frac{\sec x - 1}{\sec x - 1} = \frac{\sec x - 1}{\sec^2 x - 1}$$

The object here is to bring $\sec^2 x - 1$ into the picture, because this is, by one of the Pythagorean identities, equal to $\tan^2 x$. So,

$$\frac{1}{\sec x + 1} = \frac{\sec x - 1}{\tan^2 x} = \frac{\sec x}{\tan^2 x} - \frac{1}{\tan^2 x}$$

$$= \frac{1}{\cos x} \cdot \frac{\cos^2 x}{\sin^2 x} - \cot^2 x$$

$$= \frac{\cos x}{\sin^2 x} - (\csc^2 x - 1)$$

$$= \frac{\cos x}{\sin x} \cdot \frac{1}{\sin x} - \csc^2 x + 1$$

$$= \cot x \csc x - \csc^2 x + 1$$

EXAMPLE 7   Prove that

$$\frac{2 \sin^3 x}{1 - \cos x} = 2 \sin x(1 + \cos x)$$

Solution
$$\frac{2 \sin^3 x}{1 - \cos x} = \frac{2 \sin x(1 - \cos^2 x)}{1 - \cos x}$$

$$= \frac{2 \sin x(1 + \cos x)(1 - \cos x)}{1 - \cos x}$$

$$= 2 \sin x(1 + \cos x)$$

EXAMPLE 8   Prove the identity

$$\frac{\csc \theta - \cot \theta}{\sec \theta - 1} = \cot \theta$$

Solution
$$\frac{\csc \theta - \cot \theta}{\sec \theta - 1} = \frac{\dfrac{1}{\sin \theta} - \dfrac{\cos \theta}{\sin \theta}}{\dfrac{1}{\cos \theta} - 1}$$

$$= \frac{\dfrac{1 - \cos \theta}{\sin \theta}}{\dfrac{1 - \cos \theta}{\cos \theta}}$$

$$= \frac{1 - \cos \theta}{\sin \theta} \cdot \frac{\cos \theta}{1 - \cos \theta}$$

$$= \frac{\cos \theta}{\sin \theta}$$

$$= \cot \theta$$

A word is in order about the utility of proving identities. In calculus, as well as in more advanced courses, we are frequently confronted with an unwieldy expression involving trigonometric functions. Often, by use of the basic identities, these can be transformed into more manageable forms. So in practice we usually do not have a ready-made identity to verify, but rather an expression that is to be changed to some other, initially unknown, form. It would be more accurate to describe this procedure as deriving an identity. The value of proving identities already provided lies in the fact that it gives a goal to shoot for in transforming an expression. Without this and with little or no experience in such activity, a student may go in circles or change to a less desirable form.

EXERCISE SET 3

A   In Problems 1–49 prove that the given equation is an identity by transforming the left-hand side into the right-hand side.

1. $\dfrac{1 + \sin \theta}{\tan \theta} = \cos \theta + \cot \theta$

2. $\dfrac{\sec \theta - \cos \theta}{\tan \theta} = \sin \theta$

3. $\dfrac{\sin x \cot x}{\cos x \csc x} = \sin x$

4. $\dfrac{\sin^2 x - 1}{\cos^2 x - 1} = \csc^2 x - 1$

5. $(1 + \cot^2 \theta) \tan^2 \theta = \sec^2 \theta$

6. $(\tan x + \cot x)^2 = \sec^2 x + \csc^2 x$

7. $\sec x - \sin x \tan x = \cos x$

8. $1 - \dfrac{\tan \theta \cos \theta}{\csc \theta} = \cos^2 \theta$

9. $(\sin \phi - \cos \phi)^2 = 1 - 2 \sin \phi \cos \phi$

10. $\dfrac{1 - \sec^2 \alpha}{\cos^2 \alpha - 1} = \sec^2 \alpha$

11. $\sin \theta \tan \theta = \sec \theta - \cos \theta$

12. $\sin \theta + \cos \theta \cot \theta = \csc \theta$

13. $(\tan^2 \theta + 1)(\cos^2 \theta - 1) = 1 - \sec^2 \theta$

14. $\csc \theta - \cos \theta \cot \theta = \sin \theta$

15. $\sin^4 x - \cos^4 x = 2 \sin^2 x - 1$

16. $\dfrac{(1 - \tan \theta)^2}{\sec^2 \theta} = 1 - 2 \sin \theta \cos \theta$

17. $\dfrac{\tan \theta + 1}{\sec \theta + \csc \theta} = \sin \theta$

18. $\dfrac{\cos x \cot x}{\csc x} - 1 = -\sin^2 x$

19. $\dfrac{1}{\tan \theta + \cot \theta} = \sin \theta \cos \theta$

20. $\dfrac{\cos \theta(\tan \theta - \sec \theta)}{1 - \csc \theta} = \sin \theta$

21. $\dfrac{\sec^2 x}{1 + \cot^2 x} = \tan^2 x$

22. $\dfrac{\sec x + \tan x}{\sec^2 x} = \cos x(1 + \sin x)$

23. $(1 + \csc \theta)(\sec \theta - \tan \theta) = \cot \theta$

24. $\dfrac{1 - \cos x}{\sin x} + \dfrac{\sin x}{1 - \cos x} = 2 \csc x$

25. $\tan^2 x - \sin^2 x = \tan^2 x \sin^2 x$

26. $\dfrac{1}{1 - \sin x} + \dfrac{1}{1 + \sin x} = 2 \sec^2 x$

27. $\dfrac{\tan^2 x - 1}{\sin^2 x} = \sec^2 x - \csc^2 x$

28. $\cot^4 \theta - 1 = \cot^2 \theta \csc^2 \theta - \csc^2 \theta$

29. $\sec^4 x = \tan^2 x \sec^2 x + \sec^2 x$

30. $\dfrac{\tan^2 \alpha - \sin^2 \alpha}{\sec^2 \alpha - 1} = \sin^2 \alpha$

31. $\dfrac{1 + \tan x}{1 + \cot x} = \tan x$

32. $\dfrac{\sin x}{\cot x + \csc x} = 1 - \cos x$

33. $\dfrac{1}{\sec x - \tan x} = \sec x + \tan x$

34. $\tan^4 x = \sec^2 x \tan^2 x - \sec^2 x + 1$

35. $\dfrac{\sin x}{1 - \cos x} - \dfrac{1 - \cos x}{\sin x} = 2 \cot x$

36. $\dfrac{(\tan^2 \theta - 1) \cot \theta}{\sin \theta - \cos \theta} = \sec \theta + \csc \theta$

37. $\dfrac{1 - \sec^2 x}{1 - \csc^2 x} = \tan^2 x \sec^2 x - \sec^2 x + 1$

38. $(\cot \theta - \csc \theta)^2 = \dfrac{1 - \cos \theta}{1 + \cos \theta}$

B   39. $(1 - \cos^2 \theta)(2 + \tan^2 \theta) = \sec^2 \theta - \cos^2 \theta$

40. $\tan\theta(\sin\theta + \cos\theta)^2 + (1 - \sec^2\theta)\cot\theta = 2\sin^2\theta$

41. $2\cos x - \sec x(1 - 2\sin^2 x) = \sec x$

42. $\dfrac{\sin\theta}{1 - \cos\theta} = \csc\theta + \cot\theta$

43. $\dfrac{1}{1 - \sin\theta} = \sec^2\theta + \tan\theta\sec\theta$

44. $\dfrac{1 - \sin x}{1 + \sin x} = 2\sec^2 x - 2\sec x\tan x - 1$

45. $\dfrac{\sin\theta}{1 + \sin\theta} + \sec^2\theta = \tan\theta\sec\theta + 1$

46. $\dfrac{\sin^2 x\tan^2 x}{\tan x - \sin x} = \tan x + \sin x$

47. $\dfrac{\sec\theta - \cos\theta + \tan\theta}{\tan\theta + \sec\theta} = \sin\theta$

48. $\dfrac{\sin^3\theta - \sin^2\theta\cos\theta - \sin\theta\cos^2\theta + \cos^3\theta}{\sin\theta + \cos\theta} = (\sin\theta - \cos\theta)^2$

49. $\sqrt{\dfrac{1 - \cos\theta}{1 + \cos\theta}} = \dfrac{\sin\theta}{1 + \cos\theta}\quad(0 \le \theta < \pi)$

50. Make the substitution: $x = \sin\theta(-\pi/2 < \theta < \pi/2)$ in the expression $x^2/\sqrt{1 - x^2}$ and show the result can be written in the form $\sec\theta - \cos\theta$.

51. Let $x = 2\tan\theta(-\pi/2 < \theta < \pi/2)$ in $x/\sqrt{4 + x^2}$, and show the result is $\sin\theta$.

52. Substitute $x = 3\sec\theta$, where θ lies either in the first or third quadrants, in $(x^2 - 9)^{3/2}/x$, and show the result can be written in the form $9(\sec\theta\tan\theta - \sin\theta)$.

53. Substitute $x = \frac{3}{2}\tan\theta(-\pi/2 < \theta < \pi/2)$ in $x/\sqrt{4x^2 + 9}$ and show that the result is $\frac{1}{2}\sin\theta$.

4   The Addition Formulas for Sine and Cosine

We will develop in this section formulas for the sum and difference of two numbers (or of two angles). These are of fundamental importance in deriving other identities. We designate by α and β two numbers which we will initially restrict to be between 0 and 2π and for which $\alpha > \beta$. These restrictions will soon be removed.

In Figure 10 we show typical positions of $P(\alpha)$ and $P(\beta)$. Now the distance along the circle from $(1, 0)$ to $P(\alpha)$ is α, and the distance to $P(\beta)$ is β. So the arc

Figure 10

Figure 11

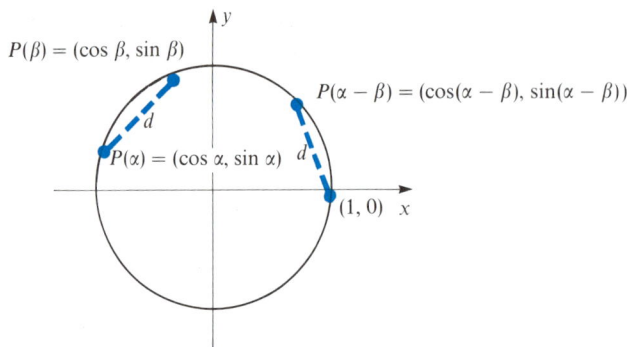

length from $P(\beta)$ to $P(\alpha)$ is $\alpha - \beta$. If we think of sliding this latter arc along the circle until the point originally at $P(\beta)$ coincides with $(1, 0)$, then the distance $\alpha - \beta$ is in standard position and the end point of the arc is correctly labeled $P(\alpha - \beta)$. Since the x and y coordinates of a point $P(\theta)$ are $\cos \theta$ and $\sin \theta$, respectively, we can show the coordinates of the three points $P(\alpha)$, $P(\beta)$, and $P(\alpha - \beta)$ as in Figure 11. Now, since the arc from $(1, 0)$ to $P(\alpha - \beta)$ is equal in length to the arc from $P(\beta)$ to $P(\alpha)$, it follows that the chords connecting these respective pairs of points are also equal. We can get these lengths using the distance formula:

$$\text{Distance from } (1, 0) \text{ to } P(\alpha - \beta) = \sqrt{[\cos(\alpha - \beta) - 1]^2 + [\sin(\alpha - \beta) - 0]^2}$$
$$\text{Distance from } P(\beta) \text{ to } P(\alpha) = \sqrt{(\cos \alpha - \cos \beta)^2 + (\sin \alpha - \sin \beta)^2}$$

Since these distances are the same, their squares are the same; so we obtain the equation

$$[\cos(\alpha - \beta) - 1]^2 + [\sin(\alpha - \beta)]^2 = (\cos \alpha - \cos \beta)^2 + (\sin \alpha - \sin \beta)^2$$

On squaring and collecting terms, and making use several times of the identity $\sin^2 \theta + \cos^2 \theta = 1$, this gives

$$\cos^2(\alpha - \beta) - 2\cos(\alpha - \beta) + 1 + \sin^2(\alpha - \beta)$$
$$= \cos^2 \alpha - 2\cos \alpha \cos \beta + \cos^2 \beta + \sin^2 \alpha - 2\sin \alpha \sin \beta + \sin^2 \beta$$
$$2 - 2\cos(\alpha - \beta) = 2 - 2(\cos \alpha \cos \beta + \sin \alpha \sin \beta)$$

or finally,

$$\cos(\alpha - \beta) = \cos \alpha \cos \beta + \sin \alpha \sin \beta \tag{1}$$

We next remove the restrictions imposed on the sizes of α and β. First, suppose $\beta > \alpha$ and both α and β are between 0 and 2π. Then, since $\cos \theta = \cos(-\theta)$,

$$\cos(\alpha - \beta) = \cos[-(\alpha - \beta)] = \cos(\beta - \alpha)$$

and now equation (1) applies, with the roles of α and β reversed. So

$$\cos(\alpha - \beta) = \cos(\beta - \alpha)$$
$$= \cos \beta \cos \alpha + \sin \beta \sin \alpha$$
$$= \cos \alpha \cos \beta + \sin \alpha \sin \beta$$

that is, equation (1) is true regardless of whether α or β is larger, as long as both are between 0 and 2π. The formula is also true if $\alpha = \beta$, because then we have

$$\cos(\alpha - \beta) = \cos 0$$

$$= \cos \alpha \cos \alpha + \sin \alpha \sin \alpha$$

$$= \cos^2 \alpha + \sin^2 \alpha$$

$$= 1$$

which is true.

Now suppose α and β are not restricted to lie between 0 and 2π. Then we can always write

$$\alpha = \alpha_1 + 2n\pi \qquad \text{and} \qquad \beta = \beta_1 + 2m\pi$$

where α_1 and β_1 do lie between 0 and 2π and m and n are appropriately chosen integers. Because of periodicity we have that $\sin \alpha = \sin(\alpha_1 + 2n\pi) = \sin \alpha_1$, and similarly for β and β_1 with the cosine:

$$\cos(\alpha - \beta) = \cos(\alpha_1 + 2n\pi - \beta_1 - 2m\pi)$$

$$= \cos[(\alpha_1 - \beta_1) + (n - m)2\pi]$$

$$= \cos(\alpha_1 - \beta_1)$$

$$= \cos \alpha_1 \cos \beta_1 + \sin \alpha_1 \sin \beta_1$$

$$= \cos \alpha \cos \beta + \sin \alpha \sin \beta$$

The third step, namely, that

$$\cos[(\alpha_1 - \beta_1) + (n - m)2\pi] = \cos(\alpha_1 - \beta_1)$$

again follows from periodicity. This establishes equation (1) for *all* numbers α and β.

From equation (1) we are able to get a number of other results. Consider first $\cos(\alpha + \beta)$. We write $\alpha + \beta = \alpha - (-\beta)$ and apply (1), replacing β by $-\beta$:

$$\cos(\alpha + \beta) = \cos(\alpha - (-\beta)) = \cos \alpha \cos(-\beta) + \sin \alpha \sin(-\beta)$$

Since $\cos(-\beta) = \cos \beta$ and $\sin(-\beta) = -\sin \beta$,

$$\mathbf{\cos(\alpha + \beta) = \cos \alpha \cos \beta - \sin \alpha \sin \beta} \qquad (2)$$

To get analogous formulas to equations (1) and (2) for the sine, we proceed as follows: In (1), replace α by $\pi/2$ and allow β to be arbitrary. Remember that $\sin \pi/2 = 1$ and $\cos \pi/2 = 0$. So,

$$\cos\left(\frac{\pi}{2} - \beta\right) = \cos \frac{\pi}{2} \cos \beta + \sin \frac{\pi}{2} \sin \beta$$

$$= 0 + \sin \beta$$

$$= \sin \beta$$

That is, for any number θ:

$$\cos\left(\frac{\pi}{2} - \theta\right) = \sin \theta \qquad (3)$$

In particular, if we take $\theta = (\pi/2) - \alpha$, we obtain

$$\cos\left[\frac{\pi}{2} - \left(\frac{\pi}{2} - \alpha\right)\right] = \sin\left(\frac{\pi}{2} - \alpha\right)$$

or

$$\cos \alpha = \sin\left(\frac{\pi}{2} - \alpha\right) \qquad (4)$$

for any number α. The letters θ and α used in equations (3) and (4) are independent of any relationships expressed between them in the derivation, that is, the formulas are self-contained. The letters are really just dummy variables, and any other letters would express the same relationships. So we could write, for example,

$$\cos\left(\frac{\pi}{2} - x\right) = \sin x$$

and

$$\sin\left(\frac{\pi}{2} - x\right) = \cos x$$

If in the first of these we take x as $\alpha + \beta$, we have, by equation (2),

$$\sin(\alpha + \beta) = \cos\left[\frac{\pi}{2} - (\alpha + \beta)\right] = \cos\left[\left(\frac{\pi}{2} - \alpha\right) - \beta\right]$$

$$= \cos\left(\frac{\pi}{2} - \alpha\right)\cos \beta + \sin\left(\frac{\pi}{2} - \alpha\right)\sin \beta$$

Now we use equations (3) and (4) again to get

$$\mathbf{\sin(\alpha + \beta) = \sin \alpha \cos \beta + \cos \alpha \sin \beta} \qquad (5)$$

This is valid for all numbers α and β. If we write $\alpha - \beta = \alpha + (-\beta)$, we can use equation (5) together with the facts that $\sin(-\theta) = -\sin \theta$ and $\cos(-\theta) = \cos \theta$ to get

$$\mathbf{\sin(\alpha - \beta)} = \sin[\alpha + (-\beta)] = \sin \alpha \cos(-\beta) + \cos \alpha \sin(-\beta)$$

$$\mathbf{= \sin \alpha \cos \beta - \cos \alpha \sin \beta} \qquad (6)$$

We summarize formulas (1), (2), (5), and (6) in the box.

The Addition Formulas for Sine and Cosine

$$\sin(\alpha + \beta) = \sin \alpha \cos \beta + \cos \alpha \sin \beta$$

$$\sin(\alpha - \beta) = \sin \alpha \cos \beta - \cos \alpha \sin \beta$$

$$\cos(\alpha + \beta) = \cos \alpha \cos \beta - \sin \alpha \sin \beta$$

$$\cos(\alpha - \beta) = \cos \alpha \cos \beta + \sin \alpha \sin \beta$$

These are of fundamental importance and should be learned. Notice that for the sine, the sign between the terms on the right agrees with the sign between

α and β on the left, whereas for the cosine these are reversed. So there really are just two basic patterns to learn.

EXAMPLE 9   Find the value of each of the following without the use of tables or a calculator:
a. $\sin(5\pi/12)$ **b.** $\sin(\pi/12)$ **c.** $\cos(13\pi/12)$ **d.** $\cos(-\pi/12)$

Solution   **a.**   We can write $5\pi/12$ as $2\pi/12 + 3\pi/12 = \pi/6 + \pi/4$. So

$$\sin\frac{5\pi}{12} = \sin\left(\frac{\pi}{6} + \frac{\pi}{4}\right)$$

$$= \sin\frac{\pi}{6}\cos\frac{\pi}{4} + \cos\frac{\pi}{6}\sin\frac{\pi}{4}$$

Now we know that we may treat $\pi/6$ and $\pi/4$ as if they are radian measures of angles. Thus,

$$\sin\frac{5\pi}{12} = \left(\frac{1}{2}\right)\left(\frac{1}{\sqrt{2}}\right) + \left(\frac{\sqrt{3}}{2}\right)\left(\frac{1}{\sqrt{2}}\right) = \frac{1+\sqrt{3}}{2\sqrt{2}}$$

b. $$\sin\frac{\pi}{12} = \sin\left(\frac{3\pi}{12} - \frac{2\pi}{12}\right) = \sin\left(\frac{\pi}{4} - \frac{\pi}{6}\right)$$

$$= \sin\frac{\pi}{4}\cos\frac{\pi}{6} - \cos\frac{\pi}{4}\sin\frac{\pi}{6}$$

$$= \left(\frac{1}{\sqrt{2}}\right)\left(\frac{\sqrt{3}}{2}\right) - \left(\frac{1}{\sqrt{2}}\right)\left(\frac{1}{2}\right) = \frac{\sqrt{3}-1}{2\sqrt{2}}$$

c. $$\cos\frac{13\pi}{12} = \cos\left(\frac{9\pi}{12} + \frac{4\pi}{12}\right) = \cos\left(\frac{3\pi}{4} + \frac{\pi}{3}\right)$$

$$= \cos\frac{3\pi}{4}\cos\frac{\pi}{3} - \sin\frac{3\pi}{4}\sin\frac{\pi}{3}$$

$$= \left(-\frac{1}{\sqrt{2}}\right)\left(\frac{1}{2}\right) - \left(\frac{1}{\sqrt{2}}\right)\left(\frac{\sqrt{3}}{2}\right) = -\frac{1+\sqrt{3}}{2\sqrt{2}}$$

d. $\cos(-\pi/12) = \cos(\pi/12)$, since $\cos(-\theta) = \cos\theta$; so,

$$\cos\left(-\frac{\pi}{12}\right) = \cos\frac{\pi}{12} = \cos\left(\frac{3\pi}{12} - \frac{2\pi}{12}\right) = \cos\left(\frac{\pi}{4} - \frac{\pi}{6}\right)$$

$$= \cos\frac{\pi}{4}\cos\frac{\pi}{6} + \sin\frac{\pi}{4}\sin\frac{\pi}{6}$$

$$= \left(\frac{1}{\sqrt{2}}\right)\left(\frac{\sqrt{3}}{2}\right) + \left(\frac{1}{\sqrt{2}}\right)\left(\frac{1}{2}\right) = \frac{\sqrt{3}+1}{2\sqrt{2}}$$

EXAMPLE 10   If $-\pi/2 \leq x \leq \pi/2$ and $0 \leq y \leq \pi$, $\sin x = \frac{3}{4}$, and $\cos y = -\frac{5}{6}$, find:
a. $\sin(x + y)$ **b.** $\cos(x - y)$

Solution   We conclude that x is between 0 and $\pi/2$, since if it were between 0 and $-\pi/2$, $\sin x$ would be negative. Similarly, we must have y between $\pi/2$ and π in order for $\cos y$ to be negative. By the Pythagorean identity, $\sin^2 x + \cos^2 x = 1$, we get

$$\cos^2 x = 1 - \sin^2 x$$

So

$$\cos x = \pm\sqrt{1 - \sin^2 x}$$

The positive sign must be chosen, since $0 \leq x \leq \pi/2$. So,

$$\cos x = \sqrt{1 - \left(\frac{3}{4}\right)^2} = \sqrt{1 - \frac{9}{16}} = \sqrt{\frac{7}{16}} = \frac{\sqrt{7}}{4}$$

Similarly,

$$\sin y = \sqrt{1 - \cos^2 y} = \sqrt{1 - \left(-\frac{5}{6}\right)^2} = \sqrt{1 - \frac{25}{36}} = \frac{\sqrt{11}}{6}$$

We now have all the necessary ingredients for obtaining the solutions.

a. $\sin(x + y) = \sin x \cos y + \cos x \sin y = \dfrac{3}{4}\left(-\dfrac{5}{6}\right) + \left(\dfrac{\sqrt{7}}{4}\right)\left(\dfrac{\sqrt{11}}{6}\right)$

$$= \frac{-15 + \sqrt{77}}{24}$$

b. $\cos(x - y) = \cos x \cos y + \sin x \sin y = \dfrac{\sqrt{7}}{4}\left(-\dfrac{5}{6}\right) + \dfrac{3}{4}\left(\dfrac{\sqrt{11}}{6}\right)$

$$= \frac{-5\sqrt{7} + 3\sqrt{11}}{24}$$

EXERCISE SET 4

A   In Problems 1–8 evaluate without using a calculator or tables.

1. $\sin(\alpha + \beta)$ and $\cos(\alpha + \beta)$, where $\alpha = \pi/4$ and $\beta = \pi/3$

2. $\sin(\alpha - \beta)$ and $\cos(\alpha - \beta)$, where $\alpha = \pi/4$ and $\beta = \pi/3$

3.   **a.** $\sin\left(\dfrac{\pi}{3} - \dfrac{3\pi}{4}\right)$ **b.** $\cos\left(\dfrac{5\pi}{6} + \dfrac{\pi}{4}\right)$

4.   **a.** $\sin\left(\dfrac{5\pi}{4} + \dfrac{11\pi}{6}\right)$ **b.** $\cos\left(\dfrac{4\pi}{3} - \dfrac{3\pi}{4}\right)$

5.   **a.** $\cos\dfrac{7\pi}{12}$ **b.** $\sin\dfrac{17\pi}{12}$

6. **a.** $\sin\left(-\dfrac{\pi}{12}\right)$ **b.** $\cos\left(-\dfrac{5\pi}{12}\right)$

7. **a.** $\sin 75°$ **b.** $\cos 15°$
8. **a.** $\cos 255°$ **b.** $\sin 195°$

9. If $\sin\alpha = -\frac{3}{5}$, $\sin\beta = -\frac{5}{13}$, $P(\alpha)$ is in the third quadrant, and $P(\beta)$ is in the fourth quadrant, find the following.
    a. $\sin(\alpha - \beta)$ **b.** $\cos(\alpha + \beta)$

10. If $\cos\alpha = \frac{12}{13}$, $\cos\beta = -\frac{4}{5}$, $P(\alpha)$ is the fourth quadrant, and $P(\beta)$ is in the second quadrant, find:
    a. $\sin(\alpha + \beta)$ **b.** $\cos(\alpha - \beta)$

11. If $\sin\alpha < 0$, $\cos\alpha = \frac{1}{3}$, $\cos\beta < 0$, and $\sin\beta = -\frac{2}{3}$, find:
    a. $\sin(\alpha + \beta)$ **b.** $\cos(\alpha - \beta)$

12. If $\tan x = -\frac{3}{4}$, $\csc x > 0$, $\sec y = \frac{13}{5}$, and $\cot y < 0$, find:
    a. $\sin(x - y)$ **b.** $\cos(x + y)$

13. If $\sin\alpha = -2/\sqrt{5}$, $\tan\alpha > 0$, $\cos\beta = -\frac{8}{17}$, and $\csc\beta > 0$, find:
    a. $\sin(\alpha - \beta)$ **b.** $\cos(\alpha + \beta)$

14. If $\cot A = -\frac{24}{7}$, $\sec A > 0$, $\tan B = \frac{4}{3}$, and $\sin B < 0$, find:
    a. $\sin(A + B)$ **b.** $\cos(A - B)$

15. If $\sin x = -\frac{3}{5}$, $\tan x > 0$, $\sec y = -\frac{13}{5}$, and $\cot y < 0$, find:
    a. $\csc(x + y)$ **b.** $\sec(x - y)$

Establish the formulas in Problems 16–20 by using addition formulas.

16. **a.** $\sin(\pi + \theta) = -\sin\theta$ **b.** $\cos(\pi + \theta) = -\cos\theta$

17. **a.** $\sin\left(\dfrac{\pi}{2} + \theta\right) = \cos\theta$ **b.** $\cos\left(\dfrac{\pi}{2} + \theta\right) = -\sin\theta$

18. **a.** $\sin\left(\dfrac{3\pi}{2} - \theta\right) = -\cos\theta$ **b.** $\cos\left(\dfrac{3\pi}{2} - \theta\right) = -\sin\theta$

19. **a.** $\sin(\pi - \theta) = \sin\theta$ **b.** $\cos(\pi - \theta) = -\cos\theta$

20. **a.** $\sin\left(\dfrac{\pi}{2} - \theta\right) = \cos\theta$ **b.** $\cos\left(\dfrac{\pi}{2} - \theta\right) = \sin\theta$

Prove the identities in Problems 21–29.

21. $\sin\alpha\cos\beta(\cot\alpha - \tan\beta) = \cos(\alpha + \beta)$

22. $\dfrac{\cos(\alpha + \beta)}{\cos(\alpha - \beta)} = \dfrac{1 - \tan\alpha\tan\beta}{1 + \tan\alpha\tan\beta}$ 23. $\dfrac{\tan\alpha - \tan\beta}{\tan\alpha + \tan\beta} = \dfrac{\sin(\alpha - \beta)}{\sin(\alpha + \beta)}$

24. $\dfrac{\sin(\alpha + \beta) + \sin(\alpha - \beta)}{\cos(\alpha + \beta) + \cos(\alpha - \beta)} = \tan\alpha$ 25. $\dfrac{\cos(\alpha - \beta) - \cos(\alpha + \beta)}{\sin(\alpha + \beta) - \sin(\alpha - \beta)} = \tan\alpha$

26. $\dfrac{\sin(\alpha + \beta)}{\sin\alpha\sin\beta} = \cot\alpha + \cot\beta$ 27. $\dfrac{\cos(\alpha - \beta)}{\sin\alpha\sin\beta} = 1 + \cot\alpha\cot\beta$

28. $\sin(x + y)\cos y - \cos(x + y)\sin y = \sin x$
29. $\sin x\sin(x + y) + \cos x\cos(x + y) = \cos y$

B 30. Prove that, in general, $\sin(\alpha + \beta) \neq \sin\alpha + \sin\beta$.
    31. Find all values of x for which $0 \le x < 2\pi$ and

$$\sin 5x\cos 4x = \cos 5x\sin 4x$$

32. Find all values of x for which $0 \leq x < 2\pi$ and

$$2 \cos 2x \cos x = 1 - 2 \sin 2x \sin x$$

33. Derive a formula for
  a. $\sin(\alpha + \beta + \gamma)$ **b.** $\cos(\alpha + \beta + \gamma)$
  Hint. First use the associative property for addition.

Prove the identities in Problems 34–36.

34. $\sin(\alpha + \beta) \sin(\alpha - \beta) = \sin^2 \alpha - \sin^2 \beta$
35. $\cos(\alpha + \beta) \cos(\alpha - \beta) = \cos^2 \alpha - \sin^2 \beta$
36. $\sin(\alpha + \beta) \cos(\alpha - \beta) = \sin \alpha \cos \alpha + \sin \beta \cos \beta$

---

5 Double-Angle, Half-Angle, and Reduction Formulas

The importance of the addition formulas in Section 4 lies primarily in the fact that so many other identities can be derived from them. We will carry out the derivations for some of the most important of these.

The **double-angle formulas** are obtained from the addition formulas for sine and cosine of α and β by putting $\beta = \alpha$. If we denote the common value of α and β by θ, we obtain

$$\sin(\theta + \theta) = \sin \theta \cos \theta + \cos \theta \sin \theta$$
$$= 2 \sin \theta \cos \theta$$

So,

$$\sin 2\theta = 2 \sin \theta \cos \theta$$

Also,

$$\cos(\theta + \theta) = \cos \theta \cos \theta - \sin \theta \sin \theta$$
$$= \cos^2 \theta - \sin^2 \theta$$

So,

$$\cos 2\theta = \cos^2 \theta - \sin^2 \theta \qquad (7)$$

Two other useful forms of $\cos 2\theta$ can be obtained by replacing, in turn, $\cos^2 \theta$ by $1 - \sin^2 \theta$ and $\sin^2 \theta$ by $1 - \cos^2 \theta$. This gives

$$\cos 2\theta = (1 - \sin^2 \theta) - \sin^2 \theta = 1 - 2 \sin^2 \theta$$

and

$$\cos 2\theta = \cos^2 \theta - (1 - \cos^2 \theta) = 2 \cos^2 \theta - 1$$

So we have

$$\cos 2\theta = 1 - 2 \sin^2 \theta \qquad (8)$$

and

$$\cos 2\theta = 2 \cos^2 \theta - 1 \qquad (9)$$

Whether to use (7), (8), or (9) depends on the objective. We will shortly see some examples where a particular form is clearly preferable.

If we solve (8) for $\sin^2 \theta$ and (9) for $\cos^2 \theta$, we obtain

$$\sin^2 \theta = \frac{1 - \cos 2\theta}{2}$$

and

$$\cos^2 \theta = \frac{1 + \cos 2\theta}{2}$$

These forms are employed extensively in calculus.

By replacing θ by $\alpha/2$ in the last two equations and then taking square roots, we get the **half-angle formulas**:

$$\sin \frac{\alpha}{2} = \pm \sqrt{\frac{1 - \cos \alpha}{2}}$$

$$\cos \frac{\alpha}{2} = \pm \sqrt{\frac{1 + \cos \alpha}{2}}$$

The ambiguity of sign has to be resolved in each particular instance according to the quadrant in which $\alpha/2$ lies.

From the addition formulas we can obtain a class of identities sometimes called **reduction formulas,** of which (3) and (4) of Section 4 are special cases. Here are some others:

$$\sin(\pi + \theta) = \sin \pi \cos \theta + \cos \pi \sin \theta$$
$$= -\sin \theta$$

and

$$\sin(\pi - \theta) = \sin \pi \cos \theta - \cos \pi \sin \theta$$
$$= \sin \theta$$

Similarly,

$$\cos(\pi + \theta) = \cos \pi \cos \theta - \sin \pi \sin \theta$$
$$= -\cos \theta$$

and

$$\cos(\pi - \theta) = \cos \pi \cos \theta + \sin \pi \sin \theta$$
$$= -\cos \theta$$

In these, we have used the facts that $\sin \pi = 0$ and $\cos \pi = -1$. Since $\sin(3\pi/2) = -1$ and $\cos(3\pi/2) = 0$, we also have

$$\sin\left(\frac{3\pi}{2} + \theta\right) = \sin \frac{3\pi}{2} \cos \theta + \cos \frac{3\pi}{2} \sin \theta$$
$$= -\cos \theta$$

and

$$\sin\left(\frac{3\pi}{2} - \theta\right) = \sin \frac{3\pi}{2} \cos \theta - \cos \frac{3\pi}{2} \sin \theta$$
$$= -\cos \theta$$

Likewise, there are similar formulas for $\cos[(3\pi/2) \pm \theta]$.

To generalize, it appears that we should consider two cases:

Case 1. Functions of $(n\pi \pm \theta)$

Case 2. Functions of $\left[\dfrac{(2n + 1)\pi}{2} \pm \theta\right]$

where n is an arbitrary integer. Note that in Case 2, an odd multiple of $\pi/2$ is involved since $(2n + 1)$ is always odd. The following identities can now be established.

Reduction Formulas for the Sine and Cosine

Case 1. $\sin(n\pi \pm \theta) = \pm\sin\theta$
$\cos(n\pi \pm \theta) = \pm\cos\theta$

Case 2. $\sin\left[\dfrac{(2n+1)\pi}{2} \pm \theta\right] = \pm\cos\theta$

$\cos\left[\dfrac{(2n+1)\pi}{2} \pm \theta\right] = \pm\sin\theta$

To determine the correct sign on the right, it suffices to determine what the sign is when θ is acute.

These are called reduction formulas since in each case the given expression is reduced to a function involving θ only. Note that in Case 1 the function on the right is the *same* as that on the left, whereas in Case 2 the function on the right is the *cofunction* of the one on the left.

We will prove the first of these formulas and leave the others as exercises. We note first that $\sin n\pi = 0$. Secondly, $\cos n\pi = (-1)^n$ since, when n is even, $n\pi$ is coterminal with 0 so that the cosine is $+1$ and, when n is odd, $n\pi$ is coterminal with π so that the cosine is -1. Using the addition formula for the sine, we have

$$\sin(n\pi + \theta) = \sin n\pi \cos\theta + \cos n\pi \sin\theta$$
$$= (0)\cos\theta + (-1)^n \sin\theta$$
$$= (-1)^n \sin\theta$$

This shows that $\sin(n\pi + \theta) = \pm\sin\theta$. Furthermore, the sign on the right is $(-1)^n$ which is independent of the size of θ. So if we determine the sign when θ is acute, it will be correct for all values of θ.

EXAMPLE 11   Reduce each of the following to a function of θ only.

a. $\sin(3\pi - \theta)$ **b.** $\cos\left(\dfrac{\pi}{2} + \theta\right)$ **c.** $\sin\left(-\dfrac{\pi}{2} + \theta\right)$

Solution   **a.** $\sin(3\pi - \theta) = \pm\sin\theta$ (Case 1)

If θ is acute, $3\pi - \theta$ is in quadrant II, so $\sin(3\pi - \theta)$ is positive. Thus,

$$\sin(3\pi - \theta) = \sin\theta$$

b. $\cos\left(\dfrac{\pi}{2} + \theta\right) = \pm\sin\theta$ (Case 2)

For θ acute, $\pi/2 + \theta$ is in quadrant II, and the cosine is negative there. So

$$\cos\left(\frac{\pi}{2} + \theta\right) = -\sin\theta$$

c. $\sin\left(-\dfrac{\pi}{2} + \theta\right) = \pm\cos\theta$ (Case 2)

For θ acute, $-\pi/2 + \theta$ is in quadrant IV, where the sine is negative. So

$$\sin\left(-\frac{\pi}{2} + \theta\right) = -\cos\theta$$

EXERCISE SET 5

A   In Problems 1–6 find $\sin 2\theta$ and $\cos 2\theta$.

1. $\sin\theta = \frac{4}{5}$ and θ terminates in quadrant II
2. $\cos\theta = -\frac{1}{3}$ and θ terminates in quadrant III
3. $\tan\theta = \frac{5}{12}$ and $\sin\theta < 0$ **4.** $\sec\theta = \sqrt{5}$ and $\csc\theta < 0$

5. $\cot\theta = -2$ and $0 \le \theta \le \pi$ **6.** $\csc\theta = \dfrac{17}{8}$ and $\dfrac{\pi}{2} \le \theta \le \dfrac{3\pi}{2}$

7. If $\sin\theta = x$ and $-\pi/2 \le \theta \le \pi/2$, find $\sin 2\theta$ and $\cos 2\theta$ in terms of x.
8. If $\cos\theta = x$ and $0 \le \theta \le \pi$, find $\sin 2\theta$ and $\cos 2\theta$ in terms of x.

In Problems 9–12 find $\sin\theta$ and $\cos\theta$.

9. $\cos 2\theta = \frac{1}{3}$ and $\pi \le 2\theta \le 2\pi$ **10.** $\sin 2\theta = -\dfrac{4}{5}$ and $\pi \le 2\theta \le \dfrac{3\pi}{2}$

11. $\sec 2\theta = \frac{25}{7}$ and $-\pi \le 2\theta \le 0$ **12.** $\tan 2\theta = -\frac{12}{5}$ and $3\pi \le 2\theta \le 4\pi$

13. Use the half-angle formulas to find

    a. $\sin\dfrac{\pi}{8}$ **b.** $\cos\dfrac{\pi}{12}$ **c.** $\sin 75°$ **d.** $\cos 67.5°$

In Problems 14–17 find $\sin(\alpha/2)$ and $\cos(\alpha/2)$.

14. $\cos\alpha = \frac{7}{25}$, $0 \le \alpha \le \pi$ **15.** $\sin\alpha = -\dfrac{12}{13}$, $\pi \le \alpha \le \dfrac{3\pi}{2}$

16. $\tan\alpha = -\frac{8}{15}$, $2\pi \le \alpha \le 3\pi$ **17.** $\sec\alpha = 3$, $-\pi \le \alpha \le 0$

18. If $P(\theta) = \left(\dfrac{1}{\sqrt{5}}, -\dfrac{2}{\sqrt{5}}\right)$, find $P(2\theta)$.

19. If $0 \le 2\theta \le \pi$ and $P(2\theta) = (-\frac{7}{25}, \frac{24}{25})$, find $P(\theta)$.

In Problems 20–22 reduce to a function involving θ only.

20. **a.** $\sin(2\pi - \theta)$ **b.** $\cos\left(\dfrac{3\pi}{2} - \theta\right)$ **c.** $\sin\left(\dfrac{5\pi}{2} + \theta\right)$

   d. $\cos(-\pi + \theta)$ **e.** $\sin\left(-\dfrac{\pi}{2} - \theta\right)$

21. **a.** $\sin(\theta - \pi)$ **b.** $\cos\left(\dfrac{\pi}{2} + \theta\right)$ **c.** $\sin\left(-\dfrac{3\pi}{2} - \theta\right)$

   d. $\cos(\theta - 3\pi)$ **e.** $\sin\left(\dfrac{\pi}{2} + \theta\right)$

22. **a.** $\cos\left(\dfrac{3\pi}{2} + \theta\right)$ **b.** $\sin(\pi + \theta)$ **c.** $\cos(\theta - 2\pi)$

   d. $\sin\left(-\dfrac{\pi}{2} + \theta\right)$ **e.** $\cos\left(\theta - \dfrac{5\pi}{2}\right)$

In Problems 23–37 prove the identities.

23. $1 - \dfrac{\cos 2x - 1}{2\cos^2 x} = \sec^2 x$

24. $\sin^4 \theta \cot^2 \theta = \tfrac{1}{4}\sin^2 2\theta$

25. $\dfrac{\cos^2 \theta - \sin^2 \theta}{\sin \theta \cos \theta} = 2\cot 2\theta$

26. $\dfrac{\sin^2 2x}{1 - \cos 2x} = 2\cos^2 x$

27. $(\sin x - \cos x)^2 = 1 - \sin 2x$

28. $\cos^4 x - \sin^4 x = \cos 2x$

29. $\dfrac{2}{1 + \cos 2x} = \sec^2 x$

30. $\dfrac{\sin 2\theta}{\sin^2 \theta - 1} + 3\tan \theta = \tan \theta$

31. $\tan \alpha + \cot \alpha = 2\csc 2\alpha$

32. $\dfrac{\cot \theta + \tan \theta}{\cot \theta - \tan \theta} = \sec 2\theta$

33. $\dfrac{\tan^2 \theta}{1 + \tan^2 \theta} = \dfrac{1 - \cos 2\theta}{2}$

34. $\sin^2 \dfrac{\theta}{2}\csc^2 \theta = \dfrac{1}{2(1 + \cos \theta)}$

35. $\dfrac{2\cos^2 \dfrac{\theta}{2}}{\sin^2 \theta} = \dfrac{1}{1 - \cos \theta}$

36. $\dfrac{2\sin^2 \dfrac{\theta}{2} + \cos \theta}{\sec \theta} = \cos \theta$

37. $\dfrac{1 - \tan^2 x}{1 + \tan^2 x} = \cos 2x$

B **38.** Prove the reduction formula for each of the following:

   a. $\sin(n\pi - \theta)$ **b.** $\cos(n\pi + \theta)$ **c.** $\cos(n\pi - \theta)$

   d. $\sin\left[\dfrac{(2n + 1)\pi}{2} + \theta\right]$ **e.** $\sin\left[\dfrac{(2n + 1)\pi}{2} - \theta\right]$ **f.** $\cos\left[\dfrac{(2n + 1)\pi}{2} + \theta\right]$

   g. $\cos\left[\dfrac{(2n + 1)\pi}{2} - \theta\right]$

39. If $\tan \theta = x$ and $-\pi/2 < \theta < \pi/2$, find $\sin 2\theta$ and $\cos 2\theta$ in terms of x.

40. If $\sec \theta = x$ and $0 \le \theta \le \pi$, $\theta \ne \pi/2$, find:
   a. $\sin 2\theta$ **b.** $\cos 2\theta$ **c.** $\sin \tfrac{1}{2}\theta$ **d.** $\cos \tfrac{1}{2}\theta$

41. By writing $3\theta = 2\theta + \theta$, find formulas for $\sin 3\theta$ and $\cos 3\theta$ in terms of functions of θ.

42. Derive the formula $\sin 4\theta = 4 \sin \theta \cos \theta - 8 \sin^3 \theta \cos \theta$.

43. Derive the formula $\cos 4\theta = 8 \cos^4 \theta - 8 \cos^2 \theta + 1$.

Prove the identities in Problems 44–50.

44. $\cos^4 x = \dfrac{3}{8} + \dfrac{\cos 2x}{2} + \dfrac{\cos 4x}{8}$

45. $\sin^6 x = \dfrac{5}{16} - \dfrac{\cos 2x}{2} + \dfrac{3 \cos 4x}{16} + \dfrac{\sin^2 2x \cos 2x}{8}$

46. $\dfrac{1 - \cos 2nx}{\sin 2nx} = \tan nx$

47. $\dfrac{\sin 3\theta}{\sin \theta} - \dfrac{\cos 3\theta}{\cos \theta} = 2$

48. $\sin 3x + \sin x = 4 \sin x \cos^2 x$

49. $\dfrac{\sin^3 x + \cos^3 x}{\sin x + \cos x} = 1 - \tfrac{1}{2} \sin 2x$

50. By calculating $\sin(\pi/12)$ in two ways, using the half-angle formulas and using the addition formulas, prove that

$$\sqrt{2 - \sqrt{3}} = \tfrac{1}{2}(\sqrt{6} - \sqrt{2})$$

6 Further Identities

To obtain addition formulas for the tangent, it is necessary only to use the fact that $\tan \theta = \sin \theta / \cos \theta$. Thus,

$$\tan(\alpha + \beta) = \frac{\sin(\alpha + \beta)}{\cos(\alpha + \beta)} = \frac{\sin \alpha \cos \beta + \cos \alpha \sin \beta}{\cos \alpha \cos \beta - \sin \alpha \sin \beta}$$

This can be improved by dividing numerator and denominator by $\cos \alpha \cos \beta$:

$$\tan(\alpha + \beta) = \frac{\dfrac{\sin \alpha \cos \beta}{\cos \alpha \cos \beta} + \dfrac{\cos \alpha \sin \beta}{\cos \alpha \cos \beta}}{\dfrac{\cos \alpha \cos \beta}{\cos \alpha \cos \beta} - \dfrac{\sin \alpha \sin \beta}{\cos \alpha \cos \beta}}$$

or

$$\tan(\alpha + \beta) = \frac{\tan \alpha + \tan \beta}{1 - \tan \alpha \tan \beta} \tag{10}$$

And in a similar manner,

$$\tan(\alpha - \beta) = \frac{\tan \alpha - \tan \beta}{1 + \tan \alpha \tan \beta} \tag{11}$$

The double-angle formula for the tangent is obtained from (10) by taking $\alpha = \beta$. If we call this common value θ, we have

$$\tan(\theta + \theta) = \frac{\tan \theta + \tan \theta}{1 - \tan \theta \tan \theta}$$

So,

$$\tan 2\theta = \frac{2 \tan \theta}{1 - \tan^2 \theta}$$

We can derive half-angle formulas for the tangent as follows:

$$\tan \tfrac{1}{2}\alpha = \frac{\sin \tfrac{1}{2}\alpha}{\cos \tfrac{1}{2}\alpha} = \frac{\sin \tfrac{1}{2}\alpha}{\cos \tfrac{1}{2}\alpha} \cdot \frac{2 \cos \tfrac{1}{2}\alpha}{2 \cos \tfrac{1}{2}\alpha}$$

$$= \frac{2 \sin \tfrac{1}{2}\alpha \cos \tfrac{1}{2}\alpha}{2 \cos^2 \tfrac{1}{2}\alpha}$$

Since $2 \sin(\alpha/2) \cos(\alpha/2) = \sin 2(\alpha/2) = \sin \alpha$ and

$$2 \cos^2 \tfrac{1}{2}\alpha = 2 \left(\sqrt{\frac{1 + \cos \alpha}{2}} \right)^2 = 1 + \cos \alpha$$

we obtain

$$\tan \tfrac{1}{2}\alpha = \frac{\sin \alpha}{1 + \cos \alpha}$$

If in this derivation we had multiplied numerator and denominator by $2 \sin(\alpha/2)$ instead of $2 \cos(\pi/2)$, we would have obtained the equivalent formula

$$\tan \tfrac{1}{2}\alpha = \frac{1 - \cos \alpha}{\sin \alpha}$$

(See Problem 35, Exercise Set 6.)

We could obtain analogous formulas for the cotangent, secant, and cosecant in a similar way, but these are so seldom used that we will not clutter up our already formidable list with them.

We do choose to list one more group of identities known as the **sum and product formulas** for the sine and cosine. These can be obtained from the addition formulas (see Problems 32 and 33 in Exercise Set 6). Although these are used less frequently than the other identities we have considered, they are indispensable at times.

Sum Formulas

$$\sin A + \sin B = 2 \sin \frac{A + B}{2} \cos \frac{A - B}{2}$$

$$\sin A - \sin B = 2 \cos \frac{A + B}{2} \sin \frac{A - B}{2}$$

$$\cos A + \cos B = 2 \cos \frac{A + B}{2} \cos \frac{A - B}{2}$$

$$\cos A - \cos B = -2 \sin \frac{A + B}{2} \sin \frac{A - B}{2}$$

Product Formulas

$$\sin \alpha \cos \beta = \tfrac{1}{2}[\sin(\alpha + \beta) + \sin(\alpha - \beta)]$$

$$\cos \alpha \sin \beta = \tfrac{1}{2}[\sin(\alpha + \beta) - \sin(\alpha - \beta)]$$

$$\sin \alpha \sin \beta = \tfrac{1}{2}[\cos(\alpha - \beta) - \cos(\alpha + \beta)]$$

$$\cos \alpha \cos \beta = \tfrac{1}{2}[\cos(\alpha + \beta) + \cos(\alpha - \beta)]$$

EXERCISE SET 6

A   **1.** Use (10) and (11) to find:

        a. $\tan \dfrac{5\pi}{12}$ **b.** $\tan \dfrac{\pi}{12}$

2. Find $\tan 2\theta$ if $P(\theta)$ is the point $(-\frac{1}{3}, 2\sqrt{2}/3)$.

3. Find $\tan 2\theta$ if $\sin \theta = -\frac{3}{5}$ and $\cos \theta = -\frac{4}{5}$.

4. Find $\tan(\alpha + \beta)$ if $\sin \alpha = \frac{4}{5}$, α is in the second quadrant, $\cos \beta = -\frac{5}{13}$, and β is in the third quadrant.

5. Find $\tan(\alpha - \beta)$ if $\sec \alpha = 3$, $\csc \alpha < 0$, $\csc \beta = -\sqrt{5}$, and $\cos \beta < 0$.

6. If $\sec \alpha = \frac{13}{5}$, $\sin \alpha < 0$, $\csc \beta = \frac{17}{8}$, and $\cos \beta < 0$, find $\tan(\alpha + \beta)$.

7. For α and β as in Problem 6, find $\tan 2\alpha$, $\tan 2\beta$, $\tan \frac{1}{2}\alpha$, and $\tan \frac{1}{2}\beta$.

8. Find the value of each of the following without using tables or a calculator.

        a. $\tan 105°$ **b.** $\tan \dfrac{\pi}{12}$ **c.** $\tan \dfrac{11\pi}{12}$ **d.** $\tan 195°$ **e.** $\tan \dfrac{\pi}{8}$

9. Find $\tan 2\theta$ and $\tan \frac{1}{2}\theta$ if $\csc \theta = \frac{5}{3}$ and $\sec \theta < 0$.

10. For the angles shown in the figures, find:

        a. $\tan(\alpha + \beta)$ **b.** $\tan 2\alpha$ **c.** $\tan(\alpha - \beta)$ **d.** $\tan 2\beta$

        e. $\tan \frac{1}{2}\alpha$ **f.** $\tan \frac{1}{2}\beta$

In Problems 11–14 evaluate by use of the sum and product formulas.

11. **a.** $\sin \dfrac{5\pi}{12} + \sin \dfrac{\pi}{12}$ **b.** $\cos \dfrac{7\pi}{12} - \cos \dfrac{\pi}{12}$

12. **a.** $\sin \dfrac{5\pi}{12} \cos \dfrac{7\pi}{12}$ **b.** $\cos \dfrac{3\pi}{8} \cos \dfrac{\pi}{8}$

13. **a.** $\sin 105° - \sin 15°$ **b.** $\cos 165° + \cos 75°$

14. **a.** $\sin 105° \sin 15°$ **b.** $\cos 165° \sin 75°$

15. **a.** Write as a product: $\sin 5x + \sin 3x$

      b. Write as a sum: $\sin 5x \cos 3x$

16. **a.** Write as a product: $\cos 7x - \cos 5x$

      b. Write as a sum: $\sin 7x \sin 5x$

17. Derive the formula

$$\cot(\alpha + \beta) = \frac{\cot \theta \cot \beta - 1}{\cot \alpha + \cot \beta}$$

18. If $\cos \theta = x$ and $\sin \theta > 0$, find $\tan 2\theta$ and $\tan \frac{1}{2}\theta$ in terms of x.

In Problems 19–29 prove the identities.

19. $\dfrac{2}{\tan 2x} = \cot x - \tan x$

20. $\csc \theta - \tan \dfrac{\theta}{2} = \cot \theta$

21. $\dfrac{1}{1 - \tan \theta} - \tan 2\theta = \dfrac{1}{1 + \tan \theta}$

22. $1 + \tan \alpha \tan \dfrac{\alpha}{2} = \sec \alpha$

23. $\cot 2\theta = \dfrac{\cot^2 \theta - 1}{2 \cot \theta}$

24. $\dfrac{2 \sin \theta - \sin 2\theta}{2 \sin \theta + \sin 2\theta} = \tan^2 \dfrac{\theta}{2}$

25. $\dfrac{\sin A - \sin B}{\cos A + \cos B} = \tan \tfrac{1}{2}(A - B)$

26. $\dfrac{\sin 7\theta - \sin 5\theta}{\cos 7\theta + \cos 5\theta} = \tan \theta$

27. $\dfrac{\cos 3\theta + \cos \theta}{\sin 3\theta + \sin \theta} = \cot 2\theta$

28. $\sin\left(\dfrac{3\pi}{4} + \theta\right) \sin\left(\dfrac{\pi}{4} - \theta\right) = \dfrac{1 - \sin 2\theta}{2}$

29. $2 \cos \dfrac{3\theta}{2} \sin \dfrac{\theta}{2} = \sin 2\theta - \sin \theta$

B **30.** Prove that

a. $\tan(n\pi \pm \theta) = \pm\tan \theta$ **b.** $\tan\left[\dfrac{(2n + 1)\pi}{2} \pm \theta\right] = \pm\cot \theta$

where the sign on the right-hand side can be determined by considering θ to be acute.

31. Prove the identity

$$\frac{\sin \theta + \sin 2\theta + \sin 3\theta}{\cos \theta + \cos 2\theta + \cos 2\theta} = \tan 2\theta$$

32. Use the addition formulas for the sine and cosine to derive the product formulas as follows:

a. Add the formulas for $\sin(\alpha + \beta)$ and $\sin(\alpha - \beta)$ to get the formula for $\sin \alpha \cos \beta$.

b. Subtract the formula for $\sin(\alpha - \beta)$ from that for $\sin(\alpha + \beta)$ to get the formula for $\cos \alpha \sin \beta$.

c. Add the formulas for $\cos(\alpha + \beta)$ and $\cos(\alpha - \beta)$ to get the formula for $\cos \alpha \cos \beta$.

d. Subtract the formula for $\cos(\alpha + \beta)$ from that for $\cos(\alpha - \beta)$ to get the formula for $\sin \alpha \sin \beta$.

33. In the addition formulas for the sine and cosine make the following substitutions: $\alpha + \beta = A$ and $\alpha - \beta = B$. Solve these two equations simultaneously for α and β in terms of A and B, and obtain the sum formulas.

34. Prove the identity

$$\frac{\sin(x + h) - \sin x}{h} = \frac{\sin \dfrac{h}{2}}{\dfrac{h}{2}} \cos\left(x + \dfrac{h}{2}\right)$$

35. Derive the formula

$$\tan \frac{\alpha}{2} = \frac{1 - \cos \alpha}{\sin \alpha}$$

7 Summary of Identities

We summarize below the identities given in Sections 2–6.

PYTHAGOREAN IDENTITIES

$\sin^2 \theta + \cos^2 \theta = 1$ $1 + \tan^2 \theta = \sec^2 \theta$ $1 + \cot^2 \theta = \csc^2 \theta$

RECIPROCAL RELATIONS

$\csc \theta = \dfrac{1}{\sin \theta}$ $\sec \theta = \dfrac{1}{\cos \theta}$ $\cot \theta = \dfrac{1}{\tan \theta}$

TANGENT AND COTANGENT IN TERMS OF SINE AND COSINE

$\tan \theta = \dfrac{\sin \theta}{\cos \theta}$ $\cot \theta = \dfrac{\cos \theta}{\sin \theta}$

ADDITION FORMULAS

$\sin(\alpha \pm \beta) = \sin \alpha \cos \beta \pm \cos \alpha \sin \beta$

$\cos(\alpha \pm \beta) = \cos \alpha \cos \beta \mp \sin \alpha \sin \beta$

$\tan(\alpha \pm \beta) = \dfrac{\tan \alpha \pm \tan \beta}{1 \mp \tan \alpha \tan \beta}$

DOUBLE-ANGLE FORMULAS

$\sin 2\theta = 2 \sin \theta \cos \theta$

$\cos 2\theta = \cos^2 \theta - \sin^2 \theta = 2 \cos^2 \theta - 1 = 1 - 2 \sin^2 \theta$

$\tan 2\theta = \dfrac{2 \tan \theta}{1 - \tan^2 \theta}$

SIN$^2 \theta$ AND COS$^2 \theta$ IN TERMS OF COS 2θ

$\sin^2 \theta = \dfrac{1 - \cos 2\theta}{2}$ $\cos^2 \theta = \dfrac{1 + \cos 2\theta}{2}$

HALF-ANGLE FORMULAS

$\sin \dfrac{\alpha}{2} = \pm \sqrt{\dfrac{1 - \cos \alpha}{2}}$ $\cos \dfrac{\alpha}{2} = \pm \sqrt{\dfrac{1 + \cos \alpha}{2}}$

$\tan \dfrac{\alpha}{2} = \dfrac{\sin \alpha}{1 + \cos \alpha} = \dfrac{1 - \cos \alpha}{\sin \alpha}$

SUM FORMULAS

$$\sin A + \sin B = 2 \sin \frac{A + B}{2} \cos \frac{A - B}{2}$$

$$\sin A - \sin B = 2 \cos \frac{A + B}{2} \sin \frac{A - B}{2}$$

$$\cos A + \cos B = 2 \cos \frac{A + B}{2} \cos \frac{A - B}{2}$$

$$\cos A - \cos B = -2 \sin \frac{A + B}{2} \sin \frac{A - B}{2}$$

PRODUCT FORMULAS

$$\sin \alpha \cos \beta = \tfrac{1}{2}[\sin(\alpha + \beta) + \sin(\alpha - \beta)]$$

$$\cos \alpha \sin \beta = \tfrac{1}{2}[\sin(\alpha + \beta) - \sin(\alpha - \beta)]$$

$$\sin \alpha \sin \beta = \tfrac{1}{2}[\cos(\alpha - \beta) - \cos(\alpha + \beta)]$$

$$\cos \alpha \cos \beta = \tfrac{1}{2}[\cos(\alpha + \beta) + \cos(\alpha - \beta)]$$

REDUCTION FORMULAS

Let f designate any trigonometric function and cf its cofunction. Then for any integer n,

$$f(n\pi \pm \theta) = \pm f(\theta)$$

$$f\left[\frac{(2n + 1)\pi}{2} \pm \theta\right] = \pm cf(\theta)$$

The sign on the right can be determined by considering θ to be acute.

Remark.   The particular letters used in these formulas are unimportant. The occurrence of α and β at some times, θ sometimes, and A and B at other times is only because of customary usage.

8   Trigonometric Equations

The solutions of most trigonometric equations cannot be obtained exactly, and we have to settle for approximate solutions obtained through some numerical procedure, usually with the aid of a calculator. There are, however, enough such equations for which elementary techniques will yield exact answers that some time devoted to these techniques is justified.

In order to make clear the sorts of solutions we are looking for, let us consider the very simple equation

$$2 \sin \theta - 1 = 0$$

The problem is to discover all real numbers θ for which this equation is true. We write the equation in the equivalent form

$$\sin \theta = \frac{1}{2}$$

and then rely on our knowledge of special angles to conclude that this is satisfied if, and only if,

$$\theta = \frac{\pi}{6}, \frac{5\pi}{6}$$

or any other number obtained from these by adding integral multiples of 2π to each. To see this, remember that the sine of a number θ is the y coordinate of the point on the unit circle that is θ units along the arc from $(1, 0)$. Thus, we are seeking those numbers θ for which the y coordinate of $P(\theta) = \frac{1}{2}$. There are only two points on the unit circle with y coordinate $\frac{1}{2}$, and our knowledge of the $30°$–$60°$ right triangle tells us that these points are $P(\pi/6)$ and $P(5\pi/6)$; see Figure 12. Since $P(\theta) = P(\theta + 2n\pi)$, we conclude that all solutions of the equation are given by $(\pi/6) + 2n\pi$ or $(5\pi/6) + 2n\pi$.

Figure 12

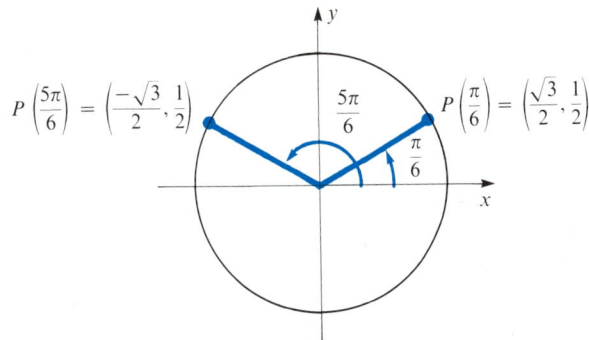

Usually, it is sufficient to give only the **primary** solutions, that is, those lying between 0 and 2π. We would know then that all other solutions are obtainable from these by adding multiples of 2π.

We can usually condense the above reasoning as follows:

1. Determine the appropriate reference angle.
2. By the sign of the function, locate all primary angles having this reference angle.
3. Write the answer as the radian measure of these angles.

In our example, since we know that $\sin 30° = \frac{1}{2}$, the reference angle is $30°$. The sine is positive in quadrants I and II, so the angles are $30°$ and $150°$. In radians these are $\pi/6$ and $5\pi/6$.

It might be useful to review at this time the values of the functions of $30°$, $45°$, and $60°$.

$$\sin 30° = \sin \frac{\pi}{6} = \frac{1}{2} \qquad \sin 45° = \sin \frac{\pi}{4} = \frac{1}{\sqrt{2}} \qquad \sin 60° = \sin \frac{\pi}{3} = \frac{\sqrt{3}}{2}$$

$$\cos 30° = \cos \frac{\pi}{6} = \frac{\sqrt{3}}{2} \qquad \cos 45° = \cos \frac{\pi}{4} = \frac{1}{\sqrt{2}} \qquad \cos 60° = \cos \frac{\pi}{3} = \frac{1}{2}$$

$$\tan 30° = \tan \frac{\pi}{6} = \frac{1}{\sqrt{3}} \qquad \tan 45° = \tan \frac{\pi}{4} = 1 \qquad \tan 60° = \tan \frac{\pi}{3} = \sqrt{3}$$

Also,

$$\sin 0° = \sin 0 = 0 \qquad \sin 90° = \sin \frac{\pi}{2} = 1$$

$$\cos 0° = \cos 0 = 1 \qquad \cos 90° = \cos \frac{\pi}{2} = 0$$

$$\tan 0° = \tan 0 = 0 \qquad \tan 90° = \tan \frac{\pi}{2} \text{ is not defined}$$

(The cotangent, secant, and cosecant are not listed because they occur less frequently and can always be obtained by the reciprocal relations.) If you feel comfortable with radian measure by now, you can omit the degree measure entirely.

If an equation can be worked around to a form such as $\sin \theta = \pm a$, $\cos \theta = \pm b$, or $\tan \theta = \pm c$, for instance, where a and b are any of the numbers 0, 1, $\frac{1}{2}$, $1/\sqrt{2}$, or $\sqrt{3}/2$, and c is any of the numbers 0, 1, $1/\sqrt{3}$, or $\sqrt{3}$, then we can obtain all solutions in the manner outlined above. For other values of a, b, and c, a calculator or tables can be used.

EXAMPLE 12   Find all values of θ, for which $0 \le \theta < 2\pi$, satisfying $2 \cos^2 \theta - \cos \theta - 1 = 0$.

Solution   We treat this first as a quadratic equation in $\cos \theta$ and factor:

$$(2 \cos \theta + 1)(\cos \theta - 1) = 0$$

This is true if and only if $2 \cos \theta + 1 = 0$ or $\cos \theta = 1$, that is, if and only if

$$\cos \theta = -\tfrac{1}{2} \quad \text{or} \quad \cos \theta = 1$$

Since $\cos 60° = \frac{1}{2}$, the reference angle in the first of these is 60°. Since the cosine is negative in quadrants II and III, it follows that we are seeking the angles 120° and 240°. In radians these are $2\pi/3$ and $4\pi/3$. The only primary angle for which $\cos \theta = 1$ is $\theta = 0°$, or 0 radians. Thus, the primary solution set for the equation is $\{0, 2\pi/3, 4\pi/3\}$.

Remark.   In many equations involving trigonometric functions the variable must be treated as a real number, which is the reason for writing the above answers as the radian measures of the angles. Recall that the values of $\sin \theta$, $\cos \theta$, and the other trigonometric functions are unchanged whether we consider θ a real number or the radian measure of an angle. An example of a mixed algebraic and trigonometric equation will perhaps help to make this point clearer. The equation

$$2 \sin x - x = 0$$

is clearly satisfied when $x = 0$, but by trial and error, using a calculator (or by some more sophisticated numerical procedure), we can find that another solution is

$$x \approx 1.8955$$

If we think of this x as the radian measure of an angle, then the degree measure of the angle is approximately $108.6°$. Now it would *not* be true that $x = 108.6°$; in fact, it would not even make sense, for we would have

$$2 \sin 108.6° - 108.6° = 0$$

which is a totally meaningless statement.

EXAMPLE 13   Find all primary solutions of $\sin 2x + \cos x = 0$.

Solution   This time we will omit most discussion and go only through the steps that would be expected in doing the problem.

$$\sin 2x + \cos x = 0$$

$$2 \sin x \cos x + \cos x = 0$$

$$\cos x (2 \sin x + 1) = 0$$

$$
\begin{array}{c|c}
\cos x = 0 & 2 \sin x = -1 \\[4pt]
x = \dfrac{\pi}{2}, \dfrac{3\pi}{2} & \sin x = -\dfrac{1}{2} \\[8pt]
& x = \dfrac{7\pi}{6}, \dfrac{11\pi}{6}
\end{array}
$$

The solution set is $\{\pi/2, 7\pi/6, 3\pi/2, 11\pi/6\}$.

EXAMPLE 14   Find all primary solutions of $\tan \alpha - 3 \cot \alpha = 0$.

Solution
$$\tan \alpha - 3 \cot \alpha = 0$$

$$\tan \alpha - \frac{3}{\tan \alpha} = 0$$

$$\tan^2 \alpha - 3 = 0$$

$$\tan \alpha = \pm\sqrt{3}$$

The reference angle is $60°$, or $\pi/3$ radians. Therefore,

$$\alpha = \frac{\pi}{3}, \frac{2\pi}{3}, \frac{4\pi}{3}, \frac{5\pi}{3}$$

Since we multiplied by an unknown expression, namely, tan α, it is essential that we check to see that this was not zero for the values of α found, which is clearly the case here, since $\tan \alpha = \pm\sqrt{3} \neq 0$. So the solution set is $\{\pi/3, 2\pi/3, 4\pi/3, 5\pi/3\}$.

EXAMPLE 15   Find all primary solutions of $\sqrt{3} \cos x = 2 + \sin x$.

Solution   The fact that $\cos^2 x = 1 - \sin^2 x$ suggests that if we square both sides of the given equation, it will be easier to work with.

$$3 \cos^2 x = 4 + 4 \sin x + \sin^2 x$$

$$3(1 - \sin^2 x) = 4 + 4 \sin x + \sin^2 x$$

$$4 \sin^2 x + 4 \sin x + 1 = 0$$

$$(2 \sin x + 1)^2 = 0$$

$$\sin x = -\tfrac{1}{2}$$

$$x = \frac{7\pi}{6}, \frac{11\pi}{6}$$

We again must check our answers, because squaring does not necessarily lead to an equivalent equation; it may introduce extraneous roots. So we check in the original equation.

When $x = 7\pi/6$, we get

$$\sqrt{3}\left(-\frac{\sqrt{3}}{2}\right) \overset{?}{=} 2 + \left(-\frac{1}{2}\right)$$

$$-\frac{3}{2} \neq \frac{3}{2}$$

So $7\pi/6$ is not a solution.

When $x = 11\pi/6$,

$$\sqrt{3}\left(\frac{\sqrt{3}}{2}\right) \overset{?}{=} 2 + \left(-\frac{1}{2}\right)$$

$$\frac{3}{2} = \frac{3}{2}$$

So $x = 11\pi/6$ is the only primary solution.

EXAMPLE 16   Find all primary solutions of $2 \sin 3\theta - \sqrt{3} \tan 3\theta = 0$.

Solution
$$2 \sin 3\theta - \frac{\sqrt{3} \sin 3\theta}{\cos 3\theta} = 0$$

$$\sin 3\theta(2 \cos 3\theta - \sqrt{3}) = 0 \quad \text{(We multiplied by } \cos 3\theta.\text{)}$$

$$\sin 3\theta = 0 \quad \Big| \quad \cos 3\theta = \frac{\sqrt{3}}{2} \quad \text{(So we did not multiply by zero.)}$$

Now we want all values of θ lying between 0 and 2π. We must therefore find all values of 3θ lying between 0 and 6π. In general, if $n\theta$ is involved, in order to find all values of θ between 0 and 2π, we find all values of $n\theta$ between 0 and $2n\pi$, and then divide by n. We have from $\sin 3\theta = 0$ that

$$3\theta = 0, \quad \pi, \quad 2\pi, \quad 3\pi, \quad 4\pi, \quad 5\pi$$

and

$$\theta = 0, \quad \frac{\pi}{3}, \quad \frac{2\pi}{3}, \quad \pi, \quad \frac{4\pi}{3}, \quad \frac{5\pi}{3}$$

From $\cos 3\theta = \sqrt{3}/2$, we have

$$3\theta = \frac{\pi}{6}, \quad \frac{11\pi}{6}, \quad \frac{13\pi}{6}, \quad \frac{23\pi}{6}, \quad \frac{25\pi}{6}, \quad \frac{35\pi}{6}$$

$$\theta = \frac{\pi}{18}, \quad \frac{11\pi}{18}, \quad \frac{13\pi}{18}, \quad \frac{23\pi}{18}, \quad \frac{25\pi}{18}, \quad \frac{35\pi}{18}$$

In both cases we found the first two values of 3θ, then added 2π once, and then 2π again. The complete solution set is

$$\left\{ 0, \quad \frac{\pi}{18}, \quad \frac{\pi}{3}, \quad \frac{11\pi}{18}, \quad \frac{2\pi}{3}, \quad \frac{13\pi}{18}, \quad \pi, \quad \frac{23\pi}{18}, \quad \frac{4\pi}{3}, \quad \frac{25\pi}{18}, \quad \frac{5\pi}{3}, \quad \frac{35\pi}{18} \right\}$$

EXAMPLE 17   Find all real solutions to $\tan x - \cot x = 2$.

Solution

$$\tan x - \cot x = 2$$

$$\frac{\sin x}{\cos x} - \frac{\cos x}{\sin x} = 2$$

$$\sin^2 x - \cos^2 x = 2 \sin x \cos x$$

$$-\cos 2x = \sin 2x$$

$$\tan 2x = -1$$

$$2x = \frac{3\pi}{4}, \quad \frac{7\pi}{4}, \quad \frac{11\pi}{4}, \quad \frac{15\pi}{4} \quad \text{(We "went around" twice.)}$$

$$x = \frac{3\pi}{8}, \quad \frac{7\pi}{8}, \quad \frac{11\pi}{8}, \quad \frac{15\pi}{8}$$

As none of these values of x makes $\sin x$, $\cos x$, or $\cos 2x$ equal to zero, we did not multiply by zero. We must also check to see that we did not lose any roots when dividing by $\cos 2x$; that is, we must check to see if any of the roots of $\cos 2x = 0$ are roots of the original equation. Since $\cos 2x = 0$ when $2x = \pi/2$, $3\pi/2$, $5\pi/2$, $7\pi/2$, and so when $x = \pi/4$, $3\pi/4$, $5\pi/4$, $7\pi/4$, we check and find that none of these is a root of the original equation. So we have found all primary solutions. To get *all* solutions, we add arbitrary multiples of 2π to each of these. So the complete solution set is

$$\left\{ \frac{3\pi}{8}, \frac{7\pi}{8}, \frac{11\pi}{8}, \frac{15\pi}{8}, \frac{19\pi}{8}, \frac{23\pi}{8}, \frac{27\pi}{8}, \frac{31\pi}{8}, \frac{35\pi}{8}, \frac{39\pi}{8}, \frac{43\pi}{8}, \frac{47\pi}{8}, \ldots \right\}$$

or we could write

$$\{3\pi/8 + 2n\pi, 7\pi/8 + 2n\pi, 11\pi/8 + 2n\pi, 15\pi/8 + 2n\pi: \quad n = 0, \pm 1, \pm 2, \ldots\}$$

We could continue with examples, each possessing its own special features, but these illustrate the main techniques. It might be useful to summarize some of the points that the examples were meant to bring out:

1. Use algebraic techniques such as factoring, multiplying by the LCD, and squaring in conjunction with basic trigonometric identities to simplify so as to obtain one or more elementary equations of the form $\sin x = \pm a$, $\cos x = \pm b$, and so on.
2. Find the radian measure of all primary angles (that is, $0 \le x < 2\pi$) satisfying the elementary equations in 1. If *all* solutions are desired, add arbitrary multiples of 2π to each of these to obtain the complete solution set.
3. If in arriving at the elementary equations both sides of an equation were squared, or if both sides were multiplied by an expression containing a variable, it is necessary to check the answers. (In the case of multiplying by an unknown, it is sufficient to check that the multiplier was not zero.) If both sides of an equation are divided by an expression containing a variable, then the values of the variable for which this expression equals zero must be checked in the original equation to see if they are solutions. (In general, such division can be avoided by factoring.)
4. If the final elementary equation(s) is of the form $\sin nx = \pm a$, $\cos nx = \pm b$, and so on, then to get all primary values of x, find all values of nx between 0 and $2n\pi$, and divide by n. This amounts to finding the angles in the first revolution and then adding 2π a total of $n - 1$ separate times and finally dividing everything by n.

EXERCISE SET 8

A   Find all primary solutions unless otherwise specified.

1. $2 \cos x = \sqrt{3}$
2. $\cot x + 1 = 0$
3. $\sec x = 2$
4. $\sin^2 x = 1$ (Give all solutions.)
5. $\cos x - 2 \cos^2 x = 0$
6. $\sin 2\theta - \cos \theta = 0$
7. $\cos 2x + \cos x = 0$
8. $2 \tan \psi - \tan \psi \sec \psi = 0$
9. $\sin^2 t - \cos^2 t = 1$
10. $\sec^2 \theta = 2 \tan \theta$
11. $2 \cos x - \cot x = 0$
12. $2 \cos^2 x + \sin x - 1 = 0$
13. $4 \tan^2 \alpha = 3 \sec^2 \alpha$
14. $\sin^2 x = 2(\cos x - 1)$
15. $\cos^2 x - \sin x + 5 = 0$
16. $\tan 2x - \cos 2x + \sec 2x = 0$

17. $\dfrac{1 - \cos x}{\sin x} = \sin x$ 18. $2 \cos^2 2\theta - 3 \cos 2\theta + 1 = 0$

19. $\sin 6\theta + \sin 3\theta = 0$ 20. $\sin^2 4\theta - \sin 4\theta - 2 = 0$

21. $\tan \dfrac{x}{2} + \cos x = 1$ 22. $\sin^2 \dfrac{x}{2} - \sin^2 x = 0$

23. $2(\sin^2 2\theta - \cos^2 2\theta) + \sqrt{3} = 0$ 24. $2 \cos x - \cot x \csc x = 0$

25. $2 \tan^2 \theta + \sec \theta + 2 = 0$

B 26. $\sin \theta + \cos \theta = 1$ (Give all solutions.)

27. $\cos 2x \tan 3x + \sqrt{3} \cos 2x = 0$ 28. $\dfrac{\sin x}{1 - \cos x} = \dfrac{\cos x}{1 + \sin x}$

29. $\sin 2\theta - 4 \sin \theta = 3(2 - \cos \theta)$ 30. $\sqrt{3} \tan \theta = 2 \sec \theta - 1$

In Problems 31–36 use a calculator or tables to find all primary solutions correct to three significant figures.

31. $12 \sin^2 x - \sin x - 6 = 0$ 32. $\cos 2x + 2 \cos x = 0$
33. $2 \sec^2 x = 5 \tan x$ 34. $3 \sin x - \tan \frac{1}{2}x = 0$
35. $2 \sin x - \csc x + 3 = 0$ 36. $\sec x - 2 = 10 \cos x$

In Problems 37–39 find all primary solutions without using a calculator or tables.

37. $\tan^3 x + \tan^2 x - 3 \tan x - 3 = 0$ 38. $8 \sin^4 \theta - 2 \sin^2 \theta - 3 = 0$
39. $2 \sin^3 x + 3 \sin^2 x - 1 = 0$

9 Graphs of the Trigonometric Functions

To obtain the graphs of $y = \sin x$ and $y = \cos x$ we make use of the definitions of the sine and cosine as the ordinate and abscissa, respectively, of a point on the unit circle (Figure 13). Notice that we have used x to represent arc length on the circle from $(1, 0)$ to $P(x)$ rather than the customary θ. We have used capital letters to label the axes. Table 1 indicates how $\sin x$ and $\cos x$ vary as x varies from 0 to 2π. These facts can be verified by visualizing the point $P(x)$ moving around the circle in a counterclockwise direction, starting at $(1, 0)$. Furthermore, it should be clear from considering Figure 13 that the ordinate

Figure 13

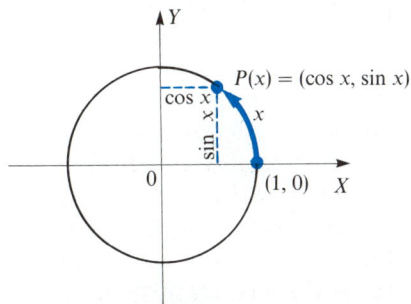

Table 1

As x goes from	sin x goes from	cos x goes from
0 to $\pi/2$	0 to 1	1 to 0
$\pi/2$ to π	1 to 0	0 to -1
π to $3\pi/2$	0 to -1	-1 to 0
$3\pi/2$ to 2π	-1 to 0	0 to 1

and abscissa of $P(x)$ (that is, sin x and cos x) vary in a uniform way, with no breaks or sudden changes, as $P(x)$ moves around the circle.

This information, together with our knowledge of sin x and cos x for $x = \pi/6$, $\pi/4$, $\pi/3$ and related values in the other quadrants, enables us to draw the graphs with reasonable accuracy. Since sin x and cos x each has period 2π, the graphs repeat every 2π units. So once we know the graphs in the interval from 0 to 2π, we can extend them indefinitely in either direction. The graphs are shown in Figures 14 and 15.

Figure 14

Figure 15

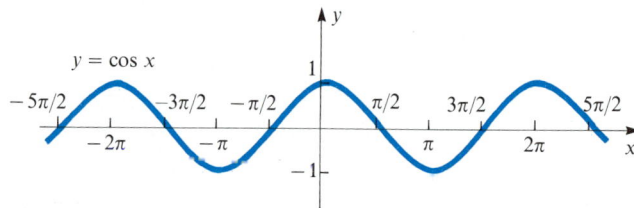

The maximum height attained by the sine curve and by the cosine curve is called the **amplitude.** So, for $y = \sin x$ and $y = \cos x$ the amplitude is 1.

To obtain the graph of $y = \tan x$ we again refer to Figure 13 and use the fact that $\tan x = \sin x/\cos x$. Therefore, we consider the ratio of the ordinate of $P(x)$ to its abscissa as $P(x)$ moves around the unit circle.

When $x = 0$, $\tan x = 0/1 = 0$, and as x increases toward $\pi/2$, the ratio of the ordinate of $P(x)$ to its abscissa steadily increases, taking on the value 1 at $x = \pi/4$. For x near $\pi/2$ the ratio becomes very large and gets larger and larger without limit as x approaches $\pi/2$. At $x = \pi/2$ the ratio is not defined. For x slightly greater than $\pi/2$ the ratio is negative, since the ordinate is positive and the abscissa is negative, but its absolute value is large. At $x = 3\pi/4$ the ratio is -1, and at π, it is back to 0. Since

$$\tan(x + \pi) = \frac{\tan x + \tan \pi}{1 - \tan x \tan \pi} = \frac{\tan x + 0}{1 - (\tan x) \cdot 0} = \tan x$$

it follows that $\tan x$ has period π. So we can draw its graph between 0 and π and duplicate this in each succeeding interval of length π. Similarly, we can extend it to the left. With this information and our knowledge of $\tan x$ for special values of x such as $\pi/6$ and $\pi/3$, we can draw the graph, as in Figure 16. The vertical lines at odd multiples of $\pi/2$ are asymptotes.

Figure 16

Figure 17

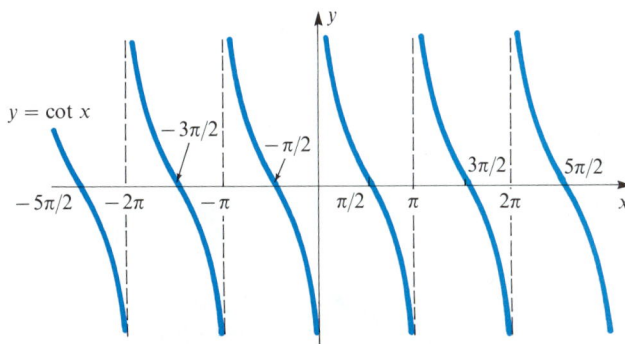

The graph of $y = \cot x$ can be similarly obtained and we show its graph in Figure 17.

The secant of x is defined as the reciprocal of the X coordinate of $P(x)$, that is, as the reciprocal of $\cos x$. Since $|\cos x| \le 1$, it follows that $|\sec x| \ge 1$. The signs of $\sec x$ and $\cos x$ are the same. When $\cos x = 1$, $\sec x = 1$, and when $\cos x = 0$, $\sec x$ is undefined. This latter occurs at $x = \pi/2, 3\pi/2, -\pi/2, 5\pi/2$, and so on. As x gets close to $\pi/2$, $\cos x$ gets close to 0; so $\sec x$ gets arbitrarily large. Using this analysis, together with the values of $\sec x$ for $x = \pi/6, \pi/4, \pi/3$, and so on, we sketch the graph in Figure 18. The graph of $y = \csc x$ can be similarly obtained (Figure 19).

Both $\sec x$ and $\csc x$ have a fundamental period of 2π. No amplitude is defined for them. They each have asymptotes; for the secant they are the lines $x = \pi/2, -\pi/2, 3\pi/2$, and so on, and for the cosecant the lines $x = 0, \pi, -\pi, 2\pi$, and so on.

Figure 18

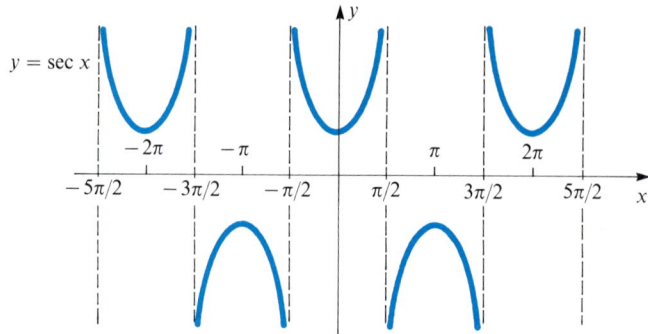

$y = \sec x$

-2π $-\pi$ π 2π

$-5\pi/2$ $-3\pi/2$ $-\pi/2$ $\pi/2$ $3\pi/2$ $5\pi/2$ x

Figure 19

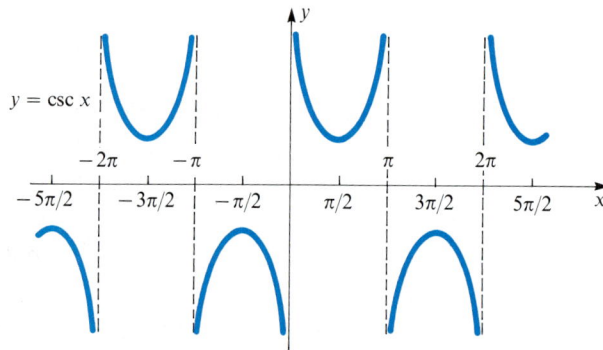

$y = \csc x$

-2π $-\pi$ π 2π

$-5\pi/2$ $-3\pi/2$ $-\pi/2$ $\pi/2$ $3\pi/2$ $5\pi/2$ x

Figure 20

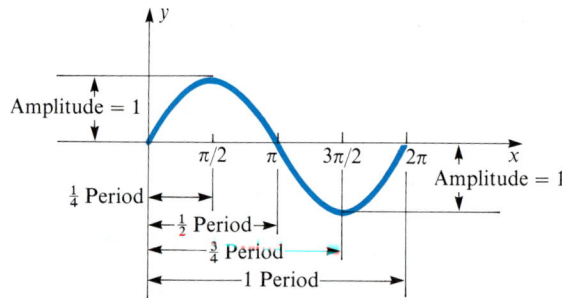

Amplitude = 1

$\pi/2$ π $3\pi/2$ 2π x

Amplitude = 1

$\frac{1}{4}$ Period

$\frac{1}{2}$ Period

$\frac{3}{4}$ Period

1 Period

What we have shown are the basic graphs of the trigonometric functions. You should become especially familiar with the first three. The crucial facts about the sine curve are illustrated in Figure 20. This, together with the knowledge of the periodicity, enables us to obtain a rapid sketch of the curve.

For the basic sine curve $y = \sin x$, the fundamental period is 2π and the amplitude is 1. Now we want to consider the effect of introducing positive constants a and b:

$$y = a \sin bx$$

We will take one at a time. First consider $y = a \sin x$. This has the effect of multiplying every y value of the basic curve by a. So when the basic curve is at its maximum height of 1, the new curve will be a units high. Thus, the ampli-

Figure 21

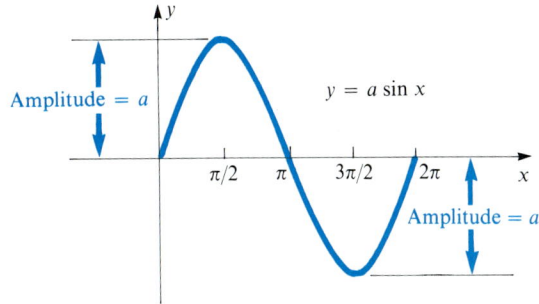

tude becomes a, and the period remains unchanged, as shown in Figure 21. We have exhibited the curve for one period only (also called one **cycle**), since the extension is obvious.

Next, let us consider $y = \sin bx$. We know that the sine curve completes one cycle when bx goes from 0 to 2π. But then x goes from 0 to $2\pi/b$. So, we conclude that the period of $\sin bx$ is $2\pi/b$. This can also be seen in another way. To say that $\sin x$ has period 2π means that $\sin(x + 2\pi) = \sin x$. Thus, $\sin(bx + 2\pi) = \sin bx$. But $\sin(bx + 2\pi) = \sin b[x + (2\pi/b)]$. So,

$$\sin b\left(x + \frac{2\pi}{b}\right) = \sin bx$$

Thus, when we add $2\pi/b$ to any x, we get the same value as $\sin bx$. That is, $\sin bx$ has period $2\pi/b$. The effect of the multiplier b in this position, then, is to alter the period; it is shortened if $b > 1$ and lengthened if $b < 1$ (Figure 22).

Figure 22

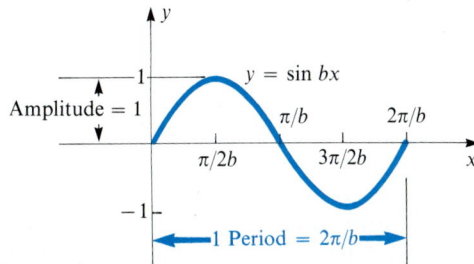

Remark. When the variable x represents time, the period is the time required to complete one cycle. The reciprocal of this, called the **frequency,** gives the number of cycles (or fraction of a cycle) completed per unit of time. Thus,

$$\text{Frequency} = \frac{1}{\text{Period}} = \frac{b}{2\pi}$$

This is a widely used concept in electronics.

Now we can put these two changes together to get the graph of $y = a \sin bx$, as shown in Figure 23. If, in addition, a constant k is added to the right-hand side, giving $y = a \sin bx + k$, this has the effect of shifting the entire graph of $y = a \sin bx$ vertically by k units—upward if $k > 0$ and downward if $k < 0$.

We consider next an equation of the form

$$y = a \sin b(x - \alpha) \tag{12}$$

Figure 23

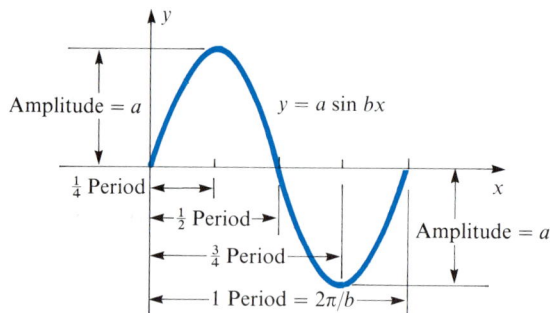

The sine will complete one cycle when $b(x - \alpha)$ goes from 0 to 2π. Setting $b(x - \alpha)$ equal to 0 gives

$$b(x - \alpha) = 0$$

$$x - \alpha = 0$$

$$x = \alpha$$

and setting $b(x - \alpha)$ equal to 2π gives

$$b(x - \alpha) = 2\pi$$

$$x - \alpha = \frac{2\pi}{b}$$

$$x = \frac{2\pi}{b} + \alpha$$

So a complete cycle occurs in the interval from α to $(2\pi/b) + \alpha$. This is a distance of $2\pi/b$, so the period of $2\pi/b$ remains unchanged, but the curve is shifted α units horizontally. If $\alpha > 0$, the shift is to the right, and if $\alpha < 0$, it is to the left. We call α the **phase shift,** and say that the curve is $|\alpha|$ units out of phase with the curve $y = a \sin bx$. This is illustrated in Figure 24.

Finally, we note the effect on the graph of $y = a \sin bx$ if either a or b is negative. If $a < 0$, every y value is the negative of what it would have been if a were positive. For example, in $y = -2 \sin x$, every y value is the negative of the corresponding y value in $y = 2 \sin x$. So the effect is to flip the graph of $y = 2 \sin x$ about the x axis. If $b < 0$, we make use of $\sin(-\theta) = -\sin \theta$.

Figure 24

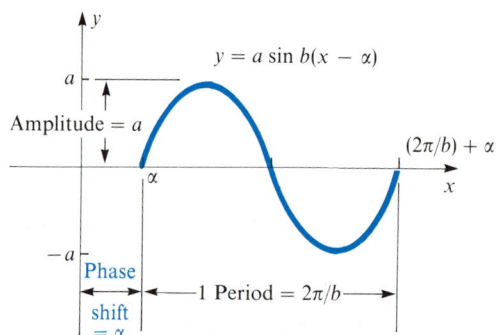

For example, we would write $y = \sin(-2x)$ as $y = -\sin 2x$, and proceed as above.

A similar analysis to that for the sine holds for the cosine function (see Figure 25). Note, however, for the cosine that $\cos(-\theta) = \cos\theta$, and so the graph of $y = \cos(-2x)$ would be identical to the graph of $y = \cos 2x$. With appropriate modifications because of the different period (for the tangent and cotangent) and lack of amplitude, the other functions, too could be analyzed in an analogous way. You will be asked to consider certain of these in Exercise Set 9.

Figure 25

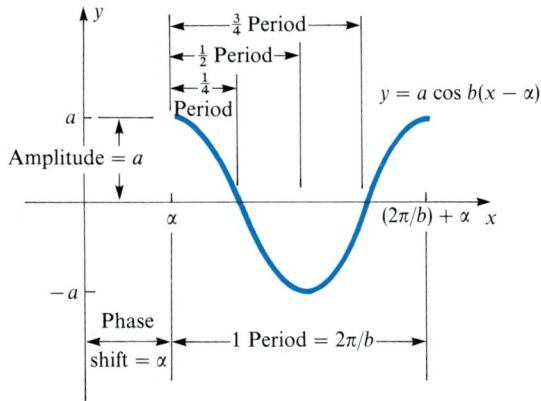

$y = a \cos b(x - \alpha)$

EXAMPLE 18   Sketch the graph of $y = 3 \sin \frac{1}{2}x$.

Solution   The amplitude is 3 and the period is $2\pi \div \frac{1}{2} = 4\pi$ (Figure 26).

Figure 26

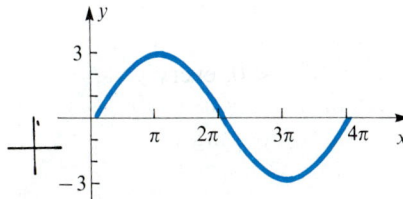

EXAMPLE 19   Sketch the graph of $y = 2 \sin(3x - \pi)$.

Solution   We first factor out the 3 to put this in the form of equation (12):

$$y = 2 \sin 3\left(x - \frac{\pi}{3}\right)$$

This is therefore a sine curve with amplitude 2, period $2\pi/3$, and phase shift $\pi/3$ units to the right (Figure 27).

Figure 27

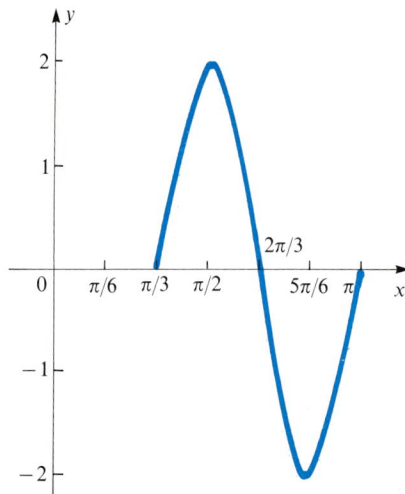

EXAMPLE 20   Sketch the graph of $y = \cos[2x + (\pi/3)]$.

Solution   We first write the equation in a form analogous to equation (12):

$$y = \cos 2\left(x + \frac{\pi}{6}\right) = \cos 2\left[x - \left(-\frac{\pi}{6}\right)\right]$$

So the phase shift α is $-\pi/6$. The curve is therefore shifted $\pi/6$ units to the left. The amplitude is 1, and the period is $2\pi/2 = \pi$ (Figure 28).

Figure 28

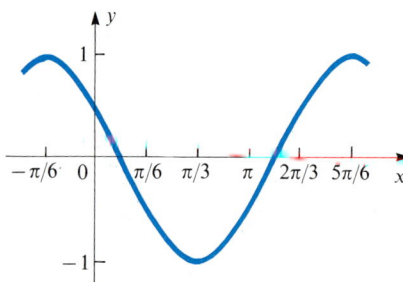

EXAMPLE 21   Sketch $y = 2 \tan \frac{1}{2}x$.

Solution   There is no amplitude defined for the tangent curve, but the effect of the coefficient 2 is to multiply all y values of the basic curve by 2; in particular, when the basic curve is 1 unit high, the new curve will be 2 units high. Since the fundamental period of the basic tangent curve is π, the period of this curve is $\pi \div \frac{1}{2} = 2\pi$. We show two complete cycles in Figure 29.

Figure 29

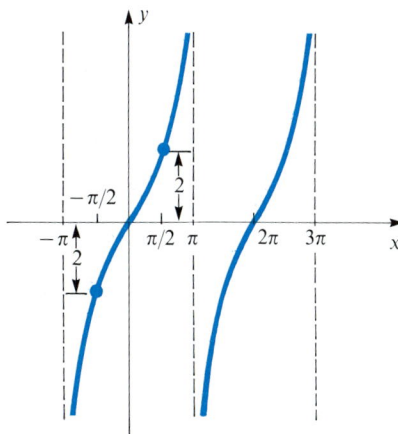

EXERCISE SET 9

In Problems 1–25 sketch one cycle of each of the curves. Give the period and, where appropriate, the amplitude and phase shift.

A
1. $y = \sin 2x$
2. $y = \cos 3x$
3. $y = 2 \sin x$
4. $y = 2 \sin 3x$
5. $y = 3 \cos(\pi x/2)$
6. $y = 4 \sin(\pi x/3)$
7. $y = 2 \sin(-3x)$
8. $y = 3 \cos(-\pi x)$
9. $y = -\sin(x/2)$
10. $y = -2 \cos x$
11. $y = \sin 2x + 1$
12. $y = 2 \cos x - 3$
13. $y = 2 \sin 3x - 1$
14. $y = 3 \cos \pi x + 2$
15. $y = \frac{1}{2} \tan \pi x$
16. $y = 2 \cot(x/2)$

17. $y = \sin\left(x - \dfrac{\pi}{3}\right)$
18. $y = \cos\left(x - \dfrac{\pi}{4}\right)$

19. $y = \sin 2\left(x + \dfrac{\pi}{4}\right)$
20. $y = \cos 3\left(x + \dfrac{\pi}{3}\right)$

B
21. $y = 2 \sin(3x + 2)$
22. $y = 3 \cos(3 - 2x)$

23. $y = 1 - 2 \sin\left(\pi x - \dfrac{\pi}{4}\right)$
24. $y = \frac{1}{2} \tan\left(2x - \dfrac{\pi}{2}\right)$

25. $y = 2 + 2 \cos\left(3x - \dfrac{\pi}{2}\right)$

26. **a.** By multiplying and dividing by $\sqrt{a^2 + b^2}$ show that $a \sin x + b \cos x$ can be written in the form

$$\sqrt{a^2 + b^2} \sin(x + \theta)$$

where θ is as shown in the accompanying sketch.

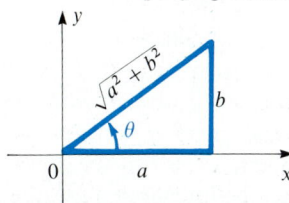

   b.   Use the technique of part a to analyze and sketch the graph of

$$y = \sin x + \sqrt{3} \cos x$$

   What is the value of θ in this case?

27.   By the technique of Problem 26, part a, write each of the following as a sine function. Determine the amplitude, period, and phase shift.
   a. $y = \sin x - \cos x$ **b.** $y = 3 \cos x - 4 \sin x$

28.   Disucss the effect on the basic secant curve of introducing positive constants a and b to obtain $y = a \sec bx$.

29.   Sketch $y = 2 \sec(x/3)$.

---

10   The Inverse Trigonometric Functions

Let us look again at the graph of $y = \sin x$ (Figure 30). It is immediately evident that this is not a one-to-one function, so it has no inverse. However, by a suitable restriction on the domain of the sine, an inverse can be found. The standard choice is to restrict x so that $-\pi/2 \le x \le \pi/2$. The sine curve with this domain will be called the **principal part** of the sine curve.

Figure 30

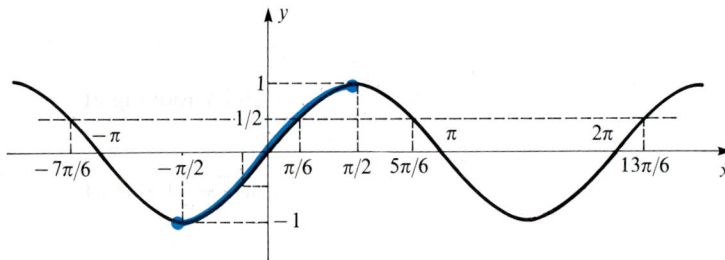

If x is so restricted, then for each y such that $-1 \le y \le 1$, there is exactly one x such that $y = \sin x$. For example, if we take $y = \frac{1}{2}$, we get $x = \pi/6$. On the other hand, if $y = -\frac{1}{2}$, then $x = -\pi/6$. The equation $y = \sin x$ expresses y in terms of x; we would like to solve this equation for x in terms of y. Unfortunately, we as yet have no way of doing this. With the aid of the graph (or tables or a calculator), we can find x for any given y, but we have no simple equation that expresses x in terms of y. What we do is invent a symbolism,

$$x = \sin^{-1} y$$

which is read "x is the inverse sine of y." Actually, we should probably read it as the "*principal* inverse sine of y," since it is the principal part of the sine curve that is used in finding x. Unless otherwise stated, we will in the future understand that $\sin^{-1} y$ means the principal value.

There is another symbol in wide use that means the same thing as $\sin^{-1} y$; it is **arcsin y,** read "arcsine of y." Its origin probably lies in the length of arc on a unit circle used in the definition of the trigonometric functions. Thus, arcsin $\frac{1}{2}$ might be interpreted as "the length of arc on the unit circle for which the sine is $\frac{1}{2}$." We know the length in this case is $\pi/6$, so

$$\sin\frac{\pi}{6} = \frac{1}{2} \quad \text{and} \quad \frac{\pi}{6} = \arcsin\frac{1}{2}$$

are two ways of viewing the same fact. The first says that the sine of the number $\pi/6$, that is, the measure of the arc on the unit circle from $(1, 0)$, is $\frac{1}{2}$. The second says that $\pi/6$ is the number, that is, the measure of arc length on the unit circle from $(1, 0)$, whose sine is $\frac{1}{2}$.

In what follows we will use both notations for the inverse sine (as well as inverses of the other trigonometric functions), since both are in wide use. Let us consider some examples.

EXAMPLE 22   Find the value of:
  a. $\sin^{-1} 1$ **b.** $\sin^{-1}(-\frac{1}{2})$ **c.** $\sin^{-1} 0$

Solution   **a.** $\sin^{-1} 1 = \pi/2$, since $\pi/2$ is that value of x on the principal part of the sine curve whose sine is 1

  b. $\sin^{-1}(-\frac{1}{2}) = -\pi/6$

It is important here to note that the answer is not $11\pi/6$, though an angle of $11\pi/6$ radians and an angle of $-\pi/6$ radians are coterminal. The distinction is most clearly seen by looking at the graph of the sine curve. On the x axis, $-\pi/6$ certainly is not the same point as $11\pi/6$, and even though the sine of each is $-\frac{1}{2}$, we choose $-\pi/6$ since it falls within the restricted range on x that defines the principal part of the sine curve.

  c. $\sin^{-1} 0 = 0$

EXAMPLE 23   Evaluate:

  a. $\arcsin\dfrac{\sqrt{3}}{2}$ **b.** $\arcsin\left(-\dfrac{1}{\sqrt{2}}\right)$ **c.** $\arcsin(-1)$

Solution   **a.** $\arcsin\dfrac{\sqrt{3}}{2} = \dfrac{\pi}{3}$ **b.** $\arcsin\left(-\dfrac{1}{\sqrt{2}}\right) = -\dfrac{\pi}{4}$ **c.** $\arcsin(-1) = -\dfrac{\pi}{2}$

To plot the graph of the inverse of the principal part of the sine curve, we follow our usual procedure with inverses of solving for x and then interchanging x and y, giving

$$y = \sin^{-1} x$$

Now, since the roles of x and y have been switched, we must restrict x so that $-1 \le x \le 1$ and y will fall in the range $-\pi/2 \le y \le \pi/2$. The graph is just the reflection of the principal part of the sine curve in a $45°$ line through the origin (Figure 31). Any value of x between -1 and 1 corresponds to a unique value

Figure 31

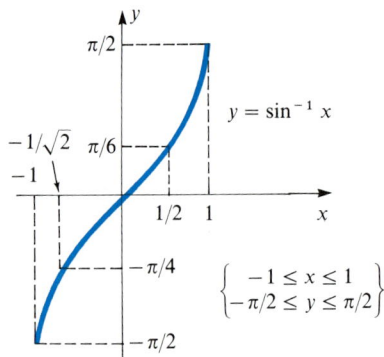

of y between $-\pi/2$ and $\pi/2$. When x is positive, y is positive, and when x is negative, y is negative. Notice that $y = \sin^{-1} x$ if and only if $\sin y = x$ and $-\pi/2 \le y \le \pi/2$. So when we wish to evaluate $\sin^{-1} x$ for a particular x, we ask what number (or what angle in radians) between $-\pi/2$ and $\pi/2$ has x as its sine.

We consider next the inverse of the tangent function, since it has much in common with the sine. The principal part (or **principal branch**) of the graph of $y = \tan x$ is that portion between $-\pi/2$ and $\pi/2$ (Figure 32). On this portion, if any value of y is specified, a unique value of x is determined. Solving $y = \tan x$ for x leads to either

$$x = \tan^{-1} y \qquad \text{or} \qquad x = \arctan y$$

Figure 32

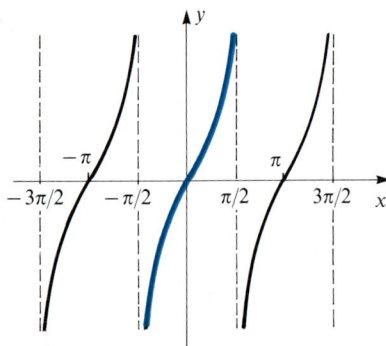

Again, we interchange the roles of x and y, and write

$$y = \tan^{-1} x \qquad \text{or} \qquad y = \arctan x$$

and restrict y such that $-\pi/2 < y < \pi/2$. The graph of this function is shown in Figure 33. With our knowledge of special angles, we conclude, for example, that

$$\tan^{-1} 1 = \frac{\pi}{4} \qquad\qquad \tan^{-1} \sqrt{3} = \frac{\pi}{3}$$

$$\tan^{-1}(-1) = -\frac{\pi}{4} \qquad\qquad \tan^{-1} 0 = 0$$

Figure 33

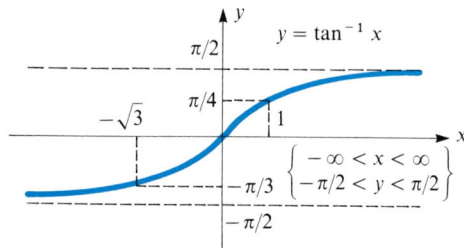

A consideration of the graph of the cosine function will make it clear that some different portion will have to be used as the principal part (Figure 34), because when x lies between $-\pi/2$ and $\pi/2$, y is always positive and hence does not assume all of its possible values. Furthermore, for a given y there is generally not a unique x determined. We choose instead the portion of the curve lying between 0 and π as the principal part. Then, for each y such that $-1 \leq y \leq 1$, there is a unique x for which $y = \cos x$. Again, we express the dependence of x on y by writing

$$x = \cos^{-1} y \qquad \text{or} \qquad x = \arccos y$$

Interchanging the roles of x and y, we obtain the graph of $y = \cos^{-1} x$ (Figure 35). When x is positive, y is positive and between 0 and $\pi/2$; when x is negative, y is positive and between $\pi/2$ and π.

Figure 34

Figure 35

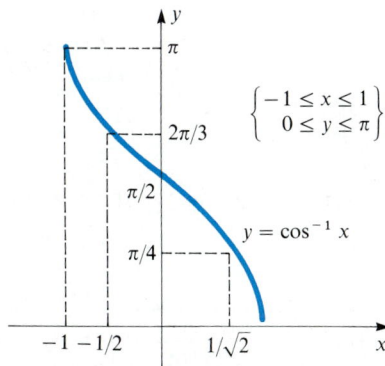

The inverse cotangent is seldom used, but is defined in much the same way as the inverse cosine. Its graph is shown in Figure 36.

The secant and cosecant present certain problems, and there is no general agreement on what parts of the curves to invert, that is, which portions to define

Figure 36

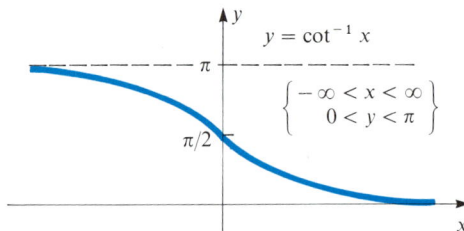

$$y = \cot^{-1} x$$

$$\left\{ \begin{array}{c} -\infty < x < \infty \\ 0 < y < \pi \end{array} \right\}$$

as the principal branches. Fortunately, this lack of agreement is not serious. The inverse cosecant is seldom used, and since it can always be circumvented, we will omit it entirely. The inverse secant is sufficiently useful to warrant consideration. For purposes of later use in calculus, there is some justification for the choice of principal parts made below. Let us consider first the graph of $y = \sec x$ (Figure 37). No single branch of the graph is suitable for defining the inverse function. While the reason is not now apparent, we select the highlighted portions in Figure 37 to define the inverse function. Thus, when $y \geq 1$, we take $0 \leq x < \pi/2$, and when $y \leq -1$, we take $\pi \leq x < 3\pi/2$. When we interchange the roles of x and y, we obtain the graph shown in Figure 38.

Figure 37

Figure 38

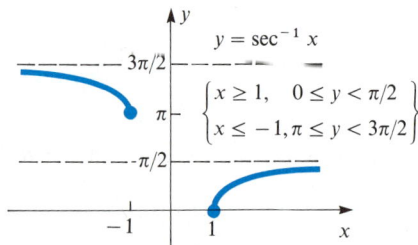

$$y = \sec^{-1} x$$

$$\left\{ \begin{array}{l} x \geq 1, \quad 0 \leq y < \pi/2 \\ x \leq -1, \pi \leq y < 3\pi/2 \end{array} \right\}$$

EXERCISE SET 10

In Problems 1–32 give the value.

A   **1.**   **a.** $\sin^{-1}(-\sqrt{3}/2)$ **b.** $\arccos(-\sqrt{3}/2)$

      2.   **a.** $\tan^{-1}(-1)$ **b.** $\text{arcsec}(-2)$

      3.   **a.** $\text{arccot}(-1)$ **b.** $\sin^{-1} 1$

4. **a.** $\arccos 1$ **b.** $\tan^{-1} 1$
5. **a.** $\operatorname{arcsec} 1$ **b.** $\sin^{-1}(-\frac{1}{2})$
6. **a.** $\arctan 0$ **b.** $\cos^{-1}(-1)$
7. **a.** $\arccos 0$ **b.** $\sec^{-1}(-2/\sqrt{3})$
8. **a.** $\cos \alpha$ if $\alpha = \sin^{-1}(-\frac{2}{3})$ **b.** $\tan \theta$ if $\theta = \arccos(-\frac{1}{4})$
9. **a.** $\sin x$ if $x = \sec^{-1}(-3)$ **b.** $\sec \theta$ if $\theta = \tan^{-1} \frac{3}{4}$
10. **a.** $\sin[\cos^{-1}(-\frac{1}{3})]$ **b.** $\sec[\sin^{-1}(-\frac{1}{4})]$
11. **a.** $\tan(\arccos \frac{3}{5})$ **b.** $\cos[\tan^{-1}(-\frac{4}{3})]$
12. **a.** $\sin(\arctan \frac{7}{12})$ **b.** $\csc[\arccos(-\frac{2}{3})]$
13. **a.** $\cos[\sin^{-1}(-\frac{1}{3})]$ **b.** $\cot[\cos^{-1}(-\frac{7}{25})]$
14. $\sin(\alpha - \beta)$ if $\alpha = \sin^{-1} \frac{3}{5}$ and $\beta = \cos^{-1}(-\frac{5}{13})$
15. $\cos(\alpha + \beta)$ if $\alpha = \arctan(-\frac{1}{2})$ and $\beta = \sec^{-1} \frac{5}{3}$
16. $\tan(\alpha + \beta)$ if $\alpha = \sin^{-1}(-\frac{4}{5})$ and $\beta = \cos^{-1}(-\frac{12}{13})$
17. $\sin 2\theta$ if $\theta = \cos^{-1}(-\frac{3}{5})$ 18. $\cos 2\theta$ if $\theta = \sin^{-1}(-\frac{1}{3})$
19. $\tan 2\theta$ if $\theta = \sin^{-1}(-\frac{5}{13})$ 20. $\cos[2 \cos^{-1}(-\frac{2}{3})]$
21. $\tan(2 \tan^{-1} \frac{1}{2})$ 22. $\sin[2 \sin^{-1}(-\frac{3}{7})]$
23. $\cos[2 \sin^{-1}(-\frac{2}{3})]$ 24. $\sin(\frac{1}{2} \cos^{-1} \frac{7}{25})$
25. $\cos[\frac{1}{2} \arcsin(-\frac{3}{5})]$ 26. $\tan \frac{1}{2}[\tan^{-1}(-\frac{12}{5})]$
27. $\sin \theta$ and $\cos \theta$ if $2\theta = \tan^{-1}(-\frac{24}{7})$
28. $\sin(\alpha/2), \cos(\alpha/2),$ and $\tan(\alpha/2)$ if $\alpha = \cos^{-1} \frac{3}{5}$
29. $\sin(\sin^{-1} \frac{12}{13} + \cos^{-1} \frac{4}{5})$ 30. $\cos[\cos^{-1} \frac{8}{17} - \sin^{-1}(-\frac{7}{25})]$
31. $\tan(\tan^{-1} \frac{2}{3} + \tan^{-1} \frac{1}{4})$

B   32. $\tan^{-1} \frac{2}{3} - \tan^{-1}(-\frac{1}{5})$
        Hint.   Call this $\alpha - \beta$ and find $\tan(\alpha - \beta)$.
33. If $\theta = \arcsin x$, show that $x/\sqrt{1 - x^2} = \tan \theta$.
34. If $\theta = \arctan x$, show that $\sqrt{1 + x^2}/x^2 = \csc \theta \cot \theta$.
35. Show that the expression $x^2/3\sqrt{x^2 + 9}$ changes to $\sec \theta - \cos \theta$ when the substitution $\theta = \tan^{-1}(x/3)$ is made.
36. Show that $\sqrt{x^2 - 4}/x = \sin \theta$ under the substitution $\theta = \sec^{-1}(x/2)$.

---

11 Trigonometric Form of Complex Numbers

An interesting and useful relationship exists between complex numbers and trigonometric functions. Let $z = a + bi$ be any complex number. We associate with this the point (a, b) in the plane. As in Figure 39, let r denote the distance from the origin to the point (a, b), and let θ denote the angle from the positive x axis to the line from the origin to the point (a, b). Then we have

$$r = \sqrt{a^2 + b^2}$$
$$a = r \cos \theta \tag{13}$$
$$b = r \sin \theta$$

The complex number $z = a + bi$ can therefore be written in the form

$$z = r(\cos \theta + i \sin \theta) \tag{14}$$

Figure 39

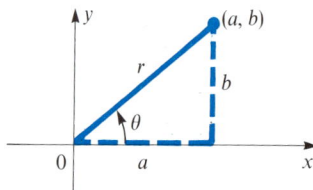

This is called the **trigonometric form** (or **polar form**) of the complex number z. The form $a + bi$ is referred to as the **rectangular form.** It should be noted that the trigonometric form is not unique, because if any integral multiple of 2π is added to θ, the value of z is unchanged. For example, if

$$z = 2\left(\cos\frac{\pi}{3} + i\sin\frac{\pi}{3}\right)$$

then also

$$z = 2\left(\cos\frac{7\pi}{3} + i\sin\frac{7\pi}{3}\right) = 2\left(\cos\frac{13\pi}{3} + i\sin\frac{13\pi}{3}\right)$$

and so on, where integral multiples of 2π are added to the angle. Normally, we choose θ to be between 0 and 2π, but there are exceptions.

The number r is called the **modulus** of z and is often denoted by $|z|$. Recall that for real number x, the absolute value $|x|$ can be interpreted geometrically as the distance on the number line between the origin and the point representing x. Similarly, $|z|$ represents the distance in the plane between the origin and the point representing z. In fact, $|z|$ is sometimes referred to as the absolute value of z. The angle θ is called the **argument** of z.

EXAMPLE 24   Find the trigonometric form of the complex number $z = \sqrt{3} + i$. What are the modulus and argument of z?

Solution   The number $\sqrt{3} + i$ is in rectangular form $a + bi$, with $a = \sqrt{3}$ and $b = 1$. So $r = \sqrt{3 + 1} = 2$, and $\theta = \pi/6$ (Figure 40). Therefore, by equation (14),

$$z = 2\left(\cos\frac{\pi}{6} + i\sin\frac{\pi}{6}\right)$$

The modulus of z is 2 and its (primary) argument is $\pi/6$.

Figure 40

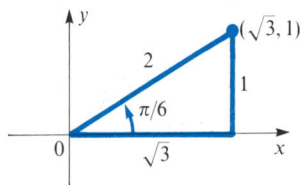

One of the advantages of the trigonometric form of complex numbers is that products, quotients, powers, and roots are particularly easy to calculate with numbers in this form. Consider first the product of two such numbers, say $z_1 = r_1(\cos \theta_1 + i \sin \theta_1)$ and $z_2 = r_2(\cos \theta_2 + i \sin \theta_2)$. On multiplication, making use of the fact that $i^2 = -1$ and arranging terms, we have

$$z_1 z_2 = r_1 r_2[(\cos \theta_1 \cos \theta_2 - \sin \theta_1 \sin \theta_2) + i(\sin \theta_1 \cos \theta_2 + \cos \theta_1 \sin \theta_2)]$$

By the addition formulas for the cosine and the sine, this can be written in the form

$$z_1 z_2 = r_1 r_2 [\cos(\theta_1 + \theta_2) + i \sin(\theta_1 + \theta_2)] \qquad (15)$$

So the modulus of the product is the product of the moduli, and the argument of the product is the sum of the arguments of the two numbers.

EXAMPLE 25   Find the product of the two complex numbers

$$z_1 = 2 \left(\cos \frac{\pi}{6} + i \sin \frac{\pi}{6} \right) \quad \text{and} \quad z_2 = 3 \left(\cos \frac{\pi}{3} + i \sin \frac{\pi}{3} \right)$$

Solution   By equation (15), the product is

$$z_1 z_2 = 2 \cdot 3 \left[\cos \left(\frac{\pi}{6} + \frac{\pi}{3} \right) + i \sin \left(\frac{\pi}{6} + \frac{\pi}{3} \right) \right]$$

$$= 6 \left(\cos \frac{\pi}{2} + i \sin \frac{\pi}{2} \right)$$

This can be put in rectangular form by evaluating the trigonometric functions:

$$z_1 z_2 = 6(0 + i \cdot 1) = 0 + 6i = 6i$$

In a similar way, we can prove that if $z_2 \neq 0$, then

$$\frac{z_1}{z_2} = \frac{r_1}{r_2} [\cos(\theta_1 - \theta_2) + i \sin(\theta_1 - \theta_2)] \qquad (16)$$

EXAMPLE 26   Find the quotient z_1/z_2 if

$$z_1 = 4 \left(\cos \frac{5\pi}{6} + i \sin \frac{5\pi}{6} \right) \quad \text{and} \quad z_2 = 2 \left(\cos \frac{\pi}{2} + i \sin \frac{\pi}{2} \right)$$

Solution

$$\frac{z_1}{z_2} = \frac{4}{2} \left[\cos \left(\frac{5\pi}{6} - \frac{\pi}{2} \right) + i \sin \left(\frac{5\pi}{6} - \frac{\pi}{2} \right) \right]$$

$$= 2 \left(\cos \frac{\pi}{3} + i \sin \frac{\pi}{3} \right)$$

In rectangular form this is

$$\frac{z_1}{z_2} = 2\left(\frac{1}{2} + i\frac{\sqrt{3}}{2}\right) = 1 + i\sqrt{3}$$

It is in raising to a power that the trigonometric form has the greatest advantage. We will state without proof the following important result due to the French mathematician Abraham De Moivre (1667–1754):

DE MOIVRE'S THEOREM   **Let $z = r(\cos\theta + i\sin\theta)$ be the trigonometric form of any complex number. Then for any natural number n**

$$z^n = r^n(\cos n\theta + i\sin n\theta)$$

Thus, the modulus of z^n is the nth power of the modulus of z, and the argument is n times the argument of z. That the result is plausible follows from a consideration of a few powers of z. By equation (15),

$$z^2 = r \cdot r[\cos(\theta + \theta) + i\sin(\theta + \theta)]$$
$$= r^2(\cos 2\theta + i\sin 2\theta)$$

Similarly, applying equation (15) again,

$$z^3 = z^2 \cdot z = r^2 \cdot r[\cos(2\theta + \theta) + i\sin(2\theta + \theta)]$$
$$= r^3(\cos 3\theta + i\sin 3\theta)$$

This process could be continued, and for any given power of z, De Moivre's theorem would be confirmed. However, this does not constitute a proof of the theorem. It can be proved using a technique called *mathematical induction*, which we will study later in this book.

EXAMPLE 27   Expand $(1 + i)^6$.

Solution   With the aid of a sketch (Figure 41) we determine that $r = \sqrt{2}$ and $\theta = \pi/4$. Writing $z = 1 + i$, we have

$$z^6 = (1 + i)^6 = \left[\sqrt{2}\left(\cos\frac{\pi}{4} + i\sin\frac{\pi}{4}\right)\right]^6$$

$$= (\sqrt{2})^6\left(\cos\frac{6\pi}{4} + i\sin\frac{6\pi}{4}\right)$$

$$= 8\left(\cos\frac{3\pi}{2} + i\sin\frac{3\pi}{2}\right)$$

In rectangular form the answer is

$$(1 + i)^6 = 8[0 + i(-1)] = -8i$$

Figure 41

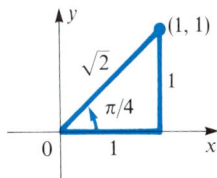

Remark.   You might wish to compare this solution with the work involved in doing this problem by expanding by the binomial theorem and simplifying the result. You will find that the method we used is much simpler.

Finally, we consider the problem of taking roots of complex numbers. Again let $z = r(\cos \theta + i \sin \theta)$, and suppose we wish to find $\sqrt[n]{z}$. We first recall that if any integral multiple of 2π is added to θ, the same value of z results. That is, for any integer k,

$$z = r[\cos(\theta + 2k\pi) + i \sin(\theta + 2k\pi)]$$

Making use of De Moivre's theorem we can prove the result

$$z^{1/n} = r^{1/n}\left[\cos\left(\frac{\theta + 2k\pi}{n}\right) + i \sin\left(\frac{\theta + 2k\pi}{n}\right)\right] \tag{17}$$

Furthermore, there are exactly n distinct roots that can be obtained by taking $k = 0, 1, 2, \ldots, n - 1$. These n roots are equally spaced on a circle of radius $r^{1/n}$.

Note.   In working with the trigonometric form of complex numbers, the angle θ may be expressed in either degrees or radians. If degrees are used, then equation (17) must be written

$$z^{1/n} = r^{1/n}\left[\cos\left(\frac{\theta + k \cdot 360°}{n}\right) + i \sin\left(\frac{\theta + k \cdot 360°}{n}\right)\right]$$

EXAMPLE 28   Find all cube roots of -8.

Solution   Let $z = -8 = -8 + 0i$. Then $r = 8$ and $\theta = \pi$ (Figure 42). So by equation (17),

$$\sqrt[3]{z} = z^{1/3} = 8^{1/3}\left[\cos\left(\frac{\pi + 2k\pi}{3}\right) + i \sin\left(\frac{\pi + 2k\pi}{3}\right)\right]$$

and the three distinct roots correspond to $k = 0$, $k = 1$, and $k = 2$. Let ζ_0, ζ_1, and ζ_2 be the roots corresponding to these values of k. Then

$$\zeta_0 = 2\left(\cos\frac{\pi}{3} + i \sin\frac{\pi}{3}\right) = 2\left(\frac{1}{2} + i\frac{\sqrt{3}}{2}\right) = 1 + i\sqrt{3}$$

$$\zeta_1 = 2\left(\cos\frac{\pi + 2\pi}{3} + i \sin\frac{\pi + 2\pi}{3}\right) = 2(\cos \pi + i \sin \pi) = -2$$

$$\zeta_2 = 2\left(\cos\frac{\pi+4\pi}{3} + i\sin\frac{\pi+4\pi}{3}\right) = 2\left(\cos\frac{5\pi}{3} + i\sin\frac{5\pi}{3}\right)$$

$$= 2\left(\frac{1}{2} - \frac{i\sqrt{3}}{2}\right) = 1 - i\sqrt{3}$$

These roots are shown graphically in Figure 43.

Figure 42

Figure 43

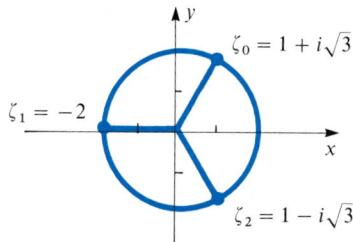

EXERCISE SET 11

A   In Problems 1–10 find the trigonometric form of the complex number. Draw a sketch in each case.

1. $1 - i$
2. $2 + 2i$
3. $\sqrt{3} - i$
4. $1 + i\sqrt{3}$
5. -4
6. $-8i$
7. $-2 - 2i\sqrt{3}$
8. $4\sqrt{2} - 4i\sqrt{2}$
9. 5
10. $i - 1$

In Problems 11–20 find the rectangular form of the complex number.

11. $2\left(\cos\frac{4\pi}{3} + i\sin\frac{4\pi}{3}\right)$
12. $4\left(\cos\frac{3\pi}{4} + i\sin\frac{3\pi}{4}\right)$
13. $5\left(\cos\frac{3\pi}{2} + i\sin\frac{3\pi}{2}\right)$
14. $7(\cos\pi + i\sin\pi)$
15. $6\left(\cos\frac{11\pi}{6} + i\sin\frac{11\pi}{6}\right)$
16. $2\left(\cos\frac{5\pi}{3} + i\sin\frac{5\pi}{3}\right)$
17. $\sqrt{2}\left(\cos\frac{7\pi}{4} + i\sin\frac{7\pi}{4}\right)$
18. $5(\cos 0 + i\sin 0)$
19. $3(\cos 150° + i\sin 150°)$
20. $8(\cos 315° + i\sin 315°)$

In Problems 21–27 find $z_1 \cdot z_2$ and z_1/z_2 using equations (15) and (16). When possible without using tables or a calculator, write answers in rectangular form.

21. $z_1 = 2\left(\cos\frac{\pi}{4} + i\sin\frac{\pi}{4}\right),\quad z_2 = 3\left(\cos\frac{5\pi}{4} + i\sin\frac{5\pi}{4}\right)$

22. $z_1 = 8(\cos \pi + i \sin \pi), \quad z_2 = 4\left(\cos \dfrac{2\pi}{3} + i \sin \dfrac{2\pi}{3}\right)$

23. $z_1 = 4\left(\cos \dfrac{\pi}{2} + i \sin \dfrac{\pi}{2}\right), \quad z_2 = 2\left(\cos \dfrac{3\pi}{4} + i \sin \dfrac{3\pi}{4}\right)$

24. $z_1 = \sqrt{2} + i\sqrt{2}, \quad z_2 = 4\sqrt{2} - 4i\sqrt{2}$

25. $z_1 = \sqrt{3} - i, \quad z_2 = 2 + 2i\sqrt{3}$

26. $z_1 = 3(\cos 70° + i \sin 70°), \quad z_2 = 5(\cos 50° + i \sin 50°)$

27. $z_1 = 4(\cos 100° + i \sin 100°), \quad z_2 = 6(\cos 70° + i \sin 70°)$

In Problems 28–34 find the indicated power using De Moivre's theorem. Express answers in rectangular form.

28. $\left[2\left(\cos \dfrac{\pi}{6} + i \sin \dfrac{\pi}{6}\right)\right]^4$ **29.** $\left[3\left(\cos \dfrac{3\pi}{4} + i \sin \dfrac{3\pi}{4}\right)\right]^6$

30. $[2(\cos 240° + i \sin 240°)]^5$ **31.** $(\sqrt{3} - i)^8$

32. $(1 - i)^{10}$ **33.** $(2 - 2i\sqrt{3})^4$

34. $(-\sqrt{2} - i\sqrt{2})^5$

B   In Problems 35–40 find all the roots indicated. Express answers in rectangular form whenever this can be done without tables or a calculator.

35. Cube roots of $8i$ **36.** Fourth roots of $-\dfrac{1}{2} - \dfrac{i\sqrt{3}}{2}$

37. Sixth roots of 1   **38.** Fourth roots of $-8 + 8i\sqrt{3}$

39. Square roots of $-16i$ **40.** Fifth roots of $-16\sqrt{3} + 16i$

In Problems 41–44 find the complete solution set.

41. $x^6 + 64 = 0$ **42.** $x^4 + 256 = 0$

43. $x^6 = 64$ **44.** $x^3 + 27i = 0$

45. Prove equation (17).
   Hint.   First write $z = r[\cos(\theta + 2k\pi) + i \sin(\theta + 2k\pi)]$, and let $\zeta = \rho(\cos \phi + i \sin \phi)$ be an unknown nth root of z. By De Moivre's theorem determine ρ and ϕ such that $\zeta^n = z$.

Problem 46 is taken from an engineering textbook.* The notation $\underline{/\theta}$ means $\cos \theta + i \sin \theta$. Use a hand calculator to evaluate.

46. Express the result of each of these complex number manipulations in polar form, using six significant figures just for the pure joy of calculating:
   (a) $(5 - 3\underline{/21.6°})(4.11\underline{/-161.9°} - 2\underline{/18.7613°})$;   (b) $1/(1\underline{/189.2°} - 1\underline{/-15.6°})$;
   (c) $2.18\underline{/57.9°} + 4.11\underline{/-161.9°} + 1.89\underline{/-49.2°}$

---

* William H. Hayt, Jr., and Jack E. Kemmerly, *Engineering Circuit Analysis*, 3d ed. (New York: McGraw-Hill Book Company, 1978), p. 755. Reprinted by permission.

12 Polar Coordinates

In all of our graphing so far we have used the rectangular coordinate system. For certain graphing problems, however, an alternative system, called the **polar coordinate system,** has definite advantages. In this system points in the plane are located by giving radial distances from a fixed point, called the **pole,** and angles from a fixed ray called the **polar axis.** The polar axis extends horizontally to the right from the pole, and we make it into the positive half of a number line, with the pole corresponding to zero. Now let θ be any angle with the pole as its vertex and the polar axis as its initial side, as in Figure 44. For a positive number r, if we measure r units from the pole along the terminal side of θ, a unique point P is determined, and we call the ordered pair (r, θ) the **polar coordinates** of P. If r is negative, we measure $|r|$ units from the pole on the ray directed opposite to the terminal side of θ. In Figure 45 we illustrate the points $(2, \pi/6)$ and $(-2, \pi/6)$.

Figure 44   **Figure 45**

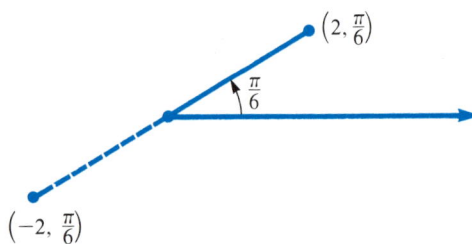

In the manner described, the ordered pair (r, θ) determines a unique point P in the plane. On the other hand, if we are given P there are infinitely many pairs of polar coordinates for it, since there are infinitely many angles having terminal side through P. For example, $(2, \pi/6)$, $(2, 13\pi/6)$, $(2, -11\pi/6)$, and $(-2, 7\pi/6)$ represent the same point. (Verify this.)

If we superimpose a rectangular coordinate system on a polar system so that the origin coincides with the pole and the positive x axis with the polar axis, as in Figure 46, we can determine relationships between rectangular and polar coordinates. Let P have coordinates (x, y) in the rectangular system and

Figure 46

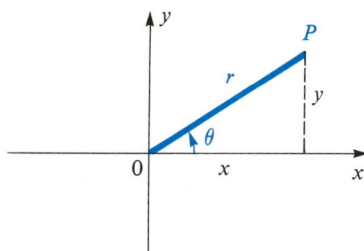

(r, θ) in the polar system. The following relationships hold true:

$$\tan \theta = \frac{y}{x} \quad (x \neq 0) \left.\vphantom{\begin{array}{c} \\ \\ \end{array}}\right\}$$
$$r^2 = x^2 + y^2 \quad\quad\;\;$$

(18)

$$\left. \begin{array}{l} x = r \cos \theta \\ y = r \sin \theta \end{array} \right\}$$

(19)

The next two examples illustrate how we can use these equations to change from one coordinate system to the other.

EXAMPLE 29   **a.**   Change $(\sqrt{3}, -1)$ to polar coordinates (r, θ), where $r > 0$ and $0 \leq \theta < 2\pi$.
  b.   Change $(-\sqrt{2}, 3\pi/4)$ to rectangular coordinates.

Solution   **a.**   From equations (18) we find that

$$\tan \theta = \frac{1}{\sqrt{3}}$$
$$r^2 = 4$$

Since $x > 0$ and $y < 0$, we know that θ is in quadrant IV, so $\theta = 11\pi/6$. The polar coordinates are therefore $(2, 11\pi/6)$.
  b.   From equations (19)

$$x = -\sqrt{2} \cos \frac{3\pi}{4} = -\sqrt{2}\left(-\frac{1}{\sqrt{2}}\right) = 1$$

$$y = -\sqrt{2} \sin \frac{3\pi}{4} = -\sqrt{2}\left(\frac{1}{\sqrt{2}}\right) = -1$$

So the rectangular coordinates are $(1, -1)$.

EXAMPLE 30   **a.**   Find the rectangular equation of the curve whose polar equation is $r = 2 \cos \theta$.
  b.   Find the polar equation of the curve whose rectangular equation is $y^2 = 2x$.

Solution   **a.**   For $r \neq 0$ we replace $\cos \theta$ by x/r to obtain

$$r = 2\frac{x}{r}$$
$$r^2 = 2x$$

Now we use the fact that $r^2 = x^2 + y^2$ to get the desired rectangular equation:

$$x^2 + y^2 = 2x$$

which we recognize as being a circle. The fact that the origin is on the circle assures us that no further points on the graph are obtained if $r = 0$, since the only point for which $r = 0$ is the pole, which coincides with the origin.

b.   From equations (19) we obtain

$$r^2 \sin^2 \theta = 2r \cos \theta$$
$$r(r \sin^2 \theta - 2 \cos \theta) = 0$$
$$r = 0 \quad | \quad r = 2 \cos \theta \csc^2 \theta \quad (\theta \neq 2k\pi)$$

The solution $r = 0$ is contained in the second equation. When $\theta = \pi/2$, the equation $r = 2 \cos \theta \csc^2 \theta$ gives $r = 0$, so $r = 2 \cos \theta \csc^2 \theta$ contains all points on the curve. Thus, the answer is

$$r = 2 \cos \theta \csc^2 \theta$$

To graph a polar equation we can make a table of values by assigning values to θ and calculating r. We typically assign to θ the function values we know without using a calculator or tables, and we use our knowledge of the behavior of the functions as θ varies from 0 to 2π. As an alternative, the graph is sometimes more easily obtained by changing to the corresponding rectangular equation. However, some of the more interesting curves in polar coordinates have complicated rectangular equations. The equation $r \cos \theta = 2$ corresponds to $x = 2$ in rectangular coordinates, so we know that its graph is a vertical line. In this case it is clearly easier to work with the rectangular equation. On the other hand, the equation $r^2 = 4 \cos 2\theta$ corresponds to $x^4 + 2x^2y^2 + y^4 - 4x^2 + 4y^2 = 0$. (Verify this.) If you attempt to draw the graph from this rectangular equation, you will soon be convinced that the polar equation is easier to work with. In the next example we show its graph.

EXAMPLE 31   Draw the graph of the equation $r^2 = 4 \cos 2\theta$.

Solution   It is sufficient to consider $0 \leq \theta < \pi$, since $\cos 2\theta$ will complete one cycle in this interval. Writing the equation in the form $r = \pm 2\sqrt{\cos 2\theta}$, we see that values of θ for which $\cos 2\theta < 0$ must be excluded. Thus we cannot have $\pi/4 < \theta < 3\pi/4$. We make a table of values as follows. Notice that we choose values for θ so that 2θ is an angle whose functions we know. The values of r are rounded to two decimal places.

θ	0	$\pi/12$	$\pi/6$	$\pi/4$	$3\pi/4$	$5\pi/6$	$11\pi/12$	π
r	± 2	± 1.86	± 1.41	0	0	± 1.41	± 1.86	± 2

The graph is shown in Figure 47. The curve is called a **lemniscate.**

Figure 47

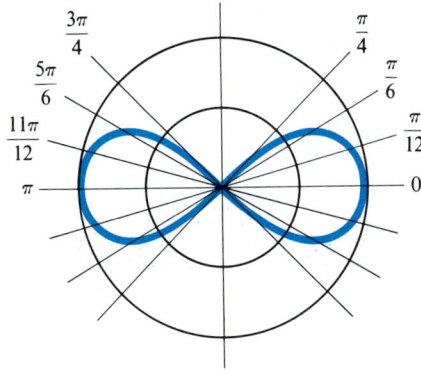

We now present a summary of some standard polar curves, showing their equations, their graphs, and their names.

Straight Lines

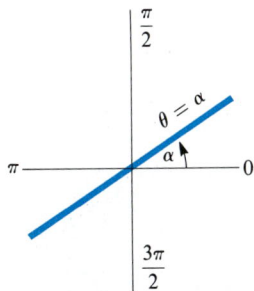

Line through pole making an angle α with polar axis

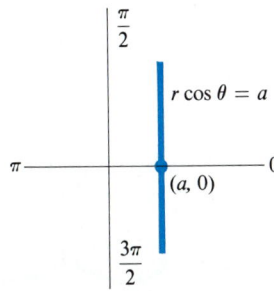

$r \cos \theta = a$
Same as $x = a$

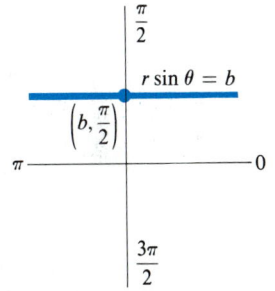

$r \sin \theta = b$
Same as $y = b$

Circles

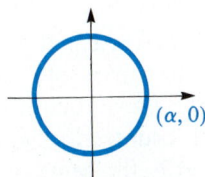

$r = a$
Circle of radius a,
center at pole

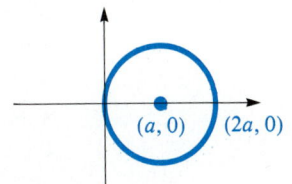

$r = 2a \cos \theta$
Circle of radius a,
center on polar axis,
passing through pole

Limacons: $r = a + b \cos \theta$

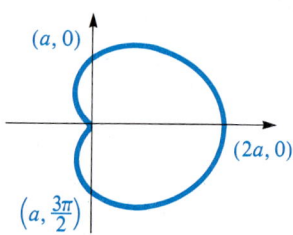

$a = b$
$r = a(1 + \cos \theta)$
Called a *cardioid* because
of heartlike shape

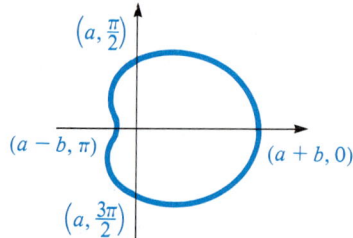

$a > b$
Limaçon without loop
(If $a \geq 2b$, the "dimple"
on the left is absent.)

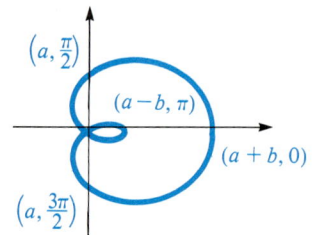

$a < b$
Limaçon with loop

Lemniscate: $r^2 = a^2 \cos 2\theta$

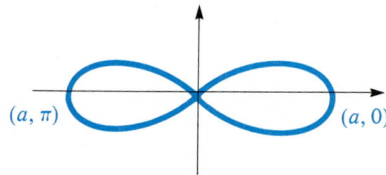

Rose Curves: $r = a \cos n\theta$

n even ($n = 2$)

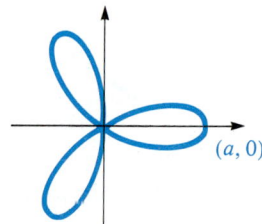

n odd ($n = 3$)

When n is even, there are $2n$ petals; when n is odd, there are n petals.

You may have noticed that each of the equations we have given involves the cosine function only and that the curves are all symmetric to the polar axis, since $\cos(-\theta) = \cos \theta$. It can be shown that if $\cos \theta$ is replaced by $\sin \theta$, the effect is to rotate the graph in a counterclockwise direction by 90°. More generally, the graph of $r = f(\theta - \alpha)$ is the same as that of $r = f(\theta)$ rotated through an angle α. Since $\cos(\theta - \pi/2) = \sin \theta$, this confirms that replacing $\cos \theta$ by $\sin \theta$ rotates the graph $\pi/2$ radians, or 90°. Similarly, since $\cos(\theta - \pi) = -\cos \theta$ and $\cos(\theta - 3\pi/2) = -\sin \theta$, replacing $\cos \theta$ by $-\cos \theta$ or by $-\sin \theta$

rotates the graph 180° or 270°, respectively. In the case of cos $n\theta$ being replaced by sin $n\theta$, the rotation is 90°/n, with similar results for the other cases. For example, the graph of the equation $r^2 = 2a \sin 2\theta$ is the lemniscate $r^2 = 2a \cos 2\theta$ rotated through an angle of 45°. We conclude this section with an example of a type of problem often encountered in calculus.

EXAMPLE 32   Draw the curves $r = 3 \cos \theta$ and $r = 1 + \cos \theta$ on the same polar coordinate system, and shade the area inside the first curve and outside the second. Also find all points of intersection of the curves.

Solution   The first curve is a circle of radius $\frac{3}{2}$ centered at $(\frac{3}{2}, 0)$; the second curve is a cardioid, as shown in Figure 48. The shaded area is the one described in the problem. To find the points of intersection we set the two r values equal to one another and solve for θ:

$$3 \cos \theta = 1 + \cos \theta$$

$$2 \cos \theta = 1$$

$$\cos \theta = \frac{1}{2}$$

$$\theta = \frac{\pi}{3}, \frac{5\pi}{3}$$

Figure 48

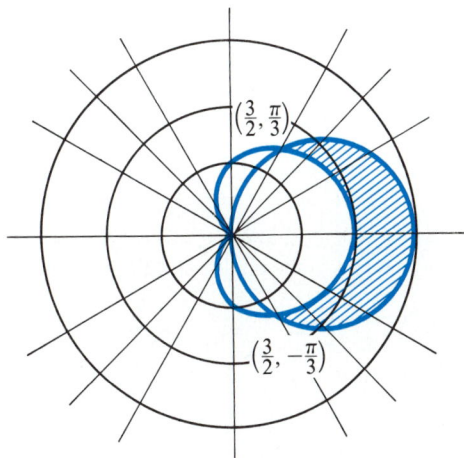

We find r to be $\frac{3}{2}$ in each case. So the curves intersect at $(\frac{3}{2}, \pi/3)$ and $(\frac{3}{2}, 5\pi/3)$. It is probably better to give the equivalent representation $(\frac{3}{2}, -\pi/3)$ for the second point.

By solving the two equations simultaneously we found two points of intersection. But from the graph we see that the curves also intersect at the pole. Why did this not show up in our solution? The answer lies in the fact that the curves pass through the pole for different values of θ. The circle goes through the pole when $\theta = \pi/2$, whereas the cardioid goes through the pole when $\theta = \pi$. Nevertheless, the pole is a point of intersection.

EXERCISE SET 12

A   In Problems 1 and 2 plot the points in a polar coordinate system.

1. **a.** $\left(1, \dfrac{2\pi}{3}\right)$ **b.** $\left(2, -\dfrac{\pi}{2}\right)$ **c.** $\left(-2, \dfrac{3\pi}{2}\right)$ **d.** $\left(3, \dfrac{\pi}{6}\right)$

    e. $\left(-1, -\dfrac{3\pi}{4}\right)$

2. **a.** $(4, \pi)$ **b.** $\left(-2, \dfrac{\pi}{2}\right)$ **c.** $\left(3, -\dfrac{5\pi}{6}\right)$ **d.** $\left(0, \dfrac{\pi}{5}\right)$

    e. $\left(-3, -\dfrac{5\pi}{3}\right)$

3. Give five different sets of polar coordinates for the point $(2, 2\pi/3)$. Include at least one set for which $r < 0$ and one for which $\theta < 0$.

In Problems 4 and 5 give the corresponding rectangular coordinates for the given polar coordinates.

4. **a.** $\left(2, \dfrac{\pi}{6}\right)$ **b.** $\left(-\sqrt{2}, \dfrac{\pi}{4}\right)$ **c.** $\left(4, \dfrac{2\pi}{3}\right)$ **d.** $\left(6, \dfrac{3\pi}{2}\right)$

    e. $\left(-8, -\dfrac{5\pi}{3}\right)$

5. **a.** $\left(2\sqrt{2}, -\dfrac{7\pi}{4}\right)$ **b.** $\left(6, \dfrac{11\pi}{6}\right)$ **c.** $\left(-10, -\dfrac{9\pi}{4}\right)$ **d.** $(4, 3\pi)$

    e. $\left(\sqrt{8}, \dfrac{9\pi}{4}\right)$

In Problems 6 and 7 give the polar coordinates (for which $r > 0$ and $0 \leq \theta < 2\pi$) corresponding to the points with the given rectangular coordinates.

6. **a.** $(1, \sqrt{3})$ **b.** $(-2, 2)$ **c.** $(0, 5)$ **d.** $(-4, 0)$
    e. $(-3, -\sqrt{3})$

7. **a.** $(4, -4)$ **b.** $(-2\sqrt{3}, 2)$ **c.** $(0, -2)$ **d.** $\left(\dfrac{1}{2}, -\dfrac{\sqrt{3}}{2}\right)$
    e. $(-3\sqrt{2}, -\sqrt{6})$

In Problems 8–18 change to the equivalent polar equation.

8. $x^2 + y^2 = 9$	**9.** $x + y = 0$
10. $2x - 3y = 4$	**11.** $x = 3$
12. $y + 1 = 0$	**13.** $x^2 + y^2 - 4y = 0$
14. $x^2 - y^2 = 4$	**15.** $xy = 2$
16. $y^2 = 2x + 1$	**17.** $(x + 1)^2 + y^2 = 1$
18. $\sqrt{x^2 + y^2} - 2 = x$	

In Problems 19–30 change to an equivalent rectangular equation.

19. $r = 4$

20. $\theta = \dfrac{\pi}{3}$

21. $r \cos \theta = 2$

22. $r \sin \theta = -1$

23. $2r \cos \theta - 3r \sin \theta = 5$

24. $r = 2 \sin \theta$

25. $r = 3 \sec \theta$

26. $r = 4 \csc \theta$

27. $r = -2 \cos \theta$

28. $\theta = \tan^{-1} \frac{2}{3}$

29. $r = \dfrac{1}{1 - \cos \theta}$

30. $r^2 \sin 2\theta = 1$

In Problems 31–52 identify the curve and draw its graph.

31. $r = 3$

32. $r = -2$

33. $\theta = \dfrac{3\pi}{4}$

34. $r \cos \theta = 2$

35. $r = -3 \csc \theta$

36. $r = 4 \cos \theta$

37. $r = 1 - \cos \theta$

38. $r = 1 + \sin \theta$

39. $r = 5 - 4 \cos \theta$

40. $r = 4 - 5 \sin \theta$

41. $r^2 = 9 \sin 2\theta$

42. $r = 2 \cos 2\theta$

43. $r = \sin 3\theta$

44. $r = -\cos 3\theta$

45. $r = 3 \sin 2\theta$

46. $r^2 = \cos^2 \theta - \sin^2 \theta$

47. $r = 2 + \sin \theta$

48. $r = 2 \cos \theta - 1$

49. $r = 2 \cos\left(\theta - \dfrac{3\pi}{4}\right)$

50. $r = 2 + 2 \cos\left(\theta + \dfrac{\pi}{6}\right)$

51. $r = 3(\sin \theta - 1)$

52. $r^2 = 8 \sin \theta \cos \theta$

B **53.** Write in polar form.
  a. $x^2 y^2 = 4(x^2 + y^2)^{3/2}$ **b.** $x^2 - y^2 - 4x = 0$
54. Write in rectangular form.

  a. $r = \dfrac{4}{1 - 2 \sin \theta}$ **b.** $r \sec^2 \theta = \sin \theta - 3 \cos \theta$

Draw the graphs in Problems 55–61.

55. $r = 2 \sin^2 \dfrac{\theta}{2}$

56. $r = \dfrac{4}{2 + \cos \theta}$

57. $r = \cos \theta + \sin \theta$
  Hint. Write in the form $r = a \cos(\theta - \alpha)$
58. $r = 3 \cos \theta - 4 \sin \theta$ (See hint to Problem 57.)

59. $r = 2 \cos \dfrac{\theta}{2}$ **60.** $r = \sqrt{4 \sin \theta}$ **61.** $r = 3 \cos 5\theta$

62. By changing to rectangular coordinates, show that the graph of $r = 4 \sec^2(\theta/2)$ is a parabola. Draw the graph.

Problems 63–65 involve three spiral curves. Draw them for the indicated values of a.

63. Spiral of Archimedes, $r = a\theta$ $(a = 1)$
64. Hyperbolic spiral, $r = a/\theta$ $(a = 2)$

65.   Logarithmic spiral, $r = e^{a\theta}$ $(a = 1)$
66.   Graph the bifolium $r = a \sin 2\theta \cos \theta$ for $a = 1$.

In Problems 67–71 show the two curves on the same coordinate system, indicate the specified area by crosshatching, and find all points of intersection.

67.   Outside $r = 2$ and inside $r = 2(1 + \cos \theta)$.
68.   Outside $r = 1 + \sin \theta$ and inside $r = 3 \sin \theta$.
69.   Inside $r = 3 \cos \theta$ and inside $r = 2 - \cos \theta$.
70.   Inside $r = -4 \cos \theta$ and outside $r = 4 + 4 \cos \theta$.
71.   Inside $r = 5 \cos \theta$ and outside $r = 2 + \cos \theta$.

13   A Useful Inequality

In this section we will derive an inequality that plays an important role in the calculus of trigonometric functions. In Figure 49 the shaded area is called a **sector** of the circle. We begin by finding a formula for the area of a sector of a circle. The area depends on the radius r and the angle θ. As usual, we use θ both to name the angle and to designate its measure in radians. We take it as known that the area of the entire circle (actually, we should say the area within the circle) is πr^2. The area of the sector is a fractional part of this, but what fractional part? It is just the ratio of θ to 2π, since θ is the measure of the central angle of the sector and 2π is the measure of the entire revolution. So we want to multiply the fraction $\theta/2\pi$ by the area of the circle:

$$\frac{\theta}{2\pi} \cdot \pi r^2 = \frac{1}{2} r^2 \theta$$

Area of a sector $= \dfrac{1}{2} r^2 \theta$

Figure 49

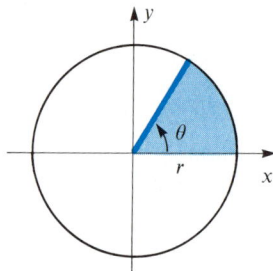

Let us now consider a unit circle and an angle θ between 0 and $\pi/2$ (Figure 50). The angle of θ radians subtends an arc length of θ units. The point $P(\theta)$ has coordinates $(\cos \theta, \sin \theta)$. So the length of the vertical line segment from $P(\theta)$ to the x axis is $\sin \theta$. If θ is small, it would appear that this vertical segment and the arc from $(1, 0)$ to $P(\theta)$ are very nearly equal, that is, $\sin \theta$ and θ are

Figure 50

Figure 51

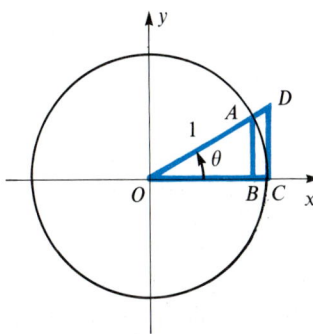

almost equal. We want to consider the ratio $(\sin\theta)/\theta$, since this plays an important role in calculus. From the observation above, it seems reasonable to expect that when θ is small, this ratio is almost 1. Of course, we cannot allow θ to be 0, because then the ratio becomes $0/0$, which is meaningless. To get a more precise estimate on the size of $(\sin\theta)/\theta$, we consider the areas shown in Figure 51. Let

$$A_1 = \text{Area of triangle } OAB$$
$$A_2 = \text{Area of sector } OAC$$
$$A_3 = \text{Area of triangle } ODC$$

Then it is evident from the geometry that $A_1 < A_2 < A_3$. The point A is what we have customarily called $P(\theta)$ and it is θ units along the arc of the circle from C, that is, arc $AC = \theta$. Also, by definition, the x and y coordinates of A are $\cos\theta$ and $\sin\theta$, respectively. Thus, $\overline{OB} = \cos\theta$ and $\overline{AB} = \sin\theta$. The area A_1 can now be calculated:

$$A_1 = \tfrac{1}{2}(\overline{OB})(\overline{AB}) = \tfrac{1}{2}\sin\theta\cos\theta$$

We have already found that

$$A_2 = \tfrac{1}{2}(1)^2 \cdot \theta = \tfrac{1}{2}\theta$$

To find A_3, note that $\overline{OC}$ of triangle OAC is 1 unit in length, since it is the radius of the circle. From that triangle we know that

$$\tan\theta = \frac{\overline{CD}}{\overline{OC}} = \frac{\overline{CD}}{1}$$

So $\overline{CD} = \tan\theta$. The area A_3 is therefore

$$A_3 = \frac{1}{2}(\overline{OC})(\overline{CD}) = \frac{1}{2}(1)(\tan\theta) = \frac{1}{2}\tan\theta = \frac{1}{2}\left(\frac{\sin\theta}{\cos\theta}\right)$$

Now the inequality $A_1 < A_2 < A_3$ can be written

$$\frac{1}{2}\sin\theta\cos\theta < \frac{1}{2}\theta < \frac{1}{2}\left(\frac{\sin\theta}{\cos\theta}\right)$$

For $0 < \theta < \pi/2$, $\sin\theta > 0$, so we can divide by $\frac{1}{2}\sin\theta$ to obtain

$$\cos\theta < \frac{\theta}{\sin\theta} < \frac{1}{\cos\theta}$$

and again using the fact that all terms are positive, we can invert each term, reversing inequality signs (since $a < b$ implies $1/a > 1/b$ for positive a and b). This gives

$$\frac{1}{\cos\theta} > \frac{\sin\theta}{\theta} > \cos\theta$$

or equivalently,

$$\cos\theta < \frac{\sin\theta}{\theta} < \frac{1}{\cos\theta} \tag{20}$$

and this is true for all θ where $0 < \theta < \pi/2$.

If θ lies in the range $-\pi/2 < \theta < 0$, we can arrive at inequality (20) again, although it is necessary to be careful with negative signs. We will not present the details. For all values of θ, then, where $-\pi/2 < \theta < \pi/2$, and $\theta \neq 0$, we have

$$\cos\theta < \frac{\sin\theta}{\theta} < \frac{1}{\cos\theta}$$

We know that $\cos 0 = 1$, and for θ very close to 0, $\cos\theta$ will be very close to, but less than, 1. Our inequality tells us, then, that for small values of θ, positive or negative, $(\sin\theta)/\theta$ is hemmed in between two numbers—one slightly less than 1 and the other slightly greater than 1. Furthermore, the closer θ is to 0, the closer both $\cos\theta$ and $1/(\cos\theta)$ are to 1. Without defining precisely what we mean by a limiting process, we can nevertheless say that $(\sin\theta)/\theta$ will be as close to 1 as we wish for all values of θ sufficiently close to 0 but not equal to 0. In calculus, this will be indicated by the symbolism

$$\lim_{\theta\to 0}\frac{\sin\theta}{\theta} = 1$$

which is read "the limit of $(\sin\theta)/\theta$ as θ approaches 0 is 1."

EXERCISE SET 13

A   **1.**   Make a table of values (using a calculator) and draw the graph of

$$y = \frac{\sin x}{x}$$

for $-\pi/2 \leq x \leq \pi/2$, $x \neq 0$. Plot several points near $x = 0$. Does your result tend to confirm the limit found in this section?

2. Show that

$$\lim_{\theta \to 0} \frac{\tan \theta}{\theta} = 1$$

Hint. $\dfrac{\tan \theta}{\theta} = \dfrac{\sin \theta}{\theta} \cdot \dfrac{1}{\cos \theta}$

3. By multiplying the numerator and denominator of $(1 - \cos \theta)/\theta$ by $1 + \cos \theta$, show that

$$\lim_{\theta \to 0} \frac{1 - \cos \theta}{\theta} = 0$$

In Problems 4–9 find the limits indicated.

4. $\displaystyle\lim_{\theta \to 0} \frac{\sin^2 \theta}{\theta}$

5. $\displaystyle\lim_{x \to 0} \frac{\sin 2x}{x}$

6. $\displaystyle\lim_{t \to 0} t \cot t$

7. $\displaystyle\lim_{x \to 0} \frac{\cos 2x - 1}{x^2}$

8. $\displaystyle\lim_{x \to 0} \frac{1}{x^2(1 + \cot^2 x)}$

9. $\displaystyle\lim_{\theta \to 0} \frac{1 - \cos 2\theta}{\theta \sin 2\theta}$

B 10. If $\alpha > 0$, show that

$$\lim_{\alpha \to 0} \frac{\sqrt{2(1 - \cos \alpha)}}{\alpha} = 1$$

Hint. Use a half-angle formula.

11. Show that

$$\lim_{x \to \infty} x \sin \frac{1}{x} = 1$$

Hint. Let $\theta = 1/x$.

12. Show that inequality (20) remains valid for $-\pi/2 < \theta < 0$.

Review Exercise Set

A 1. Evaluate each of the following without the use of tables or a calculator:
   a. $\tan(7\pi/12)$ **b.** $\sin(23\pi/12)$ **c.** $\cos(\pi/8)$ **d.** $\cos(13\pi/12)$
2. Reduce each of the following to a function involving θ only:

   a. $\sin\left(\dfrac{3\pi}{2} - \theta\right)$ **b.** $\tan(\theta + \pi)$ **c.** $\sec(4\pi - \theta)$

   d. $\cos\left(\theta - \dfrac{\pi}{2}\right)$ **e.** $\csc\left(\dfrac{9\pi}{2} + \theta\right)$

3. Evaluate:
   a. $\arccos(-\frac{1}{2})$ b. $\tan^{-1}(-\sqrt{3})$ c. $\arcsin(-\sqrt{3}/2)$
   d. $\cos^{-1}(-1)$ e. $\tan^{-1}(-1)$

4. If $\sec\theta = \frac{5}{4}$ and $\sin\theta < 0$, $0 \le \theta \le 2\pi$, find:
   a. $\cos 2\theta$ b. $\tan 2\theta$ c. $\cos\frac{1}{2}\theta$

5. If $\sin\theta = \frac{4}{5}$ and $\tan\theta < 0$, $0 \le \theta \le 2\pi$, find:
   a. $\sin 2\theta$ b. $\cos 2\theta$ c. $\sin\frac{1}{2}\theta$

6. If $\alpha = \arcsin(-\frac{3}{5})$ and $\beta = \arccos(-\frac{5}{13})$, find:
   a. $\sin(\alpha + \beta)$ b. $\cos(\alpha - \beta)$ c. $\tan(\alpha + \beta)$

7. If $\alpha = \tan^{-1}(-\frac{4}{3})$ and $\beta = \cos^{-1}(-\frac{8}{17})$, find:
   a. $\sin(\alpha - \beta)$ b. $\cos(\alpha + \beta)$ c. $\tan(\alpha - \beta)$

8. If $\tan 2\theta = -\frac{24}{7}$ and $\pi/2 < 2\theta < \pi$, find $\sin\theta$ and $\cos\theta$.

9. If $\tan\theta = \frac{15}{8}$ and $\pi < \theta < 3\pi/2$, find $\sin(\theta/2)$, $\cos(\theta/2)$, and $\tan(\theta/2)$.

10. Evaluate:
    a. $\cos[\arcsin(-\frac{3}{5})]$ b. $\sin[2\sin^{-1}(-\frac{5}{13})]$

11. Evaluate:
    a. $\tan[2\cos^{-1}(-\frac{4}{5})]$ b. $\cos(\frac{1}{2}\tan^{-1} 4\sqrt{3})$

In Problems 12–25 prove that the given equations are identities.

12. $\csc\theta - \cos\theta\cot\theta = \sin\theta$

13. $\dfrac{2}{\tan\theta + \cot\theta} = \sin 2\theta$

14. $\dfrac{\cos\theta + \cot\theta}{1 + \csc\theta} = \cos\theta$

15. $\dfrac{\cos\theta}{\sec\theta - \tan\theta} = 1 + \sin\theta$

16. $\dfrac{\cot\theta - \tan\theta}{\cot\theta + \tan\theta} = \cos 2\theta$

17. $\sin\theta\tan\theta + \cos\theta = \sec\theta$

18. $\dfrac{\tan\theta}{\sec\theta + 1} + \dfrac{\sec\theta - 1}{\tan\theta} = \dfrac{2\tan\theta}{\sec\theta + 1}$

19. $\tan\theta(\cos 2\theta + 1) = \sin 2\theta$

20. $\sin\theta + \cos\theta\cot\theta = \csc\theta$

21. $\sin 2\theta + (\cos\theta - \sin\theta)^2 = 1$

22. $1 + \dfrac{\tan^2\theta}{\sec\theta + 1} = \sec\theta$

23. $\cot\theta - \tan\theta = 2\cot 2\theta$

24. $\dfrac{1 + \tan^2\theta}{1 - \tan^2\theta} = \sec 2\theta$

25. $\dfrac{\sin 2\theta}{1 - \cos 2\theta} = \cot\theta$

In Problems 26–31 find all primary solutions.

26. $\sin x - 2\sin^2 x = 0$

27. $3\tan^3 x - \tan x = 0$

28. $\sin 2\theta + \cos\theta = 0$

29. $\cos 2\theta - \sin\theta = 0$

30. $2\cos^2 3t - 3\cos 3t - 2 = 0$

31. $2\cos^2 t = 1 - \sin t$

In Problems 32–34 sketch the graphs.

32. a. $y = 2\sin x + 1$ b. $y = 3\cos 2x$

33. a. $y = 2\tan\dfrac{\pi x}{4}$ b. $y = 2\cos\dfrac{\pi x}{2} + 3$

34. a. $y = \sin\left(3x + \dfrac{\pi}{2}\right)$ b. $y = 2\cos\left(\pi x - \dfrac{\pi}{3}\right)$

35. If

$$z_1 = 2\left(\cos\frac{5\pi}{6} + i\sin\frac{5\pi}{6}\right) \quad \text{and} \quad z_2 = 3\left(\cos\frac{4\pi}{3} + i\sin\frac{4\pi}{3}\right)$$

find $z_1 \cdot z_2$ and z_1/z_2. Express answers in rectangular form.

In Problems 36 and 37 expand using De Moivre's theorem.

36. $(1 - i)^8$ 37. $(2 + 2i\sqrt{3})^4$

38. Write in polar form.

  a. $x^2 + 8y = 16$ **b.** $x^2 - y^2 = \dfrac{2xy}{x^2 + y^2}$

39. Write in rectangular form.

  a. $r = \dfrac{4}{2 - 3\cos\theta}$ **b.** $r^2 \cos 2\theta = 4$

In Problems 40 and 41 draw the graph.

40. **a.** $r = 2 - 3\cos\theta$ **b.** $r^2 = -4\cos 2\theta$
41. **a.** $r + \cos 2\theta = 0$ **b.** $r = 2 - 2\sin\theta$

In Problems 42 and 43 evaluate the limits.

42. $\displaystyle\lim_{x\to 0}\frac{x\sin x}{1 - \cos 2x}$ 43. $\displaystyle\lim_{\theta\to 0}\frac{\sec^2\theta - 1}{\theta^2}$

B 44. Evaluate:
  a. $\cos[\tan^{-1}\frac{5}{12} - \sin^{-1}(-\frac{8}{17})]$ **b.** $\tan^{-1}\frac{1}{3} + \tan^{-1}(-2)$

In Problems 45–50 prove the identities.

45. $\dfrac{\sin\theta + \cos 2\theta - 1}{\cos\theta - \sin 2\theta} = \tan\theta$ 46. $\sin^2\theta + \dfrac{2 - \tan^2\theta}{\sec^2\theta} - 1 = \cos 2\theta$

47. $\dfrac{\sec\theta - 1}{\sec\theta + 1} = 2\csc^2\theta - 2\cot\theta\csc\theta - 1$

48. $\sec\theta\csc\theta - 2\cos\theta\csc\theta = \tan\theta - \cot\theta$

49. $\dfrac{\sin 8\theta - \sin 6\theta}{\cos 8\theta + \cos 6\theta} = \tan\theta$ 50. $\dfrac{\cos\theta}{1 - \sin\theta} = \tan\theta + \sec\theta$

In Problems 51–54 find all primary solutions.

51. $\tan^2 2x + 3\sec 2x + 3 = 0$ 52. $\cos 2\theta\sec\theta + \sec\theta = 1$
53. $\tan 2\theta = 2\cos\theta$ 54. $1 + \sin t = \cos t$
                                                        Hint. Square both sides.

55. Draw the graph of:

  a. $y = 3 - 2\cos\left(\dfrac{\pi}{3} - 2x\right)$ **b.** $y = \sqrt{3}\cos x - \sin x$

56. Find all eighth roots of 1.
57. Find all cube roots of $-64i$.

58. Find the complete solution set to the equation $x^6 + 1 = 0$.

59. Draw the curves $r = 3 - 4 \cos \theta$ and $r = 2\sqrt{3}(1 - \cos \theta)$ on the same polar coordinate system, and crosshatch the area that lies outside the first curve and inside the second. Find all points of intersection.

60. Show that if $x < 0$, then

$$\lim_{x \to 0} \frac{\sqrt{1 - \cos 2x}}{x} = -\sqrt{2}$$

Cumulative Review Exercise Set III (Chapters 8 and 9)

1. In each of the following a right triangle ABC is given, with right angle at C. Find all missing sides and angles without the use of a calculator or tables.
   a. $A = 30°$, $b = 12$ b. $B = 60°$, $a = 4$
   c. $A = 45°$, $c = 16$ d. $a = 10$, $c = 20$
   e. $b = 6\sqrt{2}$, $c = 12$

2. Without using a calculator or tables find all six trigonometric functions of each of the following. Leave answers in exact form.
   a. $4\pi/3$ b. $-3\pi/4$ c. $17\pi/6$ d. $75°$ e. $990°$
   f. $17\pi/12$ g. $-22.5°$ h. $(2n-1)\pi$, n an integer

3. Evaluate without a calculator or tables:
   a. $\sin[2 \sin^{-1}(-\frac{3}{5})]$
   b. $\cos[\cos^{-1}(-\frac{5}{13}) + \tan^{-1}(-\frac{4}{3})]$
   c. $\tan(\frac{1}{2})\theta$, where $\sec\theta = \frac{3}{2}$ and $\sin\theta < 0$

   d. $\csc\left(\dfrac{\pi}{2} - \theta\right)$, where $\cot\theta = \frac{1}{2}$ and $\cos\theta < 0$

4. Prove the identities:

   a. $\dfrac{\sec\theta - \cos\theta + \tan\theta}{\tan\theta + \sec\theta} = \sin\theta$ b. $\dfrac{(\sin\theta - \cos\theta)^2}{\cos 2\theta} = \dfrac{1 - \tan\theta}{1 + \tan\theta}$

5. Let

   $$z_1 = 4\left(\cos\frac{4\pi}{3} + i\sin\frac{4\pi}{3}\right) \quad \text{and} \quad z_2 = 2\left(\cos\frac{\pi}{6} + i\sin\frac{\pi}{6}\right)$$

   Find:

   a. $z_1 z_2$ b. z_1/z_2 c. z_2^4 d. The square roots of z_1

   Express answers in rectangular form.

6. Points A and B are on level ground on a line with the base of a tower. From the top of the tower the angles of depression of A and B, respectively, are $24.6°$ and $31.2°$. If points A and B are known to be 20 meters apart, find the height of the tower.

7. Evaluate without using a calculator or tables:
   a. $\cos[2 \sin^{-1}(-\frac{1}{3})]$ b. $\sin[2 \arctan(-3)]$
   c. $\tan \frac{1}{2}[\cos^{-1}(-\frac{7}{25})]$ d. $\cos \frac{1}{2}\alpha$, where $\csc\alpha = -\frac{5}{4}$ and $\pi \le \alpha \le 3\pi/2$

8. Find all primary solutions:
   a. $2 \sin x + \sqrt{3} \tan x = 0$ b. $2 \sin^2 \frac{1}{2}x - 2 \cos^2 x = 1$

9. A chord on a circle of radius 6 inches is 10 inches long. Find:
   a. The central angle formed by the radii to the end points of the chord
   b. The arc length cut off by the chord
   c. The area of the sector formed by this arc and the radii
   d. The area of the triangle formed by the chord and the radii

10. In each of the following, triangle ABC is a right triangle, with right angle at C. Find all unknown sides and angles.
    a. $A = 16.3°$, $b = 4.68$ b. $B = 52°40'$, $c = 171.5$
    c. $a = 13.7$, $b = 21.3$ d. $b = 50$, $c = 130$

11. a. A curve on a railroad track is in the form of a circular arc which is 1.5 kilometers long. If the central angle corresponding to this arc is $72°$, find the radius of the circle.

    b. A girl is riding a bicycle with 28 inch diameter tires which are rotating at the rate of 200 revolutions per minute. Approximately what is the speed of the bicycle in miles per hour?

12. Find all unknown sides and angles of the triangles ABC. Also, find their areas.
    a. $A = 32.4°$, $B = 47.8°$, $c = 25.3$ b. $B = 28.3°$, $b = 23.5$, $c = 39.2$
    c. $A = 98°24'$, $b = 124.3$, $c = 89.76$ d. $a = 32.5$, $b = 26.8$, $c = 18.6$

13. Prove the identities:

a. $\dfrac{\sin \theta}{\sec \theta - 1} + \dfrac{\sin \theta}{\sec \theta + 1} = 2 \cot \theta$

b. $\dfrac{\sin 2x \cos x}{(1 + \cos 2x) \cos^2(x/2)} = 2 \tan(x/2)$

14. Find all primary solutions:

a. $\sin x + \sin 2x = 0$

b. $\cos 4x = \cos 2x$

15. Find all solutions to the equation $x^3 + 64i = 0$.

16. Evaluate:

a. $\sin[\cos^{-1}(-\tfrac{4}{5}) - \tan^{-1}(-\tfrac{12}{5})]$

b. $\arctan(-2) + \arctan \tfrac{1}{2}$

c. $\cos(\alpha + 2\beta)$, where $\sec \alpha = \tfrac{13}{5}$, $\csc \alpha < 0$, $\cot \beta = 2$, $\sec \beta < 0$

17. Draw the graphs:

a. $y = 1 + 2 \sin\left(\dfrac{x}{2} - \dfrac{\pi}{3}\right)$

b. $y = \tfrac{1}{2} \cos\left(\pi x + \dfrac{\pi}{4}\right)$

18. An airplane leaves an airport at 2:00 P.M. and flies at a heading of 148° at an average cruising speed of 240 miles per hour. Another plane leaves the same airport at 2:15 P.M. with a heading of 25° and cruises at an average speed of 400 miles per hour. If they fly at the same altitude, how far apart are they at 3:30 P.M.?

19. Prove the identities:

a. $\dfrac{2 \cos^3 \theta}{1 + \sin \theta} + \sin 2\theta = 2 \cos \theta$

b. $\tan\left(\dfrac{\alpha}{2} - \dfrac{\pi}{4}\right) = \dfrac{\sin \alpha - 1}{\cos \alpha}$

20. Prove the identities:

a. $\cot \theta \sin 2\theta - \cos 2\theta = 1$

b. $\dfrac{\sin \theta}{1 - \cos \theta} - \tan \dfrac{\theta}{2} = 2 \cot \theta$

21. Draw the graphs:

a. $y = \tfrac{1}{3} \tan(\pi x/2)$

b. $y = \tfrac{1}{2} \sin^{-1}(2x) + \pi/3$

22. Observer A is stationed at a point due west of a monument, and measures the angle of elevation of the top of the monument to be 45°. Observer B is 100 feet due south of observer A, and B measures the angle of elevation of the top of the monument to be 30°. Without using a calculator or tables, find the height of the monument.

23. Find the complete solution set of each of the following:

a. $\sqrt{3} \sin x = \cos x - 1$

b. $\dfrac{\cos 3x}{\sin x} + \dfrac{\sin 3x}{\cos x} = \csc 2x$

24. An offshore oil drilling rig in the Gulf of Mexico is viewed from points A and B on the shore, with the point on the shore nearest the rig lying between A and B. In the triangle formed by the rig and the points A and B, the angle at A is 76°25′, and the angle at B is 68°54′. If A and B are 6 kilometers apart, find the distance from each of these points to the drilling rig. How far is the rig from the nearest point on shore?

25. Show the curves $r = 2 \cos \theta$ and $r^2 = 2\sqrt{3} \sin 2\theta$ on the same polar coordinate system. Crosshatch the area outside the first curve and inside the second, and find all points of intersection.

26. Prove that the area of the parallelogram having the vectors $\mathbf{V}$ and $\mathbf{W}$ as adjacent sides is $|\mathbf{V}| |\mathbf{W}| \sin \theta$, where θ is the angle between $\mathbf{V}$ and $\mathbf{W}$.

27. In the accompanying figure, triangle ABC is in the horizontal plane and line CD is vertical. If side c and angles α, β, and ϕ are known, derive the following formula for the length h of side CD:

$$h = \frac{c \sin \alpha \tan \phi}{\sin(\alpha + \beta)}$$

If $c = 21.34$, $\alpha = 18°37'$, $\beta = 43°16'$, and $\phi = 56°42'$, find h. Also find angle θ.

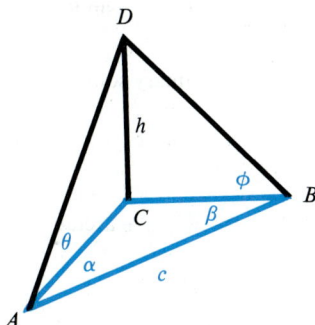

28. The pilot of a small airplane flew from town A to town B and returned the following day. The bearing of B from A is N 42.3° E, and its distance from A is 452 miles. On the trip from A to B, a 33.4 mile per hour wind was blowing from 270°; on the return trip the wind was from 305° at 29.7 miles per hour. If the pilot cruised at 182 miles per hour airspeed, find her heading on each leg of the trip. Also find her total time in the air.

10 Systems of Equations and Inequalities

Systems of equations and inequalities occur in many applications in the physical, social, and life sciences. The following example illustrates a system of linear equations occurring in a biology problem.*

Coexistence of Bacteria. Three species of bacteria coexist in a test tube and feed on three resources. Suppose that a bacterium of the ith species consumes on average an amount c_{ij} of the jth resource per day. Define $c_i = (c_{i1}, c_{i2}, c_{i3})$ to be the consumption vector for the ith species. Suppose that $c_1 = (1, 1, 1)$, $c_2 = (1, 2, 3)$, and $c_3 = (1, 3, 5)$ and suppose that there are 15,000 units of the first resource supplied each day to the test tube, 30,000 units of the second resource, and 45,000 units of the third resource. Assuming that all the resources are consumed, what are the populations of the three species that can coexist in this environment?

Solution Let x_1, x_2, and x_3 be the population of the three species that can be supported by the resources. The x_1 individuals of the first species consume x_1 units of each resource. The x_2 bacteria of the second species consume x_2, $2x_2$, and $3x_2$ units of the first, second, and third resources, respectively. The corresponding consumptions of the third species are x_3, $3x_3$, and $5x_3$ units. Equating the total consumption of each resource to the amount available, we obtain

$$\begin{aligned} x_1 + x_2 + x_3 &= 15{,}000 \\ x_1 + 2x_2 + 3x_3 &= 30{,}000 \\ x_1 + 3x_2 + 5x_3 &= 45{,}000. \end{aligned}$$

... This system does not have a unique solution but $x_1 = x_3 = (15{,}000 - x_2)/2$. The bacteria populations must be nonnegative. Therefore, $0 \le x_2 \le 15{,}000$ and $0 \le x_1 = x_3 \le 7500$. The total population that can coexist is 15,000, and the populations of the three species satisfy $x_1 = x_3$ and $x_2 = 15{,}000 - 2x_1$ if all resources are consumed.

In this chapter we will learn to solve such a system. We will see that a system such as this—in which two unknowns are found as a function of the third—is an example of what is called a *dependent system*.

---

* Reprinted with permission of Macmillan Publishing Co., Inc. from *Mathematics for the Biological Sciences* by Stanley I. Grossman and James E. Turner, pp. 132–133. Copyright © 1974 by Macmillan Publishing Co., Inc.

1   Linear Systems

We saw in Chapter 5 that the general form of the equation of a line is

$$Ax + By + C = 0$$

This is also called a **general linear equation in two variables.** The word *linear* continues to apply, however, regardless of the number of variables as long as the equation is of degree 1. Thus, $2x - 3y + 4z = 0$ and $5x_1 - 2x_2 + 3x_3 - 4x_4 + 8x_5 = 2$ are linear, whereas $x^2 - 2x + 3y = 4$, $xy - 3x + 4y - 7$, and $\sqrt{x_1} + x_2 = 4$ are not. Techniques for solving **systems of linear equations** form the basis of a large part of what is called **linear algebra.** A complete treatment of linear systems is not appropriate in this course, but a review of techniques studied in high school algebra, with an introduction to more advanced techniques, is in order.

We consider first **two linear equations in two variables.** For example,

$$\begin{cases} 2x - 3y = 4 \\ 5x + 4y = 7 \end{cases}$$

Our object is to find all pairs (x, y) that simultaneously satisfy both equations. The collection of all such pairs is the solution to the system. In this context we will refer to x and y as the unknowns, since we are seeking to determine values for them.

Since two linear equations correspond geometrically to two lines, we can reason in advance that one of three situations will occur:

1.   The lines intersect in one and only one point, and its coordinates constitute the unique solution. The equations are said to be **consistent.**
2.   The lines are parallel and hence do not intersect, so there is no simultaneous solution. The equations are said to be **inconsistent.**
3.   The lines coincide and hence intersect at infinitely many points, so there are infinitely many solutions. The equations are said to be linearly **dependent.**

Let us consider the example given above.

EXAMPLE 1   Solve the system: $\begin{cases} 2x - 3y = 4 \\ 5x + 4y = 7 \end{cases}$

Solution   By appropriate multiplications and additions or subtractions, we seek to eliminate one of the unknowns. One way is to multiply the top equation by 4 and the bottom equation by 3 and then add the resulting equations, thus eliminating y:

$$\begin{array}{r} 8x - 12y = 16 \\ 15x + 12y = 21 \\ \hline 23x \quad\quad\; = 37 \\ x = \tfrac{37}{23} \end{array}$$

This is the x coordinate of a point on both lines; we can therefore find the y coordinate by substituting into either equation. By substituting in the first equation, we have

$$2(\tfrac{37}{23}) - 3y = 4$$
$$-3y = \tfrac{18}{23}$$
$$y = \tfrac{-6}{23}$$

So this problem illustrates a consistent system. There is a unique solution $(\tfrac{37}{23}, \tfrac{-6}{23})$. The situation is graphed in Figure 1.

Figure 1

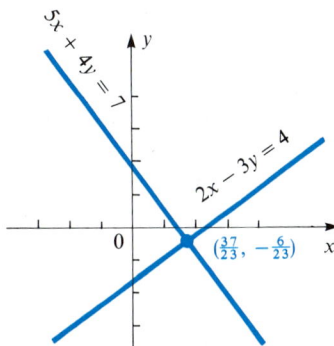

The technique used to solve the system in Example 1 is known as **elimination.** We eliminated y from the two equations and obtained an equation in x alone. Then we were able to solve for x, and y was found by substituting this value of x into one of the original equations. In general, to eliminate an unknown we use one of two methods: elimination by addition or subtraction, or elimination by substitution.

To eliminate an unknown from two equations by addition or subtraction, the coefficients of that unknown must be the same in absolute value. If they are not the same, then we make them the same by multiplying the equations by appropriate numbers. In Example 1 we multiplied both sides of the first equation by 4 and both sides of the second equation by 3. When the coefficients are the same in absolute value, we *add* if the coefficients are opposite in sign (as in Example 1) and *subtract* if they are like in sign.

To eliminate an unknown from two equations by substitution, we solve one of the equations for that unknown in terms of the other (or others) and substitute this into the other equation. Consider, for example, the system

$$\begin{cases} 3x - 4y = 7 \\ 2x - y = 3 \end{cases}$$

We can solve the second equation for y to get $y = 2x - 3$ and then substitute $2x - 3$ in place of y in the first equation:

$$3x - 4(2x - 3) = 7$$
$$3x - 8x + 12 = 7$$
$$-5x = -5$$
$$x = 1$$

Having found x, we obtain y from $y = 2x - 3$. This gives

$$y = 2(1) - 3$$
$$= -1$$

So this is a consistent system with unique solution $(1, -1)$.

The next two examples illustrate inconsistent and dependent systems, respectively.

EXAMPLE 2   Solve the system: $\begin{cases} 2x - 3y = 4 \\ 4x - 6y = 15 \end{cases}$

Solution   After multiplying both sides of the top equation by 2 and subtracting, we get $0 = -7$, which is clearly impossible. There is no simultaneous solution; that is, the lines are parallel. In fact, we could have seen in advance that the two lines had the same slope. The situation is graphed in Figure 2.

Figure 2

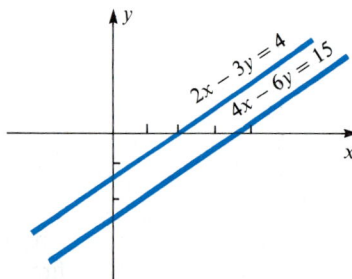

EXAMPLE 3   Solve the system: $\begin{cases} 2x - 3y = 4 \\ 4x - 6y = 8 \end{cases}$

Solution   This system differs from the one in Example 2 only in the fact that the entire second equation is obtainable from the first by multiplying both sides by 2. But this means that the second equation is really equivalent to the first and so has the same graph. Attempting to solve simultaneously would yield $0 = 0$. This is an example of a dependent system. We could say that the simultaneous solutions are the pairs (x, y) corresponding to all points on the line given by either equation. From the first equation we can solve for y to get

$$y = \frac{2x - 4}{3}$$

Now let x take on an arbitrary value, say, $x = c$; then $y = (2c - 4)/3$. So we could say that the solution set is the set of all pairs

$$\left(c, \frac{2c - 4}{3} \right)$$

where c may range over all real numbers.

Remark. The form of the solution set for a dependent system is not unique. We can see this from the preceding example by solving the first equation for x, rather than y, getting

$$x = \frac{3y + 4}{2}$$

Then if we let y be any real number c, we can write the solution set as the set of all ordered pairs of the form

$$\left(\frac{3c + 4}{2}, c \right)$$

where c is any real number. Even though this solution looks different from the solution found in Example 3, when we allow c to range over all real numbers, the set of ordered pairs obtained from either solution is the same as the set obtained from the other.

EXAMPLE 4   Solve the system:
$$\begin{cases} x + 2y + z = 3 \\ 2x - y - z = 0 \\ 3x + 4y + 2z = 8 \end{cases}$$

Solution   We will again use the process of elimination. The object is to eliminate the *same* unknown from two pairs of equations, thus obtaining two equations in two unknowns. Then one further elimination enables us to find one of the unknowns, and the others are found by substitution.

It appears that z would be particularly easy to eliminate in this case. We add corresponding sides of the first two equations:

$$\begin{array}{l} x + 2y + z = 3 \\ \underline{2x - y - z = 0} \\ 3x + y = 3 \end{array} \qquad (1)$$

Now returning to the original system, we must eliminate z from another pair of equations. It is essential to stay with z so that a second equation containing only x and y can be obtained. We multiply both sides of the second equation by 2 and add it to the third:

$$\begin{array}{l} 4x - 2y - 2z = 0 \\ \underline{3x + 4y + 2z = 8} \\ 7x + 2y = 8 \end{array} \qquad (2)$$

Now we wish to solve equations (1) and (2) simultaneously, and to this end we multiply both sides of equation (1) by -2 and add the result to equation (2):

$$\begin{array}{l} -6x - 2y = -6 \\ \underline{7x + 2y = 8} \\ x = 2 \end{array}$$

Having found x, we can substitute in either equation (1) or (2) to find y. We select (1):

$$3(2) + y = 3$$

$$y = -3$$

Finally, we substitute both x and y into any one of the original equations in order to find z. From the first equation we get

$$2 + 2(-3) + z = 3$$
$$2 - 6 + z = 3$$
$$z = 7$$

The final answer for the simultaneous solution is the triple $(2, -3, 7)$, that is, $x = 2$, $y = -3$, and $z = 7$.

Keeping track of things in the case of three equations and three unknowns is difficult enough, but with more than three the difficulty increases rapidly. For example, with four equations, three pairs are selected and from each pair the *same* unknown is eliminated. The result is a system of three equations in three unknowns, which is solved as in Example 4. When the three unknowns are found, they are substituted into any one of the original equations to find the fourth unknown.

Equations in two or more unknowns often arise in real-world problems. Sometimes problems that could be treated with one unknown are easier to handle with two, as illustrated in the following examples.

EXAMPLE 5   A saline solution containing 5% salt is to be mixed with one containing 8% salt to obtain 5 liters of a 6% salt solution. How many liters of each solution should be used?

Solution   Let

$$x = \text{Number of liters of 5\% solution required}$$
$$y = \text{Number of liters of 8\% solution required}$$

Then

$$0.05x = \text{Amount of pure salt in first solution}$$
$$0.08y = \text{Amount of pure salt in second solution}$$
$$(0.06)5 = \text{Amount of pure salt in final solution}$$

We need two equations relating x and y. Since there are to be 5 liters in all, we must have

$$x + y = 5$$

Further, the amount of pure salt from the two components must equal the amount of pure salt in the final mixture:

$$0.05x + 0.08y = (0.06)5$$

or, after multiplying by 100 and simplifying,

$$5x + 8y = 30$$

So the system we wish to solve is

$$\begin{cases} x + y = 5 \\ 5x + 8y = 30 \end{cases}$$

By multiplying both sides of the top equation by 5 and subtracting from the bottom, we get

$$5x + 8y = 30$$
$$\underline{5x + 5y = 25}$$
$$3y = 5$$
$$y = \tfrac{5}{3}$$

Finally,

$$x = 5 - y = 5 - \frac{5}{3} = \frac{15 - 5}{3} = \frac{10}{3}$$

So $3\tfrac{1}{3}$ liters of the 5% solution are needed, and $1\tfrac{2}{3}$ liters of the 8% solution are needed.

EXAMPLE 6

A boy rows 6 miles upstream in 1 hour and 20 minutes, and the return trip takes 1 hour. Find how fast he can row in still water and find the rate of the current.

Solution Let

$$x = \text{Rate in miles per hour that the boy can row in still water}$$
$$y = \text{Rate in miles per hour of the current}$$

Then

$$x - y = \text{Actual rate of progress upstream}$$
$$x + y = \text{Actual rate of progress downstream}$$

We apply the fundamental relation $d = rt$ two times, once for going upstream and once for going downstream:

$$\begin{cases} 6 = (x - y) \cdot \tfrac{4}{3} \\ 6 = (x + y) \cdot 1 \end{cases} \qquad (\tfrac{4}{3} \text{ hours} = 1 \text{ hour and 20 minutes})$$

These can be simplified to the form

$$\begin{cases} 2x - 2y = 9 \\ x + y = 6 \end{cases}$$

The solution is now easily found:

$$2x - 2y = 9$$
$$\underline{2x + 2y = 12}$$
$$4x = 21$$
$$x = \tfrac{21}{4}$$

So

$$y = 6 - \frac{21}{4} = \frac{24 - 21}{4} = \frac{3}{4}$$

The boy can row $5\tfrac{1}{4}$ miles per hour in still water, and the rate of the current is $\tfrac{3}{4}$ mile per hour.

EXAMPLE 7   Joan has a tractor mower and Charles has a hand-operated power mower. They regularly mow a certain large lawn in 4 hours by working together. On one occasion, after working together for 3 hours on the lawn, Joan's mower breaks down, and it takes Charles another 3 hours to finish the job alone. How long would it take each of them to do the entire job alone?

Solution   Let

$$x = \text{Number of hours for Joan alone}$$

$$y = \text{Number of hours for Charles alone}$$

Then

$$\frac{1}{x} = \text{Fractional part of the job Joan does per hour}$$

$$\frac{1}{y} = \text{Fractional part of the job Charles does per hour}$$

If each works 4 hours, the entire job is done:

$$\frac{4}{x} + \frac{4}{y} = 1$$

When Joan works only 3 hours, Charles has to work an additional 3 hours, or 6 hours in all, to accomplish the entire job:

$$\frac{3}{x} + \frac{6}{y} = 1$$

Now we have the system

$$\begin{cases} \dfrac{4}{x} + \dfrac{4}{y} = 1 \\[2mm] \dfrac{3}{x} + \dfrac{6}{y} = 1 \end{cases}$$

These are not linear equations, but we can use the same techniques we used above to solve them. It is probably easiest in this situation not to clear the fractions at the outset. We multiply the top equation by 3 and the bottom one by 4:

$$\frac{12}{x} + \frac{12}{y} = 3$$

$$\frac{12}{x} + \frac{24}{y} = 4$$

Now we subtract the top equation from the bottom one to obtain

$$\frac{12}{y} = 1$$

Clearing the fractions now yields $y = 12$. We may substitute into either of the original equations. We choose the first:

$$\frac{4}{x} + \frac{4}{12} = 1$$

$$\frac{4}{x} = \frac{2}{3}$$

$$x = 6$$

So Joan could do the job alone in 6 hours, and Charles could do it alone in 12 hours.

EXAMPLE 8

The units digit of a two-digit number is 1 less than twice the tens digit. If the digits are reversed, the new number is 27 greater than the old number. Find the original number.

Solution   Let

$$x = \text{Tens digit}$$
$$y = \text{Units digit}$$

Then

$$10x + y = \text{Original number}$$
$$10y + x = \text{Number with digits reversed}$$

Thus, from the given information,

$$y = 2x - 1$$
$$10y + x = 10x + y + 27$$

After simplifying the second equation, the system to be solved can be written in the form

$$\begin{cases} y = 2x - 1 \\ x - y = -3 \end{cases}$$

We eliminate y by substitution from the first equation into the second:

$$x - (2x - 1) = -3$$
$$-x + 1 = -3$$
$$x = 4$$

So $y = 2(4) - 1 = 7$. Thus, the original number is 47.

Remark.   In Example 8 we wrote the number as $10x + y$, since in our positional system the tens digit is understood to be multiplied by 10. Thus, 47 means $(4 \times 10) + 7$. Similarly, if x were the hundreds digit, y the tens digit, and z the units digit of a number, we would indicate the number as $100x + 10y + z$.

EXERCISE SET 1

A   In Problems 1–22 solve the systems.

1. $\begin{cases} x - y = 2 \\ x + y = 6 \end{cases}$

2. $\begin{cases} x + 2y = -4 \\ x - 3y = 6 \end{cases}$

3. $\begin{cases} 3x - y = 0 \\ 5x - 2y = 1 \end{cases}$
4. $\begin{cases} 2x - 3y = 18 \\ 3x + 4y = -7 \end{cases}$

5. $\begin{cases} 3x - 2y = 6 \\ x + 2y = 10 \end{cases}$
6. $\begin{cases} 2x - y = -2 \\ 3x + 2y = 1 \end{cases}$

7. $\begin{cases} 4x - y = 6 \\ 3x + 2y = 5 \end{cases}$
8. $\begin{cases} 5s - 2t = 4 \\ 3s - 2t = 0 \end{cases}$

9. $\begin{cases} 2x + 3y = 2 \\ 3x - 4y = 20 \end{cases}$
10. $\begin{cases} 5x + 2y = 8 \\ 7x - 3y = -12 \end{cases}$

11. $\begin{cases} 5s + 4t = -1 \\ 2s - 3t = -28 \end{cases}$
12. $\begin{cases} 5m - 2n = -2 \\ 4m + 5n = 16 \end{cases}$

13. $\begin{cases} x + 3y - 2z = -1 \\ 2x - y + 3z = 5 \\ -x + 5y - 4z = 1 \end{cases}$
14. $\begin{cases} 2x - 3y - 4z = -4 \\ 3x + 4y + 2z = 1 \\ 5x - 2y - 3z = 0 \end{cases}$

15. $\begin{cases} 2x + y + z = 7 \\ x - y + 2z = 11 \\ 5x + y - 2z = 1 \end{cases}$
16. $\begin{cases} 3x + 4y - z = 4 \\ 2x - 5y + 3z = -10 \\ 4x + 3y + z = 10 \end{cases}$

17. $\begin{cases} 2x + 3y + 3z = 9 \\ 5x - 2y + 8z = 6 \\ 4x - y + 5z = -1 \end{cases}$
18. $\begin{cases} 2x + 4y + 3z = -2 \\ x - 3y + 4z = 9 \\ 5x + 7y - z = -9 \end{cases}$

19. $\begin{cases} \dfrac{2}{x} - \dfrac{3}{y} = 4 \\ \dfrac{1}{x} + \dfrac{4}{y} = -10 \end{cases}$
20. $\begin{cases} \dfrac{2}{x} + \dfrac{3}{y} = -2 \\ \dfrac{5}{x} + \dfrac{4}{y} = \dfrac{5}{6} \end{cases}$

21. $\begin{cases} ax + by = c \\ bx - ay = d \end{cases}$
22. $\begin{cases} x + y = -1 \\ y + 3z = 2 \\ 4z - w = 0 \\ 2x - w = 0 \end{cases}$

In Problems 23 and 24 show that the system is dependent, and give the solution set. Draw the graph.

23. $\begin{cases} 3x - 4y = 5 \\ 8y - 6x + 10 = 0 \end{cases}$
24. $\begin{cases} 4x - 10y = 14 \\ -6x + 15y = 21 \end{cases}$

Show that the systems in Problems 25 and 26 are inconsistent, and draw their graphs.

25. $\begin{cases} 8x - 6y = 3 \\ 3y - 4x = 2 \end{cases}$
26. $\begin{cases} 8x - 10y = 7 \\ -12x + 15y = 11 \end{cases}$

27. Show that the following system is consistent. Draw the graph.

$$\begin{cases} 2x + 5y = 4 \\ x - 2y = -7 \\ 5x + 8y = 1 \end{cases}$$

28. Show that the lines whose equations are $2x - 3y = 0$, $4x + 5y = 22$, and $3x - 2y = 5$ intersect at a common point. Draw their graphs.

29. Find the two numbers whose sum is 127 and whose difference is 63.

30. The difference between two numbers is 5. Three times the larger number minus four times the smaller number is 1. Find the numbers.

31. The perimeter of a certain rectangle is 24. If the width were doubled and the length tripled, the perimeter would be 64. Find the length and width.

32. The length of a rectangle is 10 more than twice the width, and the perimeter is 50. Find the length and width.

33. Flying with the wind, an airplane makes a 1,500 mile trip in 2 hours and 30 minutes. The return trip takes 3 hours and 20 minutes. Find the average airspeed of the airplane and the average wind velocity.

34. Rowing with the current, a 10 mile trip on a river takes a boy 1 hour and 20 minutes. The return trip takes 4 hours. Find how fast the boy can row in still water and the rate of the current.

35. A girl covered a distance of $3\frac{1}{4}$ miles by alternating between jogging and walking. She walked a total of 15 minutes and jogged a total of 30 minutes. The next day she walked a total of 30 minutes and jogged 45 minutes, covering a total distance of $5\frac{1}{4}$ miles. Assuming her rates of walking and of jogging remained the same from one day to the next, find these rates.

36. The sum of the digits of a certain two-digit number is 10. By interchanging the units and tens digits, the value of the number is increased by 36. Find the number.

37. The sum of the digits of a two-digit number is 14. If the digits are reversed, the value of the number is decreased by 18. Find the number.

38. By working together for 4 hours Bill and his younger brother Tom weed one-half of a large garden. The next day they work together for 2 hours, and then Tom gets tired and quits. It takes Bill an additional 3 hours to complete the job. How long would it have taken Bill to weed the entire garden alone? How long would it have taken Tom?

39. A roofer estimates that he and his assistant working together can roof a house in 4 hours. They work together for $2\frac{1}{2}$ hours, when the assistant becomes ill and has to quit. It takes the roofer another $2\frac{1}{2}$ hours to finish the job. How long would it have taken the roofer alone to do the entire job?

40. A man has a total of $5,000 invested in two ways. Part is in a savings account earning 5% interest, and the rest is in a certificate of deposit earning 6% interest. If the earnings for the first year total $286, find how much is invested in each account.

41. A woman has two investments, one yielding 5% interest and one 7% interest annually. The amount at 7% lacks $1,000 of being double the amount at 5%. The total interest after 1 year is $690. Find how much she has invested in each account.

42. A customer in a coffee house wants a blend of two kinds of coffee: Colombian, selling at $4.00 per pound, and Brazilian, selling for $3.60 per pound. He gets 4 pounds of the blend, and the cost is $15.40. How many pounds of each kind did he buy?

43. A chemist wishes to mix a solution containing 10% sulfuric acid with a solution containing 25% sulfuric acid. She wants 30 cubic centimeters in all, and she wants the final mixture to be 18% sulfuric acid. How much of each concentration should she use?

44. An alloy that is 35% copper is to be combined with an alloy that is 60% copper to obtain 180 pounds of an alloy that is 50% copper. How many pounds of each kind of alloy should be used?

45. Twenty pounds of English breakfast tea is to be made by blending Indian and Ceylon teas. The Indian tea is priced at $6.25 per pound, and the Ceylon tea at $7.00 per pound. The price of the English breakfast tea is to be $6.60 per pound. How much Indian tea and how much Ceylon tea should be used?

46. The prices of tickets at a movie theater are $2.75 for adults and $1.50 for children. For a certain show there were 400 tickets sold for a total of $875. How many adults and how many children attended?

47. Four pounds of a certain brand of coffee and three dozen large eggs cost $19.70. Two pounds of the same brand of coffee and four dozen large eggs cost $12.10. Find the cost of 1 pound of the coffee and one dozen large eggs.

B In Problems 48–52 solve the systems,

48. $\begin{cases} 3x - 2y + 4z = 5 \\ 2x + 3y - 2z = 6 \\ 4x - 5y + 3z = -5 \end{cases}$

49. $\begin{cases} 3x + 5y - 7z = 6 \\ 4x - 2y + 8z = -5 \\ 6x + 7y - 3z = 4 \end{cases}$

50. $\begin{cases} 5x - 2y + 3z = 6 \\ 6x - 3y + 4z = 10 \\ -4x + 4y - 9z = 4 \end{cases}$

51. $\begin{cases} x + 2y - 3z - 2w = 1 \\ 3x - 4y + z - w = 3 \\ 2x + 4z + 3w = 4 \\ 3y - 2z + w = 10 \end{cases}$

52. $\begin{cases} 2x + 4y - z - 3w = 6 \\ x + 3y + 2z + 4w = -4 \\ 3x - 5y + 3z + 2w = 13 \\ 4x - 6y + z - 3w = 22 \end{cases}$

53. Show that the following system is inconsistent:

$$\begin{cases} 3x - 2y + 4z = 5 \\ 4x - y + 2z = 3 \\ x + y - 2z = 7 \end{cases}$$

In Problems 54 and 55 show that the system is dependent and give the solution set.

54. $\begin{cases} x - 3y + 4z = -1 \\ 2x + y - 5z = 3 \\ 7x - 7y + 2z = 3 \end{cases}$

55. $\begin{cases} 2x - 3y + 4z - w = 3 \\ x + y - 3z + 2w = -1 \\ 3x - y - 3z + 8w = 5 \end{cases}$

56. Find a, b, and c so that the parabola $y = ax^2 + bx + c$ passes through the points $(1, -5)$, $(-2, 10)$, and $(3, 5)$.

57. Let $f(x) = ax^2 + bx + c$. If $f(2) = 5$, $f(-1) = 2$, and $f(4) = -3$, find a, b, and c.

58. A car leaves town A going toward town B, which is 50 miles away on a straight road. At the same time, two cars leave B, one going toward A and one going away from A, both traveling at the same rate of speed. The car that left from town A meets the car going from B toward A after 30 minutes, and overtakes the one going from B away from A after $2\frac{1}{2}$ hours. Find the speed of each car.

59. A commuter finds that if she leaves the office 5 minutes earlier than usual, she can average 36 miles per hour and arrive home 10 minutes earlier than usual. However, if she leaves the office 5 minutes later than usual, she can only average 25 miles per hour and arrives home 11 minutes later than usual. Find the time it normally takes her to get home and the distance from the office to her home.

60. Brine containing 40% salt is diluted by adding pure water, resulting in a 25% salt solution. Then 20 more gallons of pure water are added, diluting the mixture to a 20% salt solution. Find how much brine there was originally and how many gallons of water were added the first time.

61. Pumps A, B, and C working simultaneously can fill a tank in 10 hours. Pumps B and C working together can fill it in 15 hours. If all three pumps work together for 4 hours and then pump C is shut off, it takes 8 more hours to fill the tank. How long would it take each pump alone to fill the tank?

2 Reduction to Triangular Form and the Use of Matrices

We will illustrate by means of the following example a technique for solving linear systems that makes the elimination of unknowns more systematic. This procedure is especially useful for systems of more than three equations and three unknowns.

EXAMPLE 9   Solve the system:
$$\begin{cases} x + 2y + 3z + 2w = 1 \\ x + 3y - z - 2w = -1 \\ 2x + 3y - 2z - w = 7 \\ 3x + 4y + z - w = -4 \end{cases}$$

Solution   The first step is to eliminate x from the bottom three equations. This is accomplished by adding to each of these, in turn, certain multiples of the first equation. Thus, we add to the second equation -1 times the first, to the third -2 times the first, and to the fourth -3 times the first. The result is the new system

$$x + 2y + 3z + 2w = 1$$
$$y - 4z - 4w = -2$$
$$-y - 8z - 5w = 5$$
$$-2y - 8z - 7w = -7$$

Next we eliminate y from the bottom two equations by adding the second equation to the third and then adding to the fourth equation 2 times the second:

$$x + 2y + 3z + 2w = 1$$
$$y - 4z - 4w = -2$$
$$-12z - 9w = 3$$
$$-16z - 15w = -11$$

The third equation can be simplified by dividing by -3:

$$x + 2y + 3z + 2w = 1$$
$$y - 4z - 4w = -2$$
$$4z + 3w = -1$$
$$-16z - 15w = -11$$

Now we eliminate z from the bottom equation by adding to it 4 times the third:

$$x + 2y + 3z + 2w = 1$$
$$y - 4z - 4w = -2$$
$$4z + 3w = -1$$
$$-3w = -15$$

The system is now in what is called **triangular form** and can be solved by working from the bottom up. We obtain from the last equation $w = 5$. Then, substituting this in the third equation, we get

$$4z + 15 = -1$$
$$4z = -16$$
$$z = -4$$

Substituting both w and z into the second equation yields

$$y + 16 - 20 = -2$$
$$y = 2$$

Finally, we get from the first equation

$$x + 4 - 12 + 10 = 1$$
$$x = -1$$

The desired solution, then, is given by the array $(-1, 2, -4, 5)$, where it is understood that the values shown are for $x, y, z,$ and $w,$ respectively.

Students should be warned that not all systems reduce to triangular form as easily as the one in Example 9. The arithmetic necessary to eliminate the desired unknowns often is more complicated. But this method always works, and it is systematic.

We will show an abbreviated version of Example 9 below, but before doing so, it will be useful to list the admissible operations for solving a system of equations. Any of the following change the system to an equivalent one, that is, to one having the same solution set:

1. Both sides of any equation may be multiplied by a nonzero number.
2. Two equations may be interchanged.
3. A multiple of any equation may be added to any other equation.

Now let us return to the original system in Example 9:

$$\begin{cases} x + 2y + 3z + 2w = 1 \\ x + 3y - z - 2w = -1 \\ 2x + 3y - 2z - w = 7 \\ 3x + 4y + z - w = -4 \end{cases}$$

We are going to represent this by means of the coefficients and the constant terms only, with the understanding that whenever it is convenient to do so, we can reinsert the letters representing the unknowns. We write this as follows:

$$\begin{bmatrix} 1 & 2 & 3 & 2 & | & 1 \\ 1 & 3 & -1 & -2 & | & -1 \\ 2 & 3 & -2 & -1 & | & 7 \\ 3 & 4 & 1 & -1 & | & -4 \end{bmatrix}$$

The vertical line is used to indicate the separation of the left-hand sides from the right. Such an array of numbers is called a **matrix,** and when used to represent a system of equations, as in the present case, it is called an **augmented matrix.** This description is used to distinguish the full matrix shown from the **coefficient matrix** only, that is,

$$\begin{bmatrix} 1 & 2 & 3 & 2 \\ 1 & 3 & -1 & -2 \\ 2 & 3 & -2 & -1 \\ 3 & 4 & 1 & -1 \end{bmatrix}$$

Now we are going to retrace the steps shown in Example 9 using the augmented matrix. We show 0 where a coefficient is eliminated. A brief indication of each step is given as a reminder of what was done to the preceding matrix to get the current one. First, we exhibit again the augmented matrix.

$$\left[\begin{array}{cccc|c} 1 & 2 & 3 & 2 & 1 \\ 1 & 3 & -1 & -2 & -1 \\ 2 & 3 & -2 & -1 & 7 \\ 3 & 4 & 1 & -1 & -4 \end{array}\right]$$

$$\left[\begin{array}{cccc|c} 1 & 2 & 3 & 2 & 1 \\ 0 & 1 & -4 & -4 & -2 \\ 0 & -1 & -8 & -5 & 5 \\ 0 & -2 & -8 & -7 & -7 \end{array}\right] \begin{array}{l} \\ \text{Row } 2 + [(-1) \cdot \text{Row } 1] \\ \text{Row } 3 + [(-2) \cdot \text{Row } 1] \\ \text{Row } 4 + [(-3) \cdot \text{Row } 1] \end{array}$$

$$\left[\begin{array}{cccc|c} 1 & 2 & 3 & 2 & 1 \\ 0 & 1 & -4 & -4 & -2 \\ 0 & 0 & -12 & -9 & 3 \\ 0 & 0 & -16 & -15 & -11 \end{array}\right] \begin{array}{l} \\ \\ \text{Row } 3 + (1 \cdot \text{Row } 2) \\ \text{Row } 4 + (2 \cdot \text{Row } 2) \end{array}$$

$$\left[\begin{array}{cccc|c} 1 & 2 & 3 & 2 & 1 \\ 0 & 1 & -4 & -4 & -2 \\ 0 & 0 & 4 & 3 & -1 \\ 0 & 0 & -16 & -15 & -11 \end{array}\right] \begin{array}{l} \\ \\ \text{Row } 3 \cdot (-\tfrac{1}{3}) \\ \\ \end{array}$$

$$\left[\begin{array}{cccc|c} 1 & 2 & 3 & 2 & 1 \\ 0 & 1 & -4 & -4 & -2 \\ 0 & 0 & 4 & 3 & -1 \\ 0 & 0 & 0 & -3 & -15 \end{array}\right] \begin{array}{l} \\ \\ \\ \text{Row } 4 + (4 \cdot \text{Row } 3) \end{array}$$

The matrix is now in triangular form, so we are ready to find the solution to the system. The last row of the matrix represents the equation

$$-3w = -15$$

so that $w = 5$. In turn we write the other equations, from the bottom up, and substitute known values as before.

EXAMPLE 10   Solve the system: $\begin{cases} 3x + 2y - 4z = -7 \\ 7x - 8y - 5z = 5 \\ -8x + 5y + 6z = -1 \end{cases}$

Solution   The augmented matrix is

$$\left[\begin{array}{ccc|c} 3 & 2 & -4 & -7 \\ 7 & -8 & -5 & 5 \\ -8 & 5 & 6 & -1 \end{array}\right]$$

It is an advantage to have 1 or -1 as the first element in Row 1, since it is then easy to choose appropriate multiples to eliminate the elements below it. We can always make the first element 1 by multiplying the first row by its reciprocal; in this case we would multiply by $\frac{1}{3}$. But this would introduce fractions, and it is generally simpler to avoid doing this. In this case we can add Row 2 to Row 3 and then interchange Rows 1 and 3:

$$\left[\begin{array}{ccc|c} 3 & 2 & -4 & -7 \\ 7 & -8 & -5 & 5 \\ -1 & -3 & 1 & 4 \end{array}\right] \quad \text{Row 3 + Row 2}$$

$$\left[\begin{array}{ccc|c} -1 & -3 & 1 & 4 \\ 7 & -8 & -5 & 5 \\ 3 & 2 & -4 & -7 \end{array}\right] \quad \begin{array}{l} \text{Row 3 interchanged with Row 1} \\ \\ \text{Row 1 interchanged with Row 3} \end{array}$$

Now we proceed to introduce zeros under the -1:

$$\left[\begin{array}{ccc|c} -1 & -3 & 1 & 4 \\ 0 & -29 & 2 & 33 \\ 0 & -7 & -1 & 5 \end{array}\right] \quad \begin{array}{l} \text{Row 2 + (7 · Row 1)} \\ \text{Row 3 + (3 · Row 1)} \end{array}$$

We are faced with messy arithmetic now unless we make some further simplifying moves. It appears that if we add -4 times Row 3 to Row 2, things will improve significantly:

$$\left[\begin{array}{ccc|c} -1 & -3 & 1 & 4 \\ 0 & -1 & 6 & 13 \\ 0 & -7 & -1 & 5 \end{array}\right] \quad \text{Row 2 + [(−4) · Row 3]}$$

Finally, we add -7 times Row 2 to Row 3:

$$\left[\begin{array}{ccc|c} -1 & -3 & 1 & 4 \\ 0 & -1 & 6 & 13 \\ 0 & 0 & -43 & -86 \end{array}\right] \quad \text{Row 3 + [(−7) · Row 2]}$$

The third equation now reads

$$-43z = -86$$

so

$$z = 2$$

The second equation is
$$-y + 6z = 13$$
which on substituting $z = 2$ yields
$$y = -1$$
The first equation can now be solved for x:
$$-x - 3y + z = 4$$
$$-x + 3 + 2 = 4$$
$$-x = -1$$
$$x = 1$$

The desired solution is $(1, -1, 2)$.

The techniques to simplify the arithmetic illustrated in this example should be kept in mind as you do problems by this method.

EXAMPLE 11   Solve the system below by reducing the augmented matrix to triangular form.

$$\begin{cases} 4x_1 + 11x_2 + 6x_3 + 22x_4 = 16 \\ x_1 + 2x_2 \qquad\quad + \quad x_4 = 7 \\ 2x_1 + 5x_2 + x_3 + 10x_4 = 7 \end{cases}$$

Solution   This example will show that the method we are employing will work even when the number of unknowns is different from the number of equations. To save one step we will mentally interchange the first two equations before writing the matrix:

$$\begin{bmatrix} 1 & 2 & 0 & 1 & \bigm| & 7 \\ 4 & 11 & 6 & 22 & \bigm| & 16 \\ 2 & 5 & 1 & 10 & \bigm| & 7 \end{bmatrix}$$

$$\begin{bmatrix} 1 & 2 & 0 & 1 & \bigm| & 7 \\ 0 & 3 & 6 & 18 & \bigm| & -12 \\ 0 & 1 & 1 & 8 & \bigm| & -7 \end{bmatrix} \quad \begin{matrix} \text{Row } 2 + [(-4) \cdot \text{Row } 1] \\ \text{Row } 3 + [(-2) \cdot \text{Row } 1] \end{matrix}$$

We could now interchange Rows 2 and 3, but we choose to multiply Row 2 by $\frac{1}{3}$ instead:

$$\begin{bmatrix} 1 & 2 & 0 & 1 & \bigm| & 7 \\ 0 & 1 & 2 & 6 & \bigm| & -4 \\ 0 & 1 & 1 & 8 & \bigm| & -7 \end{bmatrix}$$

Now we subtract Row 2 from Row 3:

$$\begin{bmatrix} 1 & 2 & 0 & 1 & \bigm| & 7 \\ 0 & 1 & 2 & 6 & \bigm| & -4 \\ 0 & 0 & -1 & 2 & \bigm| & -3 \end{bmatrix}$$

This is as far as we can go in the triangular form. The third equation now reads

$$-x_3 + 2x_4 = -3$$

While this cannot be solved for x_3 as a specific number, it can be solved in terms of x_4:

$$x_3 = 3 + 2x_4$$

From the second equation we get

$$x_2 + 2x_3 + 6x_4 = -4$$
$$x_2 = -4 - 2(3 + 2x_4) - 6x_4$$
$$= -4 - 6 - 4x_4 - 6x_4$$
$$= -10 - 10x_4$$

and from the first,

$$x_1 + 2x_2 + x_4 = 7$$
$$x_1 = 7 - 2(-10 - 10x_4) - x_4$$
$$= 7 + 20 + 20x_4 - x_4$$
$$= 27 + 19x_4$$

Summarizing, we have found

$$\begin{cases} x_1 = 27 + 19x_4 \\ x_2 = -10 - 10x_4 \\ x_3 = 3 + 2x_4 \\ x_4 = x_4 \end{cases}$$

We may select any real value for x_4. Then x_1, x_2, and x_3 are determined. Let us designate x_4 by c. Then the solution set can be written as

$$\{(27 + 19c, -10 - 10c, 3 + 2c, c): \quad c \in R\}$$

Thus, there are infinitely many points that satisfy all three equations.

EXAMPLE 12   Determine whether the following system is consistent by reducing the augmented matrix to triangular form.

$$\begin{cases} x - y + 2z = 3 \\ 2x + y \quad\quad = 4 \\ x + 3y - z = 2 \\ -x + 4y + 2z = 3 \end{cases}$$

Solution   In this case there are more equations than unknowns. While we might expect three equations in three unknowns to have a common solution, it is a special case when this solution also works for a fourth equation. So it should come as no surprise if these equations turn out to be inconsistent.

$$\begin{bmatrix} 1 & -1 & 2 & | & 3 \\ 2 & 1 & 0 & | & 4 \\ 1 & 3 & -1 & | & 2 \\ -1 & 4 & 2 & | & 3 \end{bmatrix}$$

$$\begin{bmatrix} 1 & -1 & 2 & | & 3 \\ 0 & 3 & -4 & | & -2 \\ 0 & 4 & -3 & | & -1 \\ 0 & 3 & 4 & | & 6 \end{bmatrix} \quad \begin{array}{l} \text{Row } 2 + [(-2) \cdot \text{Row } 1] \\ \text{Row } 3 + [(-1) \cdot \text{Row } 1] \\ \text{Row } 4 + (1 \cdot \text{Row } 1) \end{array}$$

$$\begin{bmatrix} 1 & -1 & 2 & | & 3 \\ 0 & -1 & -1 & | & -1 \\ 0 & 4 & -3 & | & -1 \\ 0 & 3 & 4 & | & 6 \end{bmatrix} \quad \text{Row } 2 + [(-1) \cdot \text{Row } 3]$$

$$\begin{bmatrix} 1 & -1 & 2 & | & 3 \\ 0 & -1 & -1 & | & -1 \\ 0 & 0 & -7 & | & -5 \\ 0 & 0 & 1 & | & 3 \end{bmatrix} \quad \begin{array}{l} \text{Row } 3 + (4 \cdot \text{Row } 2) \\ \text{Row } 4 + (3 \cdot \text{Row } 2) \end{array}$$

$$\begin{bmatrix} 1 & -1 & 2 & | & 3 \\ 0 & -1 & -1 & | & -1 \\ 0 & 0 & 1 & | & 3 \\ 0 & 0 & -7 & | & -5 \end{bmatrix} \quad \begin{array}{l} \text{Row } 4 \text{ interchanged with Row } 3 \\ \text{Row } 3 \text{ interchanged with Row } 4 \end{array}$$

$$\begin{bmatrix} 1 & -1 & 2 & | & 3 \\ 0 & -1 & -1 & | & -1 \\ 0 & 0 & 1 & | & 3 \\ 0 & 0 & 0 & | & 16 \end{bmatrix} \quad \text{Row } 4 + (7 \cdot \text{Row } 3)$$

The last equation now reads

$$0 = 16$$

which is not possible. Therefore, the system is inconsistent.

EXERCISE SET 2

By reducing the augmented matrix to triangular form, solve the following systems or show that no solution exists. If the system is dependent, show the solution set as in Example 11.

A **1.** $\begin{cases} x + 3y - 2z = 3 \\ y + z = 4 \\ x + 2y + 4z = 6 \end{cases}$ **2.** $\begin{cases} x - y + z = 1 \\ 2x + y + z = 4 \\ x + 5y - 2z = 1 \end{cases}$

3. $\begin{cases} x + 2y + z = 3 \\ 2x - y - z = 0 \\ 3x + 4y + 2z = 8 \end{cases}$ **4.** $\begin{cases} x + 2y + z = 1 \\ 2x + 5y + 4z = 2 \\ -x - 3y + 5z = 7 \end{cases}$

5. $\begin{cases} x + y - z = 3 \\ 3x + 4y + 2z = 3 \\ 4x - 2y - 8z = -4 \end{cases}$

6. $\begin{cases} x + 3y - 2z = -1 \\ x - 5y + 4z = -1 \\ 2x - y + 3z = 5 \end{cases}$

7. $\begin{cases} x - y = 1 \\ y + z = 1 \\ x + z = 2 \end{cases}$

8. $\begin{cases} x + 4y - 2z = -3 \\ 3x - 2y + z = 12 \\ 2x - 3y + z = 11 \end{cases}$

9. $\begin{cases} x - y + 2z = 3 \\ 2x - y + 8z = 5 \\ -3x + 5y - 3z = -11 \end{cases}$

10. $\begin{cases} 2x - 3y + z = 0 \\ 3x + 2y + 4z = 4 \\ -4x + y - 5z = -2 \end{cases}$

11. $\begin{cases} 2x - 3y + 2z = -2 \\ 3x - 8y - z = 2 \\ -5x + 10y - 3z = 4 \end{cases}$

12. $\begin{cases} 2x - 3y + 4z = 5 \\ x + y - 2z = 1 \\ 7x - 3y + 2z = 13 \end{cases}$

13. $\begin{cases} 2x + y + z = 7 \\ x - y + 2z = 11 \\ 5x + y - 2z = 1 \end{cases}$

14. $\begin{cases} 2x + 4y + 3z = -2 \\ x - 3y + 4z = 9 \\ 5x + 7y - z = -9 \end{cases}$

15. $\begin{cases} x - y - 3z = -3 \\ 2x - 3y - 2z = 0 \\ 4x - 3y + z = -1 \end{cases}$

16. $\begin{cases} x + 3y + 3z = -2 \\ 3x - 6y + 2z = 6 \\ 2x + 3y - z = 4 \end{cases}$

17. $\begin{cases} x + 2y + 3z = 9 \\ x - y + 2z = 5 \\ x + 5y + 4z = 13 \end{cases}$

18. $\begin{cases} 2x + y - 3z = 1 \\ x + 2y + z = 3 \\ 4x - y - 11z = 5 \end{cases}$

19. $\begin{cases} 2x - 3y + 4z = 0 \\ x - y - 2z = 0 \\ x - 3y + 14z = 0 \end{cases}$

20. $\begin{cases} x + y - z + w = 2 \\ 2x - 3y + 4z + 5w = -4 \\ 4x + 5y - 2z - 3w = 8 \end{cases}$

21. $\begin{cases} 4x - 2y + 3z = 5 \\ 3x + y + 2z = 3 \\ 2x - 3y + 5z = 4 \end{cases}$

22. $\begin{cases} x + 4y + z = 7 \\ 3x - 2y + 2z = 12 \\ x + 2y - z = 2 \end{cases}$

23. $\begin{cases} 3x - 2y - z = 2 \\ 5x + 3y - 4z = 6 \\ 4x - 9y + z = 3 \end{cases}$

24. $\begin{cases} 2x + 3y + 3z = 9 \\ 5x - 2y + 8z = 6 \\ 4x - y + 5z = -1 \end{cases}$

25. $\begin{cases} 5x - 2y + 3z = 6 \\ 6x - 3y + 4z = 10 \\ -4x + 4y - 9z = 4 \end{cases}$

26. $\begin{cases} 3x + 4y - z = 4 \\ 2x - 5y + 3z = -10 \\ 4x + 3y + z = 10 \end{cases}$

27. $\begin{cases} x + 2y - z + w = 1 \\ 2x - y + z - 2w = 0 \\ -x - 3y + 2z - 3w = -5 \end{cases}$

28. $\begin{cases} 2x - 3y - 2z = 1 \\ 3x - 4y - 3z = 2 \\ 4x + y + z = 10 \end{cases}$

29. $\begin{cases} 2x - 3y + 4z = 0 \\ x - y + 3z = 0 \\ 3x - 5y + 5z = 0 \end{cases}$

30. $\begin{cases} 5x - 6y + z = 1 \\ 9x - 8y + 7z = 1 \\ -3x + 4y - z = 5 \end{cases}$

31. $\begin{cases} 8x - 5y + 6z = 0 \\ 3x - 2y - 2z = -10 \\ -11x + 9y - 2z = 16 \end{cases}$

32. $\begin{cases} 2x + y + z = 1 \\ 5x + 3y - 2z = -4 \\ 3x + y + 6z = 8 \end{cases}$

33. $\begin{cases} x - y - z = -1 \\ y - z + w = 0 \\ x + 2z - 2w = 1 \\ 2x + y - w = -1 \end{cases}$

34. $\begin{cases} x + y + z + w = 1 \\ 3y - w = 0 \\ x - z = 1 \\ y - 2z - w = -2 \end{cases}$

35.
$$\begin{cases} x_1 + x_2 - x_3 + 2x_4 = 1 \\ 2x_1 - x_2 - 3x_3 + 2x_4 = -6 \\ -x_1 + 2x_2 + x_3 + 3x_4 = 2 \\ x_1 - x_2 - 2x_3 + x_4 = 0 \end{cases}$$

36.
$$\begin{cases} 3x + 5y - 7z = 6 \\ 4x - 2y + 8z = -5 \\ 6x + 7y - 3z = 4 \end{cases}$$

37.
$$\begin{cases} 3x - 2y - 2z = -1 \\ 7x + y - 2z = 0 \\ 5x - 3y + 4z = 20 \end{cases}$$

B   **38.**
$$\begin{cases} x + y + 3z - 2w = -2 \\ 2x + 4y - 2z + 4w = 1 \\ -3x - 5y - 4z - w = 4 \\ 4x + 6y - 2z + 5w = 1 \end{cases}$$

39.
$$\begin{cases} 2x_1 - x_2 + 3x_3 + x_4 = 0 \\ 4x_1 - 3x_2 + x_3 - 2x_4 = 1 \\ -3x_1 + 2x_3 - 4x_4 = -2 \\ 6x_1 - 4x_2 - 5x_3 + 3x_4 = -3 \end{cases}$$

40.
$$\begin{cases} x - y - 2z + w = -2 \\ 3x + 2y + 3z + 2w = 1 \\ 2x - 7y - 4z - 3w = 1 \\ -x + 6y + 5z + 2w = 1 \end{cases}$$

41.
$$\begin{cases} 2x - 3y + 5z + 4w = -3 \\ 3x - 2y - 2z - w = 1 \\ 5x + 2y + 6z - 8w = 1 \\ -7x + 4y - 3z + 2w = 2 \end{cases}$$

42.
$$\begin{cases} 3x - 2y + z - w = -1 \\ x + y - 3z + 3w = 3 \\ 2x - 3y + 5z - 4w = 1 \\ 4x + 2y + 4z - w = -4 \end{cases}$$

43.
$$\begin{cases} 2x - 3y + 4z + 2w = 5 \\ -3x + 2y - z + w = 2 \\ 4x - 5y + 2z - 3w = 6 \\ 5x - 4y - z - 6w = 1 \end{cases}$$

44.
$$\begin{cases} x_1 - 2x_2 + x_3 - x_4 = 2 \\ x_1 - x_2 - x_4 = 6 \\ 2x_1 - 2x_2 + x_3 = 9 \\ -x_1 + 5x_2 - 2x_3 + 5x_4 = 6 \end{cases}$$

45.
$$\begin{cases} 2s - t + 3u + v = 0 \\ 3s + 2t + 4u - v = 0 \\ 5s - 2t - 2u - v = 0 \\ -2s - 3t + 7u + 5v = 0 \end{cases}$$

46.
$$\begin{cases} x + y + 2z - w = 1 \\ -x + 2y + 3z - 2w = -3 \\ 2x - y - z + w = 4 \\ x + 2y + z - w = 1 \end{cases}$$

47.
$$\begin{cases} x_1 - 2x_2 + 3x_4 + x_5 = 2 \\ -x_1 + 3x_2 + 2x_3 - 4x_4 + x_5 = -1 \\ x_1 - 2x_2 + x_3 + 3x_4 = 0 \\ x_2 + 2x_3 - 2x_4 + 2x_5 = 7 \\ 2x_1 - 4x_2 + 2x_3 + 6x_4 + x_5 = 5 \end{cases}$$

---

3 Determinants

In Section 2 our approach made use of the augmented matrix of a system of equations. In Section 4 we will present an alternative procedure that uses the coefficient matrix and some other matrices associated with it. This procedure works only when the number of unknowns and the number of equations are the same, in which case the coefficient matrix is said to be **square**, since it has the same number of rows as columns. However, it will first be necessary to introduce a new concept—the **determinant** of a matrix. Various symbols are used to designate the determinant of a matrix; we will use the one that is probably the most common, namely, vertical bars on each side of the matrix. For example, the determinant of the matrix

$$\begin{bmatrix} 2 & 3 & 1 \\ 4 & -2 & 5 \\ 1 & 2 & 7 \end{bmatrix}$$

is designated by

$$\begin{vmatrix} 2 & 3 & 1 \\ 4 & -2 & 5 \\ 1 & 2 & 7 \end{vmatrix}$$

The number of rows (or columns) in a square matrix is called the **order** of the matrix. The determinant of a matrix of order 2 is defined as follows: Let

$$\begin{bmatrix} a & b \\ c & d \end{bmatrix}$$

designate an arbitrary matrix of order 2. Then

$$\begin{vmatrix} a & b \\ c & d \end{vmatrix} = ad - bc$$

The right-hand side is suggested by the arrows on the left. The diagonal elements from upper left to lower right, called the **principal diagonal elements,** are multiplied, and from their product is subtracted the product of the other diagonal elements. For example, we have

$$\begin{vmatrix} 2 & 3 \\ 4 & 5 \end{vmatrix} = 10 - 12 = -2$$

and

$$\begin{vmatrix} 3 & -1 \\ 5 & -2 \end{vmatrix} = -6 - (-5) = -6 + 5 = -1$$

The procedure for finding the determinant of a square matrix of order higher than 2 is more complicated and will require several preliminary steps. We will use a general matrix of order 3 to illustrate,

$$\begin{bmatrix} a_1 & b_1 & c_1 \\ a_2 & b_2 & c_2 \\ a_3 & b_3 & c_3 \end{bmatrix}$$

(subscripts are employed to avoid the use of too many different letters), but everything we do can be extended in a straightforward way to higher orders. We refer to the entries in the matrix as **elements** of the matrix. It is important to distinguish between rows (which go across) and columns (which go up and down). For example, consider the matrix

$$\begin{bmatrix} 2 & -1 & 3 \\ 4 & 2 & -7 \\ -1 & 0 & 5 \end{bmatrix}$$

The element in Row 2 and Column 3 is -7, and the element in Row 3 and Column 2 is 0.

If we delete the row and column of a given element in a square matrix, we are left with a submatrix of order 1 less than that of the original matrix. The determinant of this submatrix is called the **minor** of the element in question. For example, let us again consider the matrix

$$\begin{bmatrix} 2 & -1 & 3 \\ 4 & 2 & -7 \\ -1 & 0 & 5 \end{bmatrix}$$

and determine the minor of the element -7 in Row 2 and Column 3. We show the row

$$\begin{bmatrix} 2 & -1 & 3 \\ 4 & 2 & -7 \\ -1 & 0 & 5 \end{bmatrix}$$

and column containing this element as being deleted by dashed lines. The minor of -7 is therefore the determinant

$$\begin{vmatrix} 2 & -1 \\ -1 & 0 \end{vmatrix} = 2(0) - (-1)(-1) = 0 - 1 = -1$$

In a similar way we could find the minor of each of the elements.

If we multiply the minor of the element in the ith row and jth column by $(-1)^{i+j}$, we obtain what is called the **cofactor** of the element. So the cofactor of an element differs from the minor at most in sign. If $i + j$ is even, $(-1)^{i+j} = 1$, so the cofactor equals the minor. If $i + j$ is odd, $(-1)^{i+j} = -1$, so the cofactor is the negative of the minor. From this definition we can devise the following scheme for determining the sign that should be affixed to the minor to give the cofactor:

$$\begin{bmatrix} + & - & + \\ - & + & - \\ + & - & + \end{bmatrix}$$

Starting with a plus sign in the upper left, the signs alternate as we move either horizontally or vertically.

EXAMPLE 13   Find the cofactor of each element in the first row of the matrix.

$$\begin{bmatrix} 2 & 1 & -3 \\ -1 & 4 & 2 \\ 5 & 3 & 6 \end{bmatrix}$$

Solution   To get the minor of the first element, 2, we cross out (mentally or otherwise) the first row and first column:

$$\begin{bmatrix} 2 & 1 & -3 \\ -1 & 4 & 2 \\ 5 & 3 & 6 \end{bmatrix}$$

The minor is

$$\begin{vmatrix} 4 & 2 \\ 3 & 6 \end{vmatrix} = 24 - 6 = 18$$

Since by the scheme of signs given above, we multiply by $+1$ to get the cofactor, it follows that the cofactor of this element also is 18.

Similarly, we determine the minor of the second element in Row 1:

$$\begin{bmatrix} 2 & 1 & -3 \\ -1 & 4 & 2 \\ 5 & 3 & 6 \end{bmatrix}$$

$$\begin{vmatrix} -1 & 2 \\ 5 & 6 \end{vmatrix} = -6 - 10 = -16$$

To get the cofactor we must multiply by -1, according to the scheme of signs for determining cofactors. So the cofactor of this element is 16.

For the third element in Row 1 we proceed in a similar way:

$$\begin{bmatrix} 2 & 1 & -3 \\ -1 & 4 & 2 \\ 5 & 3 & 6 \end{bmatrix}$$

$$\begin{vmatrix} -1 & 4 \\ 5 & 3 \end{vmatrix} = -3 - 20 = -23$$

The cofactor is obtained by multiplying this minor by $+1$, so the cofactor is -23.

With a little practice you will probably be able to calculate cofactors of elements in a matrix of order 3 mentally. It is a good idea to write the correct factor $+1$ or -1 first, according to the position of the element, and then calculate the minor. To illustrate, consider again the matrix in Example 13. The cofactor of the element -1 in the second row and first column is $-(6 + 9) = -15$; the cofactor of the element 3 in the third row and second column is $-(4 - 3) = -1$; and so on. Note that the cofactor of an element depends on the position of the element but not on the value of the element itself.

We are now ready to state a **procedure for finding the value of the determinant of a square matrix of order 3 or greater.**

1. **Select any row or column of the matrix.**
2. **Multiply each element of that row or column by its cofactor.**
3. **Add the results.**

We will illustrate with the matrix used in Example 13.

EXAMPLE 14   Find the determinant of the matrix.

$$\begin{bmatrix} 2 & 1 & -3 \\ -1 & 4 & 2 \\ 5 & 3 & 6 \end{bmatrix}$$

Solution Let us select Row 1, since we have already found the cofactors of the elements in that row in Example 13, namely, 18, 16, and -23, respectively. Next, we multiply each element in the row by its own cofactor and then add the results. Thus,

$$\begin{vmatrix} 2 & 1 & -3 \\ -1 & 4 & 2 \\ 5 & 3 & 6 \end{vmatrix} = 2(18) + 1(16) + (-3)(-23) = 36 + 16 + 69 = 121$$

Note. In Step 1 above we specified that *any* row or column may be selected at the outset. It can be proved (See Problem 26, Exercise Set 3) that the same result will occur regardless of this initial choice, so long as Steps 2 and 3 are carried out for the row or column selected. To illustrate let us select Column 2 in the example above (we say "expand by Column 2"). The cofactors can be calculated mentally as we move down the column.

$$\begin{vmatrix} 2 & 1 & -3 \\ -1 & 4 & 2 \\ 5 & 3 & 6 \end{vmatrix} = 1[-(-6 - 10)] + 4[+(12 + 15)] + 3[-(4 - 3)]$$

$$= 16 + 4(27) + 3(-1) = 16 + 108 - 3 = 121$$

EXAMPLE 15 Find the determinant of the matrix

$$\begin{bmatrix} 2 & 3 & 0 \\ -1 & 2 & -4 \\ -3 & -1 & 5 \end{bmatrix}$$

Solution It is convenient to select either Row 1 or Column 3. (Why?) Let us expand by Column 3. We can ignore the cofactor of the first element 0, since whatever it is, the result will be 0 after multiplication. So we have

$$\begin{vmatrix} 2 & 3 & 0 \\ -1 & 2 & -4 \\ -3 & -1 & 5 \end{vmatrix} = 0 + (-4)[-(-2 + 9)] + 5[4 + 3]$$

$$= (-4)(-7) + 5(7) = 28 + 35 = 63$$

While the procedure outlined for finding determinants is applicable to matrices of any order greater than 2, the work involved rapidly becomes excessive as the orders increase. For example, finding the determinant of a matrix of order 4 involves multiplying each of four elements (any row or column) by their respective cofactor, each of which involves evaluating the determinant of an order 3 matrix. It is not hard to visualize how difficult it would be to find the determinant of a matrix of order 5. In these more complicated situations there are admissible preliminary steps that can be taken which introduce zeros into a given row or column without changing the value of the determinant. The more zeros present, the easier the evaluation of the determinant. We will not pursue these methods here, since in the applications of determinants to systems of equations the method to be described is practical only for relatively small systems.

EXERCISE SET 3

A In Problems 1–3 evaluate the determinants.

1. a. $\begin{vmatrix} 2 & 3 \\ -1 & 4 \end{vmatrix}$ **b.** $\begin{vmatrix} -3 & 5 \\ 12 & 6 \end{vmatrix}$ **c.** $\begin{vmatrix} 4 & -8 \\ -6 & -3 \end{vmatrix}$

2. a. $\begin{vmatrix} 3 & -1 \\ 4 & -2 \end{vmatrix}$ **b.** $\begin{vmatrix} 5 & 6 \\ -8 & 3 \end{vmatrix}$ **c.** $\begin{vmatrix} -10 & 3 \\ 14 & -5 \end{vmatrix}$

3. a. $\begin{vmatrix} 9 & 6 \\ 3 & 2 \end{vmatrix}$ **b.** $\begin{vmatrix} 0 & 5 \\ -1 & 4 \end{vmatrix}$ **c.** $\begin{vmatrix} 8 & 4 \\ -4 & -2 \end{vmatrix}$

Problems 4–8 refer to the matrix

$$\begin{bmatrix} 3 & -2 & 1 \\ -4 & 5 & -3 \\ -6 & -1 & 7 \end{bmatrix}$$

In each case for the position specified find:

a. The element in that position
b. The minor of that element
c. The cofactor of that element

4. Row 2, Column 3   **5.** Row 3, Column 2
6. Row 1, Column 3   **7.** Row 3, Column 1
8. Row 3, Column 3

9. Evaluate the determinant of the matrix used in Problems 4–8 by expanding on:
  a. The third column   **b.** The third row

In Problems 10–18 evaluate the determinants.

10. $\begin{vmatrix} 2 & -1 & -3 \\ 4 & 2 & -5 \\ -1 & 3 & 6 \end{vmatrix}$ **11.** $\begin{vmatrix} 3 & 0 & -1 \\ 2 & 5 & 0 \\ 1 & 3 & 1 \end{vmatrix}$ **12.** $\begin{vmatrix} 1 & 5 & 3 \\ -2 & -4 & 10 \\ 6 & 8 & -3 \end{vmatrix}$

13. $\begin{vmatrix} 3 & -1 & -5 \\ 0 & 2 & -4 \\ 5 & 1 & 6 \end{vmatrix}$ **14.** $\begin{vmatrix} 2 & 3 & -1 \\ -4 & 2 & 3 \\ 5 & -2 & 6 \end{vmatrix}$ **15.** $\begin{vmatrix} 1 & -1 & 4 \\ 3 & 2 & 0 \\ 4 & -1 & 6 \end{vmatrix}$

16. $\begin{vmatrix} 5 & 1 & 2 \\ -2 & 4 & 3 \\ 7 & 2 & -1 \end{vmatrix}$ **17.** $\begin{vmatrix} -2 & 1 & -5 \\ 0 & 3 & -4 \\ 6 & -1 & 2 \end{vmatrix}$ **18.** $\begin{vmatrix} 4 & -2 & -3 \\ -5 & 3 & -4 \\ 2 & -1 & -2 \end{vmatrix}$

19. Find all values of x satisfying

$$\begin{vmatrix} 1 & x & 0 \\ 2 & -4 & x-1 \\ 1 & -x & 2 \end{vmatrix} = 0$$

20. Find all values of t satisfying

$$\begin{vmatrix} -t & 2 & -1 \\ 0 & t & 4 \\ t+2 & 1 & -2 \end{vmatrix} = 0$$

21. Prove that for any number k

$$\begin{vmatrix} a & b \\ c & d \end{vmatrix} = \begin{vmatrix} a+kb & b \\ c+kd & d \end{vmatrix}$$

and

$$\begin{vmatrix} a & b \\ c & d \end{vmatrix} = \begin{vmatrix} a+kc & b+kd \\ c & d \end{vmatrix}$$

22. It can be proved that the area of a triangle with vertices (x_1, y_1), (x_2, y_2), and (x_3, y_3) is given by

$$A = \frac{1}{2} \begin{vmatrix} x_1 & y_1 & 1 \\ x_2 & y_2 & 1 \\ x_3 & y_3 & 1 \end{vmatrix}$$

Use this to find the area of the triangle with vertices $(2, -3)$, $(-4, 1)$, and $(-3, -5)$.

B Evaluate the determinants in Problems 23–25.

23. $\begin{vmatrix} 3 & 2 & -1 & 5 \\ 1 & 0 & 2 & 4 \\ -1 & 1 & 3 & 0 \\ 2 & 0 & -1 & 1 \end{vmatrix}$ **24.** $\begin{vmatrix} 1 & 0 & -2 & 3 \\ 0 & -2 & 5 & 0 \\ 2 & 3 & -1 & 1 \\ -1 & -2 & 3 & 4 \end{vmatrix}$

25. $\begin{vmatrix} 2 & -1 & 3 & 1 \\ 4 & 2 & 1 & 3 \\ -1 & 1 & 2 & 4 \\ 3 & 5 & -2 & 6 \end{vmatrix}$

26. Verify the fact that the same final result occurs regardless of which row or column is used in the calculation of the determinant of the order 3 matrix

$$\begin{bmatrix} a_1 & b_1 & c_1 \\ a_2 & b_2 & c_2 \\ a_3 & b_3 & c_3 \end{bmatrix}$$

27. Prove that if each element in any row or column of a square matrix A is multiplied by a constant k, the determinant of the resulting matrix is $k|A|$.

28. It can be proved that if any two rows or any two columns of a square matrix A are interchanged, the determinant of the resulting matrix is $-|A|$. Use this result to show that if any two rows or columns of a square matrix A are identical, then $|A| = 0$.

29. Prove that

$$\begin{vmatrix} x & y & 1 \\ x_1 & y_1 & 1 \\ x_2 & y_2 & 1 \end{vmatrix} = 0$$

is the equation of a line passing through the points (x_1, y_1) and (x_2, y_2).

30. Prove that if all elements above or below the principal diagonal of a square matrix are 0, then the determinant of the matrix equals the product of the elements along the principal diagonal.

31. Solve for x:

$$\begin{vmatrix} x & 0 & 0 & 0 \\ 15 & x-1 & 0 & 0 \\ -5 & 24 & x+2 & 0 \\ 24 & -31 & 57 & 2x+3 \end{vmatrix} = 0$$

---

4 Cramer's Rule

To see how determinants can play a role in solving systems of equations, let us consider the general case of two equations in two unknowns:

$$\begin{cases} a_1 x + b_1 y = c_1 \\ a_2 x + b_2 y = c_2 \end{cases} \tag{3}$$

We eliminate y by multiplying the top equation by b_2 and the bottom by b_1 and then subtracting:

$$\begin{aligned} a_1 b_2 x + b_1 b_2 y &= c_1 b_2 \\ a_2 b_1 x + b_1 b_2 y &= c_2 b_1 \\ \hline (a_1 b_2 - a_2 b_1) x &= c_1 b_2 - c_2 b_1 \end{aligned} \tag{4}$$

Assume for the moment that the coefficient of x is not 0. Then we can solve for x to get

$$x = \frac{c_1 b_2 - c_2 b_1}{a_1 b_2 - a_2 b_1}$$

This can be written as a quotient of determinants:

$$x = \frac{\begin{vmatrix} c_1 & b_1 \\ c_2 & b_2 \end{vmatrix}}{\begin{vmatrix} a_1 & b_1 \\ a_2 & b_2 \end{vmatrix}} \tag{5}$$

Returning to the original system of equations (3), we multiply the top equation by a_2 and the bottom by a_1, and then subtract, in order to eliminate x:

$$\begin{aligned} a_1 a_2 x + a_2 b_1 y &= a_2 c_1 \\ a_1 a_2 x + a_1 b_2 y &= a_1 c_2 \\ \hline (a_1 b_2 - a_2 b_1) y &= a_1 c_2 - a_2 c_1 \end{aligned} \tag{6}$$

(We subtracted the top equation from the bottom one.) Again, assuming the coefficient of y is nonzero, we get

$$y = \frac{a_1 c_2 - a_2 c_1}{a_1 b_2 - a_2 b_1}$$

which can be written as

$$y = \frac{\begin{vmatrix} a_1 & c_1 \\ a_2 & c_2 \end{vmatrix}}{\begin{vmatrix} a_1 & b_1 \\ a_2 & b_2 \end{vmatrix}} \tag{7}$$

Let us now examine the situation when the coefficient of x in equation (4) or of y in (6) is 0:

$$a_1 b_2 - a_2 b_1 = 0 \tag{8}$$

We will suppose that neither b_1 nor b_2 is 0, because if either was 0, both would have to be (why?); thus, the lines would both be vertical, and so either parallel or coincident. We can rewrite equation (8) in the form

$$\frac{a_1}{b_1} = \frac{a_2}{b_2}$$

The slopes of the lines are $-a_1/b_1$ and $-a_2/b_2$, respectively; we conclude that the lines are parallel or coincident. If they are parallel, no solution exists; the system is inconsistent. If they are coincident, the system is dependent. We conclude that a *unique* solution to the system exists if and only if $a_1 b_2 - b_2 a_1 \neq 0$, that is,

$$\begin{vmatrix} a_1 & b_1 \\ a_2 & b_2 \end{vmatrix} \neq 0$$

EXAMPLE 16   Solve the system below using equations (5) and (7).

$$\begin{cases} 2x - 3y = 4 \\ 7x + 5y = 6 \end{cases}$$

Solution   We have immediately

$$x = \frac{\begin{vmatrix} 4 & -3 \\ 6 & 5 \end{vmatrix}}{\begin{vmatrix} 2 & -3 \\ 7 & 5 \end{vmatrix}} = \frac{20 + 18}{10 + 21} = \frac{38}{31}$$

$$y = \frac{\begin{vmatrix} 2 & 4 \\ 7 & 6 \end{vmatrix}}{\begin{vmatrix} 2 & -3 \\ 7 & 5 \end{vmatrix}} = \frac{12 - 28}{31} = -\frac{16}{31}$$

So the solution is $(\frac{38}{31}, -\frac{16}{31})$.

It is useful to analyze the results (5) and (7):

$$x = \frac{\begin{vmatrix} c_1 & b_1 \\ c_2 & b_2 \end{vmatrix}}{\begin{vmatrix} a_1 & b_1 \\ a_2 & b_2 \end{vmatrix}} \qquad y = \frac{\begin{vmatrix} a_1 & c_1 \\ a_2 & c_2 \end{vmatrix}}{\begin{vmatrix} a_1 & b_1 \\ a_2 & b_2 \end{vmatrix}}$$

The denominators are the same, and this common denominator is seen to be the determinant of the coefficient matrix of the system. In each case the numerator differs from the denominator only in that the column of coefficients of the unknown in question is replaced by the column of constants. It is convenient to introduce notation for the matrices involved. Let D denote the coefficient matrix of the system, and let D_x and D_y be matrices that are obtained from D by replacing the column of coefficients of x and of y, respectively, by the column of constants. Then we have

$$x = \frac{|D_x|}{|D|} \qquad y = \frac{|D_y|}{|D|}$$

This same pattern holds true for higher-order systems. For example, the solution to the system of three equations in three unknowns,

$$\begin{cases} a_1 x + b_1 y + c_1 z = d_1 \\ a_2 x + b_2 y + c_2 z = d_2 \\ a_3 x + b_3 y + c_3 z = d_3 \end{cases}$$

is given by

$$x = \frac{|D_x|}{|D|} \qquad y = \frac{|D_y|}{|D|} \qquad z = \frac{|D_z|}{|D|} \qquad (D \neq 0)$$

where D_x, D_y, and D_z are obtained from the coefficient matrix D by replacing the column of coefficients of x, of y, and of z, respectively, by the column of constants appearing on the right-hand side.

As an illustration of the meanings of the matrices D, D_x, D_y, and D_z, consider the system

$$\begin{cases} x + y + z = 4 \\ 2x + y - z = 0 \\ 3x - 4y - 3z = 1 \end{cases}$$

Here,

$$D = \begin{bmatrix} 1 & 1 & 1 \\ 2 & 1 & -1 \\ 3 & -4 & -3 \end{bmatrix}$$

and so

$$D_x = \begin{bmatrix} 4 & 1 & 1 \\ 0 & 1 & -1 \\ 1 & -4 & -3 \end{bmatrix} \qquad D_y = \begin{bmatrix} 1 & 4 & 1 \\ 2 & 0 & -1 \\ 3 & 1 & -3 \end{bmatrix} \qquad D_z = \begin{bmatrix} 1 & 1 & 4 \\ 2 & 1 & 0 \\ 3 & -4 & 1 \end{bmatrix}$$

Column of constants

The general result is known as **Cramer's rule,** which we state as follows:

Cramer's Rule

Let D denote the coefficient matrix in a system of n linear equations in the n unknowns $x_1, x_2, \ldots, x_n$, where each equation is written in the form

$$a_1 x_1 + a_2 x_2 + \cdots + a_n x_n = b$$

Let D_{x_i} be the matrix obtained from D by replacing the column of coefficients of x_i by the column of constants appearing on the right-hand side of the system. Then if $D \neq 0$,

$$x_1 = \frac{|D_{x_1}|}{|D|}, \quad x_2 = \frac{|D_{x_2}|}{|D|}, \quad \cdots \quad , \quad x_n = \frac{|D_{x_n}|}{|D|}$$

Note.   In applying Cramer's rule it is important that the terms involving the unknowns in each equation be written in the same order, and that the constant terms all appear on the right. For example, before applying Cramer's rule to the system

$$\begin{cases} 2y - 3x + 4z - 7 = 0 \\ x + 2z - y = 8 \\ 3z - 4y + 2x + 5 = 0 \end{cases}$$

we would rewrite it as

$$\begin{cases} -3x + 2y + 4z = 7 \\ x - y + 2z = 8 \\ 2x - 4y + 3z = -5 \end{cases}$$

EXAMPLE 17   Solve the system below by Cramer's rule.

$$\begin{cases} x + y + z = 4 \\ 2x + y - z = 0 \\ 3x - 4y - 3z = 1 \end{cases}$$

Solution $x = \dfrac{|D_x|}{|D|} = \dfrac{\begin{vmatrix} 4 & 1 & 1 \\ 0 & 1 & -1 \\ 1 & -4 & -3 \end{vmatrix}}{\begin{vmatrix} 1 & 1 & 1 \\ 2 & 1 & -1 \\ 3 & -4 & -3 \end{vmatrix}} = \dfrac{4(-7) + 1(-2)}{1(-7) - 2(1) + 3(-2)} = \dfrac{-30}{-15} = 2$

We expanded by the first column in both cases.

$$y = \frac{|D_y|}{|D|} = \frac{\begin{vmatrix} 1 & 4 & 1 \\ 2 & 0 & -1 \\ 3 & 1 & -3 \end{vmatrix}}{-15} = \frac{-4(-3) - (-3)}{-15} = \frac{15}{-15} = -1$$

We expanded the numerator by the second column.

$$z = \frac{|D_z|}{|D|} = \frac{\begin{vmatrix} 1 & 1 & 4 \\ 2 & 1 & 0 \\ 3 & -4 & 1 \end{vmatrix}}{-15} = \frac{4(-11) + 1(-1)}{-15} = \frac{-45}{-15} = 3$$

Expansion was by the third column. So the solution is $(2, -1, 3)$.

Remark.   Cramer's rule works only when the number of equations is the same as the number of unknowns. Furthermore, it is usually impractical for systems with more than three equations. It works well for two equations and two unknowns, and is often the easiest method in this case. Depending on how adept one becomes in expanding order 3 determinants, it can be an efficient way to solve a system of three equations in three unknowns.

EXERCISE SET 4

A   Solve each of the following by Cramer's rule.

1. $\begin{cases} 2x - 3y = 7 \\ x + 4y = 3 \end{cases}$

2. $\begin{cases} 5x + 4y = 9 \\ 7x - 3y = 6 \end{cases}$

3. $\begin{cases} 3x + y = -2 \\ 2x + 5y = 4 \end{cases}$

4. $\begin{cases} x - 2y = 4 \\ 3x - 4y = 5 \end{cases}$

5. $\begin{cases} 6x - 5y = 4 \\ 8x + 7y = -3 \end{cases}$

6. $\begin{cases} 3y - 4x + 5 = 0 \\ \qquad 6x = 2y - 3 \end{cases}$

7. $\begin{cases} 7x - 8y = 10 \\ 5x - 4y = 8 \end{cases}$

8. $\begin{cases} 5x + 6y = -3 \\ 2x - 3y = 4 \end{cases}$

9. $\begin{cases} x + 2y - 3 = 0 \\ 3x - y + 4 = 0 \end{cases}$

10. $\begin{cases} 3x + 2y = 4 \\ 3y + 5x = 2 \end{cases}$

11. $\begin{cases} 3x - 5y = 2 \\ 2x - 3y = 4 \end{cases}$

12. $\begin{cases} 9y + 7x \qquad = 10 \\ 2x + 3y - 8 = 0 \end{cases}$

13. $\begin{cases} x - y + 2z = 0 \\ 2x \qquad - 3z = 1 \\ \qquad y + z = 3 \end{cases}$

14. $\begin{cases} x + 2y - 3z = 1 \\ 2x - y + z = 2 \\ x + y + 4z = 0 \end{cases}$

15. $\begin{cases} x + y \qquad = 1 \\ \qquad 2y - z = -1 \\ x \qquad + z = 0 \end{cases}$

16. $\begin{cases} 3x + y + z = 3 \\ x \qquad - z = -5 \\ \qquad 2y - z = 0 \end{cases}$

17. $\begin{cases} 3x + 5y \qquad = 2 \\ x + y - z = -1 \\ x - 3y - z = 1 \end{cases}$

18. $\begin{cases} x + y - z = 4 \\ 2x - y + z = 0 \\ x - 2y - 3z = 1 \end{cases}$

19. $\begin{cases} 3x - y + z = 1 \\ x \qquad - z = 2 \\ 2y + 3z = 4 \end{cases}$

20. $\begin{cases} x + y + z = 1 \\ 3x + 2y - 3 = 0 \\ y + 3z = 0 \end{cases}$

21. $\begin{cases} 3x - 4y + 5z = 7 \\ 2x + 3y - 8z = 5 \\ 4x - 2y + 3z = 6 \end{cases}$

22. $\begin{cases} 2x - 3y - 4z = -4 \\ 3x + 4y + 2z = 1 \\ 5x - 2y - 3z = 0 \end{cases}$

B 23. $\begin{cases} (a - 1)x + \qquad 2ay = 3 \\ (a + 1)x + (2a - 1)y = 2 \end{cases}$
Solve for x and y.

24. $\begin{cases} x^2u - 3xv = 1 \\ 2xu + 4v = 2 \end{cases}$
Solve for u and v.

25. $\begin{cases} u - 2xv = -1 \\ xu + v = x \end{cases}$
Solve for u and v.

26. $\begin{cases} ax - (a + 1)y = 2 \\ (a - 1)x - ay = 1 \end{cases}$
Solve for x and y.

27. $\begin{cases} 2m^2s + (m + 2)t = 6 \\ 4(m - 1)s + 2t = 3 \end{cases}$
Solve for s and t.

28. $\begin{cases} 3x - 4y + z = 2 \\ x + 2y - z = 3 \\ 4x - 3y - 2z = 4 \end{cases}$

29. $\begin{cases} 3x - 2y + 4z = 5 \\ 2x + 3y - 2z = 6 \\ 4x - 5y + 3z = -5 \end{cases}$

30. $\begin{cases} x + y + z + w = 1 \\ 3y \qquad - w = 0 \\ x \qquad - z \qquad = 1 \\ y - 2z - w = 2 \end{cases}$

31. $\begin{cases} x - y \qquad + w = 1 \\ 2x \qquad + 3z - w = 0 \\ 3y - z + 2w = 2 \\ x + y - z \qquad = 3 \end{cases}$

5 The Algebra of Matrices

A matrix with *m* **rows** and *n* **columns** is said to be an *m* × *n* (read "*m* by *n*") matrix, and the **size** (or **dimension**) of the matrix is said to be $m \times n$. In this section we will see how the operations of addition and multiplication are defined for matrices.

Two matrices are said to be **equal** provided they are of the same size and corresponding elements are equal. For example,

$$\begin{bmatrix} a & b \\ c & d \end{bmatrix} = \begin{bmatrix} 2 & 3 \\ 5 & 7 \end{bmatrix}$$

if and only if $a = 2$, $b = 3$, $c = 5$, and $d = 7$.

To **add** two matrices of the same size, we add their corresponding elements. For example,

$$\begin{bmatrix} 2 & -1 & 3 \\ 4 & 2 & -5 \end{bmatrix} + \begin{bmatrix} 3 & 7 & -8 \\ 5 & -2 & 4 \end{bmatrix} = \begin{bmatrix} 5 & 6 & -5 \\ 9 & 0 & -1 \end{bmatrix}$$

Addition is not defined for matrices of different sizes.

A **zero matrix,** denoted by **0,** is one in which all elements are 0. There are zero matrices of all sizes. For any matrix A, if **0** is a zero matrix of the same size as A, then $A + 0 = A$. Thus, **0** is the **additive identity.**

The **additive inverse** of a matrix A, denoted by $-A$, is the matrix whose elements are the negatives of the corresponding elements of A. For example,

$$-\begin{bmatrix} 2 & 3 \\ 4 & -2 \\ -5 & 6 \end{bmatrix} = \begin{bmatrix} -2 & -3 \\ -4 & 2 \\ 5 & -6 \end{bmatrix}$$

If A and B are matrices of the same size, then the **difference** between A and B is defined by

$$A - B = A + (-B)$$

It follows that subtraction is carried out term-by-term, as in

$$\begin{bmatrix} 4 & 2 \\ 5 & 6 \end{bmatrix} - \begin{bmatrix} 3 & 1 \\ 7 & 2 \end{bmatrix} = \begin{bmatrix} 1 & 1 \\ -2 & 4 \end{bmatrix}$$

The following properties can now be proven:

$$A + B = B + A$$
$$A + (B + C) = (A + B) + C$$
$$A + (-A) = 0$$

In each case the matrices are understood to be of the same size. For matrices of the same size, then, the commutative and associative properties hold true for addition, and each matrix has an additive inverse.

Multiplication of matrices is more complicated. First we define multiplication of a matrix by a real number. This is referred to as **scalar multiplication,** and the real number is called a **scalar.** If A is a matrix and c is a scalar, then cA is defined as the matrix obtained by multiplying every element of A by c. For example,

$$2\begin{bmatrix} 3 & 1 & -4 \\ 2 & 3 & 6 \end{bmatrix} = \begin{bmatrix} 6 & 2 & -8 \\ 4 & 6 & 12 \end{bmatrix}$$

Now let A and B denote two matrices. In order to define the product AB we require that the number of *columns in A* equal the number of *rows in B.* Before stating the general definition of the product AB, let us consider a specific example. Suppose

$$A = \begin{bmatrix} 2 & 1 & 4 \\ 3 & -2 & 0 \end{bmatrix} \quad \text{and} \quad B = \begin{bmatrix} 5 & 4 & 3 & -2 \\ 6 & -1 & 2 & 3 \\ 2 & 3 & -2 & 4 \end{bmatrix}$$

Then A is 2×3 and B is 3×4. So the requirement that the number of columns in A equals the number of rows in B is met. To find the elements of the product AB we describe first what is known as the **inner product** of a given row of A

with a given column of B. Take, for example, the first row of A and the second column of B:

$$\boxed{\begin{array}{ccc} 2 & 1 & 4 \end{array}} \boxed{\begin{array}{c} 4 \\ -1 \\ 3 \end{array}} = 2(4) + 1(-1) + 4(3) = 8 - 1 + 12 = 19$$

Observe that we multiplied corresponding elements and then added. This is what we mean by inner product. Now to obtain the element in the ith row and the jth column of AB, we find the inner product of the ith row of A and the jth column of B. In our example, we have found that 19 is the element in the first row and second column of AB. We now calculate the other elements:

$$\begin{bmatrix} 2 & 1 & 4 \\ 3 & -2 & 0 \end{bmatrix} \begin{bmatrix} 5 & 4 & 3 & -2 \\ 6 & -1 & 2 & 3 \\ 2 & 3 & -2 & 4 \end{bmatrix} = \begin{bmatrix} 24 & 19 & 0 & 15 \\ 3 & 14 & 5 & -12 \end{bmatrix}$$

We have shaded the first row of A, the second column of B, and their inner product 19, which therefore appears in the first row and second column of AB. The other elements are obtained in a similar way. (You should check these.) Notice that the size of the product matrix is 2×4, the number of rows being the same as the number of rows in A, and the number of columns being the same as the number of columns in B.

We now generalize these concepts.

DEFINITION 1   Let A be an $m \times n$ matrix and let B be an $n \times p$ matrix, and suppose the ith row of A and the jth column of B are as shown:

$$B$$

$$i\text{th row} \rightarrow \begin{bmatrix} & & & A & & & \\ \cdot & \cdot & \cdot & \cdot & \cdot & \cdot & \\ a_1 & a_2 & a_3 & \cdots & & a_n \\ \cdot & \cdot & \cdot & \cdot & \cdot & \cdot & \end{bmatrix} \qquad \begin{bmatrix} \cdot & b_1 & \cdot \\ \cdot & b_2 & \cdot \\ \cdot & b_3 & \cdot \\ \vdots & \vdots & \vdots \\ \cdot & b_n & \cdot \end{bmatrix}$$

$$\uparrow$$
$$j\text{th column}$$

The **inner product** of this row and this column is the number

$$a_1 b_1 + a_2 b_2 + a_3 b_3 + \cdots + a_n b_n$$

DEFINITION 2   If A and B are $m \times n$ and $n \times p$ matrices, respectively, then the product AB is the $m \times p$ matrix whose element in the ith row and jth column is the inner product of the ith row of A and the jth column of B.

EXAMPLE 18
$$\begin{bmatrix} 2 & -1 \\ 3 & 4 \\ 5 & -3 \end{bmatrix} \begin{bmatrix} -2 & 3 & 6 \\ 4 & 1 & -5 \end{bmatrix} = \begin{bmatrix} -8 & 5 & 17 \\ 10 & 13 & -2 \\ -22 & 12 & 45 \end{bmatrix}$$

In general, $AB \neq BA$. In fact, BA may not be defined even if AB is. For example, if

$$A = \begin{bmatrix} 3 & 1 \\ 4 & 2 \end{bmatrix} \quad \text{and} \quad B = \begin{bmatrix} 1 & 5 & 4 \\ 4 & 3 & 6 \end{bmatrix}$$

then the product AB is defined, but BA is not. Even when both AB and BA are defined, they may not be equal. For example, let

$$A = \begin{bmatrix} 3 & 4 \\ -2 & 5 \end{bmatrix} \quad \text{and} \quad B = \begin{bmatrix} -1 & 2 \\ 3 & -4 \end{bmatrix}$$

Then

$$AB = \begin{bmatrix} 3 & 4 \\ -2 & 5 \end{bmatrix} \begin{bmatrix} -1 & 2 \\ 3 & -4 \end{bmatrix} = \begin{bmatrix} 9 & -10 \\ 17 & -24 \end{bmatrix}$$

and

$$BA = \begin{bmatrix} -1 & 2 \\ 3 & -4 \end{bmatrix} \begin{bmatrix} 3 & 4 \\ -2 & 5 \end{bmatrix} = \begin{bmatrix} -7 & 6 \\ 17 & -8 \end{bmatrix}$$

So $AB \neq BA$. Matrix multiplication is therefore *noncommutative*. The following properties, however, can be shown to hold (we assume the sizes are such that all products are defined):

$$A(BC) = (AB)C \qquad \text{Associative property}$$
$$A(B + C) = AB + AC \qquad \text{Left distributive property}$$
$$(B + C)A = BA + CA \qquad \text{Right distributive property}$$

The left and right distributive properties normally yield different results because of noncommutativity.

EXERCISE SET 5

A In Problems 1–14 perform the indicated operations.

1. $\begin{bmatrix} 3 & 4 & -2 \\ 7 & 8 & 10 \end{bmatrix} + \begin{bmatrix} -1 & 2 & 5 \\ 3 & -4 & 6 \end{bmatrix}$

2. $\begin{bmatrix} 2 & 0 \\ 7 & 3 \\ -1 & 4 \end{bmatrix} + \begin{bmatrix} 5 & -3 \\ 2 & 6 \\ 3 & -7 \end{bmatrix}$

3. $\begin{bmatrix} 1 & 4 \\ -2 & 5 \end{bmatrix} - \begin{bmatrix} 3 & 2 \\ 4 & -6 \end{bmatrix}$

4. $\begin{bmatrix} 7 & -5 & 3 \\ -6 & 4 & 2 \\ 0 & 3 & -8 \end{bmatrix} - \begin{bmatrix} 5 & -8 & 1 \\ 2 & -6 & 3 \\ 4 & 0 & -2 \end{bmatrix}$

5. $\begin{bmatrix} 2 & 5 \\ 3 & -4 \end{bmatrix} + \begin{bmatrix} -1 & 2 \\ 5 & 6 \end{bmatrix} - \begin{bmatrix} 3 & -7 \\ 8 & 2 \end{bmatrix}$

6. $\begin{bmatrix} 3 & 1 & 5 \\ 2 & -3 & -6 \end{bmatrix} - \begin{bmatrix} 8 & -4 & 3 \\ -2 & 5 & -6 \end{bmatrix} + \begin{bmatrix} 4 & 6 & 9 \\ -5 & 7 & -2 \end{bmatrix}$

7. $2A + 3B,$ where $A = \begin{bmatrix} 2 & 1 \\ -1 & 4 \\ 3 & -5 \end{bmatrix}$ and $B = \begin{bmatrix} -3 & 2 \\ 4 & -3 \\ 7 & 8 \end{bmatrix}$

8. $4A - 5B,$ where A and B are as given in Problem 7

9. $\begin{bmatrix} 2 & 3 \\ -1 & 4 \end{bmatrix} \begin{bmatrix} 3 & -2 \\ 5 & 6 \end{bmatrix}$
10. $\begin{bmatrix} 1 & 2 & -4 \end{bmatrix} \begin{bmatrix} 3 & 4 \\ -2 & 6 \\ 5 & -1 \end{bmatrix}$

11. $\begin{bmatrix} 2 & 1 \\ 5 & 7 \end{bmatrix} \begin{bmatrix} 4 & -2 & 5 \\ -1 & 3 & 0 \end{bmatrix}$
12. $\begin{bmatrix} 1 & 3 & -2 \\ 0 & 4 & 5 \\ -2 & 1 & 3 \end{bmatrix} \begin{bmatrix} 4 \\ 3 \\ 2 \end{bmatrix}$

13. $\begin{bmatrix} 3 & 1 \\ 2 & -4 \\ 5 & 6 \end{bmatrix} \begin{bmatrix} 1 & 3 & -4 & 2 \\ -2 & 0 & 5 & 1 \end{bmatrix}$
14. $\begin{bmatrix} 1 & 3 & -2 \\ 4 & 0 & 1 \\ -2 & 5 & 3 \end{bmatrix} \begin{bmatrix} 1 & 2 & 0 & 5 \\ -2 & 3 & 1 & 4 \\ 3 & 0 & -5 & 6 \end{bmatrix}$

In Problems 15 and 16 solve for x and y by performing the multiplications and equating elements.

15. $\begin{bmatrix} 3 & 7 \\ 2 & -1 \end{bmatrix} \begin{bmatrix} x \\ y \end{bmatrix} = \begin{bmatrix} 1 \\ 12 \end{bmatrix}$
16. $\begin{bmatrix} 3 & 7 \\ 5 & -2 \end{bmatrix} \begin{bmatrix} x \\ y \end{bmatrix} = \begin{bmatrix} 11 \\ -9 \end{bmatrix}$

17. Perform the multiplication

$$\begin{bmatrix} 2 & -3 & 1 & -1 \\ 1 & 1 & -2 & 1 \end{bmatrix} \begin{bmatrix} 1 & 2 \\ -1 & 1 \\ 5 & 4 \\ 10 & 5 \end{bmatrix}$$

What can you conclude in general about matrices A and B if $AB = 0$?

18. Let

$$A = \begin{bmatrix} 2 & 3 \\ -1 & 4 \end{bmatrix} \qquad B = \begin{bmatrix} 1 & 0 & -2 \\ 3 & -1 & 5 \end{bmatrix} \qquad C = \begin{bmatrix} 1 & -4 \\ -2 & 3 \\ 5 & -1 \end{bmatrix}$$

Determine which of the following are defined. For those that are defined, perform the indicated multiplications.
a. ABC **b.** ACB **c.** BAC **d.** BCA **e.** CAB **f.** CBA

B **19.** Let

$$A = \begin{bmatrix} a_1 & a_2 \\ a_3 & a_4 \end{bmatrix} \qquad B = \begin{bmatrix} b_1 & b_2 \\ b_3 & b_4 \end{bmatrix} \qquad C = \begin{bmatrix} c_1 & c_2 \\ c_3 & c_4 \end{bmatrix}$$

Prove that:
a. $A + B = B + A$ **b.** $A + (B + C) = (A + B) + C$
c. $A(BC) = (AB)C$ **d.** $A(B + C) = AB + AC$
20. When AA is defined, it is customary to denote this by A^2. Prove that A^2 exists if and only if A is a square matrix.

21. For a square matrix A, we write $A^2 = AA$, $A^3 = AAA$, and so on. If

$$A = \begin{bmatrix} 1 & 1 \\ 1 & 1 \end{bmatrix}$$

find A^2, A^3, and A^4. Generalize this to A^n.

22. Use 2×2 matrices to prove that in general $(A + B)^2 \neq A^2 + 2AB + B^2$. Find a correct formula for $(A + B)^2$.

23. Use 2×2 matrices to prove that in general $(A + B)(A - B) \neq A^2 - B^2$. Find a correct formula for $(A + B)(A - B)$.

24. Let

$$A = \begin{bmatrix} 2 & -1 & 3 \\ 4 & 2 & -2 \\ -3 & 5 & 4 \end{bmatrix} \qquad X = \begin{bmatrix} x \\ y \\ z \end{bmatrix} \qquad B = \begin{bmatrix} 13 \\ -6 \\ -1 \end{bmatrix}$$

Solve the equation $AX = B$ for X.

25. The following represents a system of m linear equations in n unknowns:

$$\begin{cases} a_{11}x_1 + a_{12}x_2 + a_{13}x_3 + \cdots + a_{1n}x_n = b_1 \\ a_{21}x_1 + a_{22}x_2 + a_{23}x_3 + \cdots + a_{2n}x_n = b_2 \\ a_{31}x_1 + a_{32}x_2 + a_{33}x_3 + \cdots + a_{3n}x_n = b_3 \\ \qquad \cdots \cdots \cdots \cdots \cdots \cdots \cdots \cdots \cdots \\ a_{m1}x_1 + a_{m2}x_2 + a_{m3}x_3 + \cdots + a_{mn}x_n = b_n \end{cases}$$

Find matrices A, B, and X for which the matrix equation $AX = B$ is equivalent to this system.

26. Let

$$A = \begin{bmatrix} 0 & 1 & 1 \\ 1 & 0 & 1 \\ 1 & 1 & 0 \end{bmatrix} \qquad I = \begin{bmatrix} 1 & 0 & 0 \\ 0 & 1 & 0 \\ 0 & 0 & 1 \end{bmatrix}$$

Solve the equation $|A - \lambda I| = 0$ for λ, where λ is a scalar.

6   Inverses of Matrices

If A is a square matrix, there may be a matrix B such that $AB = BA = I$. In this case matrix B is called the **multiplicative inverse** (or simply the inverse) of A and is denoted by A^{-1}. If B is the inverse of A, then A is also the inverse of B, so that $(A^{-1})^{-1} = A$. Matrices that have inverses are said to be **nonsingular**; those that do not are called **singular.** We will give two methods for calculating inverses of nonsingular matrices. Both methods also provide means of identifying singular matrices.

Method I.   If a sequence of elementary row operations exists that transforms A into I, then A is nonsingular and A^{-1} is the matrix obtained by applying this sequence of elementary row operations to I.

We illustrate this method below, where we have written I to the right of A. Thus as an elementary row operation is applied to A it is also applied to I.

Our goal will be reached when the left-hand matrix is I. The right-hand matrix will then be A^{-1}. If it is impossible to obtain I on the left, then A is singular.

$$
\begin{array}{cc}
A & I
\end{array}
$$

$$
\left[\begin{array}{ccc|ccc}
2 & -1 & 5 & 1 & 0 & 0 \\
0 & 2 & 4 & 0 & 1 & 0 \\
1 & -2 & 0 & 0 & 0 & 1
\end{array}\right]
$$

$$
\left[\begin{array}{ccc|ccc}
1 & -2 & 0 & 0 & 0 & 1 \\
0 & 2 & 4 & 0 & 1 & 0 \\
2 & -1 & 5 & 1 & 0 & 0
\end{array}\right]
\begin{array}{l}
\text{Row 3 interchanged with Row 1} \\[1em]
\text{Row 1 interchanged with Row 3}
\end{array}
$$

$$
\left[\begin{array}{ccc|ccc}
1 & -2 & 0 & 0 & 0 & 1 \\
0 & 2 & 4 & 0 & 1 & 0 \\
0 & 3 & 5 & 1 & 0 & -2
\end{array}\right]
\quad \text{Row } 3 + (-2) \cdot \text{Row 1}
$$

$$
\left[\begin{array}{ccc|ccc}
1 & -2 & 0 & 0 & 0 & 1 \\
0 & 1 & 2 & 0 & \frac{1}{2} & 0 \\
0 & 3 & 5 & 1 & 0 & -2
\end{array}\right]
\quad (\text{Row 2}) \cdot (\tfrac{1}{2})
$$

$$
\left[\begin{array}{ccc|ccc}
1 & 0 & 4 & 0 & 1 & 1 \\
0 & 1 & 2 & 0 & \frac{1}{2} & 0 \\
0 & 0 & -1 & 1 & -\frac{3}{2} & -2
\end{array}\right]
\begin{array}{l}
\text{Row } 1 + 2 \cdot \text{Row 2} \\[1em]
\text{Row } 3 + (-3) \cdot \text{Row 2}
\end{array}
$$

$$
\left[\begin{array}{ccc|ccc}
1 & 0 & 0 & 4 & -5 & -7 \\
0 & 1 & 0 & 2 & -\frac{5}{2} & -4 \\
0 & 0 & 1 & -1 & \frac{3}{2} & 2
\end{array}\right]
\begin{array}{l}
\text{Row } 1 + 4 \cdot \text{Row 3} \\
\text{Row } 2 + 2 \cdot \text{Row 3} \\
(\text{Row 3}) \cdot (-1)
\end{array}
$$

Therefore A is nonsingular and

$$
A^{-1} = \left[\begin{array}{ccc}
4 & -5 & -7 \\
2 & -\frac{5}{2} & -4 \\
-1 & \frac{3}{2} & 2
\end{array}\right]
$$

You should check to see that $AA^{-1} = A^{-1}A = I$.

Method II. First find the matrix C obtained by replacing each element of A by its cofactor. Then interchange the rows of C with the corresponding columns. The result of this interchange of rows and columns is called the **transpose** of C and is denoted by C^{T}. Finally, divide C^{T} by the determinant of A, provided this determinant is nonzero. The result is A^{-1}. Briefly,

$$
A^{-1} = \frac{C^{\mathrm{T}}}{|A|}
$$

If $|A| = 0$, then A is singular.

Let us apply this method to the same matrix A used in illustrating method I:

$$
A = \left[\begin{array}{ccc}
2 & -1 & 5 \\
0 & 2 & 4 \\
1 & -2 & 0
\end{array}\right]
$$

Replace each element of A by its cofactor, obtaining C:

$$C = \begin{bmatrix} 8 & 4 & -2 \\ -10 & -5 & 3 \\ -14 & -8 & 4 \end{bmatrix}$$

Transpose rows and columns:

$$C^{\mathrm{T}} = \begin{bmatrix} 8 & -10 & -14 \\ 4 & -5 & -8 \\ -2 & 3 & 4 \end{bmatrix}$$

Calculate $|A|$. (Note that this can be done by taking the inner product of any row or column of A and the corresponding row or column of C.) Expanding on the first column we get

$$|A| = 2(8) + 0(-10) + 1(-14) = 2$$

So A is nonsingular and

$$A^{-1} = \frac{1}{2}\begin{bmatrix} 8 & -10 & -14 \\ 4 & -5 & -8 \\ -2 & 3 & 4 \end{bmatrix} = \begin{bmatrix} 4 & -5 & -7 \\ 2 & -\frac{5}{2} & -4 \\ -1 & \frac{3}{2} & 2 \end{bmatrix}$$

Remark.   This method shows that the condition $|A| \neq 0$ is both necessary and sufficient for A to be nonsingular.

Method II is particularly simple for 2×2 matrices. Consider, for example,

$$A = \begin{bmatrix} a & b \\ c & d \end{bmatrix}$$

We have

$$C = \begin{bmatrix} d & -c \\ -b & a \end{bmatrix} \quad \text{and} \quad C^{\mathrm{T}} = \begin{bmatrix} d & -b \\ -c & a \end{bmatrix}$$

so that if $|A| = ad - bc \neq 0$, then

$$A^{-1} = \frac{\begin{bmatrix} d & -b \\ -c & a \end{bmatrix}}{|A|}$$

Note that to get C^{T} directly from A we simply interchange the elements a and d on the major diagonal and take the negatives of the elements on the minor diagonal. For example,

$$\begin{bmatrix} 3 & -2 \\ 5 & -4 \end{bmatrix}^{-1} = \frac{\begin{bmatrix} -4 & 2 \\ -5 & 3 \end{bmatrix}}{(-12 + 10)} = \begin{bmatrix} 2 & -1 \\ \frac{5}{2} & -\frac{3}{2} \end{bmatrix}$$

For 3×3 matrices, method II may still be easier than method I, depending on how adept one is in calculating cofactors mentally. For higher-order matrices, however, method I is generally preferable.

Using inverses of matrices provides an alternative way of solving a system $AX = B$, where the number of equations is the same as the number of unknowns (so that A is square). If A^{-1} exists, we multiply both sides by A^{-1} (left multiplication on each side) to get

$$A^{-1}(AX) = A^{-1}B$$
$$(A^{-1}A)X = A^{-1}B$$
$$IX = A^{-1}B$$
$$X = A^{-1}B$$

For example, let us solve the system

$$\begin{cases} 2x - y + 5z = 3 \\ 2y + 4z = 5 \\ x - 2y = -4 \end{cases}$$

This can be written in matrix form, $AX = B$, where

$$A = \begin{bmatrix} 2 & -1 & 5 \\ 0 & 2 & 4 \\ 1 & -2 & 0 \end{bmatrix} \qquad X = \begin{bmatrix} x \\ y \\ z \end{bmatrix} \qquad B = \begin{bmatrix} 3 \\ 5 \\ -4 \end{bmatrix}$$

We have already found the inverse of A in illustrating methods I and II, so

$$X = A^{-1}B = \begin{bmatrix} 4 & -5 & -7 \\ 2 & -\frac{5}{2} & -4 \\ -1 & \frac{3}{2} & 2 \end{bmatrix} \begin{bmatrix} 3 \\ 5 \\ -4 \end{bmatrix} = \begin{bmatrix} 15 \\ \frac{19}{2} \\ -\frac{7}{2} \end{bmatrix}$$

Thus $x = 15$, $y = \frac{19}{2}$, $z = -\frac{7}{2}$.

While using inverses to solve systems of equations appears simple, the limitations on its use are severe—especially the requirements that the system be square and that A be nonsingular. Furthermore, calculation of A^{-1} is difficult for higher-order systems. In fact, there is at least as much work involved in calculating A^{-1} by method I as in solving the system by reducing the augmented matrix to triangular form as in Section 2. It should be emphasized, however, that inverses of matrices have many other uses, even if their utility is limited in solving systems of equations.

EXERCISE SET 6

A In Problems 1–15 use method I to find the inverse or to show that the inverse does not exist. When A is nonsingular, check your result by showing that $AA^{-1} = I$.

1. $\begin{bmatrix} 2 & -1 \\ 3 & -2 \end{bmatrix}$ 2. $\begin{bmatrix} -1 & 2 \\ 3 & 5 \end{bmatrix}$ 3. $\begin{bmatrix} 5 & -4 \\ 3 & -2 \end{bmatrix}$

4. $\begin{bmatrix} -2 & 6 \\ -3 & 4 \end{bmatrix}$ 5. $\begin{bmatrix} 1 & 0 & 0 \\ -1 & 2 & 0 \\ 1 & 4 & 3 \end{bmatrix}$ 6. $\begin{bmatrix} 1 & 2 & 3 \\ 0 & 1 & 4 \\ 0 & 0 & 1 \end{bmatrix}$

7. $\begin{bmatrix} 2 & 1 & 0 \\ -3 & -4 & 2 \\ 2 & 2 & -1 \end{bmatrix}$ 8. $\begin{bmatrix} 3 & -1 & 2 \\ 0 & 1 & 6 \\ 1 & 0 & 3 \end{bmatrix}$ 9. $\begin{bmatrix} -1 & 1 & 1 \\ 1 & -1 & -1 \\ -1 & 1 & -1 \end{bmatrix}$

10. $\begin{bmatrix} 2 & 0 & 1 \\ 0 & 3 & -2 \\ 1 & -2 & 2 \end{bmatrix}$

11. $\begin{bmatrix} 1 & -3 & 4 \\ -2 & 5 & 1 \\ 0 & -2 & 18 \end{bmatrix}$

12. $\begin{bmatrix} 5 & 0 & -6 \\ 3 & 2 & -3 \\ -2 & 5 & 4 \end{bmatrix}$

13. $\begin{bmatrix} 2 & 7 & -3 \\ 3 & 8 & -4 \\ -10 & 6 & 7 \end{bmatrix}$

14. $\begin{bmatrix} 2 & -3 & -3 \\ 3 & 2 & -5 \\ -4 & 3 & 6 \end{bmatrix}$

15. $\begin{bmatrix} 3 & 1 & 4 \\ -5 & -2 & 1 \\ 7 & 3 & -6 \end{bmatrix}$

16–30.   Repeat Problems 1–15 using method II.

In Problems 31–36 solve the system $AX = B$ using $X = A^{-1}B$.

31. $\begin{cases} x - y - 2z = 7 \\ 2x + 3y + 4z = -3 \\ -x + 2y + 3z = -8 \end{cases}$

32. $\begin{cases} 2x - y + z = 1 \\ x + 3y - z = 3 \\ 3x - 2y + 2z = -1 \end{cases}$

33. $\begin{cases} x - y - z = 0 \\ 2x + 4y + 5z = 5 \\ 5x - 3y - 2z = 3 \end{cases}$

34. $\begin{cases} 2x + y - z = 1 \\ 3x - 2y + 5z = 3 \\ 5x + 3y - 4z = 0 \end{cases}$

35. $\begin{cases} 5x + 3y + 2z = 21 \\ 4x - 2y - 3z = 7 \\ -3x + 4y + 5z = 1 \end{cases}$

36. $\begin{cases} 3x + 4y - 5z = -1 \\ -4x - 5y + 6z = 11 \\ 7x + 5z = 2 \end{cases}$

B   **37.**   Complete the following proof that the inverse of a nonsingular matrix is unique. Suppose A is nonsingular and B and C are inverses of A. Then $AB = AC$. (Why?) Now multiply both sides of this equation on the left by B (or by C), and use the associate property. What conclusion do you draw?

38.   Prove that if A and B are nonsingular $n \times n$ matrices, then AB is nonsingular and $(AB)^{-1} = B^{-1}A^{-1}$.

39.   Show that an "upper triangular" matrix of the form

$$\begin{bmatrix} a_{11} & a_{12} & a_{13} \\ 0 & a_{22} & a_{23} \\ 0 & 0 & a_{33} \end{bmatrix}$$

is nonsingular if, and only if, $a_{ii} \neq 0$ for $i = 1, 2, 3$, and find a formula for the inverse.

In Problems 40–43 find the inverse or show that it does not exist.

40. $\begin{bmatrix} 1 & -1 & 0 & 0 \\ 1 & 0 & 1 & -1 \\ 0 & 1 & 1 & 0 \\ 1 & -1 & 0 & 1 \end{bmatrix}$

41. $\begin{bmatrix} 1 & -1 & 2 & 0 \\ 0 & 1 & -1 & 1 \\ -1 & 1 & 1 & 2 \\ 0 & -1 & 1 & -2 \end{bmatrix}$

42. $\begin{bmatrix} 1 & 0 & -2 & 3 \\ 0 & -2 & -5 & 0 \\ 2 & 3 & -1 & 1 \\ -1 & -2 & 3 & 4 \end{bmatrix}$

43. $\begin{bmatrix} 2 & -1 & 3 & 1 \\ -1 & 4 & 2 & 1 \\ 3 & -1 & 5 & 4 \\ -2 & 3 & -1 & 1 \end{bmatrix}$

44.   Solve the following system in the form $X = A^{-1}B$.

$$\begin{cases} x_1 - 2x_2 + x_3 - x_4 = 2 \\ x_1 - x_2 - x_4 = 6 \\ 2x_1 - 2x_2 + x_3 = 9 \\ -x_1 + 5x_2 - 2x_3 + 6x_4 = 6 \end{cases}$$

45. The matrix

$$A = \begin{bmatrix} a_{11} & a_{12} & \cdots & a_{1n} \\ a_{21} & a_{22} & \cdots & a_{2n} \\ \vdots & \vdots & & \vdots \\ a_{n1} & a_{n2} & \cdots & a_{nn} \end{bmatrix}$$

is said to be **orthonormal** if

$$a_{i1}^2 + a_{i2}^2 + \cdots + a_{in}^2 = 1 \quad \text{and} \quad a_{i1}a_{i2}a_{k2} + \cdots + a_{in}a_{kn} = 0$$

for $i, k = 1, 2, \ldots, n$. Prove that if A is orthonormal, $A^{-1} = A^{\mathrm{T}}$.

46. Using the result of Problem 45, show that the following matrix is orthonormal and find its inverse.

$$\begin{bmatrix} \dfrac{1}{2} & \dfrac{1}{2} & \dfrac{1}{2} & \dfrac{1}{2} \\[2mm] \dfrac{1}{\sqrt{2}} & \dfrac{-1}{\sqrt{2}} & 0 & 0 \\[2mm] \dfrac{1}{\sqrt{6}} & \dfrac{1}{\sqrt{6}} & \dfrac{-2}{\sqrt{6}} & 0 \\[2mm] \dfrac{1}{2\sqrt{3}} & \dfrac{1}{2\sqrt{3}} & \dfrac{1}{2\sqrt{3}} & \dfrac{-\sqrt{3}}{2} \end{bmatrix}$$

47. Carry out the details of the following proof of method II for finding inverses. Let

$$A = \begin{bmatrix} a_{11} & a_{12} & \cdots & a_{1n} \\ a_{21} & a_{22} & \cdots & a_{2n} \\ \vdots & \vdots & & \vdots \\ a_{n1} & a_{n2} & \cdots & a_{nn} \end{bmatrix}$$

and let A_{ij} be the cofactor of a_{ij}. Then

$$C^{\mathrm{T}} = \begin{bmatrix} A_{11} & A_{21} & \cdots & A_{n1} \\ A_{12} & A_{22} & \cdots & A_{n2} \\ \vdots & \vdots & & \vdots \\ A_{1n} & A_{2n} & \cdots & A_{nn} \end{bmatrix}$$

Show that both AC^{T} and $C^{\mathrm{T}}A$ yield a matrix that can be written in the form $|A|I$. (In doing this you will need to know that when the elements of any row or column of A are multiplied by the respective cofactors of any *other* row or column, the result is zero. Can you see why?) Now draw the desired conclusion.

In Problems 48 and 49 use a calculator to find the inverse.

48.
$$\begin{bmatrix} 0.231 & 1.24 & -2.79 \\ 3.75 & -2.03 & 0.462 \\ 5.16 & 6.23 & -4.68 \end{bmatrix}$$

49.
$$\begin{bmatrix} 2.801 & -0.7254 & -3.042 \\ -4.731 & 6.287 & -0.2345 \\ 0.6498 & 3.976 & -8.504 \end{bmatrix}$$

7 Nonlinear Systems

No general theory exists to handle the great variety of nonlinear systems that can occur. One must deal with each particular situation and decide what will work, and of course there are times when nothing will give an exact solution. Nevertheless, we can consider some fairly common situations that may be solved by elementary means. We will illustrate these by examples.

EXAMPLE 19   Solve the system: $\begin{cases} 2x^2 - y + 3 = 0 \\ x + y = 6 \end{cases}$

Solution   This is a case of a quadratic equation and a linear equation. Typically, when-ever one equation is linear and the other is not, the best procedure is to sub-stitute from the linear equation into the other. In this problem we choose to solve the second equation for y (rather than x, since the substitution is simpler):

$$y = 6 - x$$
$$2x^2 - (6 - x) + 3 = 0$$
$$2x^2 + x - 3 = 0$$
$$(2x + 3)(x - 1) = 0$$
$$x = -\tfrac{3}{2} \quad | \quad x = 1$$

When $x = -\tfrac{3}{2}$, $y = 6 - (-\tfrac{3}{2}) = \tfrac{15}{2}$, and when $x = 1$, $y = 6 - 1 = 5$. So the solution set is $\{(1, 5), \quad (-\tfrac{3}{2}, \tfrac{15}{2})\}$. The graphs of both equations are shown in Figure 3, and the solutions are indicated.

Figure 3

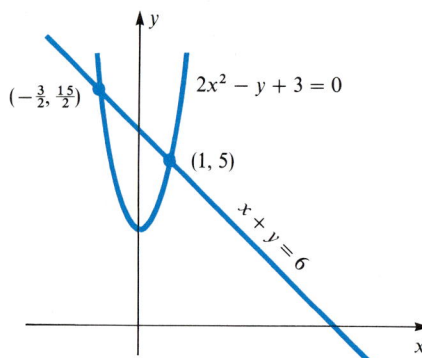

EXAMPLE 20   Solve the system: $\begin{cases} xy + 2 = 0 \\ 2x - y = 5 \end{cases}$

Solution   This is handled in a similar way, although we could easily substitute from the first equation into the second:

$$y = 2x - 5$$
$$x(2x - 5) + 2 = 0$$
$$2x^2 - 5x + 2 = 0$$
$$(2x - 1)(x - 2) = 0$$
$$x = \tfrac{1}{2} \quad | \quad x = 2$$

When $x = \tfrac{1}{2}$, $y = 2(\tfrac{1}{2}) - 5 = -4$, and when $x = 2$, $y = 2(2) - 5 = -1$. So the solution set is $\{(\tfrac{1}{2}, -4), \quad (2, -1)\}$. The graph of the first equation is obtained by plotting a few points. It is a hyperbola (Figure 4).

Figure 4

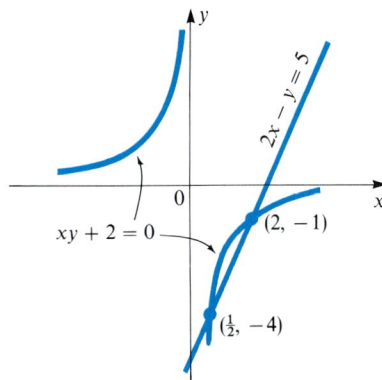

$$\begin{cases} x^2 - y^2 = 5 \\ 2x^2 + y^2 = 22 \end{cases}$$

EXAMPLE 21   Solve the system:

Solution   Even though these are quadratic equations, they are linear in form, and the techniques of solving linear systems can be used to find x^2 and y^2, from which x and y can be obtained. In particular, Cramer's rule could be used, but it is probably easier here just to eliminate y^2 by addition:

$$\begin{aligned} x^2 - y^2 &= 5 \\ 2x^2 + y^2 &= 22 \\ \hline 3x^2 &= 27 \\ x^2 &= 9 \\ x &= \pm 3 \end{aligned}$$

Now substitute $x^2 = 9$ into the first equation (since it is simpler):

$$\begin{aligned} 9 - y^2 &= 5 \\ y^2 &= 4 \\ y &= \pm 2 \end{aligned}$$

The complete solution set is $\{(3, 2), (3, -2), (-3, 2), (-3, -2)\}$. Again, it is helpful to visualize the situation graphically (Figure 5).

Figure 5

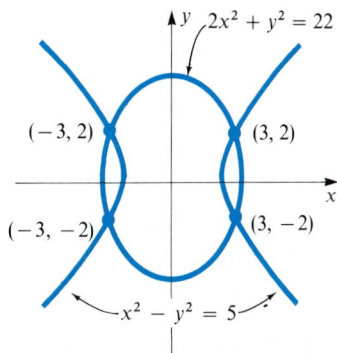

EXAMPLE 22   Solve the system:
$$\begin{cases} y = 3x - \dfrac{4}{x} \\ y = x^2 \end{cases}$$

Solution   Here, we can eliminate y to get

$$x^2 = 3x - \frac{4}{x}$$

Multiplying by x yields

$$x^3 - 3x^2 + 4 = 0^*$$

We know from Chapter 6 that the only possible rational roots are $\pm 1, \pm 2, \pm 4$. We proceed by synthetic division to test these:

x				y
0	1	-3	0	4
1	1	-2	-2	2
2	1	-1	-2	0

So $x = 2$ is a root, and the depressed equation is quadratic:

$$x^2 - x - 2 = 0$$
$$(x - 2)(x + 1) = 0$$
$$x = 2 \quad | \quad x = -1$$

Thus, $x = 2$ is a double root. When $x = 2$, $y = 4$, and when $x = -1$, $y = 1$. The solution set is $\{(2, 4), (-1, 1)\}$ with $(2, 4)$ as a double point. Graphically, the significance of the double point is that the curves are tangent to each other at that point. The graph of the first equation is somewhat more complicated this time, but again we give a sketch in Figure 6 to help visualize the situation.

Figure 6

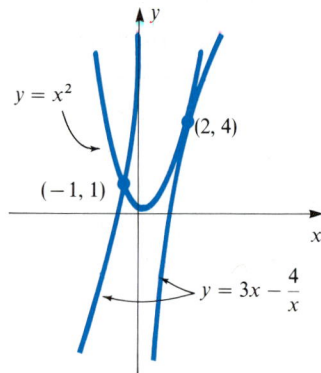

* This could lead to an extraneous root, since we may be unwittingly multiplying by 0. The answers should be checked to see that this is not the case.

EXAMPLE 23   Solve the system:
$$\begin{cases} y = \sqrt{x} \\ y^2 = \dfrac{2}{x} + 1 \end{cases}$$

Solution   Again, substitution can be used. We substitute for y from the first equation into the second:

$$x = \frac{2}{x} + 1$$

$$x^2 = 2 + x$$

$$x^2 - x - 2 = 0$$

$$(x - 2)(x + 1) = 0$$

$$x = 2 \quad | \quad x = -1$$

When $x = 2$, $y = \sqrt{2}$, and when $x = -1$, y is imaginary. So $(2, \sqrt{2})$ is the only real solution.

Notice that after finding $x = 2$ we substituted into the first equation to get y. Had we substituted into the second, we would have had

$$y^2 = \tfrac{2}{2} + 1 = 2$$

$$y = \pm\sqrt{2}$$

But $y = -\sqrt{2}$ is not possible, since the first equation implies that y is never negative; so we must reject $-\sqrt{2}$. This extraneous root resulted from squaring the first equation to substitute into the second. Whenever both sides of an equation are squared, there is a possibility of introducing extraneous roots, and so the answer should be checked. In general, after finding one unknown it is best to substitute this into the equation that imposes the greater restriction on the other unknown, if this can be identified. In solving for x, we also multiplied by the unknown, which again could introduce extraneous roots since we might have multiplied by 0. We can check mentally to see that this did not occur. The graphs are rather complicated, and we will not show them here.

The main device we have used in the above examples is that of elimination by substitution. This technique is especially useful whenever at least one of the unknowns appears to the first power in either of the equations. You should also be alert to the possibility of eliminating an unknown by addition or subtraction.

EXERCISE SET 7

A   Find the solution set in Problems 1–33.

1. $\begin{cases} x^2 + y^2 = 5 \\ x - y = 1 \end{cases}$

2. $\begin{cases} x^2 + y^2 = 10 \\ 2x - y = 1 \end{cases}$

3. $\begin{cases} x^2 + 2y^2 = 9 \\ x - 2y = 3 \end{cases}$

4. $\begin{cases} x^2 + y^2 = 5 \\ 3x + 4y = 5 \end{cases}$

5. $\begin{cases} y = x^2 - 4 \\ y = \dfrac{2x - 7}{3} \end{cases}$

6. $\begin{cases} y = 3 - x^2 \\ 2x - y + 4 = 0 \end{cases}$

7. $\begin{cases} x - y^2 = 4 \\ 2x - 3y = 10 \end{cases}$

8. $\begin{cases} xy = 4 \\ y - x = 3 \end{cases}$

9. $\begin{cases} 4x^2 + 3y^2 = 9 \\ y = 2x \end{cases}$

10. $\begin{cases} 3x^2 + 4y^2 = 63 \\ x - 2y + 3 = 0 \end{cases}$

11. $\begin{cases} y^2 = x \\ 2x - 3y = 5 \end{cases}$

12. $\begin{cases} y^2 = x \\ x^2 = y \end{cases}$

13. $\begin{cases} xy = 1 \\ 4x - 7y = 3 \end{cases}$

14. $\begin{cases} 2xy = -3 \\ 3x - 4y = 9 \end{cases}$

15. $\begin{cases} x^2 + y^2 = 3 \\ y^2 = 2x \end{cases}$

16. $\begin{cases} x^2 + y^2 = 6 \\ y^2 - 3x = 2 \end{cases}$

17. $\begin{cases} x^2 - y^2 = 7 \\ y = 2x - 5 \end{cases}$

18. $\begin{cases} 4x^2 - 5y^2 + 16 = 0 \\ 2x + 3y = 4 \end{cases}$

19. $\begin{cases} y^2 = 4x \\ x^2 - 2y^2 = 9 \end{cases}$

20. $\begin{cases} y = x^2 - 4 \\ 5x^2 - y^2 = 20 \end{cases}$

21. $\begin{cases} x^2 + y^2 - 2y = 24 \\ 2x - y = 4 \end{cases}$

22. $\begin{cases} 2x^2 - 3y^2 = 5 \\ x^2 - 2y^2 = 2 \end{cases}$

23. $\begin{cases} 4x^2 - y^2 = 7 \\ x^2 + 3y^2 = 31 \end{cases}$

24. $\begin{cases} xy + 6 = 0 \\ x^2 + y^2 = 13 \end{cases}$

25. $\begin{cases} 2x^2 - 3x + 4y^2 = 35 \\ x + 2y = 5 \end{cases}$

26. $\begin{cases} 3x^2 - 4y^2 = 12 \\ 7x^2 - y^2 = 8 \end{cases}$

27. $\begin{cases} 3x^2 - 7y^2 = 5 \\ 5x^2 + 3y^2 = 12 \end{cases}$

28. $\begin{cases} 3x^2 - y^2 = 1 \\ 7x^2 - 2y^2 = 5 \end{cases}$

29. $\begin{cases} y^2 = x - 3 \\ y^2 - 3y + 2x = 12 \end{cases}$

30. $\begin{cases} xy = 3 \\ 2x^2 - 3y^2 = 15 \end{cases}$

31. $\begin{cases} x^2 + y^2 + 2x - y = 8 \\ x^2 + y^2 = 5 \end{cases}$

32. $\begin{cases} x^2 + y^2 + 3x - 4y = -4 \\ x^2 + y^2 + 2x - 3y = 1 \end{cases}$

33. $\begin{cases} y = x^2 - 4 \\ x^2 + 3y^2 + 4y - 6 = 0 \end{cases}$

34. The perimeter of a rectangle is 40, and its area is 96. Find its dimensions.
35. The length of a rectangle is 4 more than twice its width, and its area is 126. Find its dimensions.
36. The difference between two numbers is 3, and their product is 270. Find the numbers.
37. The difference between two numbers is 4 and the difference between their squares is 80. Find the numbers.
38. The product of two numbers is 128, and the sum of their reciprocals is $\frac{3}{16}$. Find the numbers.
39. The perimeter of a rectangle is 34, and the length of its diagonal is 13. Find the length and width.
40. The length of a rectangle is 3 less than twice the width, and the square of the length of the diagonal is 306. Find the length and width.
41. A beam is to be sawed from a log of diameter 10 inches. If the height of the cross-section of the beam is to be twice the width, what are the maximum dimensions of the cross-section of the beam?

42. A driver travels the first 75 miles of a 95 mile trip without encountering congestion, but traffic is heavy on the remaining part, and his average speed is reduced by 10 miles per hour. The total time for the trip is 2 hours. Find his average speed on each part of the trip.

43. A man has a certain amount invested at simple interest, the annual income from which is $180. If he had invested it at another bank that pays $\frac{1}{2}\%$ more interest, he would have received an income of $198 per year. Find the amount he invested and the rate of interest.

B   Find the solution set in Problems 44–47.

44. $\begin{cases} x^2 - y = 2 \\ y^2 + 2y - 3x^2 - 10x = 6 \end{cases}$

45. $\begin{cases} x^2 + y = 8 \\ x^2 - 2xy + y^2 = 16 \end{cases}$

46. $\begin{cases} xy = 1 \\ x - 4y^2 + 3 = 0 \end{cases}$

47. $\begin{cases} \dfrac{1}{x} + \dfrac{2}{y} = 3 \\ xy = 1 \end{cases}$

48. The height of a certain right circular cylinder is 1 inch more than twice its radius. Its volume is 9π cubic inches. Find the height and the radius.

49. A right circular cylinder of volume 72π is inscribed in a sphere of radius 5. Find the base radius and height of the cylinder.

50. The height of a right circular cone is 1 inch less than twice its base radius. If the volume is 15π cubic inches, find the base radius and the height.

51. Find the equation of the line that passes through the points of intersection of the curves whose equations are $y^2 = x$ and $x^2 + 3xy - 2y^2 = 32$.

52. Find the equation of the line passing through the points of intersection of the curves $x^2 + y^2 = 10$ and $x^2 + y^2 - 2x + 4y = 0$.

53. An isosceles triangle with base equal to its altitude is inscribed in a circle of diameter 10. Find the altitude of the triangle.

54. A boy is in a rowboat 4 miles from the point A nearest him on the shore. In order to get to the point B on the shore 10 miles from A, he rows to point C, between A and B, and jogs the rest of the way to B. If he can row 5 miles per hour and jog 7 miles per hour, and if his time rowing equals his time jogging, find how far C is from A (see sketch).

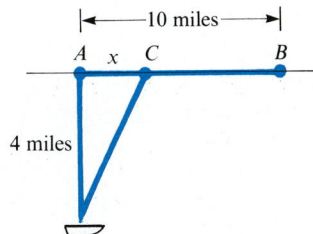

8 Systems of Inequalities

We will illustrate in this section how to determine graphic solutions to systems of inequalities. First we must see how to solve graphically a single inequality in two variables. This is illustrated in the next two examples.

EXAMPLE 24   Show the graphic solution to the inequality $2x - y < 3$.

Solution   The inequality can be written in the equivalent form $y > 2x - 3$. We wish to describe as a region in the plane the set of all points (x, y) satisfying this. One technique is to sketch first the line $y = 2x - 3$ and to observe that the solution to the given inequality consists of all points *above* this line (Figure 7). The line is dashed in the figure to indicate that it is not part of the solution set.

Figure 7

Remark.   We could equally well write the inequality in the form $x < (y + 3)/2$ and conclude that the solution set consists of all points to the *left* of the line $x = (y + 3)/2$, and this is seen to agree with what we have shown.

EXAMPLE 25   Show the graphic solution of the inequality $y \leq x^2 + 4$.

Solution   The graph of $y = x^2 + 4$ is the parabola pictured in Figure 8. All points *on the parabola or below* it satisfy the given inequality. The parabola is shown as a solid curve to indicate that it is part of the solution set.

Figure 8

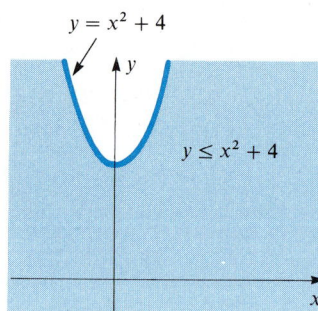

The next two examples illustrate graphic solutions to systems of linear inequalities in two variables.

EXAMPLE 26   Find the common solution set to the system: $\begin{cases} 2x + 3y > 4 \\ x + y < 3 \end{cases}$

Solution   We rewrite the inequalities in the form

$$y > \frac{4 - 2x}{3}$$

$$y < 3 - x$$

and next draw the bounding lines, as shown in Figure 9. The simultaneous solution is the shaded region in the figure, since that is where y is greater than $(4 - 2x)/3$ and at the same time less than $3 - x$.

Figure 9

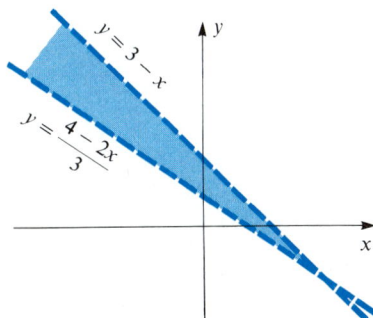

EXAMPLE 27   Exhibit graphically the simultaneous solution set to the system:

$$\begin{cases} x + 3y \le 12 \\ x + y \le 6 \\ 2x + y \le 10 \\ x \ge 0 \\ y \ge 0 \end{cases}$$

Solution   The last two inequalities restrict the solution set to the first quadrant. We rewrite the other three inequalities in the form

$$y \le \frac{12 - x}{3}$$

$$y \le 6 - x$$

$$y \le 10 - 2x$$

and draw the lines represented by the corresponding equalities (Figure 10). The simultaneous solution is the shaded region in the figure, including the boundary lines. In applications, it is usually important to know the vertices of the boundary. These are found by solving appropriate pairs of equations simultaneously and are shown in the figure.

Figure 10

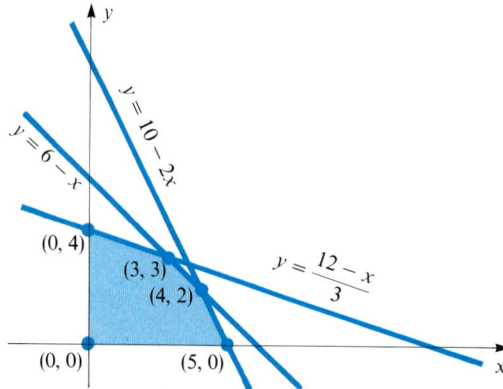

The next example involves absolute values and is equivalent to a system of simultaneous inequalities.

EXAMPLE 28 Show the graphic solution of the inequality $|x| - |y| \le 1$.

Solution We may rewrite the inequality in the form

$$|x| \le |y| + 1$$

which is equivalent to

$$-|y| - 1 \le x \le |y| + 1$$

So if $y \ge 0$, this gives

$$-y - 1 \le x \le y + 1$$

whereas if $y < 0$, we obtain

$$y - 1 \le x \le -y + 1$$

Equivalently, we may say that when $y \ge 0$, the inequality is satisfied by all pairs (x, y) which simultaneously satisfy

$$\begin{cases} x \le y + 1 \\ x \ge -y - 1 \end{cases}$$

and when $y < 0$, by the pairs (x, y) satisfying

$$\begin{cases} x \le -y + 1 \\ x \ge y - 1 \end{cases}$$

So for $y \ge 0$ we draw in the bounding lines $x = y + 1$ and $x = -y - 1$ and include all points to the *left* of the first line and at the same time to the *right* of the second; we also include points on the boundaries.

Similarly, when $y < 0$, we draw the bounding lines $x = -y + 1$ and $x = y - 1$ and include all points between as well as on these lines. The solution set is shown in Figure 11.

Figure 11

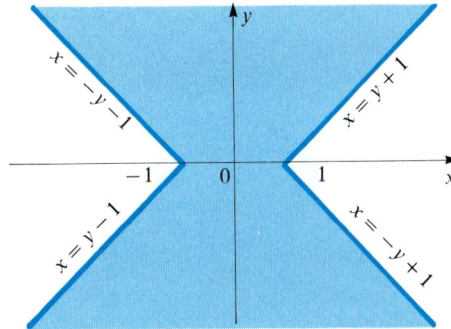

EXERCISE SET 8

Give the graphic solution to each of the following.

A

1. $y < 3x - 5$
2. $y > 4 - x$
3. $x + y < 2$
4. $2x - y > 3$
5. $3x + 2y \leq 4$
6. $5x - 4y \geq 3$
7. $3y - 4 < 2x - 5$
8. $5x + 2 > 3y - 4$
9. $4y - x^2 > 0$
10. $y - 1 < x^2$
11. $x > y^2$
12. $y - x^2 > 4$
13. $16y \leq x^2$
14. $\begin{cases} x - y > 0 \\ y - 2x < 4 \end{cases}$

15. $\begin{cases} x - 2y + 4 > 0 \\ x + y > -3 \end{cases}$
16. $\begin{cases} 3x - 2y > 4 \\ x + y \geq 1 \end{cases}$

17. $\begin{cases} 3x + 4y > 12 \\ 2x - y + 3 > 0 \end{cases}$
18. $\begin{cases} x \geq 2 \\ x \leq 2 + y \end{cases}$

19. $\begin{cases} y \leq 2x \\ 2x - y < 3 \end{cases}$
20. $\begin{cases} 2x - 5y < 6 \\ x + 2y \geq 4 \end{cases}$

21. $\begin{cases} y \leq 1 \\ x - y \leq 2 \end{cases}$
22. $\begin{cases} x < 1 \\ y > 1 \\ x - y + 3 > 0 \end{cases}$

23. $\begin{cases} x \geq 0 \\ x + y \leq 2 \\ 2x - 3y \leq 6 \end{cases}$
24. $|y| \leq x - 1$

25. $|2x - y| \leq 3$
26. $|y| > x - 1$
27. $|x| < 2y + 3$
28. $|x| \geq 2 - y$
29. $\begin{cases} x^2 - 4y \leq 0 \\ 2y - x < 2 \end{cases}$
30. $\begin{cases} y - \sqrt{x} < 0 \\ 4y - x > 0 \end{cases}$
31. $\begin{cases} y > x \\ y < 4 - x^2 \end{cases}$
32. $\begin{cases} x + y < 2 \\ x > y^2 \end{cases}$
33. $\begin{cases} x - y > 2 \\ x + y^2 \leq 4 \end{cases}$
34. $\begin{cases} 4y - x^2 > 0 \\ y^2 - 4x < 0 \end{cases}$
35. $\begin{cases} y \leq 9 - x^2 \\ y \geq x^2 \end{cases}$
36. $\begin{cases} x^2 + y \leq 3x \\ x^2 - 2y \leq 0 \end{cases}$

B 37. $\begin{cases} y \le 1 + x \\ y \le 1 - x \\ y \ge x - 1 \\ y \ge -x - 1 \end{cases}$

38. $\begin{cases} 2x + y \le 8 \\ 2x + 3y \le 12 \\ x \ge 0 \\ y \ge 0 \end{cases}$

39. $\begin{cases} x^2 - 2x + y \le 0 \\ x + y > 0 \end{cases}$

40. $\begin{cases} x^2 + y < 4 \\ 2x - y < 4 \\ 2x + y + 4 > 0 \end{cases}$

41. $|x| + |y| \le 1$

42. $|x - y| \ge 1$

9 Linear Programming

An important application of systems of linear inequalities occurs in a technique developed in the 1940's for solving problems in which a quantity is to be maximized or minimized, subject to certain limitations called **constraints.** For example, a company might want to maximize the profit on some manufactured item or to minimize the cost. Applications of this technique, called **linear programming,** can be found in many areas but are especially important in business and industry.

In a typical linear programming problem the quantity to be maximized or minimized is a linear function of two or more variables. The method we will illustrate is applicable to functions of two variables only, but other procedures exist for dealing with larger numbers of variables. This function is known as the **objective function,** and has the form $F = ax + by + c$. The constraints on x and y are expressed in the form of linear inequalities.

For example, suppose we wish to find the maximum value of the objective function $F = 3x + 4y$, subject to the constraints given by

$$\begin{cases} x + y \le 7 \\ 2x + 5y \le 20 \\ x \ge 0 \\ y \ge 0 \end{cases}$$

The four constraints have the simultaneous solution set shown by the shaded region in Figure 12. This region is called the **set of feasible solutions** to the problem. We have shown the coordinates of each vertex of the polygon bounding the region. Finding these vertices is an essential part of the problem and involves solving two or more sets of equations simultaneously. To find the values of x and y among the feasible solutions for which the objective function F is a

Figure 12

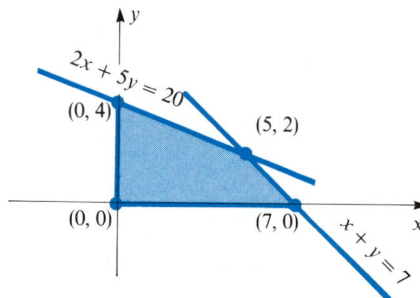

maximum, we make use of the following fundamental result, which we state without proof:

THEOREM   **The maximum and minimum values of the objective function in a linear programming problem, if they exist, occur at a vertex of the graph of the set of feasible solutions.***

Thus, to find the maximum value of F we test its value at each of the vertices $(0, 0)$, $(7, 0)$, $(5, 2)$, and $(0, 4)$. The maximum value is found to be 23, and this occurs when x is 5 and y is 2.

Vertex	F
$(0, 0)$	0
$(7, 0)$	21
$(5, 2)$	23
$(0, 4)$	16

The next two examples illustrate applications in economics.

EXAMPLE 29   A company manufactures two kinds of pocket calculators, one with and one without rechargeable batteries. The company can make at most 50 of the type with rechargeable batteries (type A) per day and 60 of the type without rechargeable batteries (type B) per day. Type A requires 3 work-hours to produce and type B requires 2 work-hours. The work force provides a total of 180 work-hours available per day. If the profit on each type A calculator is \$2.50, and the profit on each type B calculator is \$2.00, find how many of each type of calculator should be produced per day to give the maximum profit.

Solution   Let x be the number of type A and y the number of type B calculators to be produced. Then the profit P is given by

$$P = 2.50x + 2.00y$$

This is the objective function, which is to be maximized, subject to the constraints

$$\begin{cases} 0 \le x \le 50 \\ 0 \le y \le 60 \\ 3x + 2y \le 180 \end{cases}$$

---

* Both maximum and minimum values do exist if the feasibility set is bounded and is **convex,** which means that for any two points of the set the line segment joining them lies entirely within the set.

Figure 13

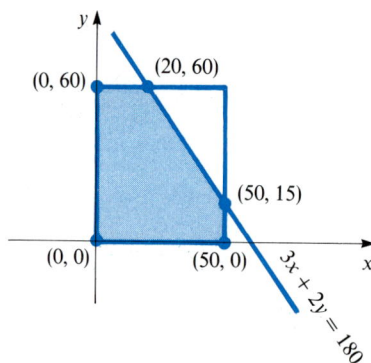

The set of feasible solutions is shown in Figure 13. Testing the value of P at each vertex, we find the maximum value to be $170, and this occurs when $x = 20$ and $y = 60$.

Vertex	P
$(0, 0)$	0
$(50, 0)$	125
$(50, 15)$	155
$(20, 60)$	170
$(0, 60)$	120

EXAMPLE 30   A machine tool company produces two kinds of parts, A and B. The weekly demand for each requires that at least 20 type A parts and 10 type B parts be produced. Limitations on capacity require that at most 60 type A and 40 type B parts be produced each week. In order to keep the work force fully employed, the combination of A and B parts produced must be at least 50 each week. If it costs $3 to produce each A part and $2 to produce each B part, how many parts of each type should be produced per week to minimize cost?

Solution   Let x be the number of type A parts and y the number of type B parts to be produced each week. The objective function is the cost C, given by

$$C = 3x + 2y$$

and this is to be minimized, subject to the constraints

$$\begin{cases} 20 \leq x \leq 60 \\ 10 \leq y \leq 40 \\ x + y \geq 50 \end{cases}$$

Figure 14

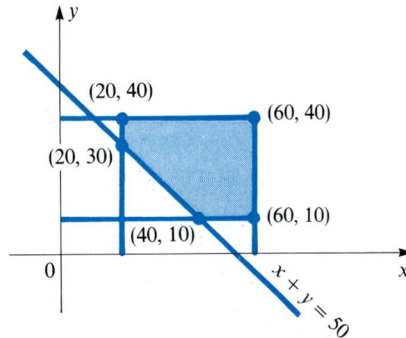

Figure 14 shows the set of feasible solutions. Calculating C at each vertex shows that the minimum value of \$120 occurs when 20 type A parts and 30 type B parts are produced each week.

Vertex	C
(60, 10)	200
(60, 40)	260
(20, 40)	140
(20, 30)	120
(40, 10)	140

EXERCISE SET 9

A In Problems 1–8 find the maximum or minimum value, as specified, of the objective function, subject to the given constraints. Give the values of x and y that produce this value.

1. Maximize $F = 2x + y$, subject to $\begin{cases} 3x + 4y \le 24 \\ x \ge 2 \\ y \ge 3 \end{cases}$

2. Minimize $C = 2x - 3y + 8$, subject to $\begin{cases} x - y \ge 0 \\ x \le 6 \\ y \ge 2 \end{cases}$

3. Maximize $G = 2x + 7y - 4$, subject to $\begin{cases} x - y \le 1 \\ 2x + 3y \le 12 \\ x \ge 0 \\ y \ge 0 \end{cases}$

4. Minimize $F = 4x - 3y + 7$, subject to $\begin{cases} y - 2x \le 0 \\ x - 2y \le 0 \\ 2 \le y \le 4 \end{cases}$

5. Minimize $H = 3x + 5y$, subject to $\begin{cases} x \le 2y + 2 \\ x \ge 6 - 2y \\ y \le x \\ x \le 6 \end{cases}$

6. Maximize $P = 2x + 3y$, subject to $\begin{cases} y \le 3x - 2 \\ 3x + 4y \le 22 \\ y \ge 1 \end{cases}$

7. Minimize $C = 4x - y + 5$, subject to $\begin{cases} x + y \le 5 \\ x + 2y \ge 6 \\ x \ge 0 \\ y \ge 0 \end{cases}$

8. Maximize $P = 10x + 6y$, subject to $\begin{cases} x + 3y \le 18 \\ x + y \le 8 \\ 2x + y \le 14 \\ x \ge 0 \\ y \ge 0 \end{cases}$

9. A grocer expects to sell between 40 and 60 cases of canned apple sauce during a 6 month period. He knows from experience that he can sell at least 20 cases of brand A and at most 30 cases of brand B apple sauce in this time period. His profit on a case of brand A is $3.00 and on a case of brand B is $3.25. Assuming he sells all the apple sauce, how much should he stock for maximum profit?

10. An oil refinery needs to produce at least 100,000 gallons of unleaded gasoline and 150,000 gallons of regular leaded gasoline each month to meet demand. In order to use the plant capacity efficiently at least 300,000 gallons of the two types combined must be produced each month, but no more than 400,000 gallons can be produced. The cost of producing unleaded gasoline is $300 per 1,000 gallons and for regular leaded gasoline it is $250 per 1,000 gallons. How many gallons of each should be produced to minimize cost?

11. A certain machine can produce two types of products, A and B. It can produce 100 type A products per hour and 150 type B products per hour. The machine can run between 6 and 12 hours per day. It is to be used at most 8 hours per day to produce product A and at least 1 but no more than 5 hours per day in the production of B. If the profit on each A item is $0.05 and on each B item $0.04, how many hours per day should the machine be used in the production of each item in order to maximize profit?

12. A woman has $20,000 which she wishes to divide between two investments, one a certificate of deposit paying $8\frac{1}{2}\%$ annual interest and requiring a minimum of $5,000, and the other a utility stock paying 10% annual interest. Because the latter involves greater risk, she wants to put no more than half as much in it as in the certificate of deposit, but she wants at least 100 shares, and it costs $20 per share. Assuming the stock price does not fluctuate, how should she invest the money for maximum income?

13. Two hardware store owners wish to buy paint of a certain kind from a wholesaler who has a stock of 1,000 gallons of the paint. The first owner will buy between 200 and 500 gallons, and the second will buy between 300 and 600 gallons. The wholesaler makes a profit of $1.10 on each gallon, but this is reduced by the cost of delivery. He estimates the cost at 5¢ per gallon for delivery to the first hardware store and 10¢ per gallon to the second. How many gallons should he sell to each owner to maximize his profits?

14. A dairy farmer plans to purchase two types of feed for his 100 cows. Type A contains 10% protein and 30% carbohydrates (by weight), and type B contains 30% protein

and 40% carbohydrates. He wants to provide each cow with a minimum of 1 pound of protein and 2 pounds of carbohydrates. If type A costs 30¢ per pound and type B costs 50¢ per pound, how many pounds of each type should he buy to minimize the cost? What is the minimum cost?

15. A machine tool company produces two types of parts that require time on a drill press and on a lathe. Part A requires 5 minutes on the drill press and 10 minutes on the lathe. Part B requires 6 minutes on the drill press and 4 minutes on the lathe. The time per day available on the drill press for producing these parts is 1 hour and 40 minutes, and the time available on the lathe is 2 hours. To meet demand, at least 5 parts of each type should be produced each day. If the profit on part A is $3 and on part B is $2, how many parts per day of each type should be made for maximum profit?

16. A baker has orders for 15 angel food cakes and 20 chocolate cakes. Each angel food cake uses 12 eggs and 1 cup of sugar, whereas each chocolate cake uses 3 eggs and 2 cups of sugar. He has available for these two items 25 dozen eggs and 36 pounds of sugar (each pound equals $2\frac{1}{4}$ cups). His profit on each angel food cake is $0.50 and on each chocolate cake is $0.75. How many cakes of each type should he make in order to meet the demand and maximize profit (assuming he can sell all the cakes he makes)?

17. A manufacturer of washing machines has two plants where three models are produced: standard, superior, and luxury. There are orders for 600 standard, 340 superior, and 200 luxury models. Plant A can produce 10 standard, 8 superior, and 3 luxury models per day, whereas plant B can produce 20 standard, 9 superior, and 8 luxury models per day. It costs $500 per day to operate plant A and $800 per day to operate plant B. How many days should each plant be used in the production of these machines to meet demand and minimize cost?

B 18. Consider the objective function $P = 5x + 2y$ and the feasibility set defined by

$$\begin{cases} x + 3y \geq 10 \\ 3x + 2y \leq 34 \\ 2x - 5y + 28 \geq 0 \\ x \geq 1 \\ y \geq 2 \end{cases}$$

Graph the feasibility set and show several members of the family obtained by setting the objective function equal to a constant, $5x + 2y = C$, for increasing values of C (if P represents profit, these are called **isoprofit** lines). Explain from what you observe why the objective function must assume both its maximum and minimum values at a vertex of the graph of the feasibility set. At which vertex do each of the extreme values of P occur and what are the maximum and minimum values of P?

19. A dairy farmer has determined that each of his cows should get three types of food supplements, A, B, and C, each day. The minimum requirements are 10 units of A, 14 units of B, and 16 units of C. There are two kinds of feed that contain all three supplements. Feed number 1 contains 2 units each of A, B, and C per pound. Feed number 2 contains 2 units of A, 3 units of B, and 4 units of C per pound. Feed number 1 costs 10¢ per pound and feed number 2 costs 12¢ per pound. How many pounds of each type of feed should the farmer purchase to meet the daily need per cow in order to minimize cost?

20. At a furniture factory, desks and tables each go through four stations where different aspects of fabrication take place. The number of work-hours required at each station, as well as the number of work-hours available each day, are shown in the table. The profit on each item also is shown. How many desks and how many tables should be produced each day to maximize profit?

	Work-hours needed				
	Station 1	Station 2	Station 3	Station 4	Profit
Desk	1	1	2	3	$80
Table	3	1	1	2	$70
Available work-hours	9	7	10	18	

21. A woman owns two orchard supply stores. She has orders from two customers for a certain type of insecticide. Customer A wants 350 gallons and customer B wants 400 gallons. The store owner has 500 gallons of this insecticide on hand at store number 1 and 600 gallons at store number 2. The cost of delivery is estimated as shown in the table. How many gallons should be sent to each customer from store 1 and from store 2 to minimize the shipping cost?

From store	To customer	Delivery cost per gallon
1	A	$0.10
2	A	$0.12
1	B	$0.11
2	B	$0.15

Review Exercise Set

A In Problems 1–7 solve the systems using the method of elimination by addition or subtraction.

1. $\begin{cases} 3x - 2y = 5 \\ x + 4y = 11 \end{cases}$

2. $\begin{cases} 5x + 3y = 6 \\ 2x - 4y = 5 \end{cases}$

3. $\begin{cases} 4x + 7y = 3 \\ 5x + 8y = 0 \end{cases}$

4. $\begin{cases} x - 2y + 4z = 1 \\ 3x + y + z = 2 \\ 2x + y - z = -1 \end{cases}$

5. $\begin{cases} x - 2y + z = 2 \\ 2x - 3y - z = 0 \\ x + y - 4z = 2 \end{cases}$

6. $\begin{cases} 2x - 3y - 5z = -1 \\ x - y - 2z = 1 \\ -4x + 5y - 6z = 14 \end{cases}$

7. $\begin{cases} x - y = 1 \\ y + z = 1 \\ x - 2w = 0 \\ x + y + 3z + w = 2 \end{cases}$

Solve Problems 8–19 by reducing the augmented matrix to triangular form.

8. $\begin{cases} x - 2y + 4z = -3 \\ 3x + y - 2z = 12 \\ 2x + y - 3z = 7 \end{cases}$

9. $\begin{cases} 2x + y - z = 1 \\ x + y + z = -3 \\ -5x - 2y + 3z = -1 \end{cases}$

10. $\begin{cases} x + 2y + 3z = 1 \\ 2x - y - z = 5 \\ -x + y - 2z = 10 \end{cases}$

11. $\begin{cases} 2x + 4y - 3z = 8 \\ 3x + 2y - z = 8 \\ 5x - 2y + 4z = 0 \end{cases}$

12. $\begin{cases} 4x + 2y - z = 0 \\ 3x - 5y - 7z = 5 \\ 7x + 3y - 5z = -1 \end{cases}$

13. $\begin{cases} 2x - y + z = 3 \\ x + 3y - 2z = 4 \\ 4x - 9y + 7z = 1 \end{cases}$

14. $\begin{cases} 3x - 2y + 4z = 6 \\ 5x - 7y - 2z = 3 \\ 7x - 23y - 34z = -20 \end{cases}$

15. $\begin{cases} x - y + z = 0 \\ y - z + 3w = 1 \\ x + z + 2w = 0 \\ x + y + 3z + w = 1 \end{cases}$

16. $\begin{cases} x + y - 2z + w = 2 \\ 3x + 2y - 4z - 2w = -19 \\ 2x - y + z + 3w = 7 \\ -x - 3y + 4z + w = 4 \end{cases}$

17. $\begin{cases} x + y - z + 3w = 1 \\ 2x - y + 3z - 4w = -13 \\ 3x + 2y + z + w = 5 \end{cases}$

18. $\begin{cases} x - 2y - z - w = -4 \\ 3x + y + 2z + w = 3 \\ 2x - 3y - z + 2w = 7 \\ x - 3y - 2z - 5w = -19 \end{cases}$

19. $\begin{cases} 2x + y + 3z = 1 \\ x - 2y - z = 3 \\ 4x - 5y + 6z = 11 \\ x - y + z = 2 \end{cases}$

Evaluate the determinants in Problems 20–22.

20. a. $\begin{vmatrix} 2 & -1 & 1 \\ 1 & 3 & 4 \\ -2 & 1 & -5 \end{vmatrix}$ **b.** $\begin{vmatrix} 4 & 1 & -2 \\ 0 & 2 & -3 \\ 5 & -3 & 6 \end{vmatrix}$

21. a. $\begin{vmatrix} 3 & -5 & 4 \\ 2 & -3 & 6 \\ -1 & 2 & 3 \end{vmatrix}$ **b.** $\begin{vmatrix} -2 & 7 & 3 \\ 3 & -8 & 4 \\ 6 & -10 & -5 \end{vmatrix}$

22. a. $\begin{vmatrix} 4 & 3 & -5 \\ 7 & 8 & 2 \\ -3 & 2 & -6 \end{vmatrix}$ **b.** $\begin{vmatrix} 2 & -1 & 0 & 3 \\ 0 & 5 & -1 & 2 \\ 1 & 6 & 3 & -2 \\ -3 & 4 & 0 & -1 \end{vmatrix}$

23. Solve for x:

$$\begin{vmatrix} 1 & 0 & x \\ 2 & -x & 1 \\ 3 & x+1 & 2 \end{vmatrix} = 3$$

Find the solution to the systems in Problems 24–28 by Cramer's rule.

24. a. $\begin{cases} 5x - 11y = 6 \\ 7x - 8y = 3 \end{cases}$ **b.** $\begin{cases} 3x + 7y + 8 = 0 \\ 2x - 3y - 4 = 0 \end{cases}$

25. a. $\begin{cases} 9x - 5y = 11 \\ -6x + 3y = 7 \end{cases}$ **b.** $\begin{cases} 4x + 3y - 5 = 0 \\ 8x - 5y + 2 = 0 \end{cases}$

26. $\begin{cases} 2x + 4y + 3z = 1 \\ 3x - 5y - 2z = 5 \\ 4x - 6y - 8z = -5 \end{cases}$

27. $\begin{cases} 3x - 5y - z = 4 \\ 2x + 4y + 3z = -1 \\ 2x + y + z = 0 \end{cases}$

28. $\begin{cases} x + 3y + z = -2 \\ 4x - 2y - 5z = -1 \\ 5x + 7y + 3z = -4 \end{cases}$

In Problems 29 and 30 find the inverse by two methods.

29. $\begin{bmatrix} 3 & -2 & 0 \\ 1 & 1 & 4 \\ -2 & 3 & 5 \end{bmatrix}$

30. $\begin{bmatrix} 1 & -1 & -2 \\ 2 & -3 & -4 \\ 2 & 1 & -2 \end{bmatrix}$

In Problems 31 and 32 solve the system $Ax = B$ in the form $x = A^{-1}B$.

31. The system of Problem 8.
32. The system of Problem 9.

33. Two drivers are initially 120 miles apart, and they drive toward each other. One averages 50 miles per hour and the other 40 miles per hour. Find how far each has driven when they meet.

34. A man in a motorboat makes a trip of 12 miles upstream in 1 hour. The return trip with the current takes 40 minutes. If he held the throttle wide open all the time, find how fast he would have gone in still water and the rate of the current.

35. Thirty cubic centimeters of a 25% sulfuric acid solution are obtained by mixing a 40% sulfuric acid solution with a 15% solution. How much of each was needed?

36. The total income from a community concert was $2,325. Admission for adults was $3.00 and for children $1.50. If 900 persons attended, how many were adults and how many were children?

37. The length of a certain rectangle is 1 more than twice the width, and the perimeter is 32. Find the length and the width.

38. Find how much nickel and how much zinc should be added to 200 kilograms of an alloy which is 15% nickel and 25% zinc in order to obtain an alloy which is 25% nickel and 30% zinc?

39. Fifty gallons of a 25% salt solution are obtained by mixing pure water with a 40% salt solution. Find how much pure water and how much of the 40% salt solution were used.

40. The sum of the digits of a two-digit number is 11. If the digits were reversed, the number would be decreased by 45. Find the number.

41. The income from an amount invested at simple interest for 1 year is $108. If the same amount were invested in an account yielding $1\frac{1}{2}$% more interest, the income for the year would be $135. Find the interest rate and the amount invested.

42. Three men working together can do a certain job in 2 hours. Mr. Jones and Mr. Smith can do the job in 3 hours, and Mr. Smith and Mr. Robinson together can do it in 4 hours. How long would it take each man working alone?

43. Two pumps working simultaneously can fill a tank in $2\frac{1}{2}$ hours. Both pumps are started at the same time, but the larger one breaks down after $1\frac{1}{2}$ hours, and it takes the smaller one an additional $2\frac{1}{2}$ hours to fill the tank. Find how long it would take each pump alone to fill the tank.

Solve the systems of equations in Problems 44–52.

44. $\begin{cases} y = x^2 - 2x \\ x + 2y = 5 \end{cases}$

45. $\begin{cases} xy + 2 = 0 \\ 2x + 3y = 4 \end{cases}$

46. $\begin{cases} x^2 - 2y^2 = 4 \\ 3x^2 + 4y^2 = 12 \end{cases}$

47. $\begin{cases} y^2 - 7x^2 = 36 \\ 3x + y = 2 \end{cases}$

48. $\begin{cases} 3y^2 - x^2 = 26 \\ x + y^2 = 12 \end{cases}$

49. $\begin{cases} x^2 - y^2 - 2x = 0 \\ 2x - 3y = 4 \end{cases}$

50. $\begin{cases} 8xy - 6x - 5y = 3 \\ \qquad 10x + y = 1 \end{cases}$

51. $\begin{cases} \dfrac{1}{x} + \dfrac{2}{y} = 4 \\ 3x + 5y = 6 \end{cases}$

52. $\begin{cases} x^2 + 3xy - 2y^2 - 8 = 0 \\ \qquad\qquad 2x - y = 3 \end{cases}$

53. Find two numbers whose difference is 8 and the sum of whose squares is 274.

54. Find two numbers whose difference is 13 and the difference of whose squares is 65.

55. The diagonal of a rectangle is 25 inches and its perimeter is 62 inches. Find the length and width.

56. The length of a certain rectangle is 4 less than 3 times the width, and the area is 160. Find the length and the width.

Show the graphic solutions of the inequalities in Problems 57–60.

57. **a.** $3x - 5y < 8$ **b.** $y \geq x^2 - 3$

58. **a.** $\begin{cases} x + 2y \leq 8 \\ 2y - x > 3 \end{cases}$ **b.** $\begin{cases} y + x^2 \leq 4 \\ 2x + y \geq 0 \end{cases}$

59. **a.** $\begin{cases} 2y - x < 8 \\ 2x - y < 5 \\ \quad x + y > 1 \end{cases}$ **b.** $\begin{cases} y - 2x \leq 3 \\ x + 2y \geq 2 \end{cases}$

60. **a.** $\begin{cases} -6 \leq x - 3y \leq 6 \\ \qquad |y - 2| \leq 1 \end{cases}$ **b.** $|x + y| > 2$

In Problems 61–64 find the maximum or minimum value, as specified, subject to the given constraints.

61. Maximize $F = 10x + 5y$, subject to $\begin{cases} 2x + 3y \leq 12 \\ x + y \geq 2 \\ x \geq 1 \\ y \geq 0 \end{cases}$

62. Minimize $C = 2x + 3y + 5$, subject to $\begin{cases} 2x + y \geq 4 \\ x \leq 8 \\ 1 \leq y \leq 4 \end{cases}$

63. Minimize $G = 3x - y + 7$, subject to $\begin{cases} 3x + 2y \geq 12 \\ x + 2y \geq 5 \\ x + y \leq 8 \\ x \leq 6 \\ y \leq 4 \end{cases}$

64. Maximize $P = 60x + 100y$, subject to $\begin{cases} x + 2y \leq 14 \\ 6 \leq x + y \leq 10 \\ y \geq 2 \\ x \geq 0 \end{cases}$

65. A farmer has 300 acres which he will divide between corn and oats. In order to meet commitments he has made he must plant at least 150 acres of corn and 50 acres of oats, and the demand for each suggests that he should plant at least twice as many acres in corn as in oats. If the profit from corn is $40 per acre and from oats is $30 per acre, how many acres should he plant of each for maximum profit?

66.   A company manufactures two types of rotary lawn mowers, a standard model and a deluxe model. At most 100 lawn mowers can be produced each week, and no more than 40 of these can be the deluxe model. To meet demand, at least 40 standard and between 20 and 40 deluxe models should be produced each week. If the profit on the standard model is $50 and on the deluxe model $70, how many of each type should be produced each week for maximum profit?

67.   The owner of an old-fashioned excursion train offers a short trip at $1.50 per person and a long trip at $5.00 per person. Each long trip he makes per day reduces by 3 the number of short trips he can make. If he makes no long trips, he can make 12 short trips, and if he makes no short trips, he can make 4 long trips. He agrees to offer at least 3 short trips and 1 long trip per day. The train holds 200 passengers, and it is 80% full on the average for short trips and 60% full for long trips. How many trips of each type should he make per day to maximize his income?

B   Solve the systems in Problems 68–73 by reducing the augmented matrix to triangular form.

68.
$$\begin{cases} 3x + 4y - 2z + w = 25 \\ x + 2y - z - w = -3 \\ 2x - y - 3z + 4w = 7 \\ -x - 3y + 5z - 2w = -7 \end{cases}$$

69.
$$\begin{cases} x - y + 2z - w = 4 \\ x + 2y - z = 5 \\ 2x - 3y + z - 4w = 7 \\ x + y - 4z - 2w = 4 \end{cases}$$

70.
$$\begin{cases} 2x - y + 5z - 4w = 0 \\ 3x - 2y - 3z + 2w = 2 \\ -5x + 3y - 4z + 6w = 10 \\ 4x + y + 2z + 3w = -1 \end{cases}$$

71.
$$\begin{cases} 2x - y + 4z - w = 0 \\ -3x + 2y + 3z - 2w = 0 \\ 4x - 3y - 10z + 5w = 0 \\ 5x + 2y + 7z + 8w = 0 \end{cases}$$

72.
$$\begin{cases} 4x - 3y + 2z - w = 0 \\ 2x - y + z - 4w = 0 \\ -5x + 6y - 8z + w = 0 \\ 7x + 2y - 5z - 5w = 0 \end{cases}$$

73.
$$\begin{cases} x + y - u = 1 \\ 2x - y + 2v - w = 3 \\ u + v + w = -1 \\ 3y - u + v - 2w = 2 \\ x + 2u + 5w = 5 \end{cases}$$

In Problems 74 and 75 solve the system $AX = B$ using $X = A^{-1}B$.

74.   The system of Problem 16.

75.   The system of Problem 68.

76.   Solve only for y by Cramer's rule:
$$\begin{cases} 2x - 3y = 3 \\ 4x + z = 5 \\ 2y - z + w = 0 \\ x + w = 4 \end{cases}$$

77.   Solve for u and v by Cramer's rule:
$$\begin{cases} (a^2 - 1)u - 3av = 3 \\ au - 4v = 2 \end{cases}$$

78.   Solve for x, y, and z by Cramer's rule:
$$\begin{cases} nx - my + mnz = 0 \\ x + mny - 2mz = 3n \\ 2mnx - y + 3nz = 4m \end{cases}$$

79.   The points $(-1, 0)$, $(2, -3)$, and $(3, 4)$ lie on a curve whose equation is of the form $y = ax^2 + bx + c$. Find a, b, and c.
      Hint.   Each point must satisfy the equation.

80. The points $(5, 1)$, $(-2, 0)$, and $(2, 2)$ lie on a circle whose equation is of the form $x^2 + y^2 + ax + by + c = 0$. Find a, b, and c.

In Problems 81 and 82 find the solution to the system.

81. $\begin{cases} x^2 + y^2 - 2x - 5y + 1 = 0 \\ x^2 + y^2 + 3x - 8y - 2 = 0 \end{cases}$

82. $\begin{cases} x^2 - 16y^2 = 5x - 20y \\ \quad\quad\quad xy = 1 \end{cases}$

83. A 40% salt solution is mixed with a 25% solution, resulting in a 30% solution. Then 4 gallons of fresh water are added to this mixture, and the final solution is 20% salt. Find how many gallons of each original solution there were.

84. A man rows 8 miles upstream and back in 3 hours. The next day the current is twice as strong, and he makes the same trip upstream and back in 4 hours and 48 minutes. Assuming no change in his rowing effort from one day to the next, find how fast he can row in still water and the rate of the current the first day.

85. Find all points of intersection of the curves whose equations are $5x^2 - 2xy + y^2 - 12x - 16 = 0$ and $x^2 - y = 2$.

86. An isosceles triangle is inscribed in a circle of radius a. The two equal sides each have length $3a/2$. Find the length of the base and the altitude of the triangle in terms of a.

87. A girl rides a bicycle a distance of 5 miles and then has a flat tire. She has to walk 2 miles to a service station. If the total elapsed time for riding and walking was 1 hour and if she rode at an average speed of 12 miles per hour faster than she walked, find her rate of riding and her rate of walking.

88. Two open-top boxes each have square bases. The base of the larger box is 2 inches larger on each side than that of the smaller, and the height of the larger box is 1 inch greater than that of the smaller box. If the volume of the larger box exceeds that of the smaller by 320 cubic inches, and the total surface area of the larger box is 124 square inches greater than that of the smaller, find the dimensions of the smaller box. (There are two solutions.)

89. A company produces two kinds of fertilizer. The first kind, for lawns, contains 20% nitrogen, 5% phosphorous, and 5% potash. The second kind, for gardens, contains 8% nitrogen, 10% phosphorous, and 8% potash. Each kind is packaged in 100 pound bags. The company has 1960 pounds of nitrogen, 850 pounds of phosphorous, and 730 pounds of potash. The owner wants to have at least 30 bags of each type of fertilizer available. His profit on the lawn fertilizer is $6 per bag and on the garden fertilizer $5 per bag. How many bags of each type should he produce to maximize his profit?

11 Sequences and Series

One of the concepts to be studied in this chapter is that of an infinite geometric series. An example of an application of such a series in economics is given by the following.*

> Thus, $1 billion worth of new export orders to New England machine-tool factories will create $1 billion of primary jobs and income. Then workers and owners may respend perhaps two-thirds of their new income on the consumption of products of Indiana and California; two-thirds of this extra income is in turn respent. The process finally comes to a halt only when the total adds up to
>
> $$3 = 1 + \tfrac{2}{3} + (\tfrac{2}{3})^2 + \cdots = 1/(1 - \tfrac{2}{3})$$
>
> —i.e., to $1 billion of initial expenditure plus $2 billion of extra secondary consumption expenditure.

The left-hand side of the equation

$$1 + \tfrac{2}{3} + (\tfrac{2}{3})^2 + \cdots = 1/(1 - \tfrac{2}{3})$$

is an infinite geometric series, and we will learn in this chapter how to find its sum, which is given here on the right-hand side.

* Paul A. Samuelson, *Economics*, 10th ed. (New York: McGraw-Hill Book Company, 1976), p. 665. Reprinted by permission.

1 Sequences

A sequence is defined as follows:

DEFINITION 1   A **sequence** is a function whose domain is the set N of natural numbers. If f is such a function, then for each natural number n, $f(n)$ is called the **nth term** of the sequence.

We will be concerned primarily with sequences whose terms are real numbers. It is customary to use subscripted variables to designate the terms of a sequence, rather than the usual functional notation. For example, we frequently use a_n instead of $f(n)$ for the nth term. For n arbitrary, the nth term of a sequence is also called the **general term.**

As an example, consider a sequence whose general term is given by

$$a_n = \frac{n}{2n + 1}$$

The sequence is now completely defined, and we can find as many of the terms as we wish. For $n = 1, 2,$ and 3 we have

$$a_1 = \frac{1}{2 \cdot 1 + 1} = \frac{1}{3}$$

$$a_2 = \frac{2}{2 \cdot 2 + 1} = \frac{2}{5}$$

$$a_3 = \frac{3}{2 \cdot 3 + 1} = \frac{3}{7}$$

It is customary to exhibit the terms in the following way:

$$\frac{1}{3}, \frac{2}{5}, \frac{3}{7}, \dots, \frac{n}{2n + 1}, \dots$$

The terms are separated by commas, three dots are shown following the last specific term, and the nth term is shown, followed by three more dots to indicate indefinite continuation. Often, we refer to such a listing of the terms of a sequence as the sequence itself, although strictly speaking the sequence is the function, and the terms constitute the range of the function.

When no ambiguity is likely to result, it is satisfactory to omit the nth term in exhibiting a sequence. For instance, we might write

$$2, 4, 6, 8, \dots$$

and it would be understood that the sequence continues in the manner which is suggested by the specific terms shown. It should be emphasized that there may be many possibilities for the continuation of this sequence but only one *reasonable* way to continue, and we will understand this to be what is intended. Thus, in this case we would infer that the general term is given by $a_n = 2n$. Contrast this with

$$1, 13, 18, 36, \dots$$

Here there is no clear pattern established, and this would not be considered a valid representation of a sequence.

To summarize, we can define a sequence either by giving the general term or by listing the first few terms of the sequence. When listing the terms, all uncertainty is removed if the nth term is shown in the list; however, it is permissible to omit it if the pattern is clearly established by the specific terms listed.

There is another way of defining a sequence which makes use of what is called a **recursion formula.** Consider, for example, the sequence for which

$$a_1 = 2$$

$$a_n = \frac{a_{n-1}}{3} \qquad n \geq 2$$

The second equation, in which a_n is given as a function of a_{n-1}, is the recursion formula. We are given a_1. Then, by the recursion formula with $n = 2$, we find

$$a_2 = \frac{a_1}{3} = \frac{2}{3}$$

Now using the recursion formula with $n = 3$, we get

$$a_3 = \frac{a_2}{3} = \frac{\frac{2}{3}}{3} = \frac{2}{9}$$

We can continue in this way to find as many terms as are desired.

It is sometimes useful to employ a **finite sequence,** by which we mean a sequence that terminates at some stage. More precisely, we have the following definition:

DEFINITION 2   A **finite sequence** is a function whose domain is a subset of N of the form $\{1, 2, 3, \ldots, n\}$ for some fixed natural number n.

In contrast to this, a sequence as defined in Definition 1 is sometimes called an **infinite sequence,** but when we say *sequence* we will always mean *infinite sequence* unless otherwise specified.

EXAMPLE 1   Write the first five terms of the sequence whose nth term is given.

a. $a_n = 2n - 1$ **b.** $a_n = \dfrac{(-1)^{n-1}}{n}$

c. $a_n = \dfrac{2^n - 1}{2^n}$ **d.** $a_n = \dfrac{(-1)^{n-1}n}{n+1}$

Solution   In each case we substitute $n = 1, 2, 3, 4,$ and 5:

a. $1, 3, 5, 7, 9, \ldots$ **b.** $1, -\frac{1}{2}, \frac{1}{3}, -\frac{1}{4}, \frac{1}{5}, \ldots$

c. $\frac{1}{2}, \frac{3}{4}, \frac{7}{8}, \frac{15}{16}, \frac{31}{32}, \ldots$ **d.** $\frac{1}{2}, -\frac{2}{3}, \frac{3}{4}, -\frac{4}{5}, \frac{5}{6}, \ldots$

Remark. Part a above shows that the nth odd natural number is $2n - 1$. Similarly, the nth even natural number is $2n$. Parts b and d illustrate a standard way of handling alternating signs. The factor $(-1)^{n-1}$ equals $+1$ for n odd and -1 for n even. These are useful facts in constructing the nth term of certain sequences.

EXAMPLE 2

Determine the nth term of each of the following sequences:

a. $1, \frac{1}{4}, \frac{1}{9}, \frac{1}{16}, \ldots$ b. $3, 6, 9, 12, \ldots$

c. $1, -\frac{1}{3}, \frac{1}{5}, -\frac{1}{7}, \ldots$ d. $5, 9, 13, 17, \ldots$

e. $1, -\frac{1}{2}, \frac{1}{4}, -\frac{1}{8}, \ldots$

Solution

a. The denominators are perfect squares. We could rewrite the sequence as

$$\frac{1}{1^2}, \frac{1}{2^2}, \frac{1}{3^2}, \frac{1}{4^2}, \ldots$$

and conclude that the general term is

$$a_n = \frac{1}{n^2}$$

b. Each term is a multiple of 3; in fact, the terms are

$$3 \cdot 1, 3 \cdot 2, 3 \cdot 3, 3 \cdot 4, \ldots$$

and the general term is

$$a_n = 3n$$

c. The denominators are the odd natural numbers in order, and the signs alternate. By the remark following Example 1, we can therefore write

$$a_n = \frac{(-1)^{n-1}}{2n-1}$$

d. Observe that each term after the first is 4 greater than the preceding term. This suggests that the terms are related to multiples of 4. In fact, each term is exactly 1 more than a multiple of 4. We can rewrite the terms as

$$4(1) + 1, 4(2) + 1, 4(3) + 1, 4(4) + 1, \ldots$$

and infer that the nth term is

$$a_n = 4n + 1$$

e. The denominators appear to be powers of 2, starting with 2^0:

$$\frac{1}{2^0}, -\frac{1}{2^1}, \frac{1}{2^2}, \frac{-1}{2^3}, \ldots$$

So we have

$$a_n = \frac{(-1)^{n-1}}{2^{n-1}}$$

EXAMPLE 3   Write the first six terms of the sequence defined recursively by:

    a. $a_1 = -2$ **b.** $a_1 = 1$

        $a_n = 1 - 2a_{n-1}, \quad n \geq 2$ $a_2 = 3$

$$a_n = \frac{a_{n-2} + a_{n-1}}{2}, \quad n \geq 3$$

Solution   **a.**
$$a_2 = 1 - 2a_1 = 1 - 2(-2) = 5$$
$$a_3 = 1 - 2a_2 = 1 - 2(5) \quad\; = -9$$
$$a_4 = 1 - 2a_3 = 1 - 2(-9) = 19$$
$$a_5 = 1 - 2a_4 = 1 - 2(19) \quad = -37$$
$$a_6 = 1 - 2a_5 = 1 - 2(-37) = 75$$

b.
$$a_3 = \frac{a_1 + a_2}{2} = \frac{1 + 3}{2} = 2$$

$$a_4 = \frac{a_2 + a_3}{2} = \frac{3 + 2}{2} = \frac{5}{2}$$

$$a_5 = \frac{a_3 + a_4}{2} = \frac{2 + \frac{5}{2}}{2} = \frac{4 + 5}{4} = \frac{9}{4}$$

$$a_6 = \frac{a_4 + a_5}{2} = \frac{\frac{5}{2} + \frac{9}{4}}{2} = \frac{10 + 9}{8} = \frac{19}{8}$$

EXERCISE SET 1

A   In Problems 1–10 write the first five terms of the sequence whose nth term is given by the indicated expression.

1. $a_n = \dfrac{2n}{3n + 1}$ **2.** $a_n = \dfrac{1}{n^2 + 1}$

3. $a_n = \dfrac{(-1)^{n-1}}{n(n + 1)}$ **4.** $a_n = \dfrac{(-1)^{n-1}n}{2n + 1}$

5. $a_n = \left(\dfrac{2}{3}\right)^{n-1}$ **6.** $a_n = \dfrac{(-1)^{n-1}n^2}{1 + n}$

7. $a_n = \dfrac{2^n}{3^n + 1}$ **8.** $a_n = \dfrac{(-1)^{n-1}}{2n^2 - 3n + 5}$

9. $a_n = \dfrac{2}{3n + 4}$ **10.** $a_n = \dfrac{(-1)^{n-1}}{e^n}$

In Problems 11–20 write the next three terms of the sequence.

11. $1, \frac{1}{3}, \frac{1}{9}, \frac{1}{27}, \frac{1}{81}, \ldots$ **12.** $2, 4, 6, 8, 10, \ldots$

13. $1, \frac{1}{3}, \frac{1}{5}, \frac{1}{7}, \frac{1}{9}, \ldots$ **14.** $1, -1, 1, -1, 1, \ldots$

15. $1, \frac{1}{2}, \frac{1}{4}, \frac{1}{8}, \frac{1}{16}, \ldots$ **16.** $1, -\frac{1}{4}, \frac{1}{7}, -\frac{1}{10}, \frac{1}{13}, \ldots$

17. $1, \frac{4}{5}, \frac{6}{10}, \frac{8}{17}, \frac{10}{26}, \ldots$ **18.** $\frac{1}{2}, \frac{2}{3}, \frac{3}{4}, \frac{4}{5}, \ldots$

19. $\frac{1}{5}, -\frac{2}{7}, \frac{3}{9}, -\frac{4}{11}, \frac{5}{13}, \ldots$ **20.** $\frac{1}{2}, \frac{3}{4}, \frac{9}{8}, \frac{27}{16}, \frac{81}{32}, \ldots$

In Problems 21–30 determine an expression for the nth term of the sequence.

21. $1, \frac{1}{3}, \frac{1}{5}, \frac{1}{7}, \ldots$

22. $1, -\frac{1}{2}, \frac{1}{4}, -\frac{1}{8}, \ldots$

23. $\frac{1}{3}, \frac{1}{6}, \frac{1}{9}, \frac{1}{12}, \ldots$

24. $\frac{1}{2}, -\frac{2}{3}, \frac{3}{4}, -\frac{4}{5}, \ldots$

25. $\frac{1}{2}, \frac{3}{4}, \frac{7}{8}, \frac{15}{16}, \ldots$

26. $\frac{1}{2}, \frac{2}{5}, \frac{3}{10}, \frac{4}{17}, \frac{5}{26}, \ldots$

27. $1, \frac{1}{4}, \frac{1}{7}, \frac{1}{10}, \ldots$

28. $\frac{1}{7}, -\frac{1}{11}, \frac{1}{15}, -\frac{1}{19}, \frac{1}{23}, \ldots$

29. $0.5, 0.05, 0.005, 0.0005, \ldots$

30. $-\frac{2}{5}, \frac{4}{7}, -\frac{6}{9}, \frac{8}{11}, \ldots$

In Problems 31–35 write the first five terms of the sequence.

31. $a_1 = 2$

$a_n = \frac{2}{3}a_{n-1}, \quad n \geq 2$

32. $a_1 = 1$

$a_n = 2a_{n-1} - 3, \quad n \geq 2$

33. $a_1 = 4$

$a_n = -\frac{a_{n-1}}{3}, \quad n \geq 2$

34. $a_1 = 1$

$a_n = \frac{a_{n-1}}{n}, \quad n \geq 2$

35. $a_1 = 2$

$a_n = -na_{n-1}, \quad n \geq 2$

B   In Problems 36–40 determine an expression for the nth term of the sequence.

36. $\frac{1}{7}, \frac{3}{10}, \frac{5}{13}, \frac{7}{16}, \ldots$

37. $-1, \frac{2}{5}, \frac{3}{15}, \frac{4}{29}, \frac{5}{47}, \ldots$

38. $1, -\frac{1}{2}, \frac{1}{6}, -\frac{1}{24}, \frac{1}{120}, -\frac{1}{720}, \ldots$

39. $\frac{1}{4}, -\frac{2}{10}, \frac{4}{28}, -\frac{8}{82}, \frac{16}{244}, \ldots$

40. $\frac{1}{2}, -\frac{3}{6}, \frac{5}{12}, -\frac{7}{20}, \frac{9}{30}, \ldots$

In Problems 41–43 write the first five terms of the sequence.

41. $a_1 = 1$

$a_2 = 1$

$a_n = a_{n-1} + a_{n-2}, \quad n \geq 3$

This is called the **Fibonacci sequence.**

42. $a_1 = 2$

$a_n = \sqrt{2 + a_{n-1}}, \quad n \geq 2$

43. $a_1 = 1$

$a_2 = 2$

$a_n = \frac{a_{n-1}}{a_{n-2}}, \quad n \geq 3$

44. Let $f(n) = (2i)^n$, where $n \in N$. Write the values of f for $n = 1, 2, 3, 4, 5$.

45. Let

$$x_n = \frac{n+4}{n} \quad \text{and} \quad y_n = \frac{2n}{n^2 + 1}$$

Plot the sequence of points (x_n, y_n) for $n = 1, 2, 3, 4, 5$. By taking $n = 10, 100, 1,000$, conjecture what point the sequence is approaching as a limit.

2 Arithmetic and Geometric Sequences

When each term after the first term of a sequence is formed by adding a fixed amount to the preceding term, the sequence is called **arithmetic.** A more precise definition is given below.

DEFINITION 3   The sequence $a_1, a_2, a_3, \ldots, a_n, \ldots$ is said to be an **arithmetic sequence** if there exists a constant d such that for all $n \geq 1$,

$$a_{n+1} - a_n = d$$

The number d is called the **common difference.**

Note.   An arithmetic sequence is also sometimes called an **arithmetic progression.**

EXAMPLE 4   Show that the sequence $2, 5, 8, 11, \ldots, 3n - 1, \ldots$ is arithmetic, and find the common difference.

Solution   From the first four terms we observe that the difference between successive terms is the constant 3. To test to see if this pattern continues, we use Definition 3. We know that $a_n = 3n - 1$. To find a_{n+1} we replace n by $n + 1$. This gives $a_{n+1} = 3(n + 1) - 1 = 3n + 2$. So

$$a_{n+1} - a_n = (3n + 2) - (3n - 1) = 3$$

and since this is a constant, independent of n, it follows that the given sequence is arithmetic, with common difference 3.

If $a_1, a_2, a_3, \ldots, a_n, \ldots$ is an arithmetic sequence with common difference d, then by Definition 3 we have

$$
\begin{array}{lll}
a_2 - a_1 = d & \text{or} & a_2 = a_1 + d \\
a_3 - a_2 = d & \text{or} & a_3 = a_2 + d = a_1 + 2d \\
a_4 - a_3 = d & \text{or} & a_4 = a_3 + d = a_1 + 3d \\
\quad \vdots & & \quad \vdots \\
a_n - a_{n-1} = d & \text{or} & a_n = a_{n-1} + d = a_1 + (n - 1)d
\end{array}
$$

The last formula enables us to find the nth term when we know a_1 and d. We restate the result for emphasis.

> In an arithmetic sequence with first term a_1 and common difference d, the nth term is given by
> $$a_n = a_1 + (n - 1)d \qquad (1)$$

Note.   While this result seems evident from the pattern exhibited above, we have not *proved* it. A proof can be based on mathematical induction, and you will be asked to carry out the details in Problem 20, Exercise Set 5.

EXAMPLE 5   Find the twenty-first term of the arithmetic sequence $2, 5, 8, 11, \ldots, 3n - 1, \ldots$.

Solution   As we saw in Example 4, the common difference is 3. So by equation (1),

$$a_{21} = 2 + (21 - 1) \cdot 3 = 2 + (20) \cdot 3 = 62$$

EXAMPLE 6   The fifth term of an arithmetic progression is 22 and the fourteenth term is 67. Find the common difference and the first term.

Solution   By equation (1), we have $a_5 = a_1 + 4d$ and $a_{14} = a_1 + 13d$. From the given values, then,

$$a_1 + 4d = 22$$
$$a_1 + 13d = 67$$

We eliminate a_1 by subtracting the members of the top equation from those of the bottom:

$$9d = 45$$
$$d = 5$$

Substituting in the equation $a_1 + 4d = 22$, we get

$$a_1 = 22 - 4(5) = 2$$

EXAMPLE 7   Insert three arithmetic means between -4 and 20.

Solution   The instructions mean to find a_2, a_3, and a_4, so that

$$a_1, a_2, a_3, a_4, a_5, \ldots$$

where $a_1 = -4$ and $a_5 = 20$, will be an arithmetic sequence. By equation (1), $a_5 = a_1 + 4d$, so that

$$20 = -4 + 4d$$
$$4d = 24$$
$$d = 6$$

So

$$a_2 = a_1 + d = -4 + 6 = 2$$
$$a_3 = a_2 + d = 2 + 6 = 8$$
$$a_4 = a_3 + d = 8 + 6 = 14$$

The five terms in arithmetic progression are $-4, 2, 8, 14, 20$.

A **geometric sequence** (or **geometric progression**) is a sequence in which each term after the first is obtained by multiplying the preceding term by a nonzero constant. We can state this in the following equivalent form:

DEFINITION 4 The sequence $a_1, a_2, a_3, \ldots, a_n, \ldots$ is said to be a **geometric sequence** if there exists a constant $r \neq 0$ such that for all $n \geq 1$,

$$\frac{a_{n+1}}{a_n} = r$$

The number r is called the **common ratio.**

EXAMPLE 8 Show that the sequence

$$1, \frac{1}{3}, \frac{1}{9}, \frac{1}{27}, \ldots, \frac{1}{3^{n-1}}, \ldots$$

is geometric, and find the common ratio.

Solution It appears from the first four terms that a given term after the first is found by multiplying the preceding term by $\frac{1}{3}$, that is, that the common ratio is $\frac{1}{3}$. To show this is always true, we use Definition 4. We are given that

$$a_n = \frac{1}{3^{n-1}}$$

So

$$a_{n+1} = \frac{1}{3^{(n+1)-1}} = \frac{1}{3^n}$$

Thus,

$$\frac{a_{n+1}}{a_n} = \frac{1/3^n}{1/3^{n-1}} = \frac{3^{n-1}}{3^n} = \frac{1}{3}$$

and since this is a nonzero constant, independent of n, it follows that the given sequence is geometric, with $r = \frac{1}{3}$.

If $a_1, a_2, a_3, \ldots, a_n, \ldots$ is a geometric sequence with common ratio r, then

$$\frac{a_2}{a_1} = r \qquad \text{or} \qquad a_2 = a_1 r$$

$$\frac{a_3}{a_2} = r \qquad \text{or} \qquad a_3 = a_2 r = a_1 r^2$$

$$\frac{a_4}{a_3} = r \qquad \text{or} \qquad a_4 = a_3 r = a_1 r^3$$

$$\vdots \qquad\qquad\qquad \vdots$$

$$\frac{a_n}{a_{n-1}} = r \qquad \text{or} \qquad a_n = a_{n-1} r = a_1 r^{n-1}$$

We restate the last general result:

In a geometric sequence with first term a_1 and common ratio r, the nth term is given by

$$a_n = a_1 r^{n-1} \qquad (2)$$

As with formula (1), this result can be proved formally by techniques we will study in Section 5.

EXAMPLE 9   Find the tenth term of the geometric sequence $1, -\frac{1}{2}, \frac{1}{4}, -\frac{1}{8}, \ldots$.

Solution   We see by inspection that the common ratio r is $-\frac{1}{2}$. So

$$a_{10} = a_1 r^9 = 1\left(-\frac{1}{2}\right)^9 = -\frac{1}{2^9} = -\frac{1}{512}$$

EXERCISE SET 2

A   In Problems 1–5 show that the given sequence is arithmetic. Find the common difference, and write the next five terms.

1. $3, 6, 9, 12, \ldots, 3n, \ldots$

2. $1, \dfrac{3}{2}, 2, \dfrac{5}{2}, \ldots, \dfrac{n+1}{2}, \ldots$

3. $5, 2, -1, -4, \ldots, 8 - 3n, \ldots$

4. $-3, 1, 5, 9, \ldots, 4n - 7, \ldots$

5. $5, \dfrac{7}{2}, 2, \dfrac{1}{2}, \ldots, \dfrac{13 - 3n}{2}, \ldots$

In Problems 6–10 show that the given sequence is geometric. Find the common ratio, and write the next four terms.

6. $\dfrac{2}{3}, \dfrac{4}{9}, \dfrac{8}{27}, \ldots, \left(\dfrac{2}{3}\right)^n, \ldots$

7. $1, -\dfrac{1}{2}, \dfrac{1}{4}, \ldots, \left(-\dfrac{1}{2}\right)^{n-1}, \ldots$

8. $0.2, 0.02, 0.002, \ldots, 2(0.1)^n, \ldots$

9. $\dfrac{1}{9}, \dfrac{1}{3}, 1, \ldots, \dfrac{3^{n-1}}{9}, \ldots$

10. $-2, 3, -\dfrac{9}{2}, \ldots, (-1)^n\left(\dfrac{3^{n-1}}{2^{n-2}}\right), \ldots$

Each sequence in Problems 11–16 is either arithmetic or geometric. Determine the nature of each, and find the specified term.

11. $-1, 2, 5, 8, \ldots;\ a_{16}$

12. $\dfrac{1}{4}, \dfrac{1}{2}, 1, 2, \ldots,\ a_{12}$

13. $-3, 1, -\dfrac{1}{3}, \dfrac{1}{9}, \ldots;\ a_{10}$

14. $1, \dfrac{1}{2}, 0, -\dfrac{1}{2}, \ldots;\ a_{30}$

15. $-10, -6, -2, 2, \ldots;\ a_{21}$

16. $8, 6, \dfrac{9}{2}, \dfrac{27}{8}, \ldots;\ a_7$

In Problems 17–30 identify the sequence as being arithmetic, geometric, or neither. If arithmetic, give the common difference, and if geometric, give the common ratio.

17. $-12, -6, -3, -\frac{3}{2}, \ldots$

18. $1, \frac{1}{2}, \frac{1}{3}, \frac{1}{4}, \ldots$

19. $3, 7, 11, 15, \ldots$

20. $1, 2, 3, 4, 5, \ldots$

21. $1, \frac{1}{4}, \frac{1}{9}, \frac{1}{16}, \ldots$

22. $1, a^2, a^4, a^6, \ldots$

23. $\frac{1}{2}, \frac{3}{4}, \frac{7}{8}, \frac{15}{16}, \ldots$

24. $0.1, 0.01, 0.001, \ldots$

25. $0.1, 0.11, 0.111, 0.1111, \ldots$

26. $2, \frac{1}{2}, -1, -\frac{5}{2}, \ldots$

27. $36, 24, 16, \frac{32}{3}, \ldots$

28. $-3, -\frac{19}{4}, -\frac{13}{2}, -\frac{33}{4}, \ldots$

29. $\frac{1}{2}, \frac{2}{3}, \frac{3}{4}, \frac{4}{5}, \ldots$

30. $x, x + 2, x + 4, x + 6, \ldots$

31. In a certain arithmetic sequence, $a_{20} = 32$ and $d = 3$. Find a_1.

32. In a certain geometric sequence, $a_8 = \frac{729}{512}$, and $r = \frac{3}{2}$. Find a_1.

33. For a certain arithmetic sequence, $a_{32} = 48$ and $a_{17} = 18$. Find a_1 and d.

34. If $x_1, x_2, x_3, \ldots$ is an arithmetic progression with $x_{15} = 19$ and $x_{28} = -\frac{1}{2}$, find the first five terms of the progression.

35. In a certain geometric sequence, $a_3 = -\frac{4}{9}$ and $a_6 = \frac{32}{243}$. Find a_1 and r.

36. If $t_1, t_2, t_3, \ldots$ is a geometric progression with $t_6 = 0.32$ and $t_{11} = 0.0001024$, find the first five terms of the progression.

37. Find x in the sequence $5, x, 20$ so that the sequence will be:
   a. Arithmetic   **b.** Geometric (two solutions)

38. Find x and y in the sequence $1, x, y, -64$ so that the sequence will be:
   a. Arithmetic   **b.** Geometric

39. Insert six arithmetic means between 11 and 32.

40. Insert four geometric means between 27 and $-\frac{32}{9}$.

B **41.** If $a_1, a_2, a_3, \ldots, a_n, \ldots$ is an arithmetic sequence, and for each $n \in N$, $x_n = a_n + 5$, prove that $x_1, x_2, x_3, \ldots, x_n, \ldots$ is also an arithmetic sequence.

42. If $a_1, a_2, a_3, \ldots, a_n, \ldots$ is a geometric sequence, and for each $n \in N$, $y_n = 8a_n$, prove that $y_1, y_2, y_3, \ldots, y_n, \ldots$ is also a geometric sequence.

43. Determine the nature of the sequence $\ln 2, \ln 4, \ln 8, \ln 16, \ldots$.

44. Determine the nature of the sequence for which

$$a_n = \log_{10} \frac{2}{3^n}$$

45. Prove that if $a_1, a_2, a_3, \ldots$ is a geometric sequence, then $\log a_1, \log a_2, \log a_3, \ldots$ is an arithmetic sequence. How are the common ratio of the first sequence and the common difference of the second related?

46. A ball is dropped to the ground from a height of 60 feet, and each time it bounces it goes two-thirds as high as it was previously. How high does it go on the eighth bounce?

47. Every person has 2 parents, 4 grandparents, 8 great-grandparents, and so on. How many ancestors does a person have in the tenth preceding generation?

48. A woman wishes to plan a program of jogging in which she will jog 10 minutes the first day and a fixed number of additional minutes each day until the twenty-first day, when she wishes to be jogging for 1 hour. How many minutes of jogging should she add each day?

49. Show that if $\$P$ are invested at $r\%$ compounded annually, the amount present after 1 year, 2 years, 3 years, $\ldots$, forms a geometric sequence. What is the common ratio? What is the nth term?

50. A woman's starting salary at a new job 5 years ago was $10,000 annually, and she has received raises of 6% each year since then. What is her salary now?

51. A piece of machinery that costs $30,000 depreciates by 20% each year. What will be its value in 6 years?

3 Series

A **series** is an indicated sum of a sequence. Some examples of series are:

a. $2 + 4 + 6 + 8$
b. $1 + \frac{1}{2} + \frac{1}{4} + \frac{1}{8} + \cdots$
c. $1 + 2 + 3 + 4 + 5 + \cdots$

The first is a **finite series,** and the other two are **infinite,** as indicated by the three dots. It is clear in series **a** how to find the sum, but in series **b** and **c** the question of whether a meaningful interpretation can be given to the sum is less clear. By adding up more and more terms in series **b** you might guess that the infinite sum is 2 (and you would be right), but this requires further explanation. It is probably also not too difficult to conclude that series **c** does not add up to any finite number. So we see that for some infinite series a number can be reasonably assigned as a sum, whereas for others this is not possible. Infinite series are studied in detail in certain advanced mathematics courses. Here, we will limit ourselves primarily to **infinite geometric series,** which are series formed by adding the terms of geometric sequences. First, however, we consider *finite* arithmetic and geometric series.

It is convenient to introduce a shorthand symbol for a series, namely the **summation symbol** $\sum$. When we write, for example,

$$\sum_{k=1}^{n} a_k$$

this means the sum of the numbers a_k, where k takes on the values from 1 to n. That is,

$$\sum_{k=1}^{n} a_k = a_1 + a_2 + a_3 + \cdots + a_n$$

The letter k as used here is called the **index of summation.** It is a "dummy variable," so-called because it does not appear in the final result, and this result would be unchanged if some other letter were used. For example,

$$\sum_{i=1}^{n} a_i = a_1 + a_2 + a_3 + \cdots + a_n$$

So

$$\sum_{k=1}^{n} a_k = \sum_{i=1}^{n} a_i$$

and, in fact, any other letter could be used as the index of summation.

EXAMPLE 10   Give the expanded form of the sums indicated.

        a. $\displaystyle\sum_{k=1}^{4} \frac{1}{2k}$ **b.** $\displaystyle\sum_{i=1}^{6} 2^{i-1}$ **c.** $\displaystyle\sum_{n=1}^{5} (3n-1)$

Solution   **a.** $\displaystyle\sum_{k=1}^{4} \frac{1}{2k} = \frac{1}{2 \cdot 1} + \frac{1}{2 \cdot 2} + \frac{1}{2 \cdot 3} + \frac{1}{2 \cdot 4} = \frac{1}{2} + \frac{1}{4} + \frac{1}{6} + \frac{1}{8}$

        b. $\displaystyle\sum_{i=1}^{6} 2^{i-1} = 2^0 + 2^1 + 2^2 + 2^3 + 2^4 + 2^5 = 1 + 2 + 4 + 8 + 16 + 32$

        c. $\displaystyle\sum_{n=1}^{5} (3n-1) = (3 \cdot 1 - 1) + (3 \cdot 2 - 1) + (3 \cdot 3 - 1) + (3 \cdot 4 - 1) + (3 \cdot 5 - 1)$

$$= (3 - 1) + (6 - 1) + (9 - 1) + (12 - 1) + (15 - 1)$$

$$= 2 + 5 + 8 + 11 + 14$$

Consider now a finite arithmetic sequence,

$$a_1, a_2, a_3, \ldots, a_n$$

The corresponding arithmetic series is

$$\sum_{k=1}^{n} a_k = a_1 + a_2 + a_3 + \cdots + a_n \qquad (3)$$

Let us represent the sum by S_n. We wish to develop a formula for finding S_n. If d is the common difference, we can write series (3) in the form

$$S_n = a_1 + (a_1 + d) + (a_1 + 2d) + (a_1 + 3d) + \cdots + [a_1 + (n-1)d] \quad (4)$$

Now we are going to rewrite series (3) once again—this time in reverse order, observing that if we begin with a_n and go in reverse, we must subtract d each time to get the next term. So we obtain

$$S_n = a_n + (a_n - d) + (a_n - 2d) + \cdots + [a_n - (n-1)d] \qquad (5)$$

Finally, we add (4) and (5), noting the terms that add to 0:

$$S_n + S_n = (a_1 + a_n) + (a_1 + a_n) + (a_1 + a_n) + \cdots + (a_1 + a_n)$$

Since there are n terms altogether, this can be written

$$2S_n = n(a_1 + a_n)$$

Therefore, we have the following:

The sum S_n of the terms of the finite arithmetic sequence $a_1, a_2, a_3, \ldots, a_n$ is

$$S_n = n\left(\frac{a_1 + a_n}{2}\right) \qquad (6)$$

An easy way to remember this is to think of multiplying the number of terms, n, by the average of the first and last term, $(a_1 + a_n)/2$.

Remark. Although formula (6) was developed for the sum of a *finite* arithmetic sequence, we may also interpret it as the *sum of the first n terms* of an infinite arithmetic sequence.

An alternate formula for the sum S_n can be found by substituting for a_n in (6) its value from equation (1). This gives

$$S_n = n\left[\frac{a_1 + a_1 + (n-1)d}{2}\right]$$

So we have:

$$S_n = \frac{n}{2}[2a_1 + (n-1)d] \qquad (7)$$

Whether to use (6) or (7) depends on the given information.

EXAMPLE 11   Find the sum of the first ten terms of the arithmetic sequence 2, 5, 8, ...

Solution   Since $a_1 = 2$ and $d = 3$, we can use equation (7) to get

$$S_{10} = \tfrac{10}{2}[2(2) + 9(3)] = 5(4 + 27) = 5(31) = 155$$

EXAMPLE 12   The first term of an arithmetic sequence is 3 and the fifteenth term is 45. Find the sum of the first fifteen terms.

Solution   This time we use equation (6):

$$S_{15} = 15\left(\frac{3+45}{2}\right) = 15(24) = 360$$

EXAMPLE 13   The first term of an arithmetic progression is -2, and the sum of the first ten terms is 20. Find the common difference.

Solution   By equation (7), we have

$$20 = \tfrac{10}{2}[2(-2) + 9d]$$
$$20 = 5(-4 + 9d)$$
$$4 = -4 + 9d$$
$$9d = 8$$
$$d = \tfrac{8}{9}$$

For a finite geometric sequence

$$a_1, a_2, a_3, \ldots, a_n$$

we wish also to develop a formula for S_n, where S_n represents the sum

$$S_n = \sum_{k=1}^{n} a_k = a_1 + a_2 + a_3 + \cdots + a_n$$

If r is the common ratio, we know that each term after the first is formed by multiplying the preceding one by r. So

$$S_n = a_1 + a_1 r + a_1 r^2 + a_1 r^3 + \cdots + a_1 r^{n-1} \qquad (8)$$

Now if we multiply both sides of equation (8) by r,

$$rS_n = a_1 r + a_1 r^2 + a_1 r^3 + \cdots + a_1 r^{n-1} + a_1 r^n$$

and then subtract this from equation (8), we get

$$S_n - rS_n = a_1 - a_1 r^n$$

or

$$S_n(1 - r) = a_1(1 - r^n)$$

If $r \neq 1$, we can solve this for S_n:

$$S_n = \frac{a_1(1 - r^n)}{1 - r} \qquad r \neq 1$$

If $r = 1$, we can find S_n from equation (8), because then it reads

$$S_n = a_1 + a_1 + a_1 + \cdots + a_1$$

and since there are n terms, this gives

$$S_n = na_1 \qquad r = 1$$

We summarize these results in the box.

If $a_1, a_2, a_3, \ldots, a_n$ is a finite geometric sequence with common ratio r, then

$$S_n = \frac{a_1(1 - r^n)}{1 - r} \quad \text{if } r \neq 1 \qquad (9)$$

$$= na_1 \qquad \text{if } r = 1$$

where $S_n = a_1 + a_2 + \cdots + a_n$.

Again we may interpret equation (9) as being the sum of the first n terms of an infinite geometric sequence.

EXAMPLE 14   Find the sum of the first eight terms of the geometric sequence 1, -2, 4, -8, ...

Solution   We see that $r = -2$. So by equation (9),

$$S_8 = \frac{1[1 - (-2)^8]}{1 - (-2)} = \frac{1 - 256}{3} = -\frac{255}{3} = -85$$

EXAMPLE 15   Find the sum

$$\sum_{k=1}^{10} \frac{1}{2^k}$$

Solution   The first thing to note is that this is a geometric series. The expanded form of the sum is

$$S_{10} = \frac{1}{2} + \frac{1}{2^2} + \frac{1}{2^3} + \cdots + \frac{1}{2^{10}}$$

The common ratio is $\frac{1}{2}$, so by equation (9) we have

$$S_{10} = \frac{\frac{1}{2}[1 - (\frac{1}{2})^{10}]}{1 - \frac{1}{2}} = 1 - \frac{1}{2^{10}} = 1 - \frac{1}{1,024} = \frac{1,023}{1,024}$$

We conclude this section with a summary of the formulas we have developed for arithmetic and geometric sequences and series.

	Arithmetic Sequence	**Geometric Sequence**
For all $n \geq 1$:	$d = a_{n+1} - a_n$	$r = \dfrac{a_{n+1}}{a_n}$
nth term:	$a_n = a_1 + (n-1)d$	$a_n = a_1 r^{n-1}$
Sum of first n terms,	$S_n = n\left(\dfrac{a_1 + a_n}{2}\right)$	$S_n = \dfrac{a_1(1 - r^n)}{1 - r}$ if $r \neq 1$
$S_n = \displaystyle\sum_{k=1}^{n} a_k :$	$= \dfrac{n}{2}[2a_1 + (n-1)d]$	$= na_1$ if $r = 1$

EXERCISE SET 3

A   Write the expanded forms of the series in Problems 1–10.

1. $\displaystyle\sum_{k=1}^{4} \frac{3k+1}{2k-1}$

2. $\displaystyle\sum_{i=1}^{5} \frac{i}{i^2+1}$

3. $\displaystyle\sum_{n=1}^{6} \frac{(-1)^{n-1}}{n(n+1)}$

4. $\displaystyle\sum_{j=1}^{5} \frac{2^{j-1}}{3^{j}}$

5. $\displaystyle\sum_{k=1}^{8} \frac{(-1)^{k-1}}{k^2+1}$

6. $\displaystyle\sum_{m=1}^{6} \frac{2^m}{m+1}$

7. $\displaystyle\sum_{k=1}^{10} (5k-3)$

8. $\displaystyle\sum_{n=1}^{5} \frac{\ln n}{n}$

9. $\displaystyle\sum_{n=1}^{6} ne^{-n}$

10. $\displaystyle\sum_{k=1}^{5} \frac{k^k}{2k-1}$

In Problems 11–18 find the sum of the first n terms of the given sequence for the specified value of n.

11. $3, 8, 13, 18, \ldots;\quad n = 20$

12. $-2, 4, -8, 16, \ldots;\quad n = 10$

13. $-6, -4, -2, 0, \ldots;\quad n = 100$

14. $1, \frac{1}{3}, \frac{1}{9}, \ldots;\quad n = 8$

15. $0.2, 0.02, 0.002, \ldots;\quad n = 12$

16. $5, \frac{7}{2}, 2, \frac{1}{2}, \ldots;\quad n = 30$

17. $0.2, 0.22, 0.24, 0.26, \ldots;\quad n = 50$

18. $-27, 18, -12, 8, \ldots;\quad n = 8$

In Problems 19–26 evaluate the indicated sums.

19. $\displaystyle\sum_{k=1}^{200} (2+3k)$

20. $\displaystyle\sum_{k=1}^{10} (-3)^{k-1}$

21. $\displaystyle\sum_{n=1}^{20} (2n-1)$

22. $\displaystyle\sum_{k=1}^{12} \frac{1}{2^{k+1}}$

23. $\displaystyle\sum_{i=1}^{8} \frac{2^i}{3^{i-1}}$

24. $\displaystyle\sum_{m=1}^{50} \left(\frac{m+3}{2}\right)$

25. $\displaystyle\sum_{j=1}^{6} \frac{(-1)^{j-1}3^j}{4^{j-1}}$

26. $\displaystyle\sum_{n=1}^{15} \left(\frac{n}{2}-3\right)$

27. Find the sum of the first 100 natural numbers.

B   Find the sums in Problems 28 and 29.

28. $\displaystyle\sum_{k=1}^{6} (2^k+3k-1)$

29. $\displaystyle\sum_{n=0}^{5} [3^n-2(n+1)]$

30. Find a formula for the sum of the first n odd positive integers.

31. Some pipes are stacked so that the bottom layer has 15 pipes, the next layer 14 pipes, the next 13, and so on, until there is only one pipe at the top. How many pipes are there in all?

32. A ball is dropped from a height of 40 feet, and each time it bounces it rises to a height three-fourths as high as previously. Find the total distance the ball has covered when it hits the ground for the fifth time.

33. A man is offered two jobs, one starting at $12,000 with constant annual raises of $700, and the other starting at $10,000 with annual raises of 8%. What would be his salary at each job during the sixth year? What would be his accumulated earnings at each job through the end of the sixth year? How many years would it be before the salary of the second job exceeded the first? How many years would it be before the accumulated earnings of the second job exceeded the first?

34. A pendulum swings a distance of 20 inches initially from one side to the other, and on each subsequent swing it goes 0.8 of the distance on the previous swing. Find the total distance covered by the pendulum after ten swings.

35. If a person were given a choice of working 30 days for 1¢ the first day, 2¢ the next, 4¢ the next, and so on, each day doubling the amount earned on the previous day, or of being paid $1,000 the first day, $2,000 the next, $3,000 the next, and so on, each day adding $1,000 to the amount on the previous day, which offer should he take? How much would he make under each arrangement?

---

4 Infinite Geometric Series

Consider an infinite sequence

$$a_1, a_2, a_3, \ldots, a_n, \ldots$$

We designate the corresponding **infinite series** by

$$\sum_{k=1}^{\infty} a_k = a_1 + a_2 + a_3 + \cdots + a_n + \cdots$$

The symbol ∞ is read "infinity." To arrive at a reasonable definition of what is meant by such an infinite sum we consider the finite sums

$$S_1 = a_1$$
$$S_2 = a_1 + a_2$$
$$S_3 = a_1 + a_2 + a_3$$
$$\ldots \ldots \ldots \ldots \ldots$$
$$S_n = a_1 + a_2 + \cdots + a_n$$

We call S_n the **nth partial sum** of the series $\sum_{n=1}^{\infty} a_n$, and we call the sequence $S_1, S_2, S_3, \ldots, S_n, \ldots$ **the sequence of partial sums.** If it happens that for larger and larger values of n, the partial sums approach as a limit some number S, then we define S to be the sum of the infinite series. This is written symbolically as

$$S = \sum_{n=1}^{\infty} a_n = \lim_{n \to \infty} S_n$$

The symbol "$\lim_{n \to \infty} S_n$" is read "the limit of S_n as n goes to infinity." Limits of sequences are studied in detail in calculus, and it is not appropriate in this course to give a precise definition. It is sufficient to say that

$$\lim_{n \to \infty} S_n = S$$

means that the partial sums S_n are arbitrarily close to S for all sufficiently large values of n.

To make these concepts more concrete let us consider the infinite geometric series

$$1 + \frac{1}{2} + \frac{1}{4} + \frac{1}{8} + \cdots + \frac{1}{2^{n-1}} + \cdots \tag{10}$$

The partial sums are

$$S_1 = 1$$
$$S_2 = 1 + \tfrac{1}{2} = \tfrac{3}{2}$$
$$S_3 = 1 + \tfrac{1}{2} + \tfrac{1}{4} = \tfrac{7}{4}$$
$$S_4 = 1 + \tfrac{1}{2} + \tfrac{1}{4} + \tfrac{1}{8} = \tfrac{15}{8}$$

. . . .

By equation (9) we can write the nth partial sum as

$$S_n = 1 + \frac{1}{2} + \frac{1}{4} + \frac{1}{8} + \cdots + \frac{1}{2^{n-1}} = \frac{1[1 - (\tfrac{1}{2})^n]}{1 - \tfrac{1}{2}} = 2\left[1 - \left(\frac{1}{2}\right)^n\right]$$

The sequence of partial sums,

$$1, \frac{3}{2}, \frac{7}{4}, \frac{15}{8}, \ldots, 2\left[1 - \left(\frac{1}{2}\right)^n\right], \ldots$$

appears to be approaching 2 as a limit. In fact,

$$\lim_{n \to \infty} S_n = \lim_{n \to \infty} 2\left[1 - \left(\frac{1}{2}\right)^n\right]$$

and since $(\tfrac{1}{2})^n$ can be made arbitrarily close to 0 by choosing n sufficiently large, it follows that $\lim_{n \to \infty} S_n = 2$.

It should be emphasized that the partial sums of an infinite series do not always approach a finite limit. If a limit is approached, we say the series **converges**; otherwise, it **diverges.** The series

$$\sum_{n=1}^{\infty} 2n = 2 + 4 + 6 + 8 + \cdots$$

clearly diverges. In fact, this is the sum of an arithmetic sequence, and by equation (6)

$$S_n = 2 + 4 + 6 + 8 + \cdots + 2n = n\left[\frac{2 + (2n)}{2}\right] = n(1 + n)$$

As n becomes arbitrarily large, S_n is unbounded.

Now we want to determine under what conditions the infinite geometric series

$$\sum_{n=1}^{\infty} a_1 r^{n-1} = a_1 + a_1 r + a_1 r^2 + a_1 r^3 + \cdots \tag{11}$$

converges. By equation (9) we know that if $r \neq 1$, the nth partial sum is given by

$$S_n = \frac{a_1(1 - r^n)}{1 - r}$$

We want to examine what happens as n gets arbitrarily large. The key lies in the term r^n. When r is less than 1 in absolute value (for example, when $r = \tfrac{1}{2}$), it is shown by calculus that r^n approaches 0. So we conclude that

$$\lim_{n \to \infty} S_n = \frac{a_1}{1 - r} \quad \text{if} \quad |r| < 1$$

On the other hand, if $|r| \geq 1$, it can be proved that no finite limit exists. For example, if $r = 2$, we see that 2^n gets arbitrarily large, so that S_n cannot approach a finite limit. Similarly, if $r = -2$, then $(-2)^n$ gets larger and larger numerically, but with alternating signs. So again, S_n does not approach a finite limit.
   The following general result can be proved:

> The infinite geometric series (11) converges if and only if $|r| < 1$. Furthermore, when $|r| < 1$, the sum S is
>
> $$S = \frac{a_1}{1 - r} \tag{12}$$

EXAMPLE 16   Show that the series below converges, and find its sum.

$$\sum_{n=1}^{\infty} \left(-\frac{2}{3}\right)^{n-1}$$

Solution   This is a geometric series with ratio $-\frac{2}{3}$, and since this is less than 1 in absolute value, the series converges. In expanded form the series is

$$1 - \tfrac{2}{3} + \tfrac{4}{9} - \tfrac{8}{27} + \cdots$$

By equation (12) the sum is

$$S = \frac{a_1}{1 - r} = \frac{1}{1 - (-\frac{2}{3})} = \frac{1}{1 + \frac{2}{3}} = \frac{3}{5}$$

It should be emphasized that we can never reach $\frac{3}{5}$ exactly by adding up any finite number of terms, but by definition, $\frac{3}{5}$ is the sum of the infinite series.

EXAMPLE 17   Show that each of the following series is divergent:

a. $1 + \dfrac{3}{2} + \dfrac{9}{4} + \dfrac{27}{8} + \cdots$ **b.** $\displaystyle\sum_{k=1}^{\infty} (-1)^{k-1}$

Solution   **a.**   The common ratio is $\frac{3}{2}$, which is greater than 1. So the series diverges.
   b.   The expanded series is $1 - 1 + 1 - 1 + \cdots$, which is a geometric series with ratio -1. Since $|-1| = 1$, the series diverges. Notice the behavior of the partial sums in this example:

$$S_1 = 1, \quad S_2 = 0, \quad S_3 = 1, \quad S_4 = 0, \ldots$$

Although these do not get arbitrarily large, no specific limit is approached.

The formula (12) for the sum of an infinite geometric series can be used to find the rational number represented by a repeating decimal. This is an alternative to the procedure given in Chapter 1. The next two examples illustrate this technique.

EXAMPLE 18   Find the rational number represented by the repeating decimal 0.242424. . . .

Solution   We treat this as the sum of the infinite series

$$0.24 + 0.0024 + 0.000024 + \cdots$$

which is geometric, with $a_1 = 0.24$ and $r = 0.01$. Thus, the sum is

$$S_n = \frac{a_1}{1-r} = \frac{0.24}{1-0.01} = \frac{0.24}{0.99} = \frac{24}{99} = \frac{8}{33}$$

EXAMPLE 19   Express 2.135135135. . . as a rational number.

Solution   We write this as

$$2 + [0.135 + 0.000135 + 0.000000135 + \cdots]$$

The portion in brackets is a geometric series with $a_1 = 0.135$ and $r = 0.001$. So its sum is

$$\frac{a_1}{1-r} = \frac{0.135}{1-0.001} = \frac{0.135}{0.999} = \frac{135}{999} = \frac{5}{37}$$

and the answer to the problem is

$$2 + \tfrac{5}{37} = \tfrac{79}{37}$$

We conclude this section with a glimpse of the larger problem of convergence of infinite series in general (not just geometric series). At this stage we cannot go into this subject in depth, since to do so would require a knowledge of calculus. It is a fascinating part of mathematics and presents some intriguing questions. There are, in fact, some famous unsolved problems in this field.

To get a hint of one aspect of the problem, consider the following infinite series:

a. $1 + \dfrac{1}{2} + \dfrac{1}{3} + \dfrac{1}{4} + \cdots$

b. $1 - \dfrac{1}{2} + \dfrac{1}{3} - \dfrac{1}{4} + \cdots$

c. $1 + \dfrac{1}{2^2} + \dfrac{1}{3^2} + \dfrac{1}{4^2} + \cdots$

d. $1 + \dfrac{1}{2^3} + \dfrac{1}{3^3} + \dfrac{1}{4^3} + \cdots$

Without any attempt at a proof, we state the following facts:

a. The series diverges. By choosing n large enough we can make S_n arbitrarily large, even though the sum of the first billion terms is only about 21. So the divergence is quite slow.

b. This series converges, and its sum is $\ln 2$.

c. This series converges, and its sum is $\pi^2/6$. How this result was first arrived at by the famous seventeenth century Swiss mathematician Leonhard Euler is a fascinating chapter in the history of mathematics.

d. This series converges, but no one knows exactly what the sum is. This is one of the unsolved problems.

EXERCISE SET 4

A   Determine which of the infinite geometric series in Problems 1–19 converge and which diverge. For those that converge, find the sum.

1. $1 + \frac{1}{3} + \frac{1}{9} + \frac{1}{27} + \cdots$

2. $1 - \frac{3}{4} + \frac{9}{16} - \frac{27}{64} + \cdots$

3. $1 + \frac{4}{3} + \frac{16}{9} + \frac{64}{27} + \cdots$

4. $\sum_{k=1}^{\infty} (-1.1)^{k-1}$

5. $\sum_{n=1}^{\infty} (-0.9)^{n-1}$

6. $\sum_{i=1}^{\infty} \frac{2^i}{3^{i+1}}$

7. $\sum_{n=1}^{\infty} \frac{(-1)^{n-1} 5^n}{6^{n-1}}$

8. $\sum_{n=1}^{\infty} 2^{-n}$

9. $\sum_{n=0}^{\infty} \left(\frac{3}{2}\right)^n$

10. $\sum_{n=0}^{\infty} \left(\frac{3}{2}\right)^{-n}$

11. $\sum_{n=1}^{\infty} 2\left(\frac{3}{5}\right)^{n-1}$

12. $\sum_{n=1}^{\infty} 3\left(-\frac{2}{3}\right)^{n-1}$

13. $36 - 12 + 4 + \cdots$

14. $0.01 + 0.02 + 0.04 + \cdots$

15. $\sum_{n=1}^{\infty} (\sqrt{2})^n$

16. $\sum_{k=1}^{\infty} (\sqrt{3})^{-k+1}$

17. $\sum_{n=1}^{\infty} 2^{-n/2}$

18. $1 + 0.1 + 0.01 + 0.001 + \cdots$

19. $1 - 0.1 + 0.01 - 0.001 + \cdots$

In Problems 20–25 find the rational number corresponding to the given decimal number using infinite series.

20. $0.333\ldots$

21. $0.151515\ldots$

22. $0.272727\ldots$

23. $1.545454\ldots$

24. $0.243243243\ldots$

25. $3.162162162\ldots$

26. Find the sum of the series $\sum_{n=1}^{\infty} x^{n-1}$ as a function of x. For what values of x is this valid?

27. Find the sum of the series $\sum_{n=0}^{\infty} (x^n/2^n)$. For what values of x is this valid?

28. If S_n is the nth partial sum of the series $\sum_{n=1}^{\infty} a_n$, show that $a_1 = S_1$, and for all $n \geq 2$, show that $a_n = S_n - S_{n-1}$.

29. Use the result of Problem 28 to construct an infinite series for which $S_n = (n + 1)/n$. Show that the series converges and that its sum is 1.
    Hint. Write S_n in the form $1 + (1/n)$ to show convergence.

B 30. Show that

$$\frac{1}{n(n + 1)} = \frac{1}{n} - \frac{1}{n + 1}$$

Use this result to find the sum of the series

$$\sum_{n=1}^{\infty} \frac{1}{n(n + 1)}$$

Hint. Use the first result, and write the expanded form of S_n. Observe the terms that add to 0.

31. Find the sum of the series

$$\sum_{n=1}^{\infty} \frac{(-1)^{n-1} x^{2n-2}}{3^n}$$

Show that this is valid only when $|x| < \sqrt{3}$.

32. A ball is dropped from a height of 50 feet, and on each bounce it goes three-fourths as high as before. Approximate the total distance traveled by the ball in coming to rest.

33. The theory of infinite geometric series continues to hold true for complex values of r, and formula (12) is valid as long as $|r| < 1$. Using this fact, find the sum of the series

$$1 + \frac{i}{2} - \frac{1}{4} - \frac{i}{8} + \frac{1}{16} + \frac{i}{32} - \cdots$$

34. Find the sum of the series $\sum_{n=0}^{\infty} (2x - 1)^n$. Find the range of values of x for which this result is valid.

In Problems 35–38 make use of formula (12) to find the infinite geometric series having the specified sum, and state the domain of validity.

35. $\dfrac{1}{1 - 2x}$

36. $\dfrac{1}{1 + (x/3)}$

37. $\dfrac{1}{2 - x}$

38. $\dfrac{3}{4 - x^2}$

Hint. Divide the numerator and denominator by 2.

39. For a certain series $\sum_{n=1}^{\infty} a_n$, the nth partial sum is $4 - (1/3^n)$. What is the sum of the series? Show that the series is geometric.
    Hint. Use Problem 28 and Definition 4.

40. In calculus it is shown that

$$e^x = 1 + x + \frac{x^2}{2!} + \frac{x^3}{3!} + \cdots + \frac{x^n}{n!} + \cdots, \text{ where } n! = 1 \cdot 2 \cdot 3 \ldots n$$

With the aid of a calculator use the first ten terms of this series to estimate the value of e by taking $x = 1$. The error in this estimate can be shown to be no greater than $3/10!$. What can you conclude is the accuracy of your estimate?

5 Mathematical Induction

In this section we present a method of proving certain statements, or formulas, about natural numbers. To illustrate how we might arrive at one such formula, let us consider the sum of the first n odd natural numbers. We observe the values for $n = 1, 2, 3$, and 4:

$$n = 1: \quad 1 = 1$$
$$n = 2: \quad 1 + 3 = 4$$
$$n = 3: \quad 1 + 3 + 5 = 9$$
$$n = 4: \quad 1 + 3 + 5 + 7 = 16$$

Since the sum in each case is the square of the number of terms added, this suggests the following general statement:

The sum of the first n odd natural numbers is n^2.

Equivalently, we could write this as the formula

$$1 + 3 + 5 + \cdots + (2n - 1) = n^2$$

But have we *proved* this formula? The answer is no. We have shown it to be true for $n = 1, 2, 3$, and 4, but that is all. Even if we continued for many more values of n and found the result true in every case, we still would not know for sure whether it was true for *all* natural numbers. It is just such situations as this where the method of proof called **mathematical induction** comes to our rescue. (We might note that the example we have used happens to be an arithmetic series, and we know a formula for the sum; however, the method of mathematical induction applies to a much wider class of problems.)

Principle of Mathematical Induction

If a statement involving natural numbers is true for $n = 1$, and if its truth for an arbitrary natural number k implies its truth for $k + 1$, then the statement is true for all natural numbers.

We will take this as an axiom, although it is possible to prove it based on other fundamental properties of the natural numbers. We will, however, show its plausibility. If we have shown that the statement in question is true for

$n = 1$, and if we have shown that its truth for $n = k$ implies its truth for $n = k + 1$, then we can let $k = 1$ and conclude that it is true also for $k + 1 = 2$. Then we can let $k = 2$ and conclude that it is true for $k + 1 = 3$. Next, letting $k = 3$, we see that it is true for $k + 1 = 4$, and so on and on. It can be seen, then, to be true for any given natural number, and hence for every natural number.

In order to state the principle of mathematical induction using fewer words, we introduce the symbol $P(n)$ for the statement to be proved (this can be thought of as a function with the natural numbers as domain and a set of statements as the range). The principle of mathematical induction can then be restated as follows:

> If (i) $P(1)$ is true, and (ii) $P(k)$ implies $P(k + 1)$ for every natural number k, then $P(n)$ is true for all natural numbers.

Both conditions (i) and (ii) are essential. To prove (i) we simply substitute $n = 1$ in the statement and see if it is true. For (ii), we *assume* the statement is true for an unspecified natural number k and show that it follows from this that the statement is true for $k + 1$. In general, it is more difficult to prove (ii) than (i).

Mathematical induction is often compared to lining up dominoes in such a way that if the first one is knocked down, all succeeding ones will fall (Figure 1). This is a pretty good analogy (provided we imagine infinitely many dominoes!). To say that the first one is knocked down is analogous to saying $P(1)$ is true. Having the dominoes spaced so that whenever any one of them (say the kth one) falls, the next one (the $k + 1$st one) will also fall, is analogous to saying that $P(k)$ implies $P(k + 1)$.

Figure 1

We illustrate the technique with several examples, the first of which is the one introduced at the beginning of this section.

EXAMPLE 20   Use mathematical induction to prove the formula

$$1 + 3 + 5 + \cdots + (2n - 1) = n^2 \qquad (13)$$

Solution   Let $P(n)$ denote the given statement, that is, formula (13). To test (i) we look at $P(1)$. The left-hand side of the formula says "add all odd natural numbers up through the nth one" (which equals $2n - 1$). But for $n = 1$ the nth term is the first term, so the left-hand side consists of the single number 1. The right-hand side is 1^2, and since $1 = 1^2$, it follows that $P(1)$ is true.

Now we assume that $P(k)$ is true and try to show that $P(k + 1)$ follows, where k represents an arbitrary natural number. So we assume that

$$1 + 3 + 5 + \cdots + (2k - 1) = k^2 \tag{14}$$

We wish to work from this and by means of valid mathematical operations obtain $P(k + 1)$. Now $P(k + 1)$ is formula (13) with n replaced by $k + 1$. The left-hand side is the sum of the first $k + 1$ odd numbers and so contains all the terms on the left-hand side of $P(k)$ plus one more term, namely $2k + 1$. So we are going to add $2k + 1$ to *both* sides of formula (14)—adding it to the left to make it what we want and adding it to the right to balance this off. This yields

$$1 + 3 + 5 + \cdots + (2k - 1) + (2k + 1) = k^2 + 2k + 1$$

or on factoring the right-hand side,

$$1 + 3 + 5 + \cdots + (2k + 1) = (k + 1)^2$$

This is exactly what formula (13) gives for $n = k + 1$; in other words, it is $P(k + 1)$. So we have shown that the truth of $P(k)$ implies that of $P(k + 1)$, and both parts (i) and (ii) of the principle of mathematical induction have been shown to be true. Therefore, formula (13) is true for all natural numbers n.

EXAMPLE 21   Prove that for all natural numbers n, $2^n \geq 2n$.

Solution   Let $P(n)$ denote the given statement. We test $P(1)$, which says

$$2^1 \geq 2 \cdot 1$$

This is true, since both sides equal 2, and since $2 \geq 2$, we see that $P(1)$ is true.

Now assume $P(k)$ is true for an arbitrary natural number k:

$$2^k \geq 2k$$

To work toward $P(k + 1)$ we can multiply both sides by 2 in order to make the left-hand side read 2^{k+1}. This gives

$$2 \cdot 2^k \geq 2 \cdot 2k$$

or

$$2^{k+1} \geq 2k + 2k$$

Since $k \geq 1$, it follows that $2k \geq 2$. Thus,

$$2^{k+1} \geq 2k + 2 = 2(k + 1)$$

Hence,

$$2^{k+1} \geq 2(k + 1)$$

which is $P(k + 1)$. Therefore the proof by mathematical induction is complete, and we conclude that $2^n \geq 2n$ for all natural numbers n.

EXAMPLE 22   Prove by mathematical induction that for all natural numbers n, the quantity $n^2 + n$ is an even number.

Solution   Let $P(n)$ represent the statement "$n^2 + n$ is an even number." Then $P(1)$ says that $1^2 + 1$ is an even number, which is true, since $1^2 + 1 = 2$. Now assume that $P(k)$ is true, that is, $k^2 + k$ is an even number. Since by definition an even number is a multiple of 2, we can say that

$$k^2 + k = 2m$$

for some integer m. For $P(k + 1)$ we want to examine $(k + 1)^2 + (k + 1)$. This can be written

$$k^2 + 2k + 1 + k + 1 = k^2 + k + 2k + 2$$
$$= (k^2 + k) + 2(k + 1)$$

By our assumption $k^2 + k = 2m$, so

$$(k + 1)^2 + (k + 1) = 2m + 2(k + 1) = 2(m + k + 1)$$

The right-hand side is a multiple of 2 and so is even. Thus, we have shown that whenever $k^2 + k$ is even, $(k + 1)^2 + (k + 1)$ is also even. So both parts of the proof by mathematical induction are complete, and we conclude that $n^2 + n$ is even for all natural numbers n.

EXAMPLE 23   Prove that

$$1^2 + 2^2 + 3^2 + \cdots + n^2 = \frac{n(n + 1)(2n + 1)}{6}$$

for all natural numbers n.

Solution   Again let $P(n)$ denote the formula to be proved. For $n = 1$ this reads

$$1^2 = \frac{1(1 + 1)(2 + 1)}{6}$$

which is seen to be true.
   Now assume that $P(k)$ is true:

$$1^2 + 2^2 + 3^2 + \cdots + k^2 = \frac{k(k + 1)(2k + 1)}{6}$$

Add $(k + 1)^2$ to both sides:

$$1^2 + 2^2 + 3^2 + \cdots + k^2 + (k + 1)^2 = \frac{k(k + 1)(2k + 1)}{6} + (k + 1)^2$$

This brings the left-hand side to the proper form for $P(k + 1)$. We want to see if the right-hand side also is in the proper form.

$$\frac{k(k + 1)(2k + 1)}{6} + (k + 1)^2 = \frac{k(k + 1)(2k + 1) + 6(k + 1)^2}{6}$$

$$= \frac{(k + 1)[k(2k + 1) + 6(k + 1)]}{6}$$

$$= \frac{(k + 1)(2k^2 + 7k + 6)}{6}$$

$$= \frac{(k + 1)(k + 2)(2k + 3)}{6}$$

$$= \frac{(k + 1)[(k + 1) + 1][2(k + 1) + 1]}{6}$$

A reexamination of the right-hand side of the original formula $P(n)$ shows that the last expression arrived at is exactly what is obtained if n is replaced by $k + 1$. So by assuming $P(k)$ to be true, we have shown that $P(k + 1)$ also is true. Therefore, the proof by induction is complete.

EXERCISE SET 5

Using mathematical induction, prove that each of the following is true for all natural numbers n.

A   **1.** $2 + 4 + 6 + \cdots + (2n) = n(n + 1)$

2. $\dfrac{1}{1 \cdot 2} + \dfrac{1}{2 \cdot 3} + \dfrac{1}{3 \cdot 4} + \cdots + \dfrac{1}{n(n + 1)} = \dfrac{n}{n + 1}$

3. $1 + 5 + 9 + \cdots + (4n - 3) = n(2n - 1)$

4. $n^2 + 1 \geq 2n$

5. $3 + 7 + 11 + \cdots + (4n - 1) = n(2n + 1)$

6. $1 + 2 + 3 + \cdots + n = \dfrac{n(n + 1)}{2}$

7. $1 + 2^1 + 2^2 + 2^3 + \cdots + 2^{n-1} = 2^n - 1$

8. 3 is a factor of $n^3 + 2n$

9. If $a > 1$, then $a^n > 1$.

10. If $0 < a < 1$, then $0 < a^n < 1$.

11. $\dfrac{1}{1 \cdot 3} + \dfrac{1}{3 \cdot 5} + \dfrac{1}{5 \cdot 7} + \cdots + \dfrac{1}{(2n - 1)(2n + 1)} = \dfrac{n}{2n + 1}$

12. 6 is a factor of $n(n + 1)(n + 2)$

13. $1 \cdot 2 + 2 \cdot 3 + 3 \cdot 4 + \cdots + n(n + 1) = \dfrac{n(n + 1)(n + 2)}{3}$

14. $\displaystyle\sum_{i=1}^{n} (3i - 2) = \dfrac{n(3n - 1)}{2}$

15. $(ab)^n = a^n b^n$

16. 2 is a factor of $n^2 - n + 2$

17. $\displaystyle\sum_{i=1}^{n} (6i - 5) = 3n^2 - 2n$

18. 3 is a factor of $4^n - 1$

19. $\sum_{k=1}^{n} (-1)^{k-1} = \dfrac{1 - (-1)^n}{2}$

20. The nth term of an arithmetic sequence having first term a_1 and common difference d is $a_1 + (n-1)d$.

21. The nth term of a geometric sequence having first term a_1 and common ratio r is $a_1 r^{n-1}$.

B **22.** $1^2 + 3^2 + 5^2 + \cdots + (2n-1)^2 = \dfrac{n(4n^2 - 1)}{3}$

23. If $x > -1$, then $(1 + x)^n \geq 1 + nx$.

24. $1^3 + 3^3 + 5^3 + \cdots + (2n-1)^3 = n^2(2n^2 - 1)$

25. $1^3 + 2^3 + 3^3 + \cdots + n^3 = (1 + 2 + 3 + \cdots + n)^2$
Hint. See Problem 6.

26. $a - b$ is a factor of $a^n - b^n$
Hint. For the second part of the proof write $a^{k+1} - b^{k+1} = a(a^k - b^k) + b^k(a - b)$.

27. $a + b$ is a factor of $a^{2n-1} + b^{2n-1}$
Hint. For the second part of the proof write $a^{2k+1} + b^{2k+1} = a^2(a^{2k-1} + b^{2k-1}) - b^{2k-1}(a^2 - b^2)$.

---

6 Proof of the Binomial Theorem

In Chapter 2 we stated the binomial theorem without proving it. Mathematical induction provides one means of proving this important result. The formula to be proved can be written as follows:

$$(a + b)^n = a^n + na^{n-1}b + \frac{n(n-1)}{1 \cdot 2} a^{n-2}b^2$$
$$+ \frac{n(n-1)(n-2)}{1 \cdot 2 \cdot 3} a^{n-3}b^3 + \cdots + b^n \tag{15}$$

We wish to show that this is true for all natural numbers n.

First we introduce a convenient symbol called the **binomial coefficient symbol**:

For $k = 1, 2, 3, \ldots, n$ we define
$$\binom{n}{k} = \frac{n(n-1)(n-2) \cdots (n-k+1)}{1 \cdot 2 \cdot 3 \cdots k} \tag{16}$$
and for $k = 0$ we define $\binom{n}{0} = 1$.

The binomial formula can now be written as

$$(a + b)^n = \binom{n}{0}a^n + \binom{n}{1}a^{n-1}b + \binom{n}{2}a^{n-2}b^2 + \cdots + \binom{n}{n}b^n \tag{17}$$
$$= \sum_{r=0}^{n} \binom{n}{r}a^{n-r}b^r$$

Note that the $(i + 1)$st term of the expansion is

$$\binom{n}{i} a^{n-i} b^i$$

Factorial notation enables us to give an alternate form of the binomial coefficient which is sometimes convenient. Recall that $r!$ means $1 \cdot 2 \cdot 3 \cdots r$, for any natural number r, and that we define $0! = 1$. We may therefore write

$$\binom{n}{k} = \frac{n(n-1)(n-2) \cdots (n-k+1)}{1 \cdot 2 \cdot 3 \cdots k}$$

$$= \frac{n(n-1)(n-2) \cdots (n-k+1)}{k!} \cdot \frac{(n-k)(n-k-1) \cdots 2 \cdot 1}{(n-k)(n-k-1) \cdots 2 \cdot 1}$$

and thus:

$$\binom{n}{k} = \frac{n!}{k!(n-k)!} \qquad k = 0, 1, 2, \ldots, n \tag{18}$$

EXAMPLE 24   Evaluate each of the following in two ways, first by equation (16) and second by (18).

a. $\binom{4}{2}$ **b.** $\binom{5}{1}$ **c.** $\binom{6}{4}$ **d.** $\binom{8}{8}$ **e.** $\binom{11}{0}$

Solution   **a.** $\binom{4}{2} = \frac{4 \cdot 3}{1 \cdot 2} = 6$ $\qquad \binom{4}{2} = \frac{4!}{2!2!} = \frac{4 \cdot 3 \cdot 2 \cdot 1}{2 \cdot 1 \cdot 2 \cdot 1} = 6$

b. $\binom{5}{1} = \frac{5}{1} = 5$ $\qquad \binom{5}{1} = \frac{5!}{1!4!} = \frac{5 \cdot 4 \cdot 3 \cdot 2 \cdot 1}{1 \cdot 4 \cdot 3 \cdot 2 \cdot 1} = 5$

c. $\binom{6}{4} = \frac{6 \cdot 5 \cdot 4 \cdot 3}{1 \cdot 2 \cdot 3 \cdot 4} = 15$ $\qquad \binom{6}{4} = \frac{6!}{4!2!} = \frac{6 \cdot 5 \cdot 4 \cdot 3 \cdot 2 \cdot 1}{4 \cdot 3 \cdot 2 \cdot 1 \cdot 2 \cdot 1} = 15$

d. $\binom{8}{8} = \frac{8 \cdot 7 \cdot 6 \cdot 5 \cdot 4 \cdot 3 \cdot 2 \cdot 1}{1 \cdot 2 \cdot 3 \cdot 4 \cdot 5 \cdot 6 \cdot 7 \cdot 8} = 1$ $\qquad \binom{8}{8} = \frac{8!}{8!0!} = \frac{8!}{(8!)1} = 1$

e. $\binom{11}{0}$ cannot be evaluated by equation (16), but it is defined to be 1; by (18) we have

$$\binom{11}{0} = \frac{11!}{0!11!} = 1$$

In the proof of the binomial theorem we will need the following result, which you will be asked to prove in Problem 24, Exercise Set 6:

$$\binom{k}{r} + \binom{k}{r-1} = \binom{k+1}{r} \tag{19}$$

Proof of the Binomial Theorem

We wish to show that

$$(a + b)^n = \binom{n}{0}a^n + \binom{n}{1}a^{n-1}b + \binom{n}{2}a^{n-2}b^2 + \cdots + \binom{n}{n-1}ab^{n-1} + \binom{n}{n}b^n$$

is true for all natural numbers n. Let this formula be designated by $P(n)$. Then $P(1)$ reads

$$(a + b)^1 = \binom{1}{0}a + \binom{1}{1}b$$

and since $\binom{1}{0} = 1$ and $\binom{1}{1} = 1$, we see that this is true.

Now assume $P(k)$ is true:

$$(a + b)^k = \binom{k}{0}a^k + \binom{k}{1}a^{k-1}b + \binom{k}{2}a^{k-2}b^2 + \cdots + \binom{k}{k-1}ab^{k-1} + \binom{k}{k}b^k$$

In order to make the left-hand side what we want for $P(k + 1)$, we multiply both sides by $a + b$. This gives

$$(a + b)^{k+1} = \binom{k}{0}a^{k+1} + \binom{k}{1}a^k b + \binom{k}{2}a^{k-1}b^2 + \cdots + \binom{k}{k}ab^k + \binom{k}{0}a^k b$$

$$+ \binom{k}{1}a^{k-1}b^2 + \cdots + \binom{k}{k-1}ab^k + \binom{k}{k}b^{k+1}$$

$$= \binom{k}{0}a^{k+1} + \left[\binom{k}{1} + \binom{k}{0}\right]a^k b + \left[\binom{k}{2} + \binom{k}{1}\right]a^{k-1}b^2$$

$$+ \cdots + \left[\binom{k}{k} + \binom{k}{k-1}\right]ab^k + \binom{k}{k}b^{k+1}$$

We can replace $\binom{k}{0}$ by $\binom{k+1}{0}$, since the value is 1 in either case. Also, $\binom{k}{k} = \binom{k+1}{k+1}$, since again each symbol has the value 1. Using these facts, together with equation (19), we get

$$(a + b)^{k+1} = \binom{k+1}{0}a^{k+1} + \binom{k+1}{1}a^k b + \binom{k+2}{2}a^{k-1}b^2$$

$$+ \cdots + \binom{k+1}{k}ab^k + \binom{k+1}{k+1}b^{k+1}$$

which is exactly $P(k + 1)$. Thus, $P(k)$ implies $P(k + 1)$. The proof by induction is therefore complete.

EXERCISE SET 6

A   **1.** Find the value of the given binomial coefficients using equation (16).

a. $\binom{3}{2}$ b. $\binom{6}{3}$ c. $\binom{8}{2}$ d. $\binom{10}{3}$ e. $\binom{9}{9}$

f. $\begin{pmatrix} 10 \\ 5 \end{pmatrix}$ **g.** $\begin{pmatrix} 30 \\ 2 \end{pmatrix}$ **h.** $\begin{pmatrix} 16 \\ 5 \end{pmatrix}$ **i.** $\begin{pmatrix} 7 \\ 6 \end{pmatrix}$ **j.** $\begin{pmatrix} 8 \\ 6 \end{pmatrix}$

2. Use equation (18) to evaluate each of the binomial coefficients in Problem 1.

Simplify the expressions in Problems 3 and 4.

3. **a.** $(k + 1)k!$ **b.** $\dfrac{(k + 1)!}{k!}$ **c.** $\dfrac{n!}{(n - 2)!}$

4. **a.** $\dfrac{1}{k!} + \dfrac{1}{(k - 1)!}$ **b.** $\begin{pmatrix} k \\ 2 \end{pmatrix} + \begin{pmatrix} k \\ 1 \end{pmatrix}$

5. Show that $\begin{pmatrix} r \\ r \end{pmatrix} = 1$ for any natural number r.

6. Show that $\begin{pmatrix} k \\ k \end{pmatrix} = \begin{pmatrix} k + 1 \\ k + 1 \end{pmatrix}$

7. Show that $\begin{pmatrix} n \\ k \end{pmatrix} = \begin{pmatrix} n \\ n - k \end{pmatrix}$

In Problems 8–15 expand, using equation (17), and simplify.

8. $(x + y)^6$

9. $(x - y)^5$
    Hint. Write $x - y = [x + (-y)]$.

10. $(2a + b)^7$

11. $(a - 3b)^4$

12. $(3x + 4y)^5$

13. $(s - 2t)^6$

14. $(3r + s^2)^4$

15. $(x^2 - 2y)^6$

In Problems 16–20 find the specified term of the expansion.

16. $(x + y)^{10}$; eighth term

17. $(x - y)^{12}$; fifth term

18. $(2x + 3y)^{12}$; ninth term

19. $(3a - b)^7$; fourth term

20. $(a - 2b)^{13}$; third term

21. Evaluate $(1.02)^6$ to three decimal places of accuracy using the binomial theorem.
     Hint. Write $(1.02)^6$ as $(1 + 0.02)^6$.

22. Evaluate $(0.99)^8$ to the nearest thousandth using the binomial theorem.

23. Show that $\begin{pmatrix} n \\ 0 \end{pmatrix} + \begin{pmatrix} n \\ 1 \end{pmatrix} + \begin{pmatrix} n \\ 2 \end{pmatrix} + \cdots + \begin{pmatrix} n \\ n \end{pmatrix} = 2^n$.
     Hint. Consider $(1 + 1)^n$.

B 24. Prove the identity (19).

25. Prove the identity

$$\frac{n - r + 1}{r} \cdot \begin{pmatrix} n \\ r - 1 \end{pmatrix} = \begin{pmatrix} n \\ r \end{pmatrix}$$

26. It can be shown that if $|x| < 1$ and α is not a positive integer, then

$$(1 + x)^\alpha = \sum_{r=0}^{\infty} \begin{pmatrix} \alpha \\ r \end{pmatrix} x^r$$

where $\binom{\alpha}{r}$ is given by equation (16). Use this to find the first five terms of $(1 + x)^{-2}$, where $|x| < 1$.

27. Use Problem 26 to write the first five terms of the expansion of $\sqrt{1+x}$, assuming $|x| < 1$.

In Problems 28 and 29 use the expansion of Problem 27 to obtain the answer to five decimal places of accuracy.

28. $\sqrt{1.02}$ **29.** $\sqrt{0.99}$

30. Use Problem 26 to evaluate $1/(1.01)^2$ to six decimal places of accuracy.

Review Exercise Set

A   Write the first four terms of the sequence whose nth term is given in Problems 1–3.

1.   **a.** $a_n = \dfrac{n}{n+1}$ **b.** $a_n = 4n - 3$

2.   **a.** $a_n = \dfrac{(-1)^{n-1}}{\sqrt{2n-1}}$ **b.** $a_n = \dfrac{(-1)^{n-1}n}{n^2+1}$

3.   **a.** $a_n = \dfrac{(-3)^{n-1}}{4^n}$ **b.** $a_n = \dfrac{(-1)^{n-1}}{n \log(n+1)}$

In Problems 4–6 find an expression for the nth term of each sequence.

4.   **a.** $1, -\frac{1}{3}, \frac{1}{5}, -\frac{1}{7}, \ldots$ **b.** $1, \frac{3}{4}, \frac{9}{16}, \frac{27}{64}, \cdots$

5.   **a.** $\dfrac{1}{1\cdot 2}, \dfrac{1}{2\cdot 3}, \dfrac{1}{3\cdot 4}, \dfrac{1}{4\cdot 5}, \cdots$ **b.** $\frac{1}{2}, \frac{2}{3}, \frac{3}{4}, \frac{4}{5}, \cdots$

6.   **a.** $1, -\frac{1}{4}, \frac{1}{16}, -\frac{1}{64}, \cdots$ **b.** $1, 4, 7, 10, \cdots$

In Problems 7–10 identify the given sequence as being arithmetic or geometric, and find the term specified.

7. $1, \frac{3}{2}, 2, \frac{5}{2}, \cdots;$ a_{20} **8.** $1, \frac{3}{2}, \frac{9}{4}, \frac{27}{8}, \cdots;$ a_8

9. $-2, \frac{1}{2}, -\frac{1}{8}, \frac{1}{32}, \cdots;$ a_7 **10.** $-1, 3, 7, 11, \cdots;$ a_{15}

11. Write the first five terms of the sequence defined by:
     a. $a_1 = 2;$ $a_n = 2a_{n-1} + 1,$ $n \geq 2$ **b.** $a_1 = 1;$ $a_n = na_{n-1},$ $n \geq 2$

12. In a certain arithmetic sequence, $a_{12} = 7$ and $a_{18} = -5$. Find a_{30}.

13. Find y so that the sequence $3, y, 15$ will be:
     a. Arithmetic   **b.** Geometric

14. Insert five arithmetic means between 3 and 11.

15. On each swing after the first a certain pendulum swings three-fourths as far as on the preceding swing. If it swings 16 inches initially, find:
     a. How far it swings on the sixth swing
     b. The total distance swung during the first six swings
     c. The approximate distance covered before coming to rest

16. Write the expanded form of each of the following sums:

     a. $\displaystyle\sum_{k=1}^{5} \frac{k^2}{2k+3}$ **b.** $\displaystyle\sum_{n=1}^{6} \frac{(-1)^{n-1}n}{n^2+1}$ **c.** $\displaystyle\sum_{m=0}^{5} \frac{(-3)^m}{(1+m)^2}$

     d. $\displaystyle\sum_{i=2}^{6} \frac{2i-3}{3i+4}$ **e.** $\displaystyle\sum_{n=1}^{10} e^{-n}\ln(n+1)$

Find the sums in Problems 17–26.

17. The sum of the first thirty terms of the sequence $-5, -1, 3, 7, \ldots$.

18. The sum of the first ten terms of the sequence $-4, 2, -1, \frac{1}{2}, \ldots$.

19. $\displaystyle\sum_{n=1}^{50} (3 - 2n)$

20. $\displaystyle\sum_{k=1}^{6} \frac{(-1)^{k-1}}{3^k}$

21. $\displaystyle\sum_{j=1}^{60} \left(\frac{1 - 2j}{3}\right)$

22. $\displaystyle\sum_{n=1}^{8} (-2)^{n-3}$

23. $\displaystyle\sum_{k=1}^{12} \left(3 - \frac{k}{4}\right)$

24. $\displaystyle\sum_{n=1}^{\infty} \left(\frac{5}{6}\right)^{n-1}$

25. $\displaystyle\sum_{k=1}^{\infty} (-1)^{k-1} \left(\frac{3}{5}\right)^k$

26. $\displaystyle\sum_{n=1}^{\infty} (0.1)^{n-1}$

27. Use a geometric series to find the rational number represented by each of the following:
    a. $0.545454\ldots$ **b.** $0.148148148\ldots$ **c.** $2.181818\ldots$
    d. $27.135135135\ldots$ **e.** $1.020202\ldots$

28. A manufacturer estimates that a piece of equipment costing \$60,000 depreciates by 25% each year. Find its value after 5 years.

29. Logs are stacked so that each layer after the bottom one has one log fewer than the layer below it. If there are 20 logs on the bottom layer and 8 logs on the top, how many logs are in the pile?

30. A culture of bacteria doubles in size every 2 hours. If initially it contains 200 bacteria, how many will it contain 10 hours later?

In Problems 31–38 use mathematical induction to prove that the given statement is true for all natural numbers.

31. $4 + 8 + 12 + \cdots + 4n = 2n(n + 1)$

32. $3 + 5 + 7 + \cdots + (2n + 1) = n^2 + 2n$

33. $\displaystyle\sum_{r=1}^{n} \frac{3}{2r(r + 1)} = \frac{3n}{2n + 2}$

34. $n^2 \geq 4(n - 1)$

35. $n < a^n$ if $a \geq 2$

36. 2 is a factor of $n^2 + 3n$

37. 4 is a factor of $2n^2 + 6n$

38. $n^2 + 1 < (n + 1)^2$

39. Evaluate each of the following binomial coefficients:
    a. $\dbinom{25}{3}$ **b.** $\dbinom{9}{6}$ **c.** $\dbinom{4}{3}$ **d.** $\dbinom{3}{0}$ **e.** $\dbinom{12}{10}$

In Problems 40 and 41 use the binomial theorem to expand, and simplify the result.

40.   **a.** $(x + 2y)^8$ **b.** $(3a - 4b)^5$

41.   **a.** $\left(x - \frac{y}{2}\right)^7$ **b.** $(1 + x^2)^{10}$

42. Find the value of each of the following correct to five decimal places, using the binomial theorem:
    a. $(1.01)^{10}$ **b.** $(0.98)^6$

43. Find the specified term of the given expansion:
    a. $(2x - y)^{12}$;   eighth term   **b.** $(x - 2)^{20}$;   tenth term

B   Find the sums in Problems 44 and 45.

44. $\displaystyle\sum_{k=1}^{8} (100k - 2^k)$

45. $\displaystyle\sum_{n=1}^{6} \frac{2 - n \cdot 3^n}{3^n}$

46. Find a formula for the sum of the first n positive integers. Use mathematical induction to prove your result.

47. In a certain city, housing costs have risen at an annual rate of 10% for the past 4 years. If, 4 years ago, a particular house cost $50,000, what would be its fair market value now?

48. A man started to work 10 years ago at a salary of $10,000 per year and has received annual raises of 6%. What is his salary now, and what is the total amount of money he has received during the past 10 years?

49. A ladder with 13 rungs is to be constructed so that each rung is shorter than the preceding one by a constant amount. If the initial rung is to be 24 inches long and the final one 15 inches long, what are the lengths of the intermediate rungs?

50. After college a boy agreed to pay off his debt of $2,550 to his father by paying $100 the first month, $110 the second month, $120 the third month, and so on. How many months were required to pay off the debt?

51. Prove the identity

$$\binom{n}{k} - \binom{n-1}{k} = \binom{n-1}{k-1}$$

52. Find the sum of the given infinite geometric series, and state the domain of validity:

a. $1 - \dfrac{x}{2} + \dfrac{x^2}{4} - \dfrac{x^3}{8} + \cdots$ **b.** $\displaystyle\sum_{n=1}^{\infty} \dfrac{x^{2n-1}}{3^{n-1}}$

53. Find the infinite geometric series having the given sum, and state the domain of validity:

a. $\dfrac{1}{1+x}$ **b.** $\dfrac{3}{2-x^2}$

In Problems 54–56 prove the given statement by mathematical induction.

54. $1 + 2 \cdot 2 + 3 \cdot 2^2 + 4 \cdot 2^3 + \cdots + n \cdot 2^{n-1} = 1 + (n-1) \cdot 2^n$

55. $\dfrac{1}{1 \cdot 2 \cdot 3} + \dfrac{1}{2 \cdot 3 \cdot 4} + \dfrac{1}{3 \cdot 4 \cdot 5} + \cdots + \dfrac{1}{n(n+1)(n+2)} = \dfrac{n(n+3)}{4(n+1)(n+2)}$

56. $|a_1 + a_2 + a_3 + \cdots + a_n| \le |a_1| + |a_2| + |a_3| + \cdots + |a_n|$

12 Probability

Probability is an essential part of statistics, the importance of which in today's world can hardly be stressed enough. Its use in business and economics and in the other social sciences is well-known. It is also useful in biology and in the physical sciences. Even in the field of history statistics is now playing an important role. While we will not study statistics per se in this chapter, we do present some elements of probability, and after having studied it you will be able to understand the following example from a statistics textbook.*

In spite of the demand for their services, competition among oil drilling contractors has increased. As a result, drilling contractors are more cost conscious and have tended to limit the number of holes they drill in any parcel of land. Suppose a drilling contractor has sufficient resources to drill up to two holes on a given parcel but will stop drilling with his first success. If the probability that he is successful on any given drill hole is .2, find the probability that the drilling contractor locates a productive well. Assume that the drilling outcomes are independent from one drill hole to another.

Solution: Let us list the events which, when they occur, satisfy the objective of the problem.

A: a productive well is found within two trials

S_1: a productive well is found on the first trial

S_2: a productive well is found on the second trial

F_1: a dry well is found on the first trial

F_2: a dry well is found on the second trial

We see that event A occurs if

1. he strikes oil on the first trial, S_1 or
2. he hits a dry well on the first trial and strikes oil on the second, $F_1 S_2$.

---

* William Mendenhall and James E. Reinmuth, *Statistics for Management and Economics*, 3d ed. (North Scituate, Mass.: Duxbury Press, 1978), pp. 96, 97. Reprinted by permission.

Thus

$$A = S_1 \cup F_1 S_2$$

Note that these events are mutually exclusive. Then, since the events S_1 and $F_1 S_2$ are mutually exclusive, we have

$$P(A) = P(S_1 \cup F_1 S_2) = P(S_1) + P(F_1 S_2)$$

We know that

$$P(S_1) = P(S_2) = .2 \qquad \text{and} \qquad P(F_1) = P(F_2) = .8$$

and the outcomes "success" or "dry" at any trial are independent of the outcome at any other trial. Applying the multiplicative law, we have

$$P(F_1 S_2) = P(F_1)P(S_2) = (.8)(.2) = .16$$

Substituting we get

$$P(A) = P(S_1) + P(F_1 S_2) = .2 + .16 = .36$$

We will learn in this chapter the meaning of such terms as *mutually exclusive events* and *independent outcomes*. We will see why, under the stated conditions, the equations

$$P(S_1 \cup F_1 S_2) = P(S_1) + P(F_1 S_2)$$

and

$$P(F_1 S_2) = P(F_1)P(S_2)$$

are true.

1   Introduction

The origin of probability dates back to the seventeenth century when two French mathematicians, Blaise Pascal and Pierre Fermat, corresponded with each other about a problem that had arisen in a game of chance. Applications to gambling of the theory that evolved flourished during the next 75 years, but it was not until the middle of the eighteenth century that probability theory was applied to other fields. Since that time probability has become a respectable and highly useful branch of mathematics. It provides the mathematical basis for the study of statistics, which is becoming increasingly important in a wide variety of fields.

Unfortunately, there is no single, clear, accepted definition of probability. There are at least three approaches. One is the **classical,** or **a priori,** approach, which can be illustrated by considering the probability of getting heads on a single toss of a coin. Before tossing the coin, we reason that the coin is just as likely to come up heads as tails. This assumes the coin is well-balanced. In this case, we would say the probability of getting heads is $\frac{1}{2}$.

A second approach to probability is the **frequency,** or **empirical,** approach. Here we refer to the proportion of the time that a certain event occurs over the long run. For example, suppose that over a 10 year period it has been observed that 65% of the families that visit the Gettysburg Battlefield stay overnight in Gettysburg. We could say on the basis of this experience that the probability that a family who visits the battlefield will spend the night in Gettysburg is approximately .65. Someone considering building a new motel would be interested in such information.

A third approach to probability is the **subjective** one in which the probability assigned to an event by an individual represents the strength of his or her belief that the event will occur. This method of assigning probabilities is often used when there is no past history to go on and no a priori basis for making the assignment. For example, a person in considering whether to give financial backing to a proposed new business might decide on the basis of his confidence in the person who would manage the business and his knowledge of the proposed location and probable clientele that he estimates the probability of success at .75.

In the theory we will develop it is not important to know which approach was used to arrive at the probabilities. The applications will illustrate all three approaches.

2   The Fundamental Principle of Counting

Before proceeding with our study of probability it is necessary to gain some sophistication in the art of counting. We will make repeated use of the following:

Fundamental Principle of Counting

If one event can occur in m ways and a second event can occur in n ways, then the number of ways in which the first event followed by the second event can occur is $m \cdot n$.

By mathematical induction it is possible to extend this to any finite sequence of events.

EXAMPLE 1   In a cafeteria there are 8 different kinds of salads and 10 different desserts. In how many ways can a person select a combination of a salad and a dessert?

Solution   By the fundamental principle this can be done in $8 \cdot 10 = 80$ different ways.

EXAMPLE 2   How many different three-digit numbers can be formed from the set $\{1, 2, 3, 4, 5\}$ if:
a.   Repeated digits are allowed?   **b.**   Repeated digits are not allowed?

Solution   **a.**   We may fill each position in any one of 5 ways. So the total number of ways of forming a three-digit number is $5 \cdot 5 \cdot 5 = 125$.

b. We may choose the first position in any one of 5 ways, but then we have only 4 choices for the second, and finally only 3 choices for the third. So the total number of ways is $5 \cdot 4 \cdot 3 = 60$.

EXAMPLE 3   In order to complete his distribution requirements a student needs a literature course, a history course, a social science course, and a physical science course. There are 8 possible courses in literature, 6 in history, 4 in social science, and 3 in physical science. In how many ways may the student complete his distribution requirements?

Solution   By the fundamental principle the answer is $8 \cdot 6 \cdot 4 \cdot 3 = 576$.

EXERCISE SET 2

A **1.** If a television viewer can select ABC, CBS, NBC, or PBS channels, and during a certain time of day all programs are of 30 minutes duration, in how many ways can the viewer choose a sequence of two programs in a 1 hour interval at this time of the day?

2. How many three-digit numbers can be formed from the set $\{1, 3, 5, 7\}$?

3. How many seven-digit telephone numbers can be formed from the set

$$\{0, 1, 2, 3, 4, 5, 6, 7, 8, 9\}$$

if 0 cannot be used as the first digit?

4. License plates are to be constructed using three letters followed by three digits. If all letters of the alphabet and all the digits 0 through 9 can be used, how many different license plates can there be?

5. There are 4 roads from town A to town B and 3 roads from town B to town C. How many different ways are there to drive from A through B to C?

6. There are 10 girls and 8 boys in a dance club. How many different dance couples can be formed (assuming a couple consists of a boy and a girl)?

7. How many three-digit numbers less than 600 can be formed using the digits $\{1, 3, 5, 7, 9\}$ if:
a. Repetitions are permitted?   **b.** Repetitions are not permitted?

8. A firm has openings for 3 keypunch operators, and there are 25 applicants for the jobs. In how many different ways can the positions be filled?

9. A multiple-choice test has 10 questions, and each question has 5 possible answers. How many different test results are possible (assuming one answer for each question)?

10. A nickel, a dime, and a quarter are tossed. How many different results are possible?

11. A die is to be rolled three times in succession, and the number showing on the upper face is to be recorded. How many different three number sequences are possible?

12. If a true–false test consists of 10 questions, how many different test results are possible?

B **13.** The Interfraternity Council at a certain college consists of 16 members, 2 from each of the 8 fraternities on campus. If the council elects 3 officers and they must be from different fraternities, in how many ways can this be done?

14. How many different numbers of at most four digits can be formed from the digits 0 through 9?

15. In the binary system the only digits used are 0 and 1. How many different numbers can be formed in this system using at most six positions? (Numbers using more than one position cannot have 0 in the leftmost position.)

16. An organization consisting of 15 women and 12 men is to elect a president, a vice-president, and a secretary. They decide in advance that not all officers should be of the same sex and that the secretary should not be a woman. In how many ways can the officers be chosen?

3 Permutations

DEFINITION 1 A **permutation** is an arrangement of a set in a certain order.

For example, suppose we have 6 books which we wish to arrange on a shelf. In how many different ways can this be done? There are 6 ways to select which book to place first. Then there are 5 ways to select the second book. So by the fundamental principle there are $6 \cdot 5 = 30$ ways to choose the first and the second book. Having made these selections, there are 4 ways to choose the third book, 3 ways to choose the fourth, 2 ways to choose the fifth, and 1 way to choose the sixth. Repeated application of the fundamental principle, then, gives the total number of arrangements, or permutations, as $6 \cdot 5 \cdot 4 \cdot 3 \cdot 2 \cdot 1 = 6! = 720$.

In exactly the same way we can conclude the following:

> The number of possible permutations of n distinct objects is $n!$.

This assumes that all n objects are to be arranged. We may be interested in arranging fewer than n of them. In the example above, for instance, we may only have room on the shelf for 4 of the 6 books. Then the number of permutations is

$$6 \cdot 5 \cdot 4 \cdot 3 = 360$$

since we may still choose the first book in any of 6 ways, the second in any of 5 ways, the third in any of 4 ways, and the fourth in any of 3 ways. The fundamental principle then gives the above result. To generalize this we consider the number of permutations of n objects when r of them are taken at a time. The symbol $P(n, r)$ is the symbol we will use to denote this, but other symbols, such as $_nP_r$, $P_{n,r}$, and P_n^r, are often used. Reasoning as above, there are n choices for the first position, $n - 1$ for the second, $n - 2$ for the third, and so on until we get to the rth position, for which there are $n - (r - 1) = n - r + 1$ choices. So by the fundamental principle,

$$P(n, r) = n(n - 1)(n - 2) \cdots (n - r + 1) \tag{1}$$

An alternate form of equation (1) can be obtained by using factorial notation. Recall that for any positive integer k, $k! = 1 \cdot 2 \cdot 3 \cdots k$. We also define

$0! = 1$. Now if we multiply and divide the right-hand side of equation (1) by $(n - r)!$, the numerator becomes $n!$ and we get

$$P(n, r) = \frac{n!}{(n - r)!} \qquad (2)$$

EXAMPLE 4   Find the number of permutations of 12 things taken 5 at a time.

Solution $$P(12, 5) = (12)(11)(10)(9)(8) = 95,040$$

EXAMPLE 5   In a committee of 7 persons, in how many ways may a chairperson, a secretary, and a treasurer be chosen?

Solution   We want the number of ways to order 3 persons out of 7, that is, the number of permutations of 7 persons, 3 at a time:

$$P(7, 3) = 7 \cdot 6 \cdot 5 = 210$$

So far we have assumed that all the objects to be arranged are distinct. To illustrate how to handle an example where this is not the case, consider the problem of finding the number of ways we can arrange the letters in the word *exercise*. There are 8 letters, but three of them are e's. For the moment let us consider the e's as distinct by writing them with subscripts, e_1, e_2, e_3. Then the number of permutations is $8!$. But for each arrangement, if the e's only are permuted among themselves, there is no actual change. Since the three e's can be permuted in $3!$ ways, it follows that we must divide $8!$ by $3!$ to arrive at the number of *different* permutations. So if P denotes the number of different permutations,

$$P = \frac{8!}{3!} = 8 \cdot 7 \cdot 6 \cdot 5 \cdot 4 = 6,720$$

As another example, consider the number of different permutations of the letters of the word *statistics*. There would be $10!$ permutations of the 10 letters if they were all distinct, but there are 3 s's, 3 t's, and 2 i's. So we have to divide out the effect of permuting these letters, getting

$$P = \frac{10!}{3!3!2!} = 50,400$$

Generalizing this, we conclude the following:

The number P of permutations of n objects where n_1 are alike of one kind, n_2 alike of another kind, . . . , and n_k alike of another kind, is given by

$$P = \frac{n!}{n_1!n_2! \cdots n_k!} \qquad (3)$$

EXAMPLE 6   How many different signals can be sent with 8 signal flags if 3 are red, 2 are blue, and 3 are white, assuming all flags are to be used?

Solution $$P = \frac{8!}{3!2!3!} = \frac{8 \cdot 7 \cdot 6 \cdot 5 \cdot 4 \cdot 3 \cdot 2 \cdot 1}{(3 \cdot 2 \cdot 1)(2 \cdot 1)(3 \cdot 2 \cdot 1)} = 560$$

EXERCISE SET 3

A   1.   Evaluate the following:

        a. $P(4, 2)$ **b.** $P(6, 5)$ **c.** $P(5, 5)$ **d.** $P(8, 3)$ **e.** $P(12, 4)$

  2.   In how many ways can 5 different books be arranged on a shelf?

  3.   There are 8 chairs in a row and 8 people to occupy them. In how many ways can they be arranged?

  4.   In Problem 3 if there are only 4 chairs, how many seating arrangements are possible?

  5.   How many three-letter "words" can be formed from the letters in the word *prime*?

  6.   How many three-digit numbers can be formed from the digits $\{1, 3, 5, 7, 9\}$ if repetitions are not allowed?

  7.   Solve for n: $P(n, 2) = 156$.
      Note. n must be a positive integer.

  8.   Solve for n: $P(n + 2, 2) = P(n - 2, 2) + 36$.

  9.   A president, a vice-president, a secretary, and a parliamentarian are to be elected from an organization of 50 members. In how many ways can this be done?

 10.   How many possible outcomes are there in a cross-country race in which there are 10 runners?

 11.   If awards are given to those placing first, second, and third in the cross-country race of Problem 10, in how many ways can these awards be given?

 12.   How many distinguishable arrangements are there of the letters of the word *book*?

 13.   How many different permutations are there of the letters of the word *algebra*?

 14.   How many distinguishable arrangements are there of the word *arrangement*?

 15.   How many different permutations are there of the letters of the word *Mississippi*?

 16.   In how many ways can 4 red blocks, 3 blue blocks, and 2 white blocks be arranged in a row so that each arrangement looks different from every other arrangement?

B   17.   In how many different ways can 6 people be seated around a round table?

 18.   In how many ways can 5 keys be arranged on a circular key ring?

 19.   Solve for n: $P(n, 3) = (6)P(n - 1, 2)$.

 20.   A student has 3 English books, 4 history books, 2 mathematics books, and 1 physics book. In how many ways can these 10 books be arranged on a shelf if those in a given subject are to be kept together?

4   Combinations

In permutations we are concerned with arranging objects in a certain order. We denoted by $P(n, r)$ the number of ways of arranging r objects out of n given objects. Sometimes we are not interested in the number of arrangements but only in the number of ways of selecting r objects from n objects. For example, we may want to know how many committees of 3 people can be selected from a group of 10 people. We are not interested in the order of the 3 people. Each such selection is called a **combination.** More generally, we have the following:

DEFINITION 2   A **combination** of n elements taken r at a time is any subset of r elements taken from the n element set, without regard to order.

We denote by $C(n, r)$ the total number of such combinations. If we are given a set of n distinct elements, we can choose r of them in $C(n, r)$ ways. If we first make a selection of r elements from the set of n elements and then permute these elements in all possible ways, and if we do this for all selections, we should obtain all the permutations of r elements taken from n elements. Since there are $r!$ ways of permuting the r elements of each of the $C(n, r)$ combinations, we must have

$$r!C(n, r) = P(n, r)$$

Therefore,

$$C(n, r) = \frac{P(n, r)}{r!}$$

Substituting formula (2) for $P(n, r)$, we obtain

$$C(n, r) = \frac{n!}{r!(n - r)!} \tag{4}$$

This result should look familiar to you. In fact, it is precisely the value of the binomial coefficient $\binom{n}{r}$. Thus,

$$C(n, r) = \binom{n}{r}$$

EXAMPLE 7   In how many ways can a committee of 3 people be chosen from a group of 10 people?

Solution   The answer is

$$C(10, 3) = \frac{10!}{3!7!} = \frac{10 \cdot 9 \cdot 8}{3 \cdot 2 \cdot 1} = 120$$

EXAMPLE 8   A committee of 7 is to be composed of 3 faculty members, 2 students, and 2 trustees. If the faculty members are to be chosen from a 25 person faculty senate, the students from the 18 member student senate, and the trustees from the 30 member board, in how many ways can the committee be chosen?

Solution   We may choose the faculty in $C(25, 3)$ ways, the students in $C(18, 2)$ ways, and the trustees in $C(30, 2)$ ways. Therefore, by the fundamental principle of counting, the number N of ways of forming the committee is

$$N = C(25, 3) \cdot C(18, 2) \cdot C(30, 2)$$

$$= \frac{25!}{3!22!} \cdot \frac{18!}{2!16!} \cdot \frac{30!}{2!28!}$$

$$= \frac{25 \cdot 24 \cdot 23}{3 \cdot 2 \cdot 1} \cdot \frac{18 \cdot 17}{2 \cdot 1} \cdot \frac{30 \cdot 29}{2 \cdot 1}$$

$$= (2{,}300)(153)(435) = 153{,}076{,}500$$

EXAMPLE 9

In how many ways can a bridge hand be dealt so as to contain 6 spades including the ace and king, and 7 cards in some one other suit?

Solution

There are 52 cards in a deck, and each bridge hand contains 13 cards. Since the ace and king of spades are specified, we may choose the other 4 spades from the remaining 11 spades in $C(11, 4)$ ways. The suit of the other 7 cards can be selected in 3 ways, and then the selection of the particular 7 cards can be made in $C(13, 7)$ ways. So by the fundamental principle of counting, we may be dealt the hand described in the following number of ways:

$$C(11, 4) \cdot 3 \cdot C(13, 7) = 3 \cdot \binom{11}{4} \cdot \binom{13}{7}$$

We will leave the answer in this form, since the numbers involved are so large.

EXERCISE SET 4

A 1. Evaluate each of the following:
   a. $C(8, 6)$ **b.** $C(5, 2)$ **c.** $C(10, 8)$ **d.** $C(6, 1)$ **e.** $C(20, 18)$

2. In how many ways can a committee of 5 persons be chosen from a group of 12 people?

3. A set contains 10 elements. How many subsets are there with exactly 4 elements?

4. The owner of a women's clothing shop has 10 styles of winter coats and wants to display 3 of them in the front window. In how many ways can she choose the 3 to display?

5. On an examination there are 10 questions, and students may omit any 2 questions. How many possible choices of questions to be answered are there?

6. To check on quality, from each set of 100 light bulbs manufactured 2 are tested. In how many ways can the 2 bulbs be selected from a batch of 100?

7. From a group of 12 men and 10 women, 2 men and 2 women are to be selected as delegates to a convention. In how many ways can this be done?

8. On an examination of 12 questions all students must answer the first 2 questions but may select any 8 of the remaining ones. How many different selections are possible?

9. An examination consists of two groups of questions, 5 in the first group and 10 in the second. Students are to select 3 from the first group and 7 from the second. In how many ways can this be done?

10. Prove that $C(n, r) = C(n, n - r)$.

11. How many different bridge hands of 13 cards can be dealt from a deck of 52 cards?

12. A jar contains 5 black and 7 white balls. In how many ways can 3 balls be withdrawn in such a way that 2 are black and 1 is white?

13. How many lines are determined by 7 points in a plane if no 3 of the points are collinear? How many triangles do these points determine?

14. In how many ways can a collection of 10 toys be divided equally between two children?

15. Fifteen geology students are going on a field trip. Nine can ride in the department van and 6 in its station wagon. In how many ways can the 15 students be divided into the two groups?

16. An employer has openings for 2 clerk–typists and 3 computer programmers. There are 10 qualified applicants for the clerk–typist positions and 12 for the programmer positions. In how many different ways can the positions be filled?

17. A joint committee of 3 faculty members from the 12 person Business Administration Department and 2 faculty members from the 6 person Mathematics Department is to be formed to study the appropriate mathematics requirement for majors in Business. In how many ways can the committee be formed?

18. In testing the effectiveness of vitamin C in curing hay fever, 20 hay fever sufferers are to receive treatment with vitamin C tablets and 20 others are to receive a placebo. There are 50 volunteers for the test. In how many ways can the two groups of 20 be formed?

B 19. A random sample of 5 manufactured parts is selected from a bin containing 100 such parts. If there are 3 defective parts, in how many ways can the sample contain all 3 defective parts?

20. In how many ways can a bridge hand have exactly 9 cards of the same suit?

21. In how many ways can a bridge hand have 6 spades and 5 hearts?

22. A poker hand consists of 5 cards. In how many ways can a hand contain all 5 cards of the same suit? (This is called a *flush*.)

23. In how many ways can a *full house* (3 of one kind and 2 of another) be dealt in a poker hand? In how many ways can 3 of a kind be dealt?

24. A truckload of 25 television sets has 2 defective ones, unknown to the purchaser. A sample of 3 of the 25 sets is selected and these are tested prior to accepting the shipment. In how many ways can the sample of 3 contain none of the defective units? In how many ways can it contain exactly 1 of the defectives? In how many ways can it contain at least 1 defective?

25. Prove that a set consisting of n elements has 2^n subsets.

5 Probability

In discussing probability we will be concerned with possible **outcomes of experiments,** but the word *experiment* is to be interpreted liberally. It may be something as simple as tossing a coin or something as complicated as determining how many people in a certain population have diabetes. A result of an experiment is called an **outcome,** and the totality of all possible outcomes for an experiment is called the **sample space.** For example, suppose a single die is tossed and the number of dots on the upper face is recorded. This is the experiment. We could list the set of all possible outcomes—that is, the sample space— as $\{1, 2, 3, 4, 5, 6\}$. Or suppose the experiment consists of tossing two coins and observing whether heads (H) or tails (T) is showing for each coin. The sample space could be listed as $\{HH, HT, TH, TT\}$.

Often we are interested in knowing something about a particular subset of the sample space, and this is called an **event.** For instance, in the case of tossing a die we might consider the event, "The number showing is 3 or greater." Or consider the tossing of two coins. The event we are interested in might be, "At least 1 head."

To help visualize sample spaces and events we sometimes employ **Venn diagrams** as in Figure 1. Here, the sample space is depicted by a rectangle, and events are depicted as circles or other closed curves within the rectangle. We have shown two events, labeled *A* and *B*. In the language of sets the sample space is the **universe,** and the events are subsets of the universe. When we refer to the occurrence of **either *A* or *B*,** we will understand this to mean the **union** of the sets *A* and *B*. When we refer to the occurrence of *A* **and *B*,** this will mean the **intersection** of *A* and *B*. These are illustrated in Figures 2 and 3, respectively.

Figure 1

Figure 2

Union

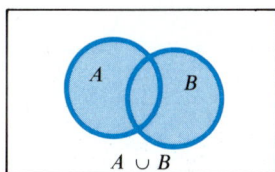

$A \cup B$

Figure 3

Intersection

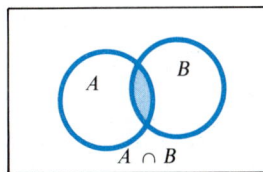

$A \cap B$

Single outcomes of the experiment are often referred to as **sample points.** This use of geometric language and diagrams to refer to experiments and their outcomes enables us to use similar language for all experiments, thus simplifying the theory to be presented.

We will limit ourselves to experiments with a finite number of outcomes. If *A* is an event associated with an experiment, then $n(A)$ is used to denote the number of sample points in *A*. For example, if we again consider tossing a die and let *A* be the event of obtaining a 3 or greater, then $n(A) = 4$, since *A* consists of the sample points {3}, {4}, {5}, and {6}.

Two events are said to be **mutually exclusive** if they have no outcome in common. In set terminology we say in this case that the sets are **disjoint.** Their intersection is the empty set. If the intersection is nonempty, we say the sets are **intersecting.** The two situations are illustrated in Figures 4 and 5.

Figure 4

Disjoint Sets

Figure 5

Intersecting Set

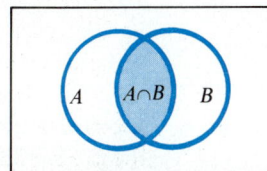

If A and B are mutually exclusive events, then we have

$$n(A \cup B) = n(A) + n(B) \qquad (5)$$

If A and B are intersecting, then $n(A) + n(B)$ counts those elements in the intersection of A and B twice, so we must subtract this number once, thus obtaining

$$n(A \cup B) = n(A) + n(B) - n(A \cap B) \qquad (6)$$

Actually, the first formula is a special case of the second, because if A and B do not intersect, then there are no elements in $A \cap B$, so $n(A \cap B) = 0$.

We need one further concept before going on to the consideration of probability, namely the notion of the **complement** of a set. If A is an event associated with an experiment, then the complement of A, denoted by A', is the set of all sample points *not* in A. Figure 6 illustrates this.

Figure 6

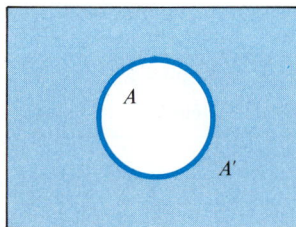

The classical, or a priori, definition of probability can now be stated:

DEFINITION 3   Let A be an event in a sample space S, and suppose the outcomes that comprise S are finite in number and are equally likely to occur. Then the **probability of A** is

$$P(A) = \frac{n(A)}{n(S)}$$

EXAMPLE 10   Find the probability that on a single toss of a die the number showing on the upper face will be 3 or greater.

Solution   The sample space S consists of six equally likely outcomes (assuming the die is not loaded). So $n(S) = 6$. If we let A denote the event in question, then as we have already seen, $n(A) = 4$. Therefore,

$$P(A) = \tfrac{4}{6} = \tfrac{2}{3}$$

EXAMPLE 11   A box contains 5 red balls and 3 blue balls. If 2 balls are drawn at random, find the probability that they will both be blue.

Solution The number of possible outcomes is $C(8, 2)$, the number of ways we can select 2 balls out of 8 balls. So this is the number of points in the sample space.

$$n(S) = C(8, 2) = \binom{8}{2} = \frac{8 \cdot 7}{2 \cdot 1} = 28$$

The event we are interested in is the selection of 2 blue balls. Let us call this event A. Then

$$n(A) = C(3, 2) = \binom{3}{2} = \frac{3 \cdot 2}{2 \cdot 1} = 3$$

since there are 3 blue balls and to be successful, we must select 2 of these. So

$$P(A) = \frac{n(A)}{n(S)} = \frac{3}{28}$$

If A and B are mutually exclusive, we have seen that $n(A \cup B) = n(A) + n(B)$. So

$$P(A \cup B) = \frac{n(A \cup B)}{n(S)} = \frac{n(A) + n(B)}{n(S)}$$

$$= \frac{n(A)}{n(S)} + \frac{n(B)}{n(S)}$$

from which it follows that

$$P(A \cup B) = P(A) + P(B) \qquad \text{if } A \text{ and } B \text{ are mutually exclusive} \qquad (7)$$

When A and B are not mutually exclusive, we use equation (6) to get

$$P(A \cup B) = P(A) + P(B) - P(A \cap B) \qquad (8)$$

EXAMPLE 12 Find the probability that on a single toss of a die the number on the upper face is either less than 3 or greater than 4.

Solution Let A be the event that the number is less than 3 and let B be the event that the number is greater than 4. Then A and B are mutually exclusive, since an outcome cannot be in both A and B. The total number, $n(S)$, of outcomes in the sample space is 6. Also, A contains the two outcomes 1 and 2, and B contains the two outcomes 5 and 6. So $n(A) = 2$ and $n(B) = 2$. Thus,

$$P(A) = \tfrac{2}{6} = \tfrac{1}{3} \qquad \text{and} \qquad P(B) = \tfrac{2}{6} = \tfrac{1}{3}$$

Therefore, by equation (7) the probability that the outcome is in either A or B is

$$P(A \cup B) = P(A) + P(B) = \tfrac{1}{3} + \tfrac{1}{3} = \tfrac{2}{3}$$

EXAMPLE 13   Two coins are tossed. What is the probability that at least one coin comes up heads?

Solution   The sample space for this experiment can be exhibited as $\{HH, HT, TH, TT\}$. We can count the number of ways that at least one coin comes up heads as 3, and since there are four possible outcomes, the desired probability is $\frac{3}{4}$. We will also calculate this in another way in order to illustrate the use of equation (8). Let A be the event of the first coin coming up heads and let B be that of the second coin coming up heads. Then we are interested in the probability of either A or B, that is, $P(A \cup B)$. This time A and B are not mutually exclusive, since it is possible that both coins come up heads. So we use

$$P(A \cup B) = P(A) + P(B) - P(A \cap B)$$

From the sample space we see that the first coin is heads two times out of the four, so that $P(A) = \frac{1}{2}$. Similarly, $P(B) = \frac{1}{2}$. Now $P(A \cap B)$ is the number of outcomes in A *and* B, divided by the total number of outcomes. In order for an outcome to be in A and B, both coins must be heads, and this occurs only once out of the four possibilities. So $P(A \cap B) = \frac{1}{4}$. Therefore,

$$P(A \cup B) = \tfrac{1}{2} + \tfrac{1}{2} - \tfrac{1}{4} = \tfrac{3}{4}$$

Formulas (7) and (8) are true even when the probabilities are not determined by Definition 1. In the next two examples the probabilities are obtained by the subjective approach and by the frequency approach, which were referred to in Section 1.

EXAMPLE 14   A football coach estimates the probability of his team's winning the next game as .75 and the game following that as .60, but he figures there is only an even chance that they will win both games. Find the probability they will win at least one of the next two games.

Solution   This is an example of probabilities that are based on subjective grounds rather than theoretical considerations. If we let A be the event of winning the next game and let B be the event of winning the one after that, then

$$P(A \cup B) = P(A) + P(B) - P(A \cap B) = .75 + .60 - .50 = .85$$

EXAMPLE 15   Weather bureau records in Taneytown, Maryland, show that in the last 100 years it has rained 32 times on April 15 and 30 times on April 16, but that it has rained on both days consecutively only 25 times. Estimate the probability that it will rain next year in Taneytown on either April 15 or April 16.

Solution   In this case, the frequency approach to probability is applicable. If we let A be the event of rain on April 15 and let B be that of rain on April 16, then based on a large number of observations we can estimate $P(A) = .32$, $P(B) = .30$, and $P(A \cap B) = .25$. Thus,

$$P(A \cup B) = P(A) + P(B) - P(A \cap B)$$
$$= .32 + .30 - .25 = .37$$

However the probability of an event A is determined, we must have **for any event A,**

$$0 \le P(A) \le 1$$

A probability of 1 indicates that the outcome is certain to be in A, and a probability of 0 indicates that the outcome cannot be in A. If we let $A = S$, that is, the entire sample space, then $P(A) = 1$, since by definition the sample space consists of all possible outcomes of the experiment in question.

Recall now that if A is any event in S, then its complement A', is the set of all outcomes in S that are not in A. So A and A' are mutually exclusive, and $A \cup A' = S$. Therefore,

$$P(A \cup A') = P(A) + P(A')$$

and also $P(A \cup A') = P(S) = 1$. So

$$P(A) + P(A') = 1 \tag{9}$$

We can often use formula (9) to simplify calculations, as the following example shows.

EXAMPLE 16

A shipment of 100 manufactured parts contains 5 defective ones, unknown to the buyer. To test the shipment the buyer selects a random sample of 6 of the parts. What is the probability that the sample contains at least 1 of the defective parts?

Solution

Let A be the event of selecting 1 or more of the defective parts. We could find $P(A)$ by adding the probabilities of 1 defective, 2 defectives, 3 defectives, 4 defectives, and 5 defectives being in the sample. But it is easier to use equation (9), in the form $P(A) = 1 - P(A')$. Now, A' is the event of selecting no defectives in the sample, since this is the complement of "at least 1 defective." There are $C(95, 6)$ ways in which all 6 parts in the sample can be selected from the 95 nondefective parts. Since there are $C(100, 6)$ ways of selecting the sample altogether, we have that $n(A') = C(95, 6)$ and $n(S) = C(100, 6)$. So

$$P(A') = \frac{C(95, 6)}{C(100, 6)} = \frac{\binom{95}{6}}{\binom{100}{6}} = \frac{\frac{(95)(94)(93)(92)(91)(90)}{6!}}{\frac{(100)(99)(98)(97)(96)(95)}{6!}}$$

$$= \frac{(94)(93)(92)(91)(90)}{(100)(99)(98)(97)(96)} = .729$$

So

$$P(A) = 1 - P(A') = .271$$

EXERCISE SET 5

A

1. An experiment consists of tossing 3 coins and observing whether each lands with heads or tails showing. Exhibit the sample space S. What is $n(S)$?

2. Two dice are thrown and the pair of numbers showing on the faces is recorded. How many outcomes does the sample space contain? Exhibit these outcomes.

3. Three red balls numbered R_1, R_2, and R_3, and 2 blue balls numbered B_1 and B_2 are in a box. Two balls are selected at random, and the identifications are observed. Exhibit the sample space S. What is $n(S)$?

4. Refer to the experiment in Problem 1 and let A be the event of at least two heads showing. Find $n(A)$. What is $P(A)$?

5. In the experiment of Problem 2, let A be the event that the sum of the numbers is less than 5. What is $n(A)$? What is $P(A)$?

6. In the experiment of Problem 3 let A be the event of selecting 1 red ball and 1 blue ball. What is $n(A)$? What is $P(A)$?

7. In the experiment of Problem 1 what is the probability of at least 1 head?

8. In the experiment of Problem 2 what is the probability that at least 1 die shows a 6? What is the probability that both show 6?

9. In the experiment of Problem 3 what is the probability that both balls selected are red? What is the probability that both are blue?

10. Three women and 2 men in an office volunteer for a certain assignment, but only 2 can be chosen. Names of the volunteers are written on slips of paper and 2 are drawn at random. What is the probability that those selected will be:
    a. 2 women?   **b.** 2 men?   **c.** 1 woman and 1 man?

11. A card is drawn from a deck of 52 playing cards. What is the probability that it is:
    a. A spade?   **b.** An ace?   **c.** The ace of spades?

12. A committee of 5 is to be chosen at random from a group of 8 men and 9 women. What is the probability that 2 men and 3 women will be selected?

13. Ten slips of paper numbered 1 though 10 are placed in a hat and thoroughly mixed. One slip is drawn from the hat. Find the probability that the number on the slip will be either less than 5 or greater than 7.

14. A card is drawn from a deck of 52 playing cards. Find the probability that it will be either a face card or a card numbered 5 or less.

15. Based on her performance to date in a chemistry course, a student estimates the following probabilities that she will receive the indicated grade on the final exam: A, .1; B, .3; C, .4; D, .15; F, .05. Using these estimates, find the probability that her grade on the final exam will be:
    a. B or C   **b.** A or B   **c.** Less than C

16. A man and his wife are both running for election to the school board. The man estimates the probability of his being elected at .5, and his wife estimates that she has a probability of .6 of being chosen, but they agree that there is only a probability of about .3 they will both be elected. Find the probability that either the man or his wife will be elected.

17. Let A and B be events in a sample space for an experiment, and suppose $P(A') = \frac{3}{8}$, $P(A \cup B) = \frac{3}{4}$, and $P(A \cap B) = \frac{1}{3}$. Find $P(A)$ and $P(B)$.

18. In a group of 8 men and 12 women, half of the men and one-third of the women have blue eyes. Find the probability that a person selected at random is a woman or has blue eyes.

19. In a certain experiment A and B are events, with $P(A) = \frac{1}{3}$, $P(B') = \frac{3}{5}$, and $P(A \cup B) = \frac{5}{8}$. Find $P(A \cap B)$.

B

20. A shipment of 25 manufactured items is received by a company, and to test for quality 5 are selected at random and tested. If the shipment actually contains 3 defective

items, find the probability that the sample contains:

a. Exactly 2 of the defective items   **b.** Either 0 or 1 defective item

c. At least 1 defective item

21. A card is drawn from a deck of 52 playing cards. Find the probability that it is either a heart or a face card.

22. If you buy 3 tickets to a lottery for which 500 tickets are sold and 5 prizes are to be awarded, what is the probability that you will win 1 or more of the prizes?

23. A group of 15 young unskilled workers are hired to do maintenance work by a contractor. Eleven of the 15 are men and 4 are women. There are 3 types of jobs to be performed, requiring 6, 5, and 4 persons, respectively. If the contractor assigns the jobs at random, find the probability that all 4 women will be chosen for the third job.

6 Conditional Probability

Sometimes we are interested in the **probability of an event, given that another event has already occurred.** Suppose, for example, a jar contains 5 red balls and 3 blue balls, and 2 balls are to be drawn in succession. We wish to know the probability that the second ball is red. This depends on the color of the first ball drawn. If the first ball is red, then of the 7 balls remaining 4 are red, so the probability is $\frac{4}{7}$ of drawing a red ball the second time. On the other hand, if the first ball is blue, the probability of the second ball being red is $\frac{5}{7}$.

This example illustrates what is known as **conditional probability.** If A is an event that has already occurred, and we want to know the probability of a second event B, then this is called the **probability of B, given A,** and it is denoted by $P(B|A)$. We can arrive at a formula for $P(B|A)$ using the following reasoning: Since we know that A has occurred, then the sample space becomes A itself, and we can find the probability of B, given A, by dividing the number of elements in B *which are also in A* by the number of elements in A. That is,

$$P(B|A) = \frac{n(B \cap A)}{n(A)}$$

Upon dividing the numerator and denominator by $n(S)$, we obtain

$$P(B|A) = \frac{P(B \cap A)}{P(A)} \qquad \textbf{This assumes } P(A) \neq 0 \qquad (10)$$

In this formula we may know $P(A)$ and $P(B|A)$ and want to find $P(B \cap A)$. This can be done by clearing of fractions,

$$P(B \cap A) = P(A) \cdot P(B|A)$$

By interchanging A and B in equation (10) and again clearing fractions, we also get

$$P(A \cap B) = P(B) \cdot P(A|B)$$

Finally, since $B \cap A = A \cap B$, we can combine the last two results to get the **multiplication formulas:**

$$P(A \cap B) = P(A) \cdot P(B|A) \quad \text{if} \quad P(A) \neq 0 \qquad (11)$$

$$= P(B) \cdot P(A|B) \quad \text{if} \quad P(B) \neq 0$$

EXAMPLE 17   Two cards are drawn in succession from an ordinary deck. Find the probability that both cards are clubs.

Solution   Let A be the event that the first card is a club, and let B be the event that the second card is a club. We want the probability of A *and* B, that is, $P(A \cap B)$. By equations (11),

$$P(A \cap B) = P(A) \cdot P(B|A)$$

Since 13 of the 52 cards are clubs, $P(A) = \frac{13}{52} = \frac{1}{4}$. Now, $P(B|A)$ is the probability that the second card is a club, given that the first card was a club. Of the 51 cards left, 12 are clubs, so $P(B|A) = \frac{12}{51} = \frac{4}{17}$. Thus,

$$P(A \cap B) = \tfrac{1}{4} \cdot \tfrac{4}{17} = \tfrac{1}{17}$$

If the probability of the occurrence of a second event is unaffected by the occurrence or nonoccurrence of a first event, then we say that the second event is **independent** of the first. More precisely, **the event A is independent of the event B provided that**

$$P(A|B) = P(A) \tag{12}$$

This says that the probability of A given B is the same as if B were not under consideration. For example, if we again draw 2 cards from a deck but this time replace the first one before drawing the second one, then the probability of drawing a club on the second draw is independent of whether a club was drawn on the first draw.

If A is independent of B, then from the second equation of (11) we get

$$P(A \cap B) = P(B) \cdot P(A) \tag{13}$$

Also from (11), $P(A \cap B) = P(A) \cdot P(B|A)$, so we obtain

$$P(A) \cdot P(B|A) = P(B) \cdot P(A)$$

which on dividing by $P(A)$ (assuming this is not 0) yields

$$P(B|A) = P(B)$$

This shows that **if A is independent of B, then B is also independent of A.** So we can speak of events being independent of each other. Equation (13) is used extensively in calculating probabilities when events are independent. It can be extended to any finite number of intersections.

EXAMPLE 18   Find the probability of two 6's on two rolls of a die.

Solution   Since the probability of rolling a 6 is $\frac{1}{6}$, and since the second roll is independent of the first, the probability is

$$P(\text{Two 6's}) = \tfrac{1}{6} \cdot \tfrac{1}{6} = \tfrac{1}{36}$$

EXERCISE SET 6

A **1.** What is the probability of a coin landing heads on each of 2 flips?

2. If we assume in advance that a baby is as likely to be one sex as another, what is the probability that a couple's 3 children will all be girls?

3. A bag contains 6 red and 4 blue marbles. Two marbles are drawn in succession. Find the probability that the first one is red and the second one is blue.

4. In the experiment of Problem 3 find the probability that both marbles are blue.

5. Find the probability of 5 successive heads in 5 tosses of a balanced coin. Given that the first 5 are heads, what is the probability of a head on the sixth toss?

6. About 5% of children inoculated against a certain type of influenza have a reaction to the shot. What is the probability that 2 children in the same family will have such a reaction after the shot?

Problems 7–10 refer to drawing 2 successive cards from a 52 card deck. Find the probability of the events indicated.

7. The first and second cards are spades.

8. The first card is a spade and the second is a heart.

9. The first card is an ace and the second is a king.

10. Both cards are aces.

Problems 11–14 refer to an experiment of drawing 2 successive poker chips from a bag containing 5 red, 3 blue, and 7 white chips. Find the probability of the events indicated.

11. The first chip is blue and the second one is white.

12. The first chip is red and the second one is blue.

13. Both chips are red.

14. Both chips are white.

15. If the probability of rain on Monday is .60 and the probability of rain on Tuesday provided it rains on Monday is .75, what is the probability it will rain on both Monday and Tuesday?

16. A certain coin is unbalanced so that the probability of its coming up heads is .6. Find the probability that on 4 successive tosses the result is H, H, H, T.

17. On a two-engine jet airplane the probability of either engine failing is estimated to be .001, but if either does fail, then the probability that the other one will also fail is .005. Find the probability that both engines will fail.

18. Consider the experiment of Problem 3. Suppose the 2 marbles are drawn in succession. Count the number of outcomes in which the first marble is red. In how many of these is the second marble also red? What probability is represented by the second number divided by the first? Calculate the result by the formula for conditional probability and show the answers are the same.

19. The probability that a new television program will be dropped after the first 12 weeks is .75, but if a program is not dropped then, the probability of its being rated in the top 10 by the end of the season is .30. Find the probability that a new program will be kept beyond 12 weeks and will be in the top 10 by the end of the season.

20. Actuarial tables show that for a married couple of certain ages the probabilities that the husband and wife, respectively, will be alive in 25 years are .7 and .8. If we assume these are independent events, find the probability that in 25 years:
a. Both will be alive.   **b.** Neither will be alive.
c. At least one will be alive.

21. A certain antihistamine is known to relieve hay fever symptoms in approximately 70% of the sufferers who take it. If 2 hay fever sufferers chosen at random take this

antihistamine, what is the probability that:
a. Both will be relieved of symptoms?   b. Only one will be relieved?
c. Neither will be relieved?

B   **22.** A soccer coach estimates that the probability of his team's winning the game this Saturday is .60 if it does not rain, but that the probability is only .40 if it rains. The weather forecast calls for a 30% chance of rain on Saturday. Find the probability that this team will win the game.

23. Prove that $P(A|B) + P(A'|B) = 1$, if $P(B) \neq 0$.

24. A box contains 1 blue and 3 red cards, and a second box contains 1 red and 2 blue cards. A blindfolded person first transfers 1 card from the first box to the second and then selects a card from the second box. What is the probability that this latter card is blue?

25. Show that in a group of 23 persons the probability is greater than $\frac{1}{2}$ that at least 2 persons have the same birthday.
Hint. The probability that a given person does *not* have the same birthday as the next person is $\frac{364}{365}$, and that these 2 have a different birthday from the next person is $\frac{363}{365}$, and so on.

26. Prove that if A and B are independent events, then A and B' are also independent.

27. In a certain test for diabetes it has been found from experience that the test is positive for about 10% of the population and that of this number 80% actually have diabetes. Also, 2% of those for which the test is negative do have diabetes. Find the probability that a person who has the test will be correctly diagnosed.

Review Exercise Set

A   **1.** How many different three-digit numbers can be formed using the digits $\{2, 4, 6, 8\}$?

2. How many 3 letter "words" can be formed using the first 10 letters of the alphabet if repetitions are not permitted? How many are possible if repetitions are permitted?

3. A firm has openings for 3 computer programmers, and there are 20 applicants. In how many different ways can the job be filled?

4. A student wishes to schedule each of 6 elective courses in different terms. If none of these has prerequisites, in how many different orders may the courses be taken?

5. A company plans to give cash bonuses to the 3 salespeople with the best, second best, and third best sales records for the year. If there are 15 salespoeple, in how many ways can the awards be made?

6. Evaluate each of the following:
a. $P(7, 3)$ b. $C(10, 4)$ c. $P(6, 6)$ d. $C(12, 10)$ e. $P(9, 6)$

7. How many different permutations are there of the letters of the word *committee*?

8. From a committee of 9 people, 3 subcommittees are to be formed consisting of 4, 3, and 2 persons, respectively. In how many ways can this be done?

9. In how many different ways can a committee of 4 be selected from 10 people?

10. In how many ways can a committee consisting of 2 boys and 3 girls be formed from a class of 12 boys and 18 girls?

11. A box contains 10 black balls and 6 white ones. Five balls are to be selected. In how many ways can the selection be made so as to include exactly 2 white balls?

12. A committee of 5 is to be chosen from a group of 8 girls and 7 boys. In how many ways can this be done if:
a. There are no restrictions?
b. The committee is to contain at least 1 boy?
c. The committee is to contain exactly 2 boys?

13. How many different triangles is it possible to draw using the sides and diagonals of an octagon (an eight-sided polygon)?

14. In how many ways can a group of 12 students be divided into:
    a. 2 teams of 6 students each?   **b.** 4 teams of 3 students each?

15. Four balls numbered 1, 2, 3, and 4 are in a box and 1 is selected at random. Find the probability that it is:
    a. Number 3   **b.** Either number 3 or number 4
    c. Not number 1

16. In the experiment of Problem 15, suppose that 2 balls are randomly selected. Find the probability that:
    a. Balls number 1 and number 2 are chosen.
    b. The sum of the numbers on the balls chosen is greater than or equal to 5.

17. Volumes number 1 through number 8 of an encyclopedia are removed from a shelf and thoroughly mixed up. They are replaced without observing the volume numbers. What is the probability they will be in the proper order?

18. Two dice are tossed. What is the probability that the sum of the numbers showing will be 7?

19. A true–false test consists of 10 questions. What is the probability of answering all 10 correctly if a person answers them without reading the questions?

20. Five light bulbs are selected from a batch of 20 bulbs in which 3 are defective. Find the probability that:
    a. No defective bulb is selected.
    b. All 3 defective bulbs are selected.
    c. Exactly 1 defective bulb is selected.
    d. At least 1 defective bulb is selected.

21. Five red cards, 5 white cards, and 5 blue cards are in a deck. For each color the cards are numbered 1 to 5. The deck is well-shuffled, and the top 5 are observed. Find the probability that:
    a. All 5 are red.   **b.** All 5 are of the same color.
    c. They are numbered 1 through 5.   **d.** Three are blue and 2 are white.

22. In the experiment of Problem 21 suppose only the top card is observed. Find the probability that it is:
    a. Either red or blue   **b.** Numbered less than 3
    c. Either numbered 2 or colored blue

23. A college has 3 runners in a cross-country race in which there are 15 entrants. Assuming all outcomes are equally likely, find the probability that this college will win:
    a. First and second place   **b.** Either first or second place.

24. A card is drawn from a 52 card deck. Find the probability that it is:
    a. A diamond or a club   **b.** A heart or a king

25. There are 8 married couples at a party, and each person's name is written on a slip of paper and placed in a hat. Two names are drawn from the hat. Find the probability that:
    a. One is male and one is female.   **b.** They are husband and wife.

26. Let A and B be events associated with an experiment and suppose $P(A) = \frac{1}{3}$, $P(B') = \frac{1}{4}$, and $P(A \cup B) = \frac{7}{8}$. Find $P(A \cap B)$.

27. Let A and B be events associated with an experiment and suppose $P(A) = \frac{3}{4}$, $P(B) = \frac{2}{3}$, and $P(A \cap B) = \frac{5}{8}$. Find $P(A|B)$ and $P(B|A)$.

28. A bag contains 8 green marbles and 6 white marbles. Three marbles are drawn from the bag in succession. Find the probability that the first one is green and the second and third ones are white.

29. In a class of 20 students, 8 have blond hair, 6 have blue eyes, and 4 have both blue eyes and blond hair. If a student chosen at random has blond hair, find the probability that the student has blue eyes.

---

30. One bag contains 3 white and 2 black marbles, and a second bag contains 2 white and 3 black marbles. One marble is drawn from each bag. Find the probability that:
  a. Both marbles are black.   **b.** One is black and 1 is white.

B.

31. Find the number of ways in which 3 history books, 4 English books, and 5 economics books can be placed on a shelf so that the books in a given subject are together.

32. In how many ways can 5 boys and 5 girls be arranged in a row if boys and girls must be alternated? Answer the same question if they are to sit around a circular table.

33. In going from town A to town B a salesperson has a choice of 5 different routes and from town B to town C a choice of 3 routes. In how many ways can he make a round trip from A through B to C and return if he does not want to travel over a given route more than once?

34. How many different 5 letter "words" can be formed using 2 vowels and 3 consonants? How many of these contain the letter s?

35. There are 6 faculty members in the Mathematics Department and 10 in the Economics Department at a certain college. How many different committees consisting of 3 mathematicians and 4 economists can be formed if the 2 chairpersons must be included?

36. A bridge hand of 13 cards is dealt from a well-shuffled 52 card deck. What is the probability that it will:
  a. Have 7 hearts and no diamonds?   **b.** Consist entirely of black cards?
  c. Have either all 4 aces or all 4 kings?

37. A shipment of 15 television sets contains 3 defective ones. On arrival they are tested one after another. Find the probability that a defective one is found:
  a. On the first and on the second test   **b.** On the second test
  c. On the first or the second test

38. If A and B are events associated with an experiment with $P(A) = \frac{1}{2}$, $P(B') = \frac{2}{3}$, and $P(A \cup B) = \frac{3}{5}$, find $P(A|B)$.

39. In the experiment of Problem 37 find the probability that the first defective set is found on test number 5.

40. A test for tuberculosis has been found in which 98% of the patients in a large hospital who have tuberculosis reacted positively to the test, whereas only 2% of those who do not have tuberculosis had a positive reaction. If 4% of the patients in the hospital have tuberculosis, find the probability that a patient selected at random:
  a. Will react positively to the test
  b. Has tuberculosis given that he or she has a positive reaction to the test
  Hint for part a. Let T be the event of having tuberculosis and let p be the event having a positive reaction. Then $P(p) = P(p \cap T) + P(p \cap T')$.

Cumulative Review Exercise Set IV (Chapters 10–12)

1. Solve the following system in three ways:
   a. By elimination using addition or subtraction and substitution
   b. By Cramer's rule
   c. By reducing the augmented matrix to triangular form.

$$\begin{cases} 2x - 6y - 3z = 8 \\ x + 2y - 4z = -1 \\ 3x + 4y + z = 5 \end{cases}$$

2. A woman selects 4 eggs from a carton of 12. Unknown to her there are 2 rotten eggs in the carton. Find the probability that she selects:
   a. No rotten egg   b. At least 1 rotten egg
   c. Both rotten eggs   d. Exactly 1 rotten egg

3. a. Multiply:

$$\begin{bmatrix} 2 & -1 & 4 & 1 \\ 3 & 2 & -5 & -2 \\ -6 & 0 & 2 & 3 \end{bmatrix} \begin{bmatrix} 1 & 4 & -3 \\ 2 & 0 & 5 \\ -1 & 3 & 2 \\ -4 & 6 & -3 \end{bmatrix}$$

   b. Using inverses, find X such that $AX = B$, where

$$A = \begin{bmatrix} 2 & 3 & 1 \\ 1 & -2 & -2 \\ 4 & 9 & 2 \end{bmatrix} \qquad X = \begin{bmatrix} x \\ y \\ z \end{bmatrix} \qquad B = \begin{bmatrix} 4 \\ -1 \\ 2 \end{bmatrix}$$

4. The proprietor of a coffee house prepared 100 pounds of a special blend of coffee using three different varieties: Colombian, Sumatran, and Brazilian. Colombian sells for $5.30 per pound, Sumatran for $5.00 per pound, and Brazilian for $4.80 per pound. He calculates that the price of the blend should be $5.04 per pound. If he used 50% more Colombian than Brazilian coffee, how many pounds of each did he use?

5. Solve the following system by matrix methods:

$$\begin{cases} 2x + y - 3z + 2w = 4 \\ 5x - 8y - 6z + 3w = 7 \\ 3x - 2y - 4z + w = 5 \end{cases}$$

6. A committee of 6 is to be chosen from a group of 10 women and 8 men. In how many ways can this be done if:
   a. There are no restrictions?
   b. There must be at least 1 man on the committee?
   c. There must be exactly 2 men on the committee?
   d. The committee must not consist entirely of persons of one sex?

7. An amusement park charges $1.20 admission for children under 18, $3.00 for adults between 18 and 65, and $1.50 for senior citizens over 65. On a given Saturday there were 3,950 tickets sold, and the receipts totaled $7,110. If the number of children exceeded the total number of adults and senior citizens by 550, how many tickets of each type were sold?

8. Solve graphically:
   a.

$$\begin{cases} y \le 2x + 5 \\ y \le 6 - x \\ y \ge x^2 - 2x \end{cases}$$

   Find the points of intersection of the boundary curves.
   b. $|x| + |y - 1| < 2$

9. For a family of 3 children let (b, g, b) indicate that the first child was a boy, the second a girl, and the third a boy, and use a similar ordered triple for other birth sequences. Give the complete sample space for the occurrence of 3 children, and answer the following:
  a. What is the probability that at least 2 children are girls?
  b. What is the probability that the first child is a boy?
  c. Are the events in parts a and b independent? Prove your result.

10. Find the indicated sums:

  a. $\displaystyle\sum_{k=1}^{20} \left(\frac{3k-5}{2}\right)$ **b.** $\displaystyle\sum_{n=0}^{\infty} e^{-2n}$

11. Solve the following system and draw the graph:

$$\begin{cases} x^2 + 2y^2 = 6 \\ 2x - y = 3 \end{cases}$$

12. A sequence is defined by

$$a_1 = \sqrt{2}$$
$$a_n = \sqrt{2 + a_{n-1}} \qquad (n \geq 2)$$

Write the first 5 terms of the sequence. Prove by mathematical induction that $a_n \leq 2$ for all n.

13. In order to determine the effectiveness of a television commercial, a local grocer conducted a telephone survey of 100 names selected at random. He found that 70% of these had seen his commerical and that 45 persons of the 100 had made purchases in his store. Of those who made purchases, only 35 had seen his commercial. Find:
  a. The probability that a person made a purchase, given that the person had seen the commercial
  b. The probability that a person who made a purchase had seen the commercial
  c. The probability that a person who did not see the commercial made a purchase

14. Nineteen pieces of pipe are to be cut so that the first piece is 2 feet long and the last piece is 14 feet long. Each piece after the first is longer than the preceding one by a fixed amount. Find this amount. Find the sum of the lengths of all the pieces of pipe.

15. **a.** Write the sixth term of the expansion of $(x^2 - 2y)^9$ and simplify your result.
  b. Expand $(1 + x)^{-1}$ to 5 terms using the binomial formula. If $|x| < 1$, it can be shown that the infinite series generated by the continuation of this expansion converges to the given function. Find the nth term of the expansion. What kind of series is this? Find the sum of the series and show that this is in agreement with the original function.

16. Prove the formula below in two ways:

$$\sum_{k=1}^{n} \log 2^k = \left(\frac{n^2 + n}{2}\right) \log 2$$

  a. By mathematical induction
  b. By showing that the sum is an arithmetic progression

17. Three red balls, 2 white balls, and 4 blue balls are placed in a bag and mixed together. The red balls are numbered 1, 2, and 3, respectively; the white balls are numbered 1 and 2; and the blue balls are numbered 1, 2, 3, and 4. Three balls are drawn in succession from the bag, without replacement. Answer the following questions:
  a. In how many different ways can the 3 balls be selected?
  b. In how many ways can 2 of the 3 balls be red and 1 white?
  c. What is the probability that the 3 balls are either all red or all blue?
  d. What is the probability that the first ball drawn will be either blue or numbered 2?
  e. What is the probability that the first ball will be numbered 1, the second numbered 2, and the third numbered 3?

    f. What is the probability that the 3 balls will have numbers 1, 2, and 3, regardless of the order?

18. Use mathematical induction to prove the formula

$$\frac{1}{3} + \frac{1}{15} + \frac{1}{35} + \cdots + \frac{1}{4n^2 - 1} = \frac{n}{2n + 1}$$

19. **a.** If the average annual inflation rate is 12% for the 5 year period beginning in 1980, what will be the purchasing power of the dollar in 1985 as compared to its value in 1980?

    b. An equilateral triangle has sides 2 centimeters long. A second triangle is inscribed in it by connecting the midpoints of its sides, and a third is inscribed in the second by connecting the midpoints of its sides, and so on. In this way a *nest* of equilateral triangles is formed. What is the area of the *n*th triangle of the nest? What is the sum of the area of all the triangles, assuming the process could be continued indefinitely?

20. As a quality-control check, out of each lot of 100 transistor radios produced by a company 2 are checked. If either is found to be defective, the lot is not accepted for shipment until each radio in the lot is checked and defective ones are replaced. Suppose a lot of 100 contains 4 defective radios. What is the probability that this lot will pass inspection and be accepted for immediate shipment?

21. Find an infinite geometric series whose sum is $1/(4 + x^2)$. For what values of x is the result valid?

22. The owner of a sporting goods store sells two types of roller skates: the standard skate on which he makes a profit of $5 per pair, and the deluxe model on which his profit is $8 per pair. From experience he expects to sell at least 50 but not more than 100 standard pairs and between 30 and 60 deluxe pairs each month. Because of limitations on storage capacity, he can handle at most 140 pairs of skates at a time. Assuming he sells all he has in stock, how many should he stock per month to maximize profit?

23. In a small machine shop, two types of parts are produced, each of which requires time on the lathe. The first type requires 10 minutes and the second type 6 minutes. Material for the first type costs $0.50 per part and material for the second type costs $0.75 per part. Labor and equipment charges for the lathe amount to $15.00 per hour. The lathe is to be used between 6 and 8 hours per day in the production of these parts. If it is necessary to produce at least 21 parts of the first type and 15 parts of the second type each day, how many parts of each type should be produced to minimize cost?

24. A balanced coin is tossed until heads first appears. What is the probability that this occurs:

    a. On the eighth trial?   **b.** On one of the first 8 trials?

    c. On an even-numbered trial?

25. The ends of a barn are in the shape of a square surmounted by an isosceles trapezoid (see sketch). The top of the trapezoid is one-half as long as the bottom, and the overall height of the barn is 32 feet. If the total area of the square and trapezoid is 580 square feet, find the dimensions of the side of the square and the height of the trapezoid. What is the overall perimeter?

26. The so-called "stress test," in which a patient walks on a treadmill while an electrocardiogram is taken, is often used to detect coronary artery disease. Recently, the reliability of this test, especially for women, has been called into question. Among women who have experienced chest pains typical of the disease, approximately 60% actually have coronary artery disease. Among women experiencing such chest pain who take the stress test, the probability of getting a "false positive" result is approximately .40; that is, the test indicates coronary artery disease in 40% of these women even though subsequent diagnosis proves they do not have the disease. On the other hand, among women with chest pains who take the stress test, the results are negative in approximately 35% of the cases when they actually have the disease. Find the probability that a woman who suffers typical chest pains and takes the stress test:
a. Will have a positive result from the test
b. Has coronary artery disease, given that the test shows a positive result

Tables

Table I

Squares, Square Roots, and Prime Factors

No.	Sq.	Sq. Rt.	Factors	No.	Sq.	Sq. Rt.	Factors
1	1	1.000		51	2,601	7.141	$3 \cdot 17$
2	4	1.414	2	52	2,704	7.211	$2^2 \cdot 13$
3	9	1.732	3	53	2,809	7.280	53
4	16	2.000	2^2	54	2,916	7.348	$2 \cdot 3^3$
5	25	2.236	5	55	3,025	7.416	$5 \cdot 11$
6	36	2.449	$2 \cdot 3$	56	3,136	7.483	$2^3 \cdot 7$
7	49	2.646	7	57	3,249	7.550	$3 \cdot 19$
8	64	2.828	2^3	58	3,364	7.616	$2 \cdot 29$
9	81	3.000	3^2	59	3,481	7.681	59
10	100	3.162	$2 \cdot 5$	60	3,600	7.746	$2^2 \cdot 3 \cdot 5$
11	121	3.317	11	61	3,721	7.810	61
12	144	3.464	$2^2 \cdot 3$	62	3,844	7.874	$2 \cdot 31$
13	169	3.606	13	63	3,969	7.937	$3^2 \cdot 7$
14	196	3.742	$2 \cdot 7$	64	4,096	8.000	2^6
15	225	3.873	$3 \cdot 5$	65	4,225	8.062	$5 \cdot 13$
16	256	4.000	2^4	66	4,356	8.124	$2 \cdot 3 \cdot 11$
17	289	4.123	17	67	4,489	8.185	67
18	324	4.243	$2 \cdot 3^2$	68	4,624	8.246	$2^2 \cdot 17$
19	361	4.359	19	69	4,761	8.307	$3 \cdot 23$
20	400	4.472	$2^2 \cdot 5$	70	4,900	8.367	$2 \cdot 5 \cdot 7$
21	441	4.583	$3 \cdot 7$	71	5,041	8.426	71
22	484	4.690	$2 \cdot 11$	72	5,184	8.485	$2^3 \cdot 3^2$
23	529	4.796	23	73	5,329	8.544	73
24	576	4.899	$2^3 \cdot 3$	74	5,476	8.602	$2 \cdot 37$
25	625	5.000	5^2	75	5,625	8.660	$3 \cdot 5^2$
26	676	5.099	$2 \cdot 13$	76	5,776	8.718	$2^2 \cdot 19$
27	729	5.196	3^3	77	5,929	8.775	$7 \cdot 11$
28	784	5.292	$2^2 \cdot 7$	78	6,084	8.832	$2 \cdot 3 \cdot 13$
29	841	5.385	29	79	6,241	8.888	79
30	900	5.477	$2 \cdot 3 \cdot 5$	80	6,400	8.944	$2^4 \cdot 5$
31	961	5.568	31	81	6,561	9.000	3^4
32	1,024	5.657	2^5	82	6,724	9.055	$2 \cdot 41$
33	1,089	5.745	$3 \cdot 11$	83	6,889	9.110	83
34	1,156	5.831	$2 \cdot 17$	84	7,056	9.165	$2^2 \cdot 3 \cdot 7$
35	1,225	5.916	$5 \cdot 7$	85	7,225	9.220	$5 \cdot 17$
36	1,296	6.000	$2^2 \cdot 3^2$	86	7,396	9.274	$2 \cdot 43$
37	1,369	6.083	37	87	7,569	9.327	$3 \cdot 29$
38	1,444	6.164	$2 \cdot 19$	88	7,744	9.381	$2^3 \cdot 11$
39	1,521	6.245	$3 \cdot 13$	89	7,921	9.434	89
40	1,600	6.325	$2^3 \cdot 5$	90	8,100	9.487	$2 \cdot 3^2 \cdot 5$
41	1,681	6.403	41	91	8,281	9.539	$7 \cdot 13$
42	1,764	6.481	$2 \cdot 3 \cdot 7$	92	8,464	9.592	$2^2 \cdot 23$
43	1,849	6.557	43	93	8,649	9.644	$3 \cdot 31$
44	1,936	6.633	$2^2 \cdot 11$	94	8,836	9.695	$2 \cdot 47$
45	2,025	6.708	$3^2 \cdot 5$	95	9,025	9.747	$5 \cdot 19$
46	2,116	6.782	$2 \cdot 23$	96	9,216	9.798	$2^5 \cdot 3$
47	2,209	6.856	47	97	9,409	9.849	97
48	2,304	6.928	$2^4 \cdot 3$	98	9,604	9.899	$2 \cdot 7^2$
49	2,401	7.000	7^2	99	9,801	9.950	$3^2 \cdot 11$
50	2,500	7.071	$2 \cdot 5^2$	100	10,000	10.000	$2^2 \cdot 5^2$

Table II

Common Logarithms

x	0	1	2	3	4	5	6	7	8	9
1.0	.0000	.0043	.0086	.0128	.0170	.0212	.0253	.0294	.0334	.0374
1.1	.0414	.0453	.0492	.0531	.0569	.0607	.0645	.0682	.0719	.0755
1.2	.0792	.0828	.0864	.0899	.0934	.0969	.1004	.1038	.1072	.1106
1.3	.1139	.1173	.1206	.1239	.1271	.1303	.1335	.1367	.1399	.1430
1.4	.1461	.1492	.1523	.1553	.1584	.1614	.1644	.1673	.1703	.1732
1.5	.1761	.1790	.1818	.1847	.1875	.1903	.1931	.1959	.1987	.2014
1.6	.2041	.2068	.2095	.2122	.2148	.2175	.2201	.2227	.2253	.2279
1.7	.2304	.2330	.2355	.2380	.2405	.2430	.2455	.2480	.2504	.2529
1.8	.2553	.2577	.2601	.2625	.2648	.2672	.2695	.2718	.2742	.2765
1.9	.2788	.2810	.2833	.2856	.2878	.2900	.2923	.2945	.2967	.2989
2.0	.3010	.3032	.3054	.3075	.3096	.3118	.3139	.3160	.3181	.3201
2.1	.3222	.3243	.3263	.3284	.3304	.3324	.3345	.3365	.3385	.3404
2.2	.3424	.3444	.3464	.3483	.3502	.3522	.3541	.3560	.3579	.3598
2.3	.3617	.3636	.3655	.3674	.3692	.3711	.3729	.3747	.3766	.3784
2.4	.3802	.3820	.3838	.3856	.3874	.3892	.3909	.3927	.3945	.3962
2.5	.3979	.3997	.4014	.4031	.4048	.4065	.4082	.4099	.4116	.4133
2.6	.4150	.4166	.4183	.4200	.4216	.4232	.4249	.4265	.4281	.4298
2.7	.4314	.4330	.4346	.4362	.4378	.4393	.4409	.4425	.4440	.4456
2.8	.4472	.4487	.4502	.4518	.4533	.4548	.4564	.4579	.4594	.4609
2.9	.4624	.4639	.4654	.4669	.4683	.4698	.4713	.4728	.4742	.4757
3.0	.4771	.4786	.4800	.4814	.4829	.4843	.4857	.4871	.4886	.4900
3.1	.4914	.4928	.4942	.4955	.4969	.4983	.4997	.5011	.5024	.5038
3.2	.5051	.5065	.5079	.5092	.5105	.5119	.5132	.5145	.5159	.5172
3.3	.5185	.5198	.5211	.5224	.5237	.5250	.5263	.5276	.5289	.5302
3.4	.5315	.5328	.5340	.5353	.5366	.5378	.5391	.5403	.5416	.5428
3.5	.5441	.5453	.5465	.5478	.5490	.5502	.5514	.5527	.5539	.5551
3.6	.5563	.5575	.5587	.5599	.5611	.5623	.5635	.5647	.5658	.5670
3.7	.5682	.5694	.5705	.5717	.5729	.5740	.5752	.5763	.5775	.5786
3.8	.5798	.5809	.5821	.5832	.5843	.5855	.5866	.5877	.5888	.5899
3.9	.5911	.5922	.5933	.5944	.5955	.5966	.5977	.5988	.5999	.6010
4.0	.6021	.6031	.6042	.6053	.6064	.6075	.6085	.6096	.6107	.6117
4.1	.6128	.6138	.6149	.6160	.6170	.6180	.6191	.6201	.6212	.6222
4.2	.6232	.6243	.6253	.6263	.6274	.6284	.6294	.6304	.6314	.6325
4.3	.6335	.6345	.6355	.6365	.6375	.6385	.6395	.6405	.6415	.6425
4.4	.6435	.6444	.6454	.6464	.6474	.6484	.6493	.6503	.6513	.6522
4.5	.6532	.6542	.6551	.6561	.6571	.6580	.6590	.6599	.6609	.6618
4.6	.6628	.6637	.6646	.6656	.6665	.6675	.6684	.6693	.6702	.6712
4.7	.6721	.6730	.6739	.6749	.6758	.6767	.6776	.6785	.6794	.6803
4.8	.6812	.6821	.6830	.6839	.6848	.6857	.6866	.6875	.6884	.6893
4.9	.6902	.6911	.6920	.6928	.6937	.6946	.6955	.6964	.6972	.6981
5.0	.6990	.6998	.7007	.7016	.7024	.7033	.7042	.7050	.7059	.7067
5.1	.7076	.7084	.7093	.7101	.7110	.7118	.7126	.7135	.7143	.7152
5.2	.7160	.7168	.7177	.7185	.7193	.7202	.7210	.7218	.7226	.2735
5.3	.7243	.7251	.7259	.7267	.7275	.7284	.7292	.7300	.7308	.7316
5.4	.7324	.7332	.7340	.7348	.7356	.7364	.7372	.7380	.7388	.7396
x	0	1	2	3	4	5	6	7	8	9

Table II   Common Logarithms (continued)

x	0	1	2	3	4	5	6	7	8	9
5.5	.7404	.7412	.7419	.7427	.7435	.7443	.7451	.7459	.7466	.7474
5.6	.7482	.7490	.7497	.7505	.7513	.7520	.7528	.7536	.7543	.7551
5.7	.7559	.7566	.7574	.7582	.7589	.7597	.7604	.7612	.7619	.7627
5.8	.7634	.7642	.7649	.7657	.7664	.7672	.7679	.7686	.7694	.7701
5.9	.7709	.7716	.7723	.7731	.7738	.7745	.7752	.7760	.7767	.7774
6.0	.7782	.7789	.7796	.7803	.7810	.7818	.7825	.7832	.7839	.7846
6.1	.7853	.7860	.7868	.7875	.7882	.7889	.7896	.7903	.7910	.7917
6.2	.7924	.7931	.7938	.7945	.7952	.7959	.7966	.7973	.7980	.7987
6.3	.7993	.8000	.8007	.8014	.8021	.8028	.8035	.8041	.8048	.8055
6.4	.8062	.8069	.8075	.8082	.8089	.8096	.8102	.8109	.8116	.8122
6.5	.8129	.8136	.8142	.8149	.8156	.8162	.8169	.8176	.8182	.8189
6.6	.8195	.8202	.8209	.8215	.8222	.8228	.8235	.8241	.8248	.8254
6.7	.8261	.8267	.8274	.8280	.8287	.8293	.8299	.8306	.8312	.8319
6.8	.8325	.8331	.8338	.8344	.8351	.8357	.8363	.8370	.8376	.8382
6.9	.8388	.8395	.8401	.8407	.8414	.8420	.8426	.8432	.8439	.8445
7.0	.8451	.8457	.8463	.8470	.8476	.8482	.8488	.8494	.8500	.8506
7.1	.8513	.8519	.8525	.8531	.8537	.8543	.8549	.8555	.8561	.8567
7.2	.8573	.8579	.8585	.8591	.8597	.8603	.8609	.8615	.8621	.8627
7.3	.8633	.8639	.8645	.8651	.8657	.8663	.8669	.8675	.8681	.8686
7.4	.8692	.8698	.8704	.8710	.8716	.8722	.8727	.8733	.8739	.8745
7.5	.8751	.8756	.8762	.8768	.8774	.8779	.8785	.8791	.8797	.8802
7.6	.8808	.8814	.8820	.8825	.8831	.8837	.8842	.8848	.8854	.8859
7.7	.8865	.8871	.8876	.8882	.8887	.8893	.8899	.8904	.8910	.8915
7.8	.8921	.8927	.8932	.8938	.8943	.8949	.8954	.8960	.8965	.8971
7.9	.8976	.8982	.8987	.8993	.8998	.9004	.9009	.9015	.9020	.9025
8.0	.9031	.9036	.9042	.9047	.9053	.9058	.9063	.9069	.9074	.9079
8.1	.9085	.9090	.9096	.9101	.9106	.9112	.9117	.9122	.9128	.9133
8.2	.9138	.9143	.9149	.9154	.9159	.9165	.9170	.9175	.9180	.9186
8.3	.9191	.9196	.9201	.9206	.9212	.9217	.9222	.9227	.9232	.9238
8.4	.9243	.9248	.9253	.9258	.9263	.9269	.9274	.9279	.9284	.9289
8.5	.9294	.9299	.9304	.9309	.9315	.9320	.9325	.9330	.9335	.9340
8.6	.9345	.9350	.9355	.9360	.9365	.9370	.9375	.9380	.9385	.9390
8.7	.9395	.9400	.9405	.9410	.9415	.9420	.9425	.9430	.9435	.9440
8.8	.9445	.9450	.9455	.9460	.9465	.9469	.9474	.9479	.9484	.9489
8.9	.9494	.9499	.9504	.9509	.9513	.9518	.9523	.9528	.9533	.9538
9.0	.9542	.9547	.9552	.9557	.9562	.9566	.9571	.9576	.9581	.9586
9.1	.9590	.9595	.9600	.9605	.9609	.9614	.9619	.9624	.9628	.9633
9.2	.9638	.9643	.9647	.9652	.9657	.9661	.9666	.9671	.9675	.9680
9.3	.9685	.9689	.9694	.9699	.9703	.9708	.9713	.9717	.9722	.9727
9.4	.9731	.9736	.9741	.9745	.9750	.9754	.9759	.9763	.9768	.9773
9.5	.9777	.9782	.9786	.9791	.9795	.9800	.9805	.9809	.9814	.9818
9.6	.9823	.9827	.9832	.9836	.9841	.9845	.9850	.9854	.9859	.9863
9.7	.9868	.9872	.9877	.9881	.9886	.9890	.9894	.9899	.9903	.9908
9.8	.9912	.9917	.9921	.9926	.9930	.9934	.9939	.9943	.9948	.9952
9.9	.9956	.9961	.9965	.9969	.9974	.9978	.9983	.9987	.9991	.9996
x	0	1	2	3	4	5	6	7	8	9

Table III

Exponential Functions

x	e^x	e^{-x}	x	e^x	e^{-x}
0.00	1.0000	1.0000	1.5	4.4817	0.2231
0.01	1.0101	0.9901	1.6	4.9530	0.2019
0.02	1.0202	0.9802	1.7	5.4739	0.1827
0.03	1.0305	0.9705	1.8	6.0496	0.1653
0.04	1.0408	0.9608	1.9	6.6859	0.1496
0.05	1.0513	0.9512	2.0	7.3891	0.1353
0.06	1.0618	0.9418	2.1	8.1662	0.1225
0.07	1.0725	0.9324	2.2	9.0250	0.1108
0.08	1.0833	0.9231	2.3	9.9742	0.1003
0.09	1.0942	0.9139	2.4	11.023	0.0907
0.10	1.1052	0.9048	2.5	12.182	0.0821
0.11	1.1163	0.8958	2.6	13.464	0.0743
0.12	1.1275	0.8869	2.7	14.880	0.0672
0.13	1.1388	0.8781	2.8	16.445	0.0608
0.14	1.1503	0.8694	2.9	18.174	0.0550
0.15	1.1618	0.8607	3.0	20.086	0.0498
0.16	1.1735	0.8521	3.1	22.198	0.0450
0.17	1.1853	0.8437	3.2	24.533	0.0408
0.18	1.1972	0.8353	3.3	27.113	0.0369
0.19	1.2092	0.8270	3.4	29.964	0.0334
0.20	1.2214	0.8187	3.5	33.115	0.0302
0.21	1.2337	0.8106	3.6	36.598	0.0273
0.22	1.2461	0.8025	3.7	40.447	0.0247
0.23	1.2586	0.7945	3.8	44.701	0.0224
0.24	1.2712	0.7866	3.9	49.402	0.0202
0.25	1.2840	0.7788	4.0	54.598	0.0183
0.30	1.3499	0.7408	4.1	60.340	0.0166
0.35	1.4191	0.7047	4.2	66.686	0.0150
0.40	1.4918	0.6703	4.3	73.700	0.0136
0.45	1.5683	0.6376	4.4	81.451	0.0123
0.50	1.6487	0.6065	4.5	90.017	0.0111
0.55	1.7333	0.5769	4.6	99.484	0.0101
0.60	1.8221	0.5488	4.7	109.95	0.0091
0.65	1.9155	0.5220	4.8	121.51	0.0082
0.70	2.0138	0.4966	4.9	134.29	0.0074
0.75	2.1170	0.4724	5.0	148.41	0.0067
0.80	2.2255	0.4493	5.5	244.69	0.0041
0.85	2.3396	0.4274	6.0	403.43	0.0025
0.90	2.4596	0.4066	6.5	665.14	0.0015
0.95	2.5857	0.3867	7.0	1096.6	0.0009
1.0	2.7183	0.3679	7.5	1808.0	0.0006
1.1	3.0042	0.3329	8.0	2981.0	0.0003
1.2	3.3201	0.3012	8.5	4914.8	0.0002
1.3	3.6693	0.2725	9.0	8103.1	0.0001
1.4	4.0552	0.2466	10.0	22026	0.00005

Table IV

Natural Logarithms of Numbers

n	$\log_e n$	n	$\log_e n$	n	$\log_e n$
	*	4.5	1.5041	9.0	2.1972
0.1	7.6974	4.6	1.5261	9.1	2.2083
0.2	8.3906	4.7	1.5476	9.2	2.2192
0.3	8.7960	4.8	1.5686	9.3	2.2300
0.4	9.0837	4.9	1.5892	9.4	2.2407
0.5	9.3069	5.0	1.6094	9.5	2.2513
0.6	9.4892	5.1	1.6292	9.6	2.2618
0.7	9.6433	5.2	1.6487	9.7	2.2721
0.8	9.7769	5.3	1.6677	9.8	2.2824
0.9	9.8946	5.4	1.6864	9.9	2.2925
1.0	0.0000	5.5	1.7047	10	2.3026
1.1	0.0953	5.6	1.7228	11	2.3979
1.2	0.1823	5.7	1.7405	12	2.4849
1.3	0.2624	5.8	1.7579	13	2.5649
1.4	0.3365	5.9	1.7750	14	2.6391
1.5	0.4055	6.0	1.7918	15	2.7081
1.6	0.4700	6.1	1.8083	16	2.7726
1.7	0.5306	6.2	1.8245	17	2.8332
1.8	0.5878	6.3	1.8405	18	2.8904
1.9	0.6419	6.4	1.8563	19	2.9444
2.0	0.6931	6.5	1.8718	20	2.9957
2.1	0.7419	6.6	1.8871	25	3.2189
2.2	0.7885	6.7	1.9021	30	2.4012
2.3	0.8329	6.8	1.9169	35	3.5553
2.4	0.8755	6.9	1.9315	40	3.6889
2.5	0.9163	7.0	1.9459	45	3.8067
2.6	0.9555	7.1	1.9601	50	3.9120
2.7	0.9933	7.2	1.9741	55	4.0073
2.8	1.0296	7.3	1.9879	60	4.0943
2.9	1.0647	7.4	2.0015	65	4.1744
3.0	1.0986	7.5	2.0149	70	4.2485
3 1	1 1314	7.6	2.0281	75	4.3175
3.2	1.1632	7.7	2.0412	80	4.3820
3.3	1.1939	7.8	2.0541	85	4.4427
3.4	1.2238	7.9	2.0669	90	4.4998
3.5	1.2528	8.0	2.0794	100	4.6052
3.6	1.2809	8.1	2.0919	110	4.7005
3.7	1.3083	8.2	2.1041	120	4.7875
3.8	1.3350	8.3	2.1163	130	4.8676
3.9	1.3610	8.4	2.1282	140	4.9416
4.0	1.3863	8.5	2.1401	150	5.0106
4.1	1.4110	8.6	2.1518	160	5.0752
4.2	1.4351	8.7	2.1633	170	5.1358
4.3	1.4586	8.8	2.1748	180	5.1930
4.4	1.4816	8.9	2.1861	190	5.2470

* Subtract 10 for $n < 1$. Thus, $\log_e 0.1 = 7.6974 - 10 = -2.3026$.

Table V   Values of Trigonometric Functions

Angle θ

Degrees	Radians	sin θ	csc θ	tan θ	cot θ	sec θ	cos θ		
0° 00′	.0000	.0000	No value	.0000	No value	1.000	1.0000	1.5708	90° 00′
10	029	029	343.8	029	343.8	000	000	679	50
20	058	058	171.9	058	171.9	000	000	650	40
30	087	087	114.6	087	114.6	000	1.0000	621	30
40	116	116	85.95	116	85.94	000	.9999	592	20
50	145	145	68.76	145	68.75	000	999	563	10
1° 00′	.0175	.0175	57.30	.0175	57.29	1.000	.9998	1.5533	89° 00′
10	204	204	49.11	204	49.10	000	998	504	50
20	233	233	42.98	233	42.96	000	997	475	40
30	262	262	38.20	262	38.19	000	997	446	30
40	291	291	34.38	291	34.37	000	996	417	20
50	320	320	31.26	320	31.24	001	995	388	10
2° 00′	.0349	.0349	28.65	.0349	28.64	1.001	.9994	1.5359	88° 00′
10	378	378	26.45	378	26.43	001	993	330	50
20	407	407	24.56	407	24.54	001	992	301	40
30	436	436	22.93	437	22.90	001	990	272	30
40	465	465	21.49	466	21.47	001	989	243	20
50	495	494	20.23	495	20.21	001	988	213	10
3° 00′	.0524	.0523	19.11	.0524	19.08	1.001	.9986	1.5184	87° 00′
10	553	552	18.10	553	18.07	002	985	155	50
20	582	581	17.20	582	17.17	002	983	126	40
30	611	610	16.38	612	16.35	002	981	097	30
40	640	640	15.64	641	15.60	002	980	068	20
50	669	669	14.96	670	14.92	002	978	039	10
4° 00′	.0698	.0698	14.34	.0699	14.30	1.002	.9976	1.5010	86° 00′
10	727	727	13.76	729	13.73	003	974	981	50
20	756	756	13.23	758	13.20	003	971	952	40
30	785	785	12.75	787	12.71	003	969	923	30
40	814	814	12.29	816	12.25	003	967	893	20
50	844	843	11.87	846	11.83	004	964	864	10
5° 00′	.0873	.0872	11.47	.0875	11.43	1.004	.9962	1.4835	85° 00′
10	902	901	11.10	904	11.06	004	959	806	50
20	931	929	10.76	934	10.71	004	957	777	40
30	960	958	10.43	963	10.39	005	954	748	30
40	.0989	.0987	10.13	.0992	10.08	005	951	719	20
50	.1018	.1016	9.839	.1022	9.788	005	948	690	10
6° 00′	.1047	.1045	9.567	.1051	9.514	1.006	.9945	1.4661	84° 00′
10	076	074	9.309	080	9.255	006	942	632	50
20	105	103	9.065	110	9.010	006	939	603	40
30	134	132	8.834	139	8.777	006	936	573	30
40	164	161	8.614	169	8.556	007	932	544	20
50	193	190	8.405	198	8.345	007	929	515	10
7° 00′	.1222	.1219	8.206	.1228	8.144	1.008	.9925	1.4486	83° 00′
10	251	248	8.016	257	7.953	008	922	457	50
20	280	276	7.834	287	7.770	008	918	428	40
30	309	305	7.661	317	7.596	009	914	399	30
40	338	334	7.496	346	7.429	009	911	370	20
50	367	363	7.337	376	7.269	009	907	341	10
8° 00′	.1396	.1392	7.185	.1405	7.115	1.010	.9903	1.4312	82° 00′
10	425	421	7.040	435	6.968	010	899	283	50
20	454	449	6.900	465	827	011	894	254	40
30	484	478	765	495	691	011	890	224	30
40	513	507	636	524	561	012	886	195	20
50	542	536	512	554	435	012	881	166	10
9° 00′	.1571	.1564	6.392	.1584	6.314	1.012	.9877	1.4137	81° 00′
		cos θ	sec θ	cot θ	tan θ	csc θ	sin θ	Radians	Degrees

Angle θ

Table V   Values of Trigonometric Functions (continued)

Angle θ

Degrees	Radians	sin θ	csc θ	tan θ	cot θ	sec θ	cos θ		
9° 00′	.1571	.1564	6.392	.1584	6.314	1.012	.9877	1.4137	81° 00′
10	600	593	277	614	197	013	872	108	50
20	629	622	166	644	6.084	013	868	079	40
30	658	650	6.059	673	5.976	014	863	050	30
40	687	679	5.955	703	871	014	858	1.4021	20
50	716	708	855	733	769	015	853	1.3992	10
10° 00′	.1745	.1736	5.759	.1763	5.671	1.015	.9848	1.3963	80° 00′
10	774	765	665	793	576	016	843	934	50
20	804	794	575	823	485	016	838	904	40
30	833	822	487	853	396	017	833	875	30
40	862	851	403	883	309	018	827	846	20
50	891	880	320	914	226	018	822	817	10
11° 00′	.1920	.1908	5.241	.1944	5.145	1.019	.9816	1.3788	79° 00′
10	949	937	164	.1974	5.066	019	811	759	50
20	.1978	965	089	.2004	4.989	020	805	730	40
30	.2007	.1994	5.016	035	915	020	799	701	30
40	036	.2022	4.945	065	843	021	793	672	20
50	065	051	876	095	773	022	787	643	10
12° 00′	.2094	.2079	4.810	.2126	4.705	1.022	.9781	1.3614	78° 00′
10	123	108	745	156	638	023	775	584	50
20	153	136	682	186	574	024	769	555	40
30	182	164	620	217	511	024	763	526	30
40	211	193	560	247	449	025	757	497	20
50	240	221	502	278	390	026	750	468	10
13° 00′	.2269	.2250	4.445	.2309	4.331	1.026	.9744	1.3439	77° 00′
10	298	278	390	339	275	027	737	410	50
20	327	306	336	370	219	028	730	381	40
30	356	334	284	401	165	028	724	352	30
40	385	363	232	432	113	029	717	323	20
50	414	391	182	462	061	030	710	294	10
14° 00′	.2443	.2419	4.134	.2493	4.011	1.031	.9703	1.3265	76° 00′
10	473	447	086	524	3.962	031	696	235	50
20	502	476	4.039	555	914	032	689	206	40
30	531	504	3.994	586	867	033	681	177	30
40	560	532	950	617	821	034	674	148	20
50	589	560	906	648	776	034	667	119	10
15° 00′	.2618	.2588	3.864	.2679	3.732	1.035	.9659	1.3090	75° 00′
10	647	616	822	711	689	036	652	061	50
20	676	644	782	742	647	037	644	032	40
30	705	672	742	773	606	038	636	1.3003	30
40	734	700	703	805	566	039	628	1.2974	20
50	763	728	665	836	526	039	621	945	10
16° 00′	.2793	.2756	3.628	.2867	3.487	1.040	.9613	1.2915	74° 00′
10	822	784	592	899	450	041	605	886	50
20	851	812	556	931	412	042	596	857	40
30	880	840	521	962	376	043	588	828	30
40	909	868	487	.2944	340	044	580	799	20
50	938	896	453	.3026	305	045	572	770	10
17° 00′	.2967	.2924	3.420	.3057	3.271	1.046	.9563	1.2741	73° 00′
10	.2996	952	388	089	237	047	555	712	50
20	.3025	.2979	357	121	204	048	546	683	40
30	054	.3007	326	153	172	048	537	654	30
40	083	035	295	185	140	049	528	625	20
50	113	062	265	217	108	050	520	595	10
18° 00′	.3142	.3090	3.236	.3249	3.078	1.051	.9511	1.2566	72° 00′
		cos θ	sec θ	cot θ	tan θ	csc θ	sin θ	Radians	Degrees

Angle θ

Table V Values of Trigonometric Functions (continued)

Angle θ									
Degrees	Radians	sin θ	csc θ	tan θ	cot θ	sec θ	cos θ		
18° 00′	.3142	.3090	3.236	.3249	3.078	1.051	.9511	1.2566	72° 00′
10	171	118	207	281	047	052	502	537	50
20	200	145	179	314	3.018	053	492	508	40
30	229	173	152	346	2.989	054	483	479	30
40	258	201	124	378	960	056	474	450	20
50	287	228	098	411	932	057	465	421	10
19° 00′	.3316	.3256	3.072	.3443	2.904	1.058	.9455	1.2392	71° 00′
10	345	283	046	476	877	059	446	363	50
20	374	311	3.021	508	850	060	436	334	40
30	403	338	2.996	541	824	061	426	305	30
40	432	365	971	574	798	062	417	275	20
50	462	393	947	607	773	063	407	246	10
20° 00′	.3491	.3420	2.924	.3640	2.747	1.064	.9397	1.2217	70° 00′
10	520	448	901	673	723	065	387	188	50
20	549	475	878	706	699	066	377	159	40
30	578	502	855	739	675	068	367	130	30
40	607	529	833	772	651	069	356	101	20
50	636	557	812	805	628	070	346	072	10
21° 00′	.3665	.3584	2.790	.3839	2.605	1.071	.9336	1.2043	69° 00′
10	694	611	769	872	583	072	325	1.2014	50
20	723	638	749	906	560	074	315	1.1985	40
30	752	665	729	939	539	075	304	956	30
40	782	692	709	.3973	517	076	293	926	20
50	811	719	689	.4006	496	077	283	897	10
22° 00′	.3840	.3746	2.669	.4040	2.475	1.079	.9272	1.1868	68° 00′
10	869	773	650	074	455	080	261	839	50
20	898	800	632	108	434	081	250	810	40
30	927	827	613	142	414	082	239	781	30
40	956	854	595	176	394	084	228	752	20
50	985	881	577	210	375	085	216	723	10
23° 00′	.4014	.3907	2.559	.4245	2.356	1.086	.9205	1.1694	67° 00′
10	043	934	542	279	337	088	194	665	50
20	072	961	525	314	318	089	182	636	40
30	102	.3987	508	348	300	090	171	606	30
40	131	.4014	491	383	282	092	159	577	20
50	160	041	475	417	264	093	147	548	10
24° 00′	.4189	.4067	2.459	.4452	2.246	1.095	.9135	1.1519	66° 00′
10	218	094	443	487	229	096	124	490	50
20	247	120	427	522	211	097	112	461	40
30	276	147	411	557	194	099	100	432	30
40	305	173	396	592	177	100	088	403	20
50	334	200	381	628	161	102	075	374	10
25° 00′	.4363	.4226	2.366	.4663	2.145	1.103	.9063	1.1345	65° 00′
10	392	253	352	699	128	105	051	316	50
20	422	279	337	734	112	106	038	286	40
30	451	305	323	770	097	108	026	257	30
40	480	331	309	806	081	109	013	228	20
50	509	358	295	841	066	111	.9001	199	10
26° 00′	.4538	.4384	2.281	.4877	2.050	1.113	.8988	1.1170	64° 00′
10	567	410	268	913	035	114	975	141	50
20	596	436	254	950	020	116	962	112	40
30	625	462	241	.4986	2.006	117	949	083	30
40	654	488	228	.5022	1.991	119	936	054	20
50	683	514	215	059	977	121	923	1.1025	10
27° 00′	.4712	.4540	2.203	.5095	1.963	1.122	.8910	1.0996	63° 00′
		cos θ	sec θ	cot θ	tan θ	csc θ	sin θ	Radians	Degrees
								Angle θ	

Table V Values of Trigonometric Functions (continued)

Angle θ									
Degrees	Radians	sin θ	csc θ	tan θ	cot θ	sec θ	cos θ		
27° 00′	.4712	.4540	2.203	.5095	1.963	1.122	.8910	1.0996	63° 00′
10	741	566	190	132	949	124	897	966	50
20	771	592	178	169	935	126	884	937	40
30	800	617	166	206	921	127	870	908	30
40	829	643	154	243	907	129	857	879	20
50	858	669	142	280	894	131	843	850	10
28° 00′	.4887	.4695	2.130	.5317	1.881	1.133	.8829	1.0821	62° 00′
10	916	720	118	354	868	134	816	792	50
20	945	746	107	392	855	136	802	763	40
30	.4974	772	096	430	842	138	788	734	30
40	.5003	797	085	467	829	140	774	705	20
50	032	823	074	505	816	142	760	676	10
29° 00′	.5061	.4848	2.063	.5543	1.804	1.143	.8746	1.0647	61° 00′
10	091	874	052	581	792	145	732	617	50
20	120	899	041	619	780	147	718	588	40
30	149	924	031	658	767	149	704	559	30
40	178	950	020	696	756	151	689	530	20
50	207	.4975	010	735	744	153	675	501	10
30° 00′	.5236	.5000	2.000	.5774	1.732	1.155	.8660	1.0472	60° 00′
10	265	025	1.990	812	720	157	646	443	50
20	294	050	980	851	709	159	631	414	40
30	323	075	970	890	698	161	616	385	30
40	352	100	961	930	686	163	601	356	20
50	381	125	951	.5969	675	165	587	327	10
31° 00′	.5411	.5150	1.942	.6009	1.664	1.167	.8572	1.0297	59° 00′
10	440	175	932	048	653	169	557	268	50
20	469	200	923	088	643	171	542	239	40
30	498	225	914	128	632	173	526	210	30
40	527	250	905	168	621	175	511	181	20
50	556	275	896	208	611	177	496	152	10
32° 00′	.5585	.5299	1.887	.6249	1.600	1.179	.8480	1.0123	58° 00′
10	614	324	878	289	590	181	465	094	50
20	643	348	870	330	580	184	450	065	40
30	672	373	861	371	570	186	434	036	30
40	701	398	853	412	560	188	418	1.0007	20
50	730	422	844	453	550	190	403	.9977	10
33° 00′	.5760	.5446	1.836	.6494	1.540	1.192	.8387	.9948	57° 00′
10	789	471	828	536	530	195	371	919	50
20	818	495	820	577	520	197	355	890	40
30	847	519	812	619	511	199	339	861	30
40	876	544	804	661	501	202	323	832	20
50	905	568	796	703	492	204	307	803	10
34° 00′	.5934	.5592	1.788	.6745	1.483	1.206	.8290	.9774	56° 00′
10	963	616	781	787	473	209	274	745	50
20	.5992	640	773	830	464	211	258	716	40
30	.6021	644	766	873	455	213	241	687	30
40	050	688	758	916.	446	216	225	657	20
50	080	712	751	.6959	437	218	208	628	10
35° 00′	.6109	.5736	1.743	.7002	1.428	1.221	.8192	.9599	55° 00′
10	138	760	736	046	419	223	175	570	50
20	167	783	729	089	411	226	158	541	40
30	196	807	722	133	402	228	141	512	30
40	225	831	715	177	393	231	124	483	20
50	254	854	708	221	385	233	107	454	10
36° 00′	.6283	.5878	1.701	.7265	1.376	1.236	.8090	.9425	54° 00′
		cos θ	sec θ	cot θ	tan θ	csc θ	sin θ	Radians	Degrees
								Angle θ	

Table V Values of Trigonometric Functions (continued)

Degrees	Radians	sin θ	csc θ	tan θ	cot θ	sec θ	cos θ		
36° 00′	.6283	.5878	1.701	.7265	1.376	1.236	.8090	.9425	54° 00′
10	312	901	695	310	368	239	073	396	50
20	341	925	688	355	360	241	056	367	40
30	370	948	681	400	351	244	039	338	30
40	400	972	675	445	343	247	021	308	20
50	429	.5995	668	490	335	249	.8004	279	10
37° 00′	.6458	.6018	1.662	.7536	1.327	1.252	.7986	.9250	53° 00′
10	487	041	655	581	319	255	969	221	50
20	516	065	649	627	311	258	951	192	40
30	545	088	643	673	303	260	934	163	30
40	574	111	636	720	295	263	916	134	20
50	603	134	630	766	288	266	898	105	10
38° 00′	.6632	.6157	1.624	.7813	1.280	1.269	.7880	.9076	52° 00′
10	661	180	618	860	272	272	862	047	50
20	690	202	612	907	265	275	844	.9018	40
30	720	225	606	.7954	257	278	826	.8988	30
40	749	248	601	.8002	250	281	808	959	20
50	778	271	595	050	242	284	790	930	10
39° 00′	.6807	.6293	1.589	.8098	1.235	1.287	.7771	.8901	51° 00′
10	836	316	583	146	228	290	753	872	50
20	865	338	578	195	220	293	735	843	40
30	894	361	572	243	213	296	716	814	30
40	923	383	567	292	206	299	698	785	20
50	952	406	561	342	199	302	679	756	10
40° 00′	.6981	.6428	1.556	.8391	1.192	1.305	.7660	.8727	50° 00′
10	.7010	450	550	441	185	309	642	698	50
20	039	472	545	491	178	312	623	668	40
30	069	494	540	541	171	315	604	639	30
40	098	517	535	591	164	318	585	610	20
50	127	539	529	642	157	322	566	581	10
41° 00′	.7156	.6561	1.524	.8693	1.150	1.325	.7547	.8552	49° 00′
10	185	583	519	744	144	328	528	523	50
20	214	604	514	796	137	332	509	494	40
30	243	626	509	847	130	335	490	465	30
40	272	648	504	899	124	339	470	436	20
50	301	670	499	.8952	117	342	451	407	10
42° 00′	.7330	.6691	1.494	.9004	1.111	1.346	.7431	.8378	48° 00′
10	359	713	490	057	104	349	412	348	50
20	389	734	485	110	098	353	392	319	40
30	418	756	480	163	091	356	373	290	30
40	447	777	476	217	085	360	353	261	20
50	476	799	471	271	079	364	333	232	10
43° 00′	.7505	.6820	1.466	.9325	1.072	1.367	.7314	.8203	47° 00′
10	534	841	462	380	066	371	294	174	50
20	563	862	457	435	060	375	274	145	40
30	592	884	453	490	054	379	254	116	30
40	621	905	448	545	048	382	234	087	20
50	650	926	444	601	042	386	214	058	10
44° 00′	.7679	.6947	1.440	.9657	1.036	1.390	.7193	.8029	46° 00′
10	709	967	435	713	030	394	173	.7999	50
20	738	.6988	431	770	024	398	153	970	40
30	767	.7009	427	827	018	402	133	941	30
40	796	030	423	884	012	406	112	912	20
50	825	050	418	.9942	006	410	092	883	10
45° 00′	.7854	.7071	1.414	1.000	1.000	1.414	.7071	.7854	45° 00′
		cos θ	sec θ	cot θ	tan θ	csc θ	sin θ	Radians	Degrees

Angle θ

Answers to Selected Problems

The solutions manual that accompanies this text is available from your local bookstore.

Note. Answers to certain problems can be given in different forms. Thus your answer may be correct even if it appears different from the one given.

Chapter 1

Exercise Set 1, page 2

1. a. $0.666\ldots$ **b.** 0.625 **c.** $0.181818\ldots$ **d.** -1.6 **e.** $0.370370\ldots$
3. Correct to two decimal places **5. a.** Rational **b.** Rational **c.** Irrational **d.** Rational
e. Rational **7. a.** Rational **b.** May be either rational or irrational
c. Rational if $x = 0$; otherwise irrational **9. a.** $\frac{2}{3}$ **b.** $\frac{28}{9}$ **11. a.** $\frac{9}{37}$ **b.** $\frac{1,709}{333}$
13. a. By the Pythagorean theorem, the diagonal of the square is $\sqrt{2}$.
b. Construct a rectangle 2 units long by 1 unit high. The diagonal will be $\sqrt{5}$.

Exercise Set 2, page 7

1. a. Distributive property **b.** Definition of additive inverse **c.** Definition of multiplicative inverse
d. Definition of additive identity **e.** Definition of multiplicative identity **f.** Associative property for addition
g. Associative property for multiplication **h.** Commutative property for addition
i. Commutative property for multiplication **j.** Property of additive identity **3. a.** -6 **b.** 15 **c.** 2
d. $\frac{1}{3}$ **e.** 19 **5. a.** 0 **b.** 1 **c.** -1 **d.** No
7. a. No. For example, $7 - (5 - 3) = 7 - 2 = 5$, but $(7 - 5) - 3 = 2 - 3 = -1$.
b. No. For example, $12 \div (4 \div 2) = 12 \div 2 = 6$, but $(12 \div 4) \div 2 = 3 \div 2 = \frac{3}{2}$.
9. a. 5 **b.** 2 **c.** 0 **d.** 5 **e.** 3
11. Taken in order, the properties used are: equality property 4, property of additive identity, associative property of addition, property of additive inverse, property of additive identity.
13. Let $a \in R$, $a \neq 0$. Suppose $a \cdot b = 1$. Then

$a^{-1} \cdot (a \cdot b) = a^{-1} \cdot 1$ Equality property 4

$a^{-1} \cdot (a \cdot b) = a^{-1}$ Property of multiplicative identity

$(a^{-1} \cdot a) \cdot b = a^{-1}$ Associative property for multiplication

$1 \cdot b = a^{-1}$ Property of multiplicative inverse

$b = a^{-1}$ Property of multiplicative identity

15. $a(b - c) = a[b + (-c)] = ab + a(-c) = ab + [-(ac)] = ab - ac$ **17.** $1/b = 1 \cdot b^{-1} = b^{-1}$
19. $(a^{-1} \cdot b^{-1}) \cdot (ab) = (b^{-1} \cdot a^{-1}) \cdot (ab) = b^{-1}(a^{-1} \cdot a) \cdot b = b^{-1} \cdot 1 \cdot b = b^{-1} \cdot b = 1$
So $a^{-1}b^{-1}$ is the inverse of ab.
21. a. -1 **b.** 0 **c.** 1 **d.** 5 **e.** -2

Exercise Set 3, page 11

1. a. $<$ **b.** $>$ **c.** $<$ **d.** $>$ **e.** $<$ **3. a.** $7 - 3 = 4$ is positive
b. $4 - (-2) = 4 + 2 = 6$ is positive   **c.** $-1 - (-4) = -1 + 4 = 3$ is positive   **d.** $5 - 2 = 3$ is positive
e. $-3 - (-5) = -3 + 5 = 2$ is positive   **5. a.** $2 < x < 5$ **b.** $-1 < x \le 0$ **c.** $0 \le x < 2$
d. $0 \le x \le 6$ **e.** $3 < x \le 4$ **7. a.**

b.

c.

d.

e.

9. a. $-2 < x < 2$ **b.** $y > 1$ or $y < -1$ **c.** $-3 \le t \le 3$ **d.** $w \ge 2$ or $w \le -2$ **11. a.** $\{x: \ |x| < 5\}$
b. $\{x: \ |x| > 6\}$ **c.** $\{x: \ |x| \le 4\}$ **d.** $\{x: \ |x| \ge 8\}$

13. If $a > 0$, then $a^2 = a \cdot a$ is positive since R^+ is closed under multiplication. If $a < 0$, then $(-a) > 0$, and $(-a)(-a) = a^2 > 0$.

15. If $a < b$, then $b - a$ is positive. If c is positive, then by closure of R^+ under multiplication, $(b - a) \cdot c$ is positive. But $(b - a)c = bc - ac$. So by definition, $ac < bc$. If c is negative, then $-c$ is positive. So $(b - a)(-c)$ is positive. But $(b - a)(-c) = -bc + ac = ac - bc$. So, since this is positive, $bc < ac$, or equivalently, $ac > bc$.

17. If $a < b$ and $c < d$, then by property 3, $a + c < b + c$ and $b + c < b + d$. Thus, by property 6, $a + c < b + d$.

19. If $a < b$, then $\begin{cases} a/c < b/c & \text{if } c > 0 \\ a/c > b/c & \text{if } c < 0 \end{cases}$

If $c > 0$, by Problem 18, $c^{-1} > 0$. So by property 4, $ac^{-1} < bc^{-1}$. But $ac^{-1} = a/c$ and $bc^{-1} = b/c$. If $c < 0$, then $c^{-1} < 0$, since otherwise the product of c and c^{-1} would not be positive. Thus, by property 4, $ac^{-1} > bc^{-1}$, and so $a/c > b/c$.

21. False. For example, $6 < 7$ and $3 < 5$. But $(6 - 3) > (7 - 5)$.

Exercise Set 4, page 17

1. a. 2 **b.** -3 **c.** -6 **d.** -2 **e.** 8 **3. a.** -6 **b.** -20 **c.** 30 **d.** -5 **e.** -1
5. a. 4 **b.** 7 **c.** 15 **d.** 15 **e.** 12 **7. a.** $\frac{19}{12}$ **b.** $\frac{11}{24}$ **9. a.** $\frac{13}{12}$ **b.** 1 **11. a.** $\frac{13}{5}$
b. $-\frac{11}{6}$ **13. a.** $-\frac{4}{7}$ **b.** $\frac{9}{4}$ **15. a.** $-\frac{5}{108}$ **b.** $\frac{43}{1,260}$ **17. a.** $\frac{1}{10}$ **b.** $\frac{61}{72}$ **19. a.** 16
b. 26 **c.** 28 **d.** 64 **e.** 45

21. First assume Definition 2. Then $a \div b = a \cdot b^{-1}$. Let $c = a \cdot b^{-1}$. Multiply both sides by b, giving $cb = (a \cdot b^{-1})b = a \cdot (b^{-1} \cdot b) = a \cdot 1 = a$, or $a = bc$. So c is a number which when multiplied by b gives a. Now assume the definition as stated in this problem. Then we have

$$a \div b = c$$

where $bc = a$. Since $b \ne 0$, then b^{-1} exists, and we multiply by b^{-1} to get

$$b^{-1}(bc) = b^{-1}a$$
$$(b^{-1}b)c = ab^{-1}$$
$$1 \cdot c = ab^{-1}$$
$$c = ab^{-1}$$

Therefore, $a \div b = ab^{-1}$.

23. a. $\frac{109}{30}$ **b.** $\frac{5}{6}$ **25. a.** $-\frac{9}{8}$ **b.** $-\frac{17}{30}$

Exercise Set 5, page 20

1. $\frac{2}{11}$ **3.** $-\frac{29}{8}$ **5.** $-\frac{14}{11}$ **7.** $-\frac{33}{40}$ **9.** $-\frac{1}{11}$ **11.** 2 **13.** $-\frac{16}{63}$ **15.** $\frac{1}{3}$ **17.** $\frac{9}{8}$ **19.** $\frac{5}{4}$

Exercise Set 6, page 27

1. a. 81 **b.** $\frac{1}{4}$ **c.** -8 **d.** 1 **e.** 4 **3. a.** $\frac{1}{16}$ **b.** $\frac{2}{3}$ **c.** -27 **d.** $\frac{243}{5}$ **e.** $\frac{2}{9}$
5. a. x^7 **b.** x^4 **c.** x^{12} **d.** $x^4 y^6$ **e.** 1

7. a. $-27a^6$ **b.** $\dfrac{8}{a^5}$ **c.** $\dfrac{a^4}{4}$ **d.** $\dfrac{4a^2 b^4}{9}$ **e.** $\dfrac{3a^5}{4}$ **9. a.** $\dfrac{y^6}{x^5}$ **b.** $\dfrac{r^2 t^3}{s^3}$ **c.** $\dfrac{2b^6}{3a^3}$

11. a. $\dfrac{x^4 y^3}{27z}$ **b.** $-\dfrac{xz^4}{2y^3}$ **13. a.** $\dfrac{b^6}{a^3 c^6 d^4}$ **b.** $\dfrac{x^{10}}{y^{16}}$

15. $\frac{7}{8}$ **17. a.** 2×10^{12} **b.** 7×10^{-6} **c.** 3.1×10^6 **d.** 1.3×10^{-1} **e.** 2.54×10^8

19. a. 6.58×10^4 **b.** $(-2.5) \times 10^3$ **21.** 2.5

23. a. 1.673×10^{-24} **b.** $602{,}300{,}000{,}000{,}000{,}000{,}000{,}000$

25. a. Let $n = -p, p > 0$. Then

$$(a^m)^n = (a^m)^{-p} = \frac{1}{(a^m)^p} = \frac{1}{a^{mp}} = a^{-(mp)} = a^{m(-p)} = a^{mn}$$

b. Let $m = -p, p > 0$. Then

$$(a^m)^n = (a^{-p})^n = \left(\frac{1}{a^p}\right)^n = \frac{1^n}{(a^p)^n} = \frac{1}{a^{pn}} = a^{-pn} = a^{(-p)n} = a^{mn}$$

c. Let $m = -p, n = -q, p > 0, q > 0$. Then

$$(a^m)^n = (a^{-p})^{-q} = (\frac{1}{a^p})^{-q} = (a^p)^q = a^{pq} = a^{(-p)(-q)} = a^{mn}$$

d. If $n = 0$, then $(a^m)^n = (a^m)^0 = 1 = a^0 = a^{m \cdot 0} = a^{mn}$.

27. 1.874×10^{20}

Exercise Set 7, page 31

1. a. $5\sqrt{5}$ **b.** $2\sqrt[3]{5}$ **3. a.** $7\sqrt{5}$ **b.** $-17\sqrt{2}$ **5.** $5x^2y^3\sqrt{2y}$ **7.** $3xz^2\sqrt{2xz}$ **9.** $10ac^2\sqrt{3}/b^3$

11. $\frac{5b^4c^5}{a^3}$ **13.** $3x^3y^2\sqrt{2}$ **15.** $-3ab^2\sqrt[3]{3a^2}$ **17. a.** $\sqrt{6}/3$ **b.** $2\sqrt{10}/5$ **c.** $2\sqrt{7}/7$ **d.** $\sqrt[3]{2}/2$

e. $3\sqrt{6}/10$ **19. a.** $\frac{a\sqrt{ab}}{b}$ **b.** $\frac{\sqrt{3ab}}{3b^2}$ **21.** $4y^5\sqrt{6}/3x^3$ **23. a.** $2^{13/12}$ **b.** $3^{1/6}$ **c.** $\frac{1}{3}$ **d.** 1

25. a. $6x^{5/6}$ **b.** $x^{1/12}y^{1/6}$ **c.** $4x^{5/6}$ **27. a.** a^2 **b.** $\frac{8}{a}$ **c.** $\frac{4a}{b^4}$ **29. a.** $2x^2$ **b.** $4a^2/b$

c. $-5y^4/x^3$ **31. a.** $256a^8b^{12}$ **b.** $-128a^7/b^{14}$ **c.** $216a^3b^6$ **33. a.** $\frac{x^{1/2}}{4y^{4/3}}$ **b.** $\frac{b^2c^{3/2}}{81a}$

35. a. $\frac{9b^4}{4a^2}$ **b.** $-\frac{8a^6}{27b^3}$ **37. a.** $\frac{27b}{8a^2}$ **b.** $\frac{9y}{4x^3}$ **39. a.** $2x^{5/2}y^{3/2}$ **b.** $2^{3/2}a^6b^{3/2}$ **c.** $2^{4/3}x^{10/3}y^{4/3}$

41. $\sqrt[k]{a^{km}} = a^{km/kn} = a^{m/n} = \sqrt[n]{a^m}$ **43.** $\sqrt[m]{\sqrt[n]{a}} = (a^{1/n})^{1/m} = a^{(1/n) \cdot (1/m)} = a^{1/nm} = a^{1/mn} = \sqrt[mn]{a}$

45. $\left(\frac{a}{b}\right)^{-m/n} = \left(\frac{a}{b}\right)^{(-1) \cdot (m/n)} = \left[\left(\frac{a}{b}\right)^{-1}\right]^{m/n} = \left(\frac{b}{a}\right)^{m/n}$ **47.** $\frac{\sqrt{2}}{2}$ **49.** $\frac{11\sqrt[3]{4}}{6}$ **51.** $\frac{9a^2b^3\sqrt[3]{4c}}{8c^2}$

Review Exercise Set, page 33

1. a. 0.6875 **b.** 3.125 **c.** $0.428571428571\ldots$ **d.** $0.185185185\ldots$ **e.** $-2.1666\ldots$ **3. a.** Rational
b. Rational   **c.** Irrational   **d.** Rational   **e.** Rational   **f.** Irrational   **g.** Rational   **h.** Rational
i. Irrational   **j.** Irrational   **5. a.** 3 **b.** 5 **c.** 12 **d.** 2 **e.** 13

7. a.   **b.**

c.   **d.**

e.

9. a. $\frac{1}{18}$ **b.** $\frac{59}{72}$ **11. a.** $\frac{59}{1{,}680}$ **b.** $-\frac{3}{4}$ **13. a.** $\frac{39}{2}$ **b.** $\frac{5}{14}$ **15. a.** 3.94×10^5

b. -3.585×10^{-5} **c.** 5×10^{-4} **17. a.** $\frac{3^6z^2}{x^2y^3}$ **b.** $4a^2b^2$ **19. a.** $\frac{27y^9z^3}{x^6}$ **b.** $\frac{x^{10}}{4y^6}$

21. a. $5xy^2\sqrt{2x}$ **b.** $\frac{-2a^2}{b}\sqrt[3]{4}$ **23. a.** $\frac{\sqrt{6}}{3}$ **b.** $\frac{2\sqrt{5}}{5}$ **c.** $\frac{2\sqrt[3]{6}}{3}$ **d.** $\frac{\sqrt{6xy}}{4y}$

25. If $a > b$, then $a - b$ is positive. Therefore, $(a - c) - (b - c) = a - c - b + c = a - b$ is positive, so that $a - c > b - c$.

27. If $a \neq 0$, then a^{-1} exists, and from $ab = 0$, we get

$$a^{-1}(ab) = a^{-1} \cdot 0$$
$$(a^{-1}a)b = 0$$
$$1 \cdot b = 0$$
$$b = 0$$

Thus, if $a \neq 0$, then b must be 0. So either $a = 0$ or $b = 0$.

29. $-\frac{33}{5}$ **31.** 4   **33.** 17.3

Chapter 2

Exercise Set 2, page 41

1. $5x^2 + 10x + 13$ **3.** $8y^3 + 2y^2 + 2y - 11$ **5.** $t^2 - 3t + 14$ **7.** $7x^2 + 4xy + 2y^2$ **9.** $2x^2 + x + 3$
11. $x^2 + 7x + 12$ **13.** $x^2 + x - 12$ **15.** $x^2 + 3xy + 2y^2$ **17.** $2 - x - x^2$ **19.** $6x^2 + 17x + 7$
21. $8t^2 - 8t - 6$ **23.** $10y^2 - 23y + 12$ **25.** $8 - 14x + 3x^2$ **27.** $x^2 - 16$ **29.** $4x^2 - 1$ **31.** $a^2 - 4b^2$
33. $9a^2 - 49b^2c^2$ **35.** $x^2 - 4x + 4$ **37.** $x^2 - 4xy + 4y^2$ **39.** $4x^2 - 12x + 9$ **41.** $a^4 - 6a^2b^2 + 9b^4$
43. $2x^2 + 11x - 44; R = 172$ **45.** $4x^2 + 12x + 29; R = 77x - 21$ **47.** $x^3 - 5x + 2$ **49.** $x^4 - 4x^3 + 9x^2 - 10x + 8$
51. $x^2 + 2xy + y^2 - 4$ **53.** $x^2 - y^2 + 2y - 1$ **55.** $16 - x^2 + 2xy - y^2$ **57.** $4x^2 + 9y^2 + 16 - 12xy + 16x - 24y$
59. $\frac{2}{3}x^3 - \frac{17}{9}x + \frac{5}{3}; R = \frac{68}{9}x - \frac{44}{3}$

Exercise Set 3, page 45

1. $a^7 + 7a^6b + 21a^5b^2 + 35a^4b^3 + 35a^3b^4 + 21a^2b^5 + 7ab^6 + b^7$ **3.** $a^6 - 6a^5b + 15a^4b^2 - 20a^3b^3 + 15a^2b^4 - 6ab^5 + b^6$
5. $1 + 6x + 15x^2 + 20x^3 + 15x^4 + 6x^5 + x^6$ **7.** $16x^4 + 32x^3y + 24x^2y^2 + 8xy^3 + y^4$
9. $16x^4 + 96x^3y + 216x^2y^2 + 216xy^3 + 81y^4$ **11.** $125x^3 - 75x^2y + 15xy^2 - y^6$
13. $\frac{32}{s^5} - \frac{240}{s^4} + \frac{720}{s^3} - \frac{1{,}080}{s^2} + \frac{810}{s} - 243$ **15.** $x^{10} - 10x^8y + 40x^6y^2 - 80x^4y^3 + 80x^2y^4 - 32y^5$ **17.** $-120a^3b^7$
19. $-48{,}384x^5y^3$ **21.** Write $(a - b)^n = [a + (-b)]^n$. The factor $(-b)$ appears alternately to even and odd powers in the expansion, and since $(-b)^k = [(-1)b]^k = (-1)^k \cdot b^k$, the sign is that of $(-1)^k$, which is plus when k is even and minus when k is odd.   **23.** **a.** $-25{,}344x^{10}y^7$ **b.** $61{,}236x^{3/2}$ **25.** $17{,}920a^8b^{12}$
27. $32{,}768a^{30} - 737{,}280a^{28}b^{-2} + 7{,}741{,}440a^{26}b^{-4} - 50{,}319{,}360a^{24}b^{-6}$

Exercise Set 4, page 51

1. **a.** $2ab(a - 2b)$ **b.** $3a^2b^3c(2ab + 3c)$ **3.** **a.** $8x^2y^2(3x - 5x^3yz + 6y^2z^2)$ **b.** $52a^3b(3a - 5b)$
5. **a.** $2x^{1/3}(x - 2)$ **b.** $6x^{1/3}(2 + 3x)$ **7.** **a.** $(x + 2)(y + 1)$ **b.** $(1 - a)(b - 1)$ **9.** **a.** $(x + y)(x - 1)$
  b. $(xy + 1)(x - 1)$ **11.** **a.** $(x - 2)^2$ **b.** $(a + 4)^2$ **13.** **a.** $(3x - 5)^2$ **b.** $(7a + 2b)^2$
15. **a.** $(x - 1)(x - 3)$ **b.** $(a + 3)(a + 4)$ **17.** **a.** $(t - 4)(t + 3)$ **19.** **a.** $(2x + 1)(x + 3)$ **b.** $(3x + 2)(x + 3)$
21. **a.** $(2x + 3)(2x - 3)$ **b.** $(4m + 5n)(4m - 5n)$ **23.** **a.** $(a - 1)(a + 1)(a^2 + 1)(a^4 + 1)$ **b.** $y^2(xy + 1)(xy - 1)$
25. **a.** $(x - 2 + y)(x - 2 - y)$ **b.** $(x + y - 2)(x - y + 2)$ **27.** **a.** $(x + 2 + y)(x + 2 - y)$
  b. $(4a - 5 - 5b)(4a - 5 + 5b)$ **29.** **a.** $(x - 4)(x^2 + 4x + 16)$ **b.** $(3a + 2)(9a^2 - 6a + 4)$ **31.** $(x + y)^3$
33. $(a - b)^4$ **35.** $(x + 3)^3$ **37.** $2(3x - 4)(2x + 5)$ **39.** $(x + 2)(x - 2)(x + 1)(x - 1)$ **41.** $(a + b)(a^2 + b^2)$
43. $(x - y + 2)(x - y - 2)$ **45.** $(16a - 9b)(3a + 4b)$ **47.** $(x + 1)(x + 2)(x - 2)$
49. $(x - 2)(x^2 + 2x + 4)(x + 2)(x^2 - 2x + 4)$ **51.** $(a - b)(a + b - 2b^2)$ **53.** $(9a - 4b)(2a + 5b)$
55. $(m - 3)(2m - n)$ **57.** $(5 - 2x)(2 + x)$ **59.** $(t - 4)^3$ **61.** $(2u - 3v)(4u^2 + 6uv + 9v^2)$ **63.** $2(3x - 7y)^2$
65. $2ab(4a + 9b)^2$ **67.** $(2x + 3)(20x - 21)$ **69.** $(x - 2y + 1)^2$ **71.** **a.** $(x - 2)(x^2 + 2x + 4)(x + 2)(x^2 - 2x + 4)$
  b. $(x^2 + 4)(x^4 - 4x^2 + 16)$ **73.** $(x - y + z - 2)(x - y - z + 2)$
75. $(a^2 + b^2)(a^4 - a^2b^2 + b^4)(a - b)(a^2 + ab + b^2)(a + b)(a^2 - ab + b^2)$ **77.** $(x - 3)^5$ **79.** $(a - b)(a^2 + ab + b^2 + 1)$
81. $(x - y)(x - y - 4)$

Exercise Set 5, page 57

1. **a.** $\dfrac{x - 1}{x + 2}$ **b.** $\dfrac{2x - 3}{x + 2}$ **3.** $\dfrac{2x^2 + x - 6}{x^2 - 5x + 4}$ **5.** $\dfrac{x^2 + x + 1}{x - 6}$ **7.** $\dfrac{2x - 1}{x + 3}$ **9.** $\dfrac{4x - 2}{x^2 + 2x - 8}$ **11.** $\dfrac{3x - 1}{x^2 - 1}$

13. $\dfrac{7}{x^2 - x - 12}$ **15.** $\dfrac{1}{x+2}$ **17.** $\dfrac{4}{x-1}$ **19.** $\dfrac{x^2 - 7x + 4}{x^2 - 2x}$ **21.** $\dfrac{3x+18}{x+4}$ **23.** $\dfrac{x+2}{x-2}$

25. $\dfrac{1}{2x^2 + 3x + 1}$ **27.** $-\dfrac{x+2}{4x^2}$ **29.** $\dfrac{1}{2-x}$ **31.** $x - y$ **33.** $-\dfrac{2}{a^2 + ah}$ **35.** $\dfrac{1}{z+2}$

37. $\dfrac{ax + 2x + 2a}{ax + 2x + 2a + 4}$ **39.** $\dfrac{-2(2x+h)}{x^2(x+h)^2}$ **41.** $\dfrac{3 - 2x}{(x-1)(x^4 + x)}$ **43.** $\dfrac{(x+4)^2(2x-25)}{(2x-3)^3}$

45. $\dfrac{x + a - 2ax}{(1 - 2x)(1 - 2a)}$ **47.** $2x + 8$

Exercise Set 6, page 61

1. $\dfrac{y - x}{xy}$ **3.** $\dfrac{b - a}{ab}$ **5.** $-\dfrac{x+4}{x^3}$ **7.** $\dfrac{x^2 - 2x - 3}{x^2 - 2x + 1}$ **9.** $\dfrac{x-2}{x+1}$ **11.** $\dfrac{1-x}{2\sqrt{x}}$ **13.** $\dfrac{1-x}{\sqrt{1-2x}}$

15. $\dfrac{x-1}{\sqrt{x^2+4}}$ **17.** $\dfrac{4}{(4-x^2)^{3/2}}$ **19.** $\dfrac{2y - y^3}{(1-y^2)^{3/2}}$ **21.** $\sqrt{3} + \sqrt{2}$ **23.** $9\sqrt{2} + 12$ **25.** $-(\sqrt{x+1} + \sqrt{x+2})$

27. $\dfrac{1}{\sqrt{x+1}}$ **29.** $\dfrac{1}{\sqrt{x+1}+1}$ **31.** $\dfrac{2}{\sqrt{2(x+h)+1} + \sqrt{2x+1}}$ **33.** $\dfrac{4(x^2 - 3)}{9(x^2 - 1)^{4/3}}$ **35.** $\dfrac{2x - x^2}{(1 - 2x)^{5/2}}$

37. $\dfrac{-1}{\sqrt{x}\sqrt{x+h}(\sqrt{x} + \sqrt{x+h})}$ **39.** $\dfrac{x^2 - 3}{3(x^2 - 1)^{4/3}}$ **41.** $\dfrac{-x(x^2 + 5)}{3(x^2 - 1)^{2/3}(x^2 - 4)^{3/2}}$

Review Exercise Set, page 62

1. **a.** $5x^2 + 4x - 9$ **b.** $2x^2 - 2y^2$ **3.** **a.** $10x^2 - 7xy - 12y^2$ **b.** $x^2 - 4y^2$ **c.** $9x^2 - 30x + 25$
d. $x^4 + x^3 - 5x^2 + 7x - 4$ **5.** **a.** $x^2 + 4; R = 7$ **b.** $2x^2 - 6x + 15; R = -59x + 37$
7. **a.** $27a^3 + 108a^2b + 144ab^2 + 64b^3$ **b.** $x^{12} - 18x^{10} + 135x^8 - 540x^6 + 1{,}215x^4 - 1{,}458x^2 + 729$
9. **a.** $-336{,}798a^6b^{10}$ **b.** $2^{16} \cdot 3^5 \cdot 5 \cdot 17 \cdot 19x^8$ **11.** **a.** $(3x + 1)(x - 2)$ **b.** $xy(x - 6y)^2$
13. **a.** $(2x^2 + 3)(x + 2)(x - 2)$ **b.** $(x + 2 + y)(x + 2 - y)$ **15.** **a.** $x(8x + 3y)(3x - 4y)$ **b.** $(a - 3)(a + 3)^2$

17. **a.** $(2 - x + y)(2 + x - y)$ **b.** $(3x^2 + 2y)(2x^2 - 3y)$ **19.** **a.** $\left(x^2 - \dfrac{y}{2}\right)\left(x^4 + \dfrac{x^2 y}{2} + \dfrac{y^2}{4}\right)$

b. $(x^4 + 1)(x^2 + 1)(x + 1)(x - 1)$ **21.** **a.** $3(2a - 3b)^2$ **b.** $(s + 4t^2)(s^2 - 4st^2 + 16t^4)$

23. **a.** $x(x + 1)^{1/2}(x - 1)^{1/2}(2x - 1)(x + 2)$ **b.** $2x(1 - 2x)^{1/3}(3 - 10x)$ **25.** $\dfrac{2}{2 - x}$ **27.** $\dfrac{6}{x - 3}$

29. $-\dfrac{3x + 8}{(x^2 - 4)^{3/2}}$ **31.** $\dfrac{1}{(1 - x^2)^{3/2}}$ **33.** $\dfrac{-8x}{3(x^2 + 1)^{1/3}(x^2 - 1)^{5/3}}$ **35.** **a.** $\dfrac{\sqrt{x+3}+2}{x-1}$ **b.** $\dfrac{a - \sqrt{a^2 - 16}}{4}$

37. **a.** $(x - 2y + 2)(x - 2y - 2)$ **b.** $(x - 1)(x - 2)(x^2 + x + 1)$ **39.** **a.** $(2x - 3y + z + 3)(2x - 3y - z - 3)$

b. $\dfrac{-5}{(2x - 3)^{4/3}(x + 1)^{2/3}}$ **41.** $\dfrac{(3x + 2)^2(6x - 53)}{(2x - 5)^2}$ **43.** $\dfrac{x - 3}{2\sqrt{x+1}(3x - 1)^{4/3}}$

Chapter 3

Exercise Set 2, page 68

1. $\{4\}$ **3.** $\{-11\}$ **5.** $\{-2\}$ **7.** $\{-6\}$ **9.** $\{\frac{7}{2}\}$ **11.** $\{\frac{4}{3}\}$ **13.** $\{\frac{15}{4}\}$ **15.** $\{\frac{1}{7}\}$ **17.** $\{-\frac{11}{2}\}$

19. $\{\frac{26}{29}\}$ **21.** $\{-\frac{2}{7}\}$ **23.** $\{\frac{11}{8}\}$ **25.** $\{-\frac{31}{29}\}$ **27.** $\dfrac{b+d}{a-c}$ **29.** $\dfrac{2y+7}{5y+3}$ **31.** $k = \frac{4}{9}$

Exercise Set 3, page 71

1. $\{2, 1\}$ **3.** $\{-2, -3\}$ **5.** $\{\frac{1}{3}, 4\}$ **7.** $\{\frac{2}{3}, -4\}$ **9.** $\{-\frac{3}{4}, 2\}$ **11.** $\{\frac{3}{2}, -\frac{3}{2}\}$ **13.** $\{\frac{2}{5}, \frac{4}{3}\}$
15. $\{-1, \frac{3}{2}\}$ **17.** $\{\frac{5}{6}, -\frac{3}{2}\}$ **19.** $\{-1, \frac{1}{2}\}$ **21.** $\{5, -2\}$ **23.** $\{1, -\frac{1}{2}\}$ **25.** $\{\frac{4}{3}, \frac{1}{2}\}$ **27.** $\{-2, \frac{3}{2}\}$

29. $\{-\frac{4}{3}, 1\}$ **31.** $\left\{\dfrac{3b}{2a}, -\dfrac{5b}{4a}\right\}$ **33.** $\left\{\dfrac{m}{2}, -\dfrac{m}{3}\right\}$ **35.** $k = 1$ or $k = 3$

Exercise Set 4, page 75

1. $\{2, -6\}$ **3.** $\{3, -1\}$ **5.** $\{2, -5\}$ **7.** $\{8, -3\}$ **9.** $\{2 \pm \sqrt{2}\}$ **11.** $\{4, -\frac{8}{3}\}$ **13.** $\left\{\dfrac{5 \pm \sqrt{37}}{2}\right\}$

15. $\{3, -\frac{3}{2}\}$ **17.** $\{1 \pm \sqrt{3}\}$ **19.** $\left\{\dfrac{-5 \pm \sqrt{61}}{2}\right\}$ **21.** $\left\{\dfrac{1 \pm \sqrt{41}}{4}\right\}$ **23.** $\left\{\dfrac{1 \pm \sqrt{7}}{3}\right\}$ **25.** $\left\{\dfrac{1 \pm \sqrt{61}}{10}\right\}$

27. $\left\{\dfrac{1 \pm \sqrt{13}}{4}\right\}$ **29.** $\left\{\dfrac{3 \pm \sqrt{41}}{4}\right\}$ **31.** $\left\{\dfrac{3 \pm \sqrt{33}}{4}\right\}$ **33.** $\left\{\dfrac{v_0 \pm \sqrt{v_0^2 + 2gs_0}}{g}\right\}$ **35.** $\left\{\dfrac{x(w + \sqrt{mgw})}{mg - w}\right\}$

37. $\left\{-\sqrt{3}\,k, \dfrac{3\sqrt{3}\,k}{2}\right\}$ **39.** $\left\{1, -\dfrac{3k + 2}{2}\right\}$ **41.** $\{77.88, -13.13\}$

Exercise Set 5, page 79

1. **a.** $9 - 2i$ **b.** $-2 - 5i$ **c.** $-1 + 9i$ **d.** $6 - 3i$ **3.** **a.** $18 + i$ **b.** 5 **c.** $-83 - i$

 d. $15 - 5i$ **5.** **a.** $\dfrac{1 - i}{2}$ **b.** $\dfrac{3 + 2i}{13}$ **c.** $-i$ **d.** $\dfrac{7 - 8i}{113}$ **7.** **a.** i **b.** $-i$ **c.** $\dfrac{3 + 29i}{34}$

 d. $\dfrac{9 + 23i}{61}$ **9.** **a.** $2i$ **b.** $9i\sqrt{2}$ **c.** $2i\sqrt{10}$ **d.** -6 **e.** -4 **11.** **a.** $-i$ **b.** i **c.** 1

 d. i **e.** -1 **13.** **a.** $\{\pm 2i\}$ **b.** $\left\{\dfrac{1 \pm i\sqrt{7}}{2}\right\}$ **15.** **a.** $\left\{\dfrac{-3 \pm i\sqrt{3}}{2}\right\}$ **b.** $\left\{\dfrac{3 \pm i}{2}\right\}$

17. **a.** $\left\{\dfrac{2 \pm i\sqrt{14}}{3}\right\}$ **b.** $\left\{\dfrac{2 \pm i\sqrt{6}}{5}\right\}$ **19.** **a.** $\left\{\dfrac{3 \pm i\sqrt{5}}{2}\right\}$ **b.** $\left\{\dfrac{-3 \pm i\sqrt{11}}{5}\right\}$ **21.** **a.** Real and unequal

 b. Imaginary   **23.** **a.** Real and unequal   **b.** Imaginary   **25.** **a.** $-7 - 24i$ **b.** $-117 - 44i$
27. $-20 + 20i$

29. **a.** $\overline{z_1 z_2} = \overline{(a + bi)(c + di)} = \overline{(ac - bd) + (ad + bc)i} = (ac - bd) - (ad + bc)i$

 $\overline{z_1} \cdot \overline{z_2} = \overline{(a + bi)}\,\overline{(c + di)} = (a - bi)(c - di) = ac - adi - bci + bdi^2 = (ac - bd) - (ad + bc)i$

 b.   First calculate z_1/z_2:

$$\frac{z_1}{z_2} = \frac{a + bi}{c + di} = \frac{a + bi}{c + di} \cdot \frac{c - di}{c - di} = \frac{(ac + bd) + (bc - ad)i}{c^2 + d^2}$$

$$\overline{\left(\frac{z_1}{z_2}\right)} = \frac{(ac + bd) + (ad - bc)i}{c^2 + d^2}$$

$$\frac{\overline{z_1}}{\overline{z_2}} = \frac{a - bi}{c - di} = \frac{a - bi}{c - di} \cdot \frac{c + di}{c + di} = \frac{(ac + bd) + (ad - bc)i}{c^2 + d^2}$$

Exercise Set 6, page 86

1. $\{\pm 1, \pm\frac{3}{2}\}$ **3.** $\{\frac{1}{3}, -\frac{1}{2}\}$ **5.** $\{\pm 1, \pm 2i\}$ **7.** $\{\pm 2, \pm\frac{3}{2}\}$ **9.** $\{-1, 27\}$ **11.** $\{5\}$ **13.** $\{12, -2\}$
15. $\{-8\}$ **17.** $\{\frac{6}{5}\}$ **19.** $\{3, \frac{5}{2}\}$ **21.** $\{4, \frac{1}{2}\}$ **23.** $\{0, \frac{17}{2}\}$ **25.** $\{-5\}$ **27.** No solution   **29.** $\{2\}$
31. $\{-3\}$ **33.** $\{5\}$ **35.** $\{-3, -\frac{4}{3}\}$ **37.** $\{3, \frac{9}{5}\}$ **39.** $\{\frac{1}{3}, -2\}$ **41.** $\{3, -1\}$ **43.** $\{6\}$ **45.** $\{-3\}$
47. $\{\pm\sqrt{\sqrt{3} - 1}, \pm i\sqrt{\sqrt{3} + 1}\}$ **49.** $\{\pm\frac{1}{8}, \pm 8i/27\}$

Exercise Set 7, page 94

1. **a.** Let t = time train A travels, $t - \frac{1}{2}$ = time train B travels, $60t$ = distance train A travels,
 $90(t - \frac{1}{2})$ = distance train B travels   **b.** $60t = 90(t - \frac{1}{2})$
 c. $t = 1\frac{1}{2}$ hours, so distance from Washington = 90 miles
3. **a.** Let x = speed of jogger, $2x$ = speed of cyclist, $4/x$ = time of jogger, $4/2x$ = time of cyclist
 b. $4/2x = (4/x) - (1/4)$ **c.** $x = 8$ kilometers per hour
5. **a.** Let x = width, $2x$ = length, perimeter = $2x + 2(2x) = 6x$ **b.** $2.50(6x) + 1.00x = 584$
 c. $x = 36.5$ feet, $2x = 73$ feet
7. **a.** Let x = width, $2x - 3$ = length   **b.** $2x + 2(2x - 3) = 72$ **c.**   Width = 13 feet, length = 23 feet
9. **a.** Let x = smallest number, $x + 2$ = next, $x + 4$ = next   **b.** $x + (x + 2) + (x + 4) = 375$ **c.**   123, 125, 127

11. a. Let x = grade on fourth exam   **b.** $\dfrac{3(78) + x}{4} = 80$ **c.** $x = 86$

13. a. Let x = number of grandstand tickets sold, $22{,}796 - x$ = number of bleacher tickets sold
b. $3.50x + 2.00(22{,}796 - x) = 63{,}943$ **c.** 12,234 grandstand, 10,562 bleacher

15. a. Let x = necessary average speed, speeder's time to reach state line = $20/80 = 1/4$ hour, patrolman's time to overtake speeder = $20/x$ hours   **b.** $20/x = (1/4) - (1/12)$ **c.** $x = 120$ miles per hour

17. a. Let x = amount of 50% solution, $200 + x$ = amount of final mixture, $0.50x$ = amount of pure alcohol in 50% solution, $0.25(200)$ = amount of pure alcohol in 25% solution, $0.30(200 + x)$ = amount of alcohol in final mixture
b. $0.50x + 0.25(200) = 0.30(200 + x)$ **c.** $x = 50$ cubic centimeters

19. a. Let t = time in seconds to strike the ground   **b.** $16t^2 + 1{,}200t - 6{,}400 = 0$ **c.** $t = 5$ seconds

21. a. Let x = original price, $0.70x$ = reduced price   **b.** $70x = 87.50$ **c.** $x = \$125$

23. a. Let x = amount invested at $5\frac{1}{2}\%$, $10{,}000 - x$ = amount invested at 7%   **b.** $0.055x + 0.07(10{,}000 - x) = 652$
c. \$3,200 at $5\frac{1}{2}\%$, \$6,800 at 7%

25. a. Let x = number of pounds to be added, $0.30x$ = cost of fattening each calf, $0.42(530 + x)$ = selling price
b. $0.42(530 + x) - (0.30x + 150) = 150$ **c.** $x = 645$ pounds

27. a. Let x = number of hours plumber worked, $t - 1$ = number of hours assistant worked, $9t$ = amount received by plumber, $5(t - 1)$ = amount received by assistant   **b.** $9t + 5(t - 1) + 25 + 12 = 81$
c. $t = 3\frac{1}{2}$ hours for plumber, $t - 1 = 2\frac{1}{2}$ hours for assistant

29. a. Let n = the smaller integer, $n + 2$ = the larger   **b.** $\dfrac{1}{n} + \dfrac{1}{n + 2} = \dfrac{5}{12}$ **c.** $n = 4,\ n + 2 = 6$

31. a. Let x = number in excess of 40, $40 + x$ = total number, $15 - 0.25x$ = price of each ticket
b. $(40 + x)(15 - 0.25x) = 625$ **c.** $x = 10$, so 50 people go

33. a. Let x = width of picture, $x + 10$ = height of picture, $x + 4$ = overall width, $x + 16$ = overall height
b. $(x + 4)(x + 16) = 468$ **c.** width = 12, height = 22

35. a. Let x = number in excess of 200, $200 + x$ = total number, $10 - 0.02x$ = price of each ticket
b. $(200 + x)(10 - 0.02x) = 2{,}450$ **c.** $x = 150$, so 350 people go

37. a. Let x = number of 1¢ fare reductions, $200{,}000 + 7{,}500x$ = average daily ridership, $0.50 - 0.01x$ = fare
b. $(200{,}000 + 7{,}500x)(0.50 - 0.01x) = 110{,}200$ **c.** $x = 12$, so fare = 38¢ and average ridership = 290,000

39. a. Let x = number of gallons of 96-octane gasoline, $200 - x$ = number of gallons of 87-octane gasoline
b. $0.96x + 0.87(200 - x) = 0.93(200)$ **c.** $133\frac{1}{3}$ gallons 96-octane gasoline, $66\frac{2}{3}$ gallons 87-octane gasoline

41. a. Let x = number of days to fill reservoir, $\frac{1}{8}$ = fractional part first pump can do per day, $\frac{1}{6}$ = fractional part second pump can do per day   **b.** $(x/8) + (3/6) = 1$ **c.** $x = 4$ days

43. a. Let x = distance from B to D, $150 - x$ = distance from D to C, $\sqrt{x^2 + (120)^2}$ = distance from A to D
b. $4\sqrt{x^2 + (120)^2} + 2(150 - x) = 720$ **c.** Two solutions: $x = 50$ feet or 90 feet

45. a. $.0024t/1{,}990$ **b.** 99.5 minutes

Exercise Set 8, page 100

1. $\{x:\ x < 1\}$

3. $\{x:\ x < 2\}$

5. $\{x:\ x < -\frac{7}{3}\}$

7. $\{x:\ x < 2\}$

9. $\{x:\ x > \frac{7}{3}\}$

11. $\{x:\ x > -\frac{16}{5}\}$

13. $\{x:\ x > -\frac{7}{12}\}$

15. $\{x:\ x > -\frac{6}{7}\}$

17. $\{x:\ 2 < x < 3\}$

19. $\{x:\ -2 < x < 2\}$

21. $\{x:\ \frac{2}{3} < x \le \frac{10}{3}\}$

23. $\{x:\ -\frac{1}{2} \le x \le \frac{3}{2}\}$

25. $\{x:\ 1.495 < x < 1.505\}$

27. $25 \le {}^\circ C \le 30$

29. 6 inches $\le$ Width $\le$ 15 inches

31. $\frac{-15}{8} < x \le \frac{5}{2}$

33. $\{x:\ x < 2\} \cup \{x:\ x > 3\}$

35. 80

Exercise Set 9, page 104

3. $|a|^2 = |a| \cdot |a| = \begin{cases} a \cdot a = a^2 & \text{if } a \geq 0 \\ (-a) \cdot (-a) = a^2 & \text{if } a < 0 \end{cases}$

$|a|^3 = |a| \cdot |a| \cdot |a| = \begin{cases} a \cdot a \cdot a = a^3 & \text{if } a \geq 0 \\ (-a) \cdot (-a) \cdot (-a) = -a^3 & \text{if } a < 0 \end{cases}$

So $|a|^3 \neq a^3$ if $a < 0$.

5. $\{x: \ -3 < x < 11\}$ 7. $\{x: \ -\frac{3}{2} < x < -\frac{1}{2}\}$ 9. $\{x: \ x < 1\} \cup \{x: \ x > 3\}$ 11. $\{x: \ -\frac{2}{3} \leq x \leq 2\}$
13. $\{x: \ x < -\frac{1}{2}\} \cup \{x: \ x > \frac{7}{2}\}$ 15. $\{x: \ x < \frac{1}{2}\} \cup \{x: \ x > 2\}$ 17. $\{x: \ x \leq b - 3\} \cup \{x: \ x \geq b + 3\}$
19. $\{x: \ 1 \leq x \leq 4\}$ 21. $\{x: \ -13 < x < 23\}$ 23. $\{x: \ 1.99 < x < 2.01\}$ 25. $\{x: \ x < \frac{9}{8}\} \cup \{x: \ x > \frac{15}{8}\}$
27. **a.** $|x - 2| < 1$ **b.** $0 < |x - 2| < 1$ 29. $|a^{-1}||a| = |a^{-1}a| = |1| = 1$.   So $|a^{-1}| = |a|^{-1}$.
31. $|a + b + c| = |(a + b) + c| \leq |a + b| + |c| \leq |a| + |b| + |c|$ 33. $\{x: \ a - \delta < x < a + \delta\}$
35. $\{x: \ -4 \leq x \leq 1, x \neq -\frac{3}{2}\}$

Exercise Set 10, page 109

1. $(-1, 3)$ 3. $[-1, 4]$ 5. $(-2, 2)$ 7. $(-4, 3)$ 9. $[-\frac{2}{3}, 1]$ 11. $(-\infty, -1) \cup (2, \infty)$
13. $(-\infty, -2] \cup [\frac{2}{3}, \infty)$ 15. $(-2, 3)$ 17. $(-\infty, -2) \cup (3, \infty)$ 19. $[-4, \frac{1}{2}] \cup [3, \infty)$
21. $\{x: \ -3 < x < 3, \ x \neq -1\}$ 23. $(-\infty, -5) \cup (-1, 3)$ 25. $(-2, -\frac{3}{2}) \cup (3, 5)$ 27. $(-\infty, -5) \cup (2, \infty)$
29. $(-\infty, \frac{3}{2}) \cup (5, \infty)$ 31. $(-6, 0) \cup (1, 2)$ 33. $(-\frac{3}{2}, -1) \cup (3, 4)$ 35. $\{k: \ k \leq -\frac{8}{5}\} \cup \{k: \ k > 0\}$
37. $\{c: \ -3 < c < 1\}$ 39. $(-\infty, -\frac{5}{3}) \cup (-1, \frac{3}{2}) \cup (2, \infty)$ 41. $\{t: \ 0 \leq t \leq 3\}$ 43. $d_{\min} = 10$ inches

Review Exercise Set, page 110

1. **a.** $\{\frac{14}{13}\}$ **b.** $\{\frac{29}{36}\}$ 3. **a.** $\{\frac{65}{36}\}$ **b.** $\{\frac{38}{21}\}$ 5. **a.** $\{\frac{3}{2}, -\frac{5}{3}\}$ **b.** $\{\frac{3}{4}, \frac{4}{3}\}$ 7. **a.** $\{1, 3\}$

b. $\left\{\dfrac{1 \pm \sqrt{13}}{3}\right\}$ 9. **a.** $\left\{\dfrac{5 \pm i\sqrt{7}}{4}\right\}$ **b.** $\left\{\dfrac{2 \pm i\sqrt{2}}{3}\right\}$ 11. **a.** $\{\frac{4}{5}, -\frac{2}{3}\}$ **b.** $\left\{\dfrac{2 \pm \sqrt{13}}{3}\right\}$

13. **a.** $\{\frac{31}{14}\}$ **b.** $\{-\frac{5}{3}\}$ 15. **a.** $\{4, -2\}$ **b.** $\{1, 2\}$ 17. **a.** $\{-\frac{13}{2}\}$ **b.** $\{-1, -2\}$ 19. **a.** $\{6\}$

b. $\{1\}$ 21. **a.** $\{\pm 2i, \pm\frac{2}{3}\}$ **b.** $\{\frac{3}{2}, -\frac{4}{3}\}$ 23. **a.** $23 + 2i$ **b.** $\dfrac{6 + 17i}{25}$ **c.** $-236 - 115i$

25. **a.** $\left\{\dfrac{5 \pm i\sqrt{7}}{4}\right\}$ **b.** $\left\{\dfrac{-1 \pm \sqrt{19}}{3}\right\}$ 27. **a.** Imaginary   **b.** Real and unequal   **c.** Real and equal

d. Imaginary   29. Width = 13 feet, Length = 19 feet   31. 117 kilometers   33. $8,000 at 5%,
$13,000 at 6%   35. $4\frac{2}{3}$ gallons   37. M's speed = 55 miles per hour, N's speed = 60 miles per hour
39. $2\frac{1}{2}$ inches   41. 20 kilograms   43. **a.** $[-1, 5)$ **b.** $(\frac{3}{8}, \frac{27}{8})$ 45. **a.** $(-3, -2] \cup (3, \infty)$
b. $(-\infty, -4) \cup (1, 2)$ 47. **a.** $(-\infty, -4] \cup [2, \frac{10}{3}]$ **b.** $(-1, 3) \cup (5, \infty)$ 49. **a.** $[1, \frac{5}{3}]$
b. $(-\infty, -1) \cup (5, \infty)$ 51. **a.** $|x - 5| < 2$ **b.** $0 < |x + 3| < 1$ 53. $15 \leq {}^\circ C \leq 30$

55. **a.** $\{k \pm i\sqrt{k^2 - 1}\}$ **b.** $\dfrac{2ab}{a + b}$ 57. $\{k: \ k \leq \frac{2}{5}\} \cup \{k: \ k \geq 2\}$ 59. $\{-2\}$ 61. $\{\frac{1}{4}, -1\}$

63. $(-1, 0] \cup (1, 3) \cup [7, \infty)$ 65. 37, $6.80   67. 60 kph, 80 kph   69. 135, $8

Cumulative Review Exercise Set I (Chapters 1–3), page 115

1. $\dfrac{4 - x}{2x - 3}$

3. If $a < b$ and $c > 0$, then $ac < bc$. Also, if $c < d$ and $b > 0$, $bc < bd$. By transitivity, $ac < bd$. Suppose $a = -2, b = 4$, $c = -3, d = -2$. Then $-2 < 4$ and $-3 < -2$, but $(-2)(-3) = 6 \not< (-2)(4) = -8$.

5. **a.** $\frac{79}{370}$

b. Let $r_1 = \dfrac{-b + \sqrt{b^2 - 4ac}}{2a}, r_2 = \dfrac{-b - \sqrt{b^2 - 4ac}}{2a}$

$r_1 + r_2 = -b/a$, which is rational
$r_1 \cdot r_2 = c/a$, which is rational

7. $\dfrac{25(x^2+1)}{(3x+4)(4x-3)}$ **9.** $2\frac{1}{2}$ feet   **11. a.** $\dfrac{2}{\sqrt{2x+2h-3}+\sqrt{2x-3}}$ **b.** $\dfrac{17\sqrt{6}}{12}$ **13. a.** $(x+2)(x-2)(3-xy)$

b. $2x(9x+8y)(4x-3y)$ **15. a.** $s=\dfrac{Fr+1}{r-2F}$ **b.** $t=\dfrac{-v_0+\sqrt{v_0^2+2gs}}{g}$ **17. a.** $\dfrac{4a^7b}{125}$ **b.** 6×10^2

19. $-\dfrac{x^2+3}{3(x^2-1)^{5/3}}$ **21. a.** $(-3,1)$ **b.** $(-11,-5]\cup(1,5]$ **23.** 15 hours, 10 hours

25. 90 suits sold during the sale; regular price = \$210

Chapter 4

Exercise Set 2, page 121

1. a.

x	0	1	3	-1
y	1	2	4	0

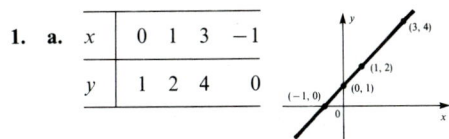

b.

x	0	1	2	-1
y	-2	-1	0	-3

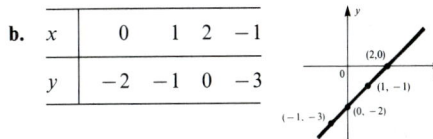

3. a.

x	0	1	2	-1
y	0	2	4	-2

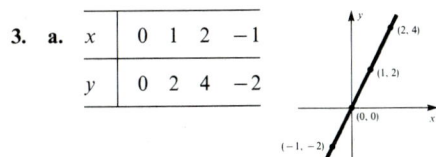

b.

x	0	1	2	-1
y	3	4	5	2

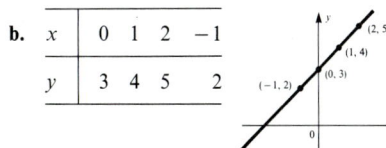

5. a. $y=1-x$

x	0	1	2	-1
y	1	0	-1	2

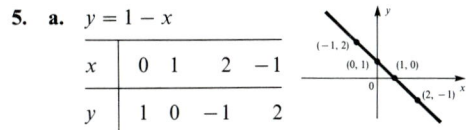

b. $y=x-2$

x	0	1	2	-1
y	-2	-1	0	-3

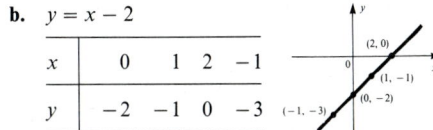

7. a. $y=\dfrac{5x-4}{3}$

x	0	1	2	-1
y	$-\frac{4}{3}$	$\frac{1}{3}$	2	-3

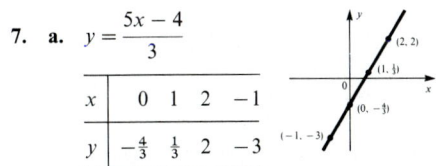

b. $y=-\dfrac{4x+7}{5}$

x	0	1	2	-1
y	$-\frac{7}{5}$	$-\frac{11}{5}$	-3	$-\frac{3}{5}$

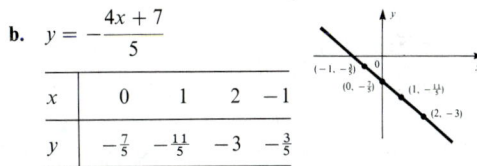

9. a.

x	0	1	2	-1
y	0	1	2	-1

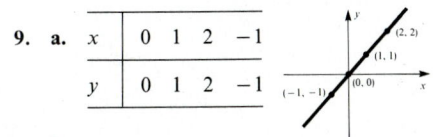

b. $y=-x$

x	0	1	2	-1
y	0	-1	-2	1

11. a. $x=3$

b. $y=-1$

13. a.

x	0	±1	±2	±3
y	0	1	4	9

b.

x	0	±1	±2	±3
y	4	3	0	-5

15. a. $y = \pm\sqrt{x}$

x	0	1	4	9
y	0	± 1	± 2	± 3

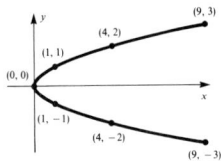

b. $y = \pm\sqrt{25 - x^2}$

x	0	± 3	± 4	± 5
y	± 5	± 4	± 3	0

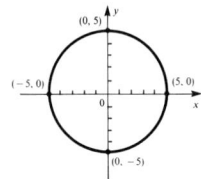

17. a.

x	0	± 1	± 2	± 3
y	1	$\frac{1}{2}$	$\frac{1}{5}$	$\frac{1}{10}$

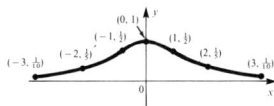

b.

x	0	± 1	± 2	± 3	± 4	± 5	± 6
y	6	$\sqrt{35}$	$\sqrt{32}$	$\sqrt{27}$	$\sqrt{20}$	$\sqrt{11}$	0

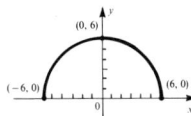

19. a.

x	0	1	2	3	-1	-2	-3	0.5	-0.5
y	0	0	6	24	0	-6	-24	-0.375	0.375

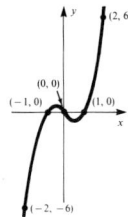

b.

x	1	2	3	-1	-2	-3	$\frac{1}{2}$	$-\frac{1}{2}$
y	0	$\frac{1}{2}$	$\frac{2}{3}$	2	$\frac{3}{2}$	$\frac{4}{3}$	-1	3

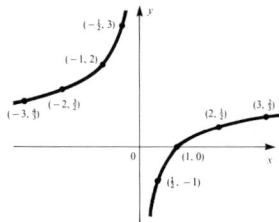

21. a. $x + y = \pm 1$
$y = 1 - x$ or $y = -1 - x$

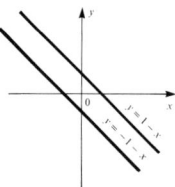

b. If $x \geq 0, y \geq 0$, then $y = 1 - x$.
If $x \geq 0, y < 0$, then $y = x - 1$.
If $x < 0, y \geq 0$, then $y = 1 + x$.
If $x < 0, y < 0$, then $y = -1 - x$.

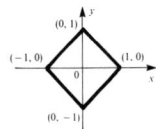

Exercise Set 3, page 128

1. a. -1 **b.** 1 **c.** -5 **d.** 9   **3. a.** 3 **b.** -1 **c.** 0 **d.** $\frac{1}{2}$ **5. a.** 1 **b.** 2 **c.** 0
d. $\sqrt{2x - 1}$ **7. a.** $\frac{7}{2}$ **b.** $-\frac{4}{11}$ **c.** $-\frac{8}{39}$ **d.** $-\frac{13}{6}$ **9. a.** -2 **b.** 4 **c.** $2a^2 - 4$

d. $2x^2 + 4x - 2$ **e.** $2x^2 + 4hx + 2h^2 - 4$ **11. a.** 0 **b.** $\sqrt{2t - t^2}$ **c.** $\dfrac{\sqrt{t^2 - 1}}{|t|}$

d. $\sqrt{1 - t^2 - 2t(\Delta t) - (\Delta t)^2}$ **13. a.** Domain $= R$, range $= R$
b. Domain $= \{x:\ x \neq 0\}$, range $= \{y:\ y \neq 0\}$ **15. a.** Domain $= \{x:\ |x| \leq 1\}$, range $= \{y:\ 0 \leq y \leq 1\}$
b. Domain $= \{x:\ x \neq 4\}$, range $= \{y:\ y \neq 1\}$ **17. a.** 4 **b.** -1 **c.** -1 **d.** 0   **19. a.** 1

b. 1 **c.** 0 **d.** 0   **21.** $-\dfrac{3}{1 + h}$ **23. a.** $(-\infty, -2) \cup [1, \infty)$ **b.** $\{t: |t| \geq 2\}$

25. $P = 2w + 24$ **27.** $C = \pi d$ **29.** $A = 10{,}000(1.07)^t$ **31. a.** $2\pi r^3$ **b.** $4\pi r^2$ **c.** $6\pi r^2$

33. $f(1/x) = \dfrac{1/x + 2}{2/x + 1} = \dfrac{1 + 2x}{2 + x} = \dfrac{1}{f(x)}$ **35. a.** Even **b.** Odd **c.** Neither **d.** Neither **e.** Even

37. a. $f(x) = 200,000 - 40,000x$ **b.** Domain $= \{x: \ 0 \le x \le 5\}$ **39.** $(-5, -2] \cup [4, \infty)$ **41.** $A = \dfrac{s^2\sqrt{3}}{4}$

43. $V = 2\pi r^2\sqrt{a^2 - r^2}$ **45.** $A = \dfrac{4(10 - h)^2}{25}$ **47.** $f(x) = \begin{cases} 0.015x \text{ if } x \le 1000 \\ 0.01x + 5 \text{ if } x > 1000 \end{cases}$ **49.** $V = \dfrac{\pi r^2}{3}(a + \sqrt{a^2 - r^2})$

51. Since we must have $x \ge 0$, it follows that $f(x) \ge 1$. So the range is contained in the given set. Now let k be any number greater than or equal to 1. Solving $1 + \sqrt{x} = k$ yields $x = (k - 1)^2$, and this is in the domain. Thus, every k in the set $\{y: \ y \ge 1\}$ is the image of an x in the domain. So $\{y: \ y \ge 1\}$ is the range.

Exercise Set 4, page 134

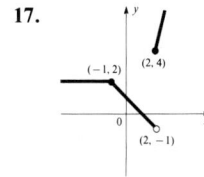

19. a. Function **b.** Not a function **c.** Function **d.** Function **e.** Function **f.** Not a function
21. Increasing on $(-\infty, -10], [-6, 0], [4, 8]$; decreasing on $[-10, -6], [0, 4], [8, \infty)$
23. $y_1 = \sqrt{4 - x^2}; y_2 = -\sqrt{4 - x^2}$

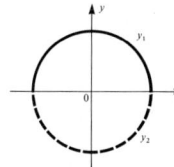

25. $y_1 = \sqrt{x^2 - 1}, \quad x \ge 1; y_2 = -\sqrt{x^2 - 1}, \quad x \ge 1$ **27.**

Exercise Set 5, page 139

1. c, e
15. Domain $= \{x: \ x \ne 0\}$; range $= \{y: \ y \ne 0\}$; ϕ is 1–1
17. Function ϕ is not 1–1, since, for example, $\phi(2) = \phi(-2)$.

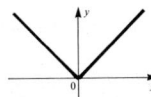

21. Domain $= \{t: \quad t \neq -1\}$; f is 1–1

23. ϕ is not 1–1

25. Domain $= \{x: \quad x \geq 1\}$; h is 1–1

27. b. Restricted domain $= \{x: \quad x \geq 0\}$

29. $f(-1) = f(1) = f(4)$; so f is not 1–1

31. Let f be increasing. Suppose $x_1 \neq x_2$. We may suppose, in particular, that $x_1 < x_2$. Then $f(x_1) < f(x_2)$, and hence $f(x_1) \neq f(x_2)$. So f is 1–1. A similar argument applies if f is decreasing.

35. b. No. There is no x for which $f(x) = 1$.

Exercise Set 6, page 146

1. $(f \circ g)(x) = 2x$; $(g \circ f)(x) = 2x - 1$ **3.** $(f \circ g)(x) = 1 - 3x$; $(g \circ f)(x) = 7 - 3x$

5. $(f \circ g)(x) = 2x^2 + 8x + 8$; $(g \circ f)(x) = 2x^2 + 2$ **7.** $(f \circ g)(x) = \dfrac{x-3}{x-2}$; $(g \circ f)(x) = -\dfrac{x+1}{3x+2}$

9. $(f \circ g)(x) = 4x^2 - 16x + 16$; $(g \circ f)(x) = 2x^2 - 4x - 1$ **11.** $(f \circ g)(x) = \dfrac{2}{2-x}$; $(g \circ f)(x) = \dfrac{2x-2}{x}$

13. $(f \circ g)(x) = \sqrt{x^2 - 1}$, domain $= \{x: \quad |x| \geq 1\}$; $(g \circ f)(x) = x - 1$, domain $= \{x: \quad x \geq 1\}$

15. $(f \circ g)(x) = 2\sqrt{x^2 - 3x + 2}$, domain $= \{x: \quad x \geq 2\} \cup \{x: \quad x \leq 1\}$; $(g \circ f)(x) = 2\sqrt{x^2 - 1} - 3$, domain $= \{x: \quad |x| \geq 1\}$

17. **a.** $\dfrac{2x^2 - 9}{5}$ **b.** $\dfrac{4x^2 - 12x - 66}{25}$ **c.** x **d.** x **e.** $\dfrac{25x^2 + 30x - 3}{4}$ **19.** $f^{-1}(x) = \dfrac{x-5}{2}$

21. $g^{-1}(x) = 2x - 8$ **23.** $G^{-1}(x) = \dfrac{7x+4}{3}$ **25.** $g^{-1}(x) = \dfrac{1 - 2x}{x}$, $x \neq 0$ **27.** $G^{-1}(x) = x^2$, $x \geq 0$

29. $h^{-1}(t) = \dfrac{3t}{1-t}$, $t \neq 1$ **31.** $F^{-1}(z) = \sqrt{z^2 + 4}$, $z \geq 0$

33. If $f(x_1) = f(x_2)$, then $\dfrac{x_1 + 1}{3} = \dfrac{x_2 + 1}{3}$, so that $x_1 + 1 = x_2 + 1$ and $x_1 = x_2$. Thus f is 1–1, and $f^{-1}(x) = 3x - 1$.

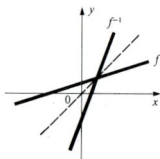

35. If $f(x_1) = f(x_2)$, then $2x_1 - 5 = 2x_2 - 5$, and so $x_1 = x_2$. Thus, f is $1 - 1$, and $f^{-1}(x) = (x + 5)/2$.

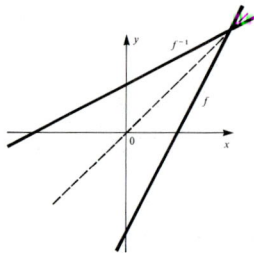

37. If $h(x_1) = h(x_2)$, then $\dfrac{3x_1 + 4}{5} = \dfrac{3x_2 + 4}{5}$, so that $3x_1 + 4 = 3x_2 + 4$ and $x_1 = x_2$. So h is 1–1, and $h^{-1}(x) = \dfrac{5x - 4}{3}$.

39. a.

b.

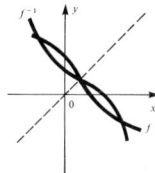

41. $f^{-1}(x) = \sqrt{x+4}$ on domain $\{x: \ x \geq -4\}$ **43.** $h^{-1}(x) = 1 + \sqrt{x+1}$ on domain $\{x: \ x \geq -1\}$

45. $f^{-1}(x) = \dfrac{bx - a}{1 - x}$, $x \neq 1$; domain of $f = \{x: \ x \neq -b\}$; range of $f = \{y: \ y \neq 1\}$; domain of $f^{-1} = \{x: \ x \neq 1\}$;

range of $f^{-1} = \{y: \ y \neq -b\}$

47. $(h \circ f)(t) = \dfrac{62{,}784}{(6{,}400 + 4t - 0.0001t^2)^2}$

Exercise Set 7, page 152

1. $u = kv$ **3.** $z = kxy$ **5.** $s = k/\sqrt{t}$ **7.** $F = km_1m_2/r^2$ **9.** $s = kt^2$ **11.** $\frac{20}{3}$ **13.** 12   **15.** 336
17. 32 pounds   **19.** 22 amperes   **21.** $k = \pi/3$; $V = 1/3\pi r^2 h$; $V = 120\pi$ **23.** 6°F per minute
25. 7 cases per day   **27.** Approximately 671 days   **29.** 375 pounds   **31.** 302.5 : 1

Review Exercise Set, page 154

1. **a.**

x	0	1	2	-1	-2
y	-1	1	3	-3	-5

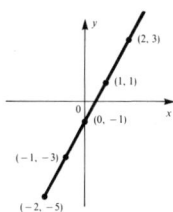

b.

x	0	1	2	3	-1	-2
y	$\frac{4}{3}$	$\frac{2}{3}$	0	$-\frac{2}{3}$	2	$\frac{8}{3}$

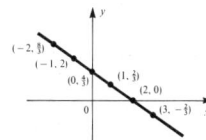

3. **a.**

x	0	2	4	-2
y	-2	3	8	-7

b.

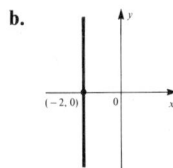

5. **a.**

x	0	± 1	± 2	± 3
$f(x)$	1	0	-3	-8

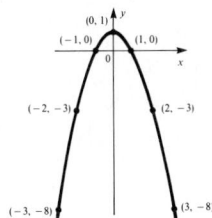

b.

x	0	1	-3	-8
$g(x)$	0	1	-1	-2

7. **a.** -1 **b.** 0   **c.** 15   **d.** $a^2 - 1$ **e.** $x^2 + 2xh + h^2 - 1$ **9.** Domain $\{t: \ t \neq 3\}$ **a.** -1 **b.** $\frac{4}{5}$

c. $\dfrac{2}{1 - 3t}$ **d.** $\dfrac{2(t + \Delta t)}{t + \Delta t - 3}$ **11.** **a.** 49   **b.** 0   **c.** 4   **d.** 7   **e.** 3   **13.** $-\dfrac{x + 2}{4x^2}$

17. $d = s\sqrt{2}$ **19.** $A = 5{,}000(1.06)^t$ **21.** $C(x) = 0.30x + 30.50$ **25.** **a.** Even   **b.** Odd   **c.** Neither

d. Odd   **e.** Even   **27.** $(\phi \circ \psi)(x) = -\dfrac{4x + 13}{35}$; $(\psi \circ \phi)(x) = \dfrac{26 - 4x}{35}$

29. $(f \circ g)(t) = -t - 2$, domain $= \{t: \ t \le 1\}$; $(g \circ f)(t) = \sqrt{4 - t^2}$, domain $= \{t: \ |t| \le 2\}$ **31.** $(g \circ f)(x) = \dfrac{T}{Ak(1 + ax)}$

33. $f^{-1}(x) = \dfrac{3x - 7}{5}$ **35.** $h^{-1}(t) = \dfrac{2 - 5t}{3}$ **37.** $g^{-1}(x) = \dfrac{2x^2 + 1}{x^2}, \quad x > 0$ **39.** $h^{-1}(x) = \dfrac{3x + 2}{x - 1}, \quad x \ne 1$

41. a. Not a function   **b.** Function; no inverse   **c.** Function; no inverse   **d.** Function; has inverse
e. Not a function   **f.** Function; no inverse

43. $f^{-1}(x) = x^2 - 1, \quad x \ge 0$

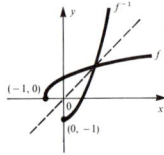

45. $\frac{80}{9}$ **47.** $S = 4\pi r^2; \ 100\pi$

49. a.

x	0	± 1	± 2	± 3
y	$\pm 3\sqrt{2}$ ≈ 4.2	± 4	$\pm\sqrt{10}$ ≈ 3.2	0

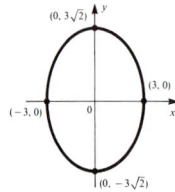

b.

x	0	1	2	-1	-2	-3
$f(x)$	2	0	-4	2	0	-4

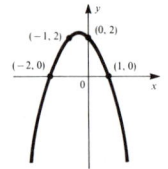

51. a. 4   **b.** -1 **c.** 2   **d.** 0   **e.** 1   **53.** $A = \dfrac{\pi s^2}{12}$

55. $f(3) = f(1)$, so f is not 1–1. On $\{x: \ x > 2\}$, $f^{-1}(x) = 2 + \dfrac{2}{\sqrt{x}}$.   **57.** Strength increased by factor of 16.

Chapter 5

Exercise Set 2, page 165

1. a. 5

b. $\frac{3}{4}$

c. $-\frac{7}{5}$

d. -1

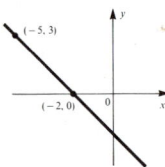

3. $m_{AB} = -\frac{1}{4}, \ m_{BC} = -\frac{7}{3}, \ m_{AC} = 1$

5. 5 units horizontal; 4 units vertical   **7.** $y = 7$

9. $m_{AB} = \frac{3}{4}$, $m_{BC} = \frac{1}{4}$, $m_{CD} = \frac{3}{4}$, $m_{AD} = \frac{1}{4}$; parallelogram, since opposite sides have same slope

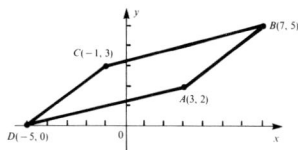

11. $y + 2x - 2 = 0$ **13.** $8x + 3y - 1 = 0$ **15.** $4x - 3y + 12 = 0$ **17.** $2x - 3y + 6 = 0$
19. $m = 3$, $b = -4$

21. $m = -\frac{1}{3}$, $b = \frac{7}{6}$

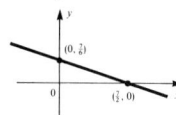

23. $m = \frac{3}{5}$, $b = -\frac{4}{5}$

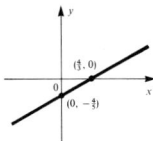

25. **a.** $y = 2$ **b.** $x = 3$
    c. $y + 3 = 0$ **d.** $x + 1 = 0$

27. Since $(a, 0)$ and $(0, b)$ are on the line, the slope is $-b/a$. So the equation is

$$y = \left(-\frac{b}{a}\right)x + b$$
$$ay = -bx + ab$$
$$bx + ay = ab$$
$$\frac{x}{a} + \frac{y}{b} = 1$$

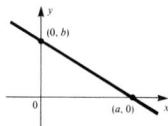

29. Let $A = (2, 2)$, $B = (-1, -7)$, $C = (3, 5)$. Method 1: $m_{AB} = 3$, $m_{BC} = 3$, so they are collinear. Method 2: Equation of line AB is $3x - y - 4 = 0$, and C satisfies this equation.
31. Let $A = (0, -3)$, $B = (2, 1)$, $C = (-1, -5)$. Method 1: $m_{AB} = 2$, $m_{BC} = 2$, so they are collinear. Method 2: Equation of line AB is $y = 2x - 3$, and C satisfies this equation.
33. **a.** $3x - 2y + C = 0$ has slope $\frac{3}{2}$. **b.** $C = 17$; $3x - 2y + 17 = 0$
35. Method 1 (point–slope): $y + 4 = \frac{1}{2}(x - 3)$ Method 2 (method of Problem 33): $x - 2y + C = 0$
                    $x - 2y - 11 = 0$ $C = -11$
                                                                    $x - 2y - 11 = 0$

37. All have slope $\frac{2}{3}$; the lines are all parallel.

Exercise Set 3, page 168

1. a. 5 **b.** $(\frac{1}{2}, 5)$ **3. a.** $\sqrt{13}$ **b.** $(1, \frac{1}{2})$ **5. a.** 13 **b.** $(\frac{1}{2}, 5)$ **7. a.** 17 **b.** $(-\frac{2}{3}, -1)$
9. $x = 11$ or -5 **11.** $(5, -11)$ **13.** Let $A = (-2, 4)$, $B = (3, -6)$, $C = (6, -2)$. Then $\overline{AB}^2 = 125$, $\overline{AC}^2 = 100$,
    $\overline{BC}^2 = 25$. So $\overline{AB}^2 = \overline{AC}^2 + \overline{BC}^2$ **15.** Each side $= 10$ units **17.** $2x - y - 7 = 0$
19. $y = 1$, $3x + y + 3 = 0$, $6x - 5y + 13 = 0$ **21.** $(3, -3), (-1, 3), (5, 7)$ **23.** $d(x) = \sqrt{5x^2 - 18x + 18}$

Exercise Set 4, page 172

1. $3x - 4y - 27 = 0$ **3.** $x + 3y - 5 = 0$ **5.** $5x - 2y = 0$ **7.** $3x + 4y - 22 = 0$ **9.** $3x + 4y - 8 = 0$
11. $x - y - 10 = 0$ **13.** $x - 3 = 0$ **15.** $x - 2 = 0$ **17.** $4x + 10y + 15 = 0$
19. Let $A = (2, 1)$, $B = (6, 9)$, $C = (-2, 3)$. Then $m_{AB} = 2$, $m_{AC} = -\frac{1}{2}$, so angle A is a right angle.
21. Let $A = (2, 2)$, $B = (0, -1)$, $C = (-4, 1)$, $D = (-2, 4)$. Then $m_{AB} = \frac{3}{2}$, $m_{BC} = -\frac{1}{2}$, $m_{CD} = \frac{3}{2}$, $m_{AD} = -\frac{1}{2}$, so opposite sides are parallel.
23. $3x - 4y + C = 0$; $9x - 12y + 32 = 0$ **25.** $4x - 3y - 16 = 0$
27. $2x + y + 1 = 0$, $5x - 9y + 49 = 0$, $x - 11y + 47 = 0$ **29.** $x - 2y + 6 = 0$ **31.** $2x + 2y - 3 = 0$
33. Tangent: $4x - y - 5 = 0$; normal: $x + 4y - 14 = 0$

Exercise Set 5, page 175

1. Line with slope 3 and y intercept -2

3. Slope $= \frac{5}{3}$, y intercept $= -\frac{4}{3}$

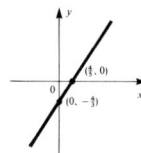

5. $f(x) = -\frac{2}{3}x + \frac{8}{3}$ **7.** $g(x) = 2x - 1$ **9.** $h(x) = -\frac{2}{3}x + \frac{7}{3}$ **11.** No, a linear function is 1–1; $f(x) = 3$

13. $f(x) = 0.2x + 18$; $93   **15.** $F(x) = 8x$; 64 pounds   **17.** $(f \circ g)(x) = a_1b_1x + (a_0 + a_1b_0)$, which is linear

19. Let $f(x) = ax + b$, $a \neq 0$. If $f(x_1) = f(x_2)$, then

$$ax_1 + b = ax_2 + b$$
$$ax_1 = ax_2$$
$$x_1 = x_2 \qquad \text{since } a \neq 0$$

So f is 1–1. If $k \in R$, then $f\left(\dfrac{k - b}{a}\right) = k$; so f is 1–1 from R onto R.

21. Let the slope of the graph of f be m. Then the slope of the graph of g is $-1/m$. So $f(x) = mx + b_1$ and $g(x) = (-1/m)x + b_2$, where b_1 and b_2 are the respective y intercepts.

$$(f \circ g)(x) = m\left(-\frac{1}{m}x + b_2\right) + b_1 = -x + (mb_2 + b_1)$$

$$(g \circ f)(x) = -\frac{1}{m}(mx + b_1) + b_2 = -x + \left(-\frac{b_1}{m} + b_2\right)$$

In each case the slope of the graph is -1.

23. $V(t) = \left(\dfrac{R - C}{N}\right)t + C$; $V(8) = \$6,200$ **25.** $C(0.6000) \approx 0.8252$

Exercise Set 6, page 183

1. Vertex $(0, 0)$, axis $x = 0$

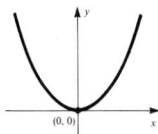

3. Vertex $(0, 4)$, axis $x = 0$

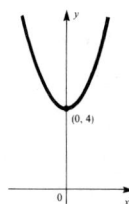

5. Vertex $(2, 1)$, axis $x = 2$

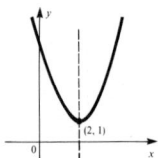

7. Vertex $(3, -1)$, axis $x = 3$

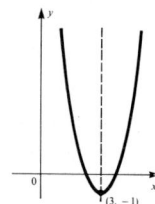

9. Vertex $(-2, 1)$, axis $x = -2$

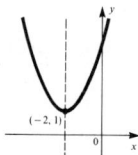

11. Vertex $(1, 5)$, axis $x = 1$

13. Vertex $(\frac{3}{2}, \frac{9}{4})$, axis $x = \frac{3}{2}$

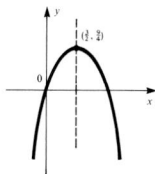

15. Vertex $(\frac{1}{3}, \frac{11}{3})$, axis $x = \frac{1}{3}$

17. Vertex $(-1, \frac{9}{2})$, axis $x = -1$

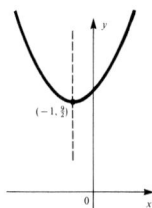

19. Vertex $(\frac{3}{2}, -\frac{19}{2})$, axis $x = \frac{3}{2}$

21. Maximum value 1 when $x = 1$ **23.** Minimum value $-\frac{3}{2}$ when $x = \frac{3}{2}$ **25.** Minimum value $-\frac{16}{5}$ when $x = \frac{1}{5}$

27. Maximum value $\frac{16}{3}$ when $x = \frac{4}{3}$ **29.** 60 items, minimum cost = $400 **31.** 576 feet

33. $f(h + t) = a(h + t - h)^2 + k = at^2 + k$,
$f(h - t) = a(h - t - h)^2 + k = a(-t)^2 + k = at^2 + k$
So $f(h + t) = f(h - t)$.

35. If x is the number of 10¢ reductions, then the average attendance is $100 + 10x$ and the price of each ticket is $3.00 - 0.10x$. So the revenue $R(x) = (3.00 - 0.10x)(100 + 10x) = 300 + 20x - x^2$.

37. $P(x) = 90x - 0.05x^2 - 10,000$, $x = 900$ gives maximum profit of $30,500, selling price for maximum profit = $55

Exercise Set 7, page 185

1. $(-\infty, 0) \cup (2, \infty)$ **3.** $[-5, 1]$ **5.** $(-\frac{1}{3}, 2)$ **7.** $(-\infty, -4] \cup [\frac{3}{2}, \infty)$ **9.** $(-\infty, -1) \cup (\frac{3}{2}, \infty)$

11. $[-\frac{2}{3}, \frac{1}{2}]$ **13.** $(\frac{4}{5}, \frac{3}{2})$ **15.** $(-\infty, -\frac{5}{6}) \cup (\frac{3}{2}, \infty)$ **17.** $[-1 - \sqrt{2}, -1 + \sqrt{2}]$ **19.** $(-\frac{6}{5}, 1)$

21. $P(x) = 26x - x^2 - 105$, $P(x)$ is positive for $5 < x < 21$, maximum profit = 64 when $x = 13$

23. Write in form $4x^2 - 4x + 1 \geq 0$. Since left-hand side $= (2x - 1)^2$, this is always nonnegative.

Exercise Set 8, page 191

1. Parabola

3. Circle

5. Hyperbola

7. Circle

9. Ellipse

11. Parabola

13. Parabola

15. Hyperbola

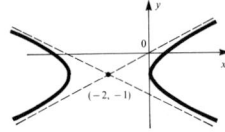

17. Upper half of circle, $x^2 + y^2 = 4$

19. Upper half of ellipse, $\dfrac{x^2}{9} + \dfrac{y^2}{4} = 1$

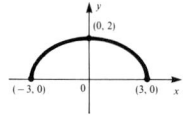

21. Upper half of parabola, $y^2 = x + 2$

23. $x - 2 = \frac{1}{2}(y - 3)^2$, parabola

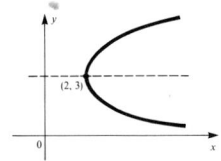

25. $\dfrac{(x - 2)^2}{9} + \dfrac{y^2}{4} = 1$, ellipse

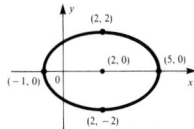

27. $x + 3 = -2(y - 4)^2$, parabola

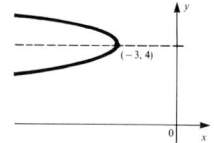

29. $\dfrac{(x + 1)^2}{1} - \dfrac{(y + 2)^2}{4} = 1$, hyperbola

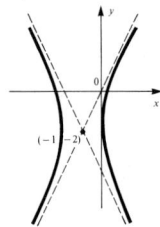

31. $(x - \frac{4}{3})^2 + (y + \frac{5}{3})^2 = \frac{62}{9}$; circle

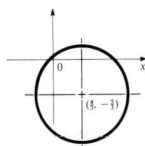

33. $\dfrac{(x - 2)^2}{9/4} + \dfrac{(y + 1)^2}{4} = 1$; ellipse

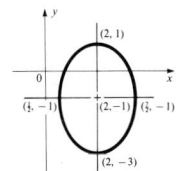

Review Exercise Set, page 192

1. **a.** $-\frac{7}{6}$ **b.** -4 **3.** **a.** $y = 3$ **b.** $x = 2$ **5.** **a.** $3x - 2y - 4 = 0$ **b.** $x - y + 5 = 0$
7. **a.** $3x - 7y + 21 = 0$ **b.** $9x + 7y - 24 = 0$ **9.** **a.** $m = \frac{3}{2}, a = 6, b = -9$ **b.** $m = -\frac{6}{5}, a = \frac{7}{3}, b = \frac{14}{5}$

11. **a** $(\frac{1}{2}, -\frac{3}{2})$ **b.** $(2, \frac{3}{2})$ **c.** $(\frac{3}{2}, 4)$ **d.** $(2, \frac{3}{2})$ **e.** $(\frac{5}{2}, -1)$
13. Let $A = (-1, 5), B = (3, -2), C = (-2, -3)$. Then $\overline{AB} = \overline{AC} = \sqrt{65}$.
15. **a.** $5x + 4y - 1 = 0$ **b.** $3x + 4y + 14 = 0$ **17.** **a.** $3x + 2y - 27 = 0$ **b.** $2x - 3y + 8 = 0$
19. $3x + 5y - 7 = 0$ **21.** **a.** $8x + 3y + C = 0, 8x + 3y - 7 = 0$ **b.** $x + 3y + C = 0, x + 3y - 14 = 0$

23. $g(x) = x - 3$, $m = 1$

25. $(f \circ g)(x) = \dfrac{10 - 9x}{5}$, $(g \circ f)(x) = -\dfrac{2 + 9x}{5}$

27. $T = -\dfrac{h}{500} + T_0$; $36°$F

29. a. $y = (x - 3)^2 - 5$; vertex $(3, -5)$, axis $x = 3$

b. $y = -2(x - 1)^2 - 1$; vertex $(1, -1)$, axis $x = 1$

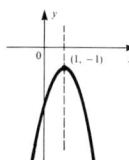

31. a. Minimum is $-\frac{11}{4}$ when $x = \frac{3}{2}$ **b.** Maximum is 12 when $x = -2$ **33.** 100 parts; minimum cost is $10,000

35. a. $(-1, 2)$ **b.** $(-3, 1)$ **37. a.** $\left(-\infty, \frac{1}{2}\right] \cup \left[\frac{4}{3}, \infty\right)$ **b.** $\left[-2, \frac{4}{3}\right]$

39. a. Hyperbola **b.** Hyperbola

41. a. Circle **b.** Ellipse

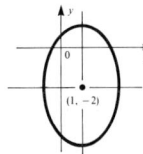

43. Let $A = (-5, 2)$, $B = (-3, -2)$, $C = (6, 1)$, $D = (4, 5)$. Then $m_{AB} = -2$, $m_{BC} = \frac{1}{3}$, $m_{CD} = -2$, $m_{AD} = \frac{1}{3}$, so opposite sides are parallel, and the figure is a parallelogram.

AB: $2x + y + 8 = 0$; BC: $x - 3y - 3 = 0$; CD: $2x + y - 13 = 0$; AD: $x - 3y + 11 = 0$

45. $3x + y - 9 = 0$ **47.** Tangent: $x + y + 2 = 0$; normal: $x - y = 0$

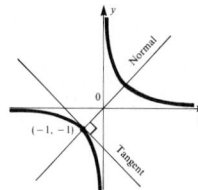

49. a. $(x - 1)^2 + (y + 2)^2 = 4$, circle

b. $\dfrac{(x + 3)^2}{4} + \dfrac{(y - 2)^2}{1} = 1$, ellipse

51. The center of the circle is $(2, -1)$, so the slope of the radius to the point $(-1, 3)$ is $-\frac{4}{3}$. Therefore, the slope of the tangent line is $\frac{3}{4}$. The point $(-1, 3)$ does lie on the circle. The given line has slope $\frac{3}{4}$, and the point $(-1, 3)$ lies on the line. So it is the tangent.

53. 350 people produce maximum revenue of $2,450

Chapter 6

Exercise Set 3, page 202

1. $x - 1$, $R = -5$ 3. $x^2 + 4x + 7$, $R = 17$ 5. $x^2 + 4x + 12$, $R = 32$ 7. $3x^2 - 6x + 8$, $R = -11$
9. $2x^2 - 4x + 5$, $R = 0$; $x + 2$ is a factor of $2x^2 - 3x + 10$ 11. $x^3 + x^2 + 3x + 9$, $R = 2$
13. $x^4 - x^3 - x^2 - x - 1$, $R = 2$ 15. $3x^3 + x^2 - x + 2$, $R = -5$ 17. $x^4 - 2x^3 + 4x^2 - 8x + 16$, $R = -113$
19. 11   21. 16   23. 2   25. 0   27. 65   29. 478   31. 202   33. 644   35. -14
37. $4x^3 - x^2 - (x/2) + \frac{3}{4}$, $R = -\frac{29}{8}$ 39. $(x^2/2) - (9x/4) + \frac{3}{8}$, $R = -\frac{29}{8}$
41. By substitution, $P(-3) = 0$. By synthetic division, remainder on division by $x + 3$ is 0.
43. Remainder is 0 on dividing by $x + 6$.   45. $\frac{59}{16}$ 47. $\frac{25}{4}$
49. Remainder on division by $x + 3$ is 0, so $x = -3$ is a root of the equation. Factors are $(x + 3)(x^2 - x + 1)$. There are no real roots of $x^2 - x + 1 = 0$ since $B^2 - 4AC = -3 < 0$.
51. a. 21.62   b. -39.04

Exercise Set 4, page 206

7. $x^3 - 3x^2 - 4x + 12 = 0$ 9. $x^4 - 5x^3 + 6x^2 + 4x - 8$ 13. a. $x^2 + 2x + 2 = 0$ b. $x^2 - x - 2 = 0$
c. $x^2 - 2x + 1 = 0$ 15. The other root is -2.   17. $x^4 - 10x^3 + 54x^2 - 130x + 125$

Exercise Set 5, page 214

1. a. $\pm\frac{1}{4}, \pm\frac{1}{2}, \pm\frac{3}{4}, \pm1, \pm\frac{3}{2}, \pm3$ b. $\pm\frac{1}{6}, \pm\frac{1}{3}, \pm\frac{1}{2}, \pm\frac{2}{3}, \pm\frac{5}{6}, \pm1, \pm\frac{4}{3}, \pm\frac{5}{3}, \pm2, \pm\frac{5}{2}, \pm\frac{10}{3}, \pm4, \pm5, \pm\frac{20}{3}, \pm10, \pm20$
3. Upper bound 3, lower bound -4; root between 2 and 3   5. a. 2 or 0 positive roots, 0 negative roots
6. 2 or 0 positive roots, 3 or 1 negative roots   7. $x = 2, -1$; -1 is a double root   9. $x = 4, -1 \pm i$
11. $x = -\frac{3}{4}, 1 \pm i\sqrt{3}$ 13. $x = -3, -1, \frac{5}{2}$ 15. $x = -1, 1 \pm i$; -1 is a double root   17. $x = 1, 2, 4, -2$
19. $x = -1, 3$; -1 is a triple root   21. $(x - 1)(x + 4)(x - 3)$ 23. $(x - 3)(x + 1)(x^2 + 4)$
25. $(x + 1)(x - 3)(x^2 + 2x + 2)$ 27. $(x + 1)(x + 2)(2x - 3)^2$ 29. $x = \frac{2}{3}, -4$; -4 is a double root
31. $x = -6$; there is a sign change between $x = 1$ and $x = 2$, between $x = 0$ and $x = -1$, and between $x = -1$ and $x = -2$, so there are three irrational roots and one rational root

Exercise Set 6, page 218

1. 1.28   3. -1.80 5. 2.25   7. $2, -1.51$ 9. $-3, 2.55$ 11. $2.54, -0.69, -2.84$ 13. $1.49, -2.36$
15. $5, -1, 1.39$

Exercise Set 7, page 222

1. $x = 1$ is the only real zero

x	0	1	2	3	-1	-2
y	-1	0	7	26	-2	-9

3. Zeros are $1, 3, -3$

x	0	1	2	3	4	-1	-2	-3	-4
y	9	0	-5	0	21	16	15	0	-35

5. Zeros are $0, 2, -2$

x	0	1	2	3	-1	-2	-3
y	0	3	0	-15	-3	0	15

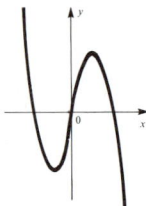

7. Zeros are 6, -2, $\frac{5}{2}$

x	0	1	2	3	4	5	6	7	-1	-2	-3
y	60	45	16	-15	-36	-35	0	81	49	0	-99

9. Zeros are -1 (double), $\frac{1}{2}$, 4

x	0	1	2	3	4	5	-1	-2	-3
y	4	-12	-54	-80	0	324	0	30	196

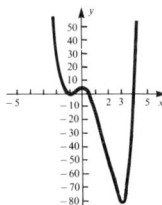

11. Zeros are 1 (double), -2

x	0	1	2	3	-1	-2	-3
y	2	0	4	20	4	0	-16

13. Rational zero -3, irrational zeros between 3 and 4 and between -1 and -2; these irrational zeros are $1 + \sqrt{5}$ and $1 - \sqrt{5}$

x	0	1	2	3	4	-1	-2	-3	-4
y	-12	-20	-20	-6	28	-2	4	0	-20

15. Zeros are 0 (double), 4, -2

x	0	1	2	3	4	5	-1	-2	-3
y	0	9	32	45	0	-175	5	0	-63

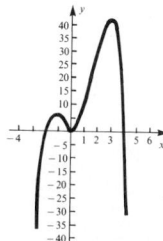

17. Zeros are 1, 3, -1, -4

x	0	1	2	3	4	-1	-2	-3	-4	-5
y	12	0	-18	0	120	0	-30	-48	0	192

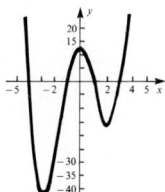

19. Real zeros are 2, $-\frac{3}{2}$

x	0	1	2	3	-1	-2
y	-12	-5	0	45	-15	40

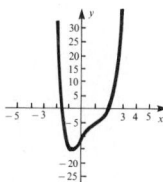

21. Zeros are 2 (double), -2, -4

x	0	1	2	3	-1	-2	-3	-4	-5
y	32	15	0	35	27	0	-25	0	147

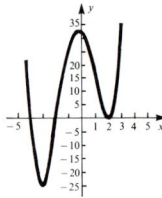

23. $(-6, \frac{4}{3}) \cup (5, \infty), x \neq -4$ **25.** $[-1, 2] \cup [4, \infty)$ **27.** $(-\infty, -2) \cup (-2, 1) \cup (3, \infty)$
29. $(-\infty, -3) \cup (-1, 2) \cup (2, \infty)$ **31.** $(-\infty, -2] \cup [1, \infty)$
33. Zeros are 0, 1, 3, -2 **35.** Zeros are 2, 4, -1 (double), -3

x	0	1	2	3	4	-1	-2	-3
y	0	0	-8	0	72	-8	0	72

x	0	1	2	3	4	5	-1	-2	-3	-4
y	24	48	0	-96	0	864	0	24	0	-432

Exercise Set 8, page 226

1. **a.** $x = 4$ **b.** $x = 1, x = -1$ **3.** **a.** $x = -1, x = \frac{5}{2}$ **b.** $x = 0, x = 5$ **5.** **a.** $x = 3, x = 4, x = -3$
  b. $x = 0, x = -1$ **7.** **a.** $y = 1$ **b.** $y = \frac{1}{2}$ **9.** **a.** $y = -1$ **b.** None
11. **a.** None **b.** $y = 0$
13. x intercept: $-\frac{3}{2}$; y intercept: -3; vertical **15.** x intercept: 1; y intercept: $\frac{1}{9}$; vertical asymptotes:
  asymptote: $x = 1$; horizontal asymptote: $y = 2$ $x = 3, x = -3$; horizontal asymptote: $y = 0$

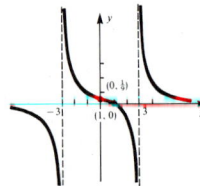

17. x intercept: 2; y intercept: $\frac{2}{3}$; vertical asymptotes: **19.** x intercepts: 4, -2; y intercept: none; vertical
  $x = 3, x = -1$; horizontal asymptote: $y = 0$ asymptotes: $x = 0, x = 2$; horizontal asymptote: $y = 1$

21. Vertical asymptotes: $x = 1, x = 4, x = -2$; **23.** Vertical asymptotes: $x = 1, x = -1, x = 2$; horizontal
  horizontal asymptote: $y = -2$ asymptote: none

25. x intercepts: 1, -3; y intercept: $-\frac{1}{2}$; vertical asymptotes: $x = 3$, $x = -2$; horizontal asymptote: $y = -1$

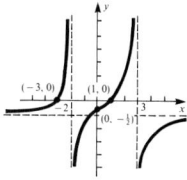

27. x intercepts: 1, -1; y intercept: $-\frac{1}{2}$; vertical asymptote: $x = -2$; horizontal asymptote: none

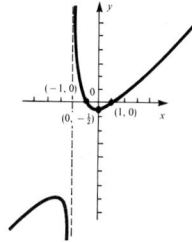

Exercise Set 9, page 231

1. $\dfrac{3}{x-1} + \dfrac{2}{x+3}$ **3.** $\dfrac{3}{x+4} - \dfrac{2}{x-3}$ **5.** $\dfrac{4}{x+2} - \dfrac{1}{x+3}$ **7.** $\dfrac{2}{x-4} - \dfrac{2}{x-5}$ **9.** $\dfrac{5}{x+3} + \dfrac{4}{x-2} - \dfrac{6}{x+4}$

11. $\dfrac{2}{x} + \dfrac{4}{x+1} - \dfrac{3}{x-1}$ **13.** $1 + \dfrac{1}{x+2} + \dfrac{1}{x-1}$ **15.** $x - 3 + \dfrac{1}{x+3} - \dfrac{2}{x+1}$ **17.** $\dfrac{1}{x-1} - \dfrac{1}{x+2} + \dfrac{2}{(x-1)^2}$

19. $\dfrac{4}{x-1} - \dfrac{2}{(x-1)^2} + \dfrac{3}{(x-1)^3}$ **21.** $\dfrac{1}{x} + \dfrac{2}{x^2} - \dfrac{2}{x+2}$ **23.** $\dfrac{2}{x-2} - \dfrac{2x-1}{x^2+4}$ **25.** $\dfrac{2}{x+1} - \dfrac{1}{(x+1)^2} - \dfrac{2x}{x^2+3}$

27. $\dfrac{1}{x-1} - \dfrac{3}{x-3} + \dfrac{2}{x+2}$ **29.** $\dfrac{5}{2(x-1)} - \dfrac{3x+2}{2(x^2+x+2)}$ **31.** $\dfrac{a}{ax+b} - \dfrac{c}{cx+d}$ **33.** $\dfrac{6}{x-1} - \dfrac{4}{(x+2)^2}$

35. $\dfrac{-2}{x} + \dfrac{2x+5}{x^2-3x+4} + \dfrac{4}{(x^2-3x+4)^2}$ **37.** $x - 1 + \dfrac{3}{2x-1} - \dfrac{2}{5x+3}$ **39.** $\dfrac{1}{x-2} + \dfrac{1}{(x-2)^2} - \dfrac{x}{x^2+4}$

41. $\dfrac{3x-4}{x^2+4} - \dfrac{2x-1}{x^2+1}$

Review Exercise Set, page 232

1. a. $2x^2 + 7x + 10$, $R = 25$ **b.** $x^2 - 3x + 6$, $R = -14$ **3. a.** $3x^3 - 14x^2 + 56x - 223$, $R = 887$
  b. $2x^4 + 4x^3 - 2x^2 - 4x - 8$, $R = 0$; so $x - 2$ is a factor of the polynomial   **5.** $2x^4 + x^3 + 12x^2 + 9x - 54$
7. a. $\pm\frac{1}{3}, \pm\frac{2}{3}, \pm 1, \pm\frac{4}{3}, \pm 2, \pm\frac{8}{3}, \pm 4, \pm 8$; 2 or 0 positive roots, 1 negative root
  b. $\pm\frac{1}{10}, \pm\frac{1}{5}, \pm\frac{3}{10}, \pm\frac{2}{5}, \pm\frac{1}{2}, \pm\frac{3}{5}, \pm\frac{4}{5}, \pm 1, \pm\frac{6}{5}, \pm\frac{3}{2}, \pm 2, \pm\frac{12}{5}, \pm 3, \pm 4, \pm 6, \pm 12$; 2 or 0 positive roots,
    2 or 0 negative roots   **9.** $\{3, -2\}$; 3 is a double root   **11.** $\{\frac{1}{2}, -\frac{4}{3}, \pm 2i\}$
13. $\{-1, -2, \frac{3}{2}\}$; $\frac{3}{2}$ is a double root   **15.** $(2x - 5)(x^2 - 2x + 4)$
17. Zeros are 0, -1, $\frac{5}{2}$

x	0	1	2	3	-1	-2
y	0	-6	-6	12	0	-18

19. Zeros are 3 (double), $-\frac{1}{2}$, -4

x	0	1	2	3	4	-1	-2	-3	-4	-5
y	36	60	30	0	72	-48	-150	-180	0	576

21. Zeros are $\frac{1}{2}$, 3, -1, -3

x	0	1	2	3	4	-1	-2	-3	-4
y	9	-16	-45	0	245	0	-25	0	189

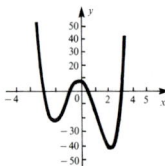

23. $(-\infty, -1) \cup (-1, 2)$ **25.** $[-\frac{3}{2}, \infty)$

27. x intercept: 0; y intercept: 0; vertical asymptotes: $x = 1, x = -1$; horizontal asymptote: $y = 0$

29. x intercepts: 2, $-\frac{1}{2}$; y intercept: none; vertical asymptotes: $x = 0, x = 5$; horizontal asymptote: $y = 2$

31. $\dfrac{2}{x-2} - \dfrac{1}{x+4}$ **33.** $\dfrac{2}{x+1} - \dfrac{3}{x-1} + \dfrac{2}{(x-1)^2}$ **35.** $\dfrac{-4}{x+2} + \dfrac{2}{(x+2)^2} + \dfrac{4x-2}{x^2+2}$ **37.** -2.60

39. $2x^4 - 13x^3 + 22x^2 + 47x - 130$ **41.** $\{\frac{4}{3}, -\frac{3}{2}, \pm\sqrt{2}i\}$

43. Rational zero -3, irrational zero between 0 and 1, two zeros are imaginary

x	0	1	2	-1	-2	-3	-4
y	-6	4	40	-14	-20	0	94

45. $(-\infty, -3) \cup (1, 2) \cup [4, \infty)$ and the isolated point $x = 0$

47. x intercepts: 0, -1; y intercept: 0; vertical asymptote: $x = 1$; horizontal asymptote: none

49. $\dfrac{-2}{2x-1} + \dfrac{5}{(2x-1)^2} + \dfrac{x-1}{x^2+x+3}$ **51.** $-1.29, 0.40, 3.90$

Chapter 7

Exercise Set 1, page 243

1. **a.** 2.6651   **b.** 31.5443   **c.** 0.0906   **d.** 7.3891   **e.** 0.3679

3.

x	0	1	2	3	-1	-2
y	1	4	16	64	0.25	0.0625

5.

x	0	1	2	-1	-2
y	1	2.7	7.39	0.37	0.14

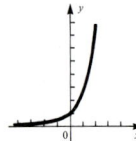

7.

x	0	1	2	3	-1	-2	-3
y	1	$\frac{2}{3}$	$\frac{4}{9}$	$\frac{8}{27}$	$\frac{3}{2}$	$\frac{9}{4}$	$\frac{27}{8}$

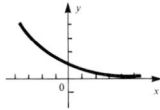

9.

x	0	1	2	3	4	-1	-2
y	$\frac{1}{2}$	1	2	4	8	$\frac{1}{4}$	$\frac{1}{8}$

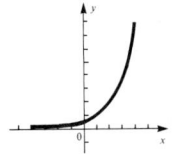

11.

x	0	1	2	3	-1	-2	-3
y	1.7	1	0.58	0.33	3	5.20	9

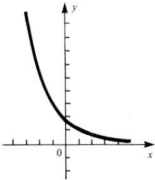

13.

x	0	1	2	3	-1	-2
y	0	0.63	0.86	0.95	-1.72	-6.39

15.

x	0	±1	±2	±3
y	2	1	$\frac{1}{8}$	$\frac{1}{256}$

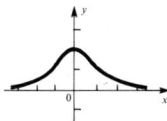

17.

x	0	1	2	3	4	-1	-2
y	$\frac{4}{3}$	1	$\frac{3}{4}$	$\frac{9}{16}$	$\frac{27}{64}$	$\frac{16}{9}$	$\frac{64}{27}$

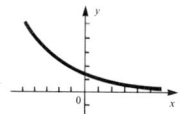

19.

x	0	1	2	3	4	5	-1
y	$\frac{1}{4}$	$\frac{1}{2}$	1	2	4	8	$\frac{1}{8}$

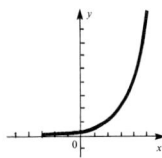

21. a. $2,477.65   **b.** $2,488.42   **c.** $2,492.15

23. 70.71 grams   **25.** 120 years   **27.** 4 times as many, 16 times as many   **29.** $3.00   **31.** 5

33.

x	0	±1	±2	±3
y	1	1.54	3.76	10.07

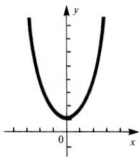

35.

x	0	1	2	3	-1	-2	-3
y	0	0.76	0.96	0.995	-0.76	-0.96	-0.995

37. $-6.25°$ **39.** $2(\frac{3}{2})^{7/3}$ billion ≈ 5.15 billion   **41.** 9.6 pounds per square inch

Exercise Set 2, page 250

1. a. 3   **b.** 3   **3. a.** x **b.** x **5. a.** 4   **b.** -3 **7. a.** 3   **b.** -4 **9. a.** 2   **b.** -2
11. a. 5   **b.** -5 **13. a.** 3   **b.** $\frac{1}{9}$ **15. a.** 3   **b.** 0.001   **17. a.** 0   **b.** $\frac{27}{8}$ **19. a.** -1
b. 2   **21. a.** $\frac{1}{27}$ **b.** $\frac{2}{3}$ **23. a.** 10   **b.** -3 **25. a.** $\log_4 64 = 3$ **b.** $\log_3 \frac{1}{9} = -2$
27. a. $\log_2 256 = 8$ **b.** $\log_2 0.125 = -3$ **29. a.** $2^4 = 16$ **b.** $10^2 = 100$ **31. a.** $5^{-1} = 0.2$
b. $8^{2/3} = 4$
33. $x = 2^y$

x	1	2	4	8	$\frac{1}{2}$	$\frac{1}{4}$	$\frac{1}{8}$
y	0	1	2	3	-1	-2	-3

35. $x = 2^y - 1$

x	0	1	3	7	$-\frac{1}{2}$	$-\frac{3}{4}$	$-\frac{7}{8}$
y	0	1	2	3	-1	-2	-3

37. $x = \frac{1}{2}(4^y + 3)$

x	2	$\frac{7}{2}$	$\frac{19}{2}$	$\frac{13}{8}$	$\frac{49}{32}$	$\frac{5}{2}$	$\frac{7}{4}$
y	0	1	2	-1	-2	$\frac{1}{2}$	$-\frac{1}{2}$

39. $x = \pm 2^{y/2}$

x	± 1	± 2	± 4	± 8	$\pm\frac{1}{2}$	$\pm\frac{1}{4}$	$\pm\frac{1}{8}$
y	0	2	4	6	-2	-4	-6

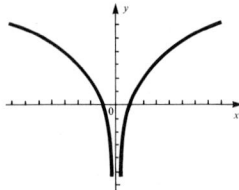

41. $x = -e^y$

x	-1	-2.7	-7.39	-20.09	-0.37	-0.14	-0.05
y	0	1	2	3	-1	-2	-3

43. Approximately 6.76 years   **45.** 12.6 years   **47.** 6.21 years   **49.** 110 decibels
51. Approximately 38.88 hours   **53.** Approximately 47.25 minutes   **55.** 33.22 feet

Exercise Set 3, page 256

1. a. $\log(x + 1) + \log(x - 2)$ **b.** $\log(x + 1) - \log(x - 2)$ **3. a.** $4\log(x - 2)$ **b.** $\frac{3}{2}\log(2x + 1)$
5. a. $\log(x - 3) + \log(x + 1)$ **b.** $\log(x + 2) + \log(x - 2) - \log(x - 3)$ **7. a.** $\frac{2}{3}\log(x + 1)$
   b. $-\frac{1}{2}\log(3x - 4)$ **9. a.** $\frac{1}{2}\log(x^2 + y^2)$ **b.** $\frac{1}{2}[\log(x + y) + \log(x - y)]$ **11.** $\frac{1}{3}\log(1 - 2x) - 2\log(x + 3)$
13. $\log(2x - 5) + \log(3x + 4) - [\log(x + 2) + \log(x - 1)]$ **15.** $\frac{3}{2}\log(x - 1) - \frac{1}{2}\log(x + 2)$
17. $\log 3 + 4\log x - \frac{3}{2}\log(2x + 1)$ **19.** $2\log x + \frac{1}{2}\log(1 - 3x) - \log(1 + 2x)$
21. $\frac{3}{2}\log(2x + 3) + 4\log(x + 1) - [\log 3 + \log x + \frac{1}{2}\log(1 - x)]$
23. $\log 3 + \log x + 2\log(x^2 + 4) - [\log(x + 2) + \frac{1}{2}\log(2x + 3)]$ **25.** $-\frac{1}{2}[\log(2x - 3) + \log(x + 1)]$ **27. a.** 81

   b. 25   **29. a.** $-\frac{10}{3}$ **b.** $\frac{15}{2}$ **31. a.** $\log(x/y)$ **b.** $\log x^2(x + 1)^3$ **33. a.** $\log\dfrac{2\sqrt{x - 1}}{(x + 2)^3}$

   b. $\log\dfrac{(x + 2)^3}{\sqrt{x - x^2}}$ **35. a.** $\log\dfrac{\sqrt{5x + 3}}{(x + 2)^2(3x + 1)}$ **b.** $\log\dfrac{2Cx}{\sqrt{x + 1}}$ **37. a.** $x = \dfrac{\ln 3}{\ln 4}$ **b.** $x = \dfrac{\ln 5}{\ln 5 - \ln 3}$

39. a. $x = \dfrac{\ln 8}{1 + \ln 2}$ **b.** $x = \dfrac{\ln 2 - \ln 3}{\ln 48}$ **41.** $x = 4$ **43.** $x = 3$ **45.** $x = 10$ **47.** $x = \frac{9}{2}$

49. $x = -1$ **51.** $x = 1$ **53.** (E)   **55.** $y = 2x^{3/2}$ **57.** $y = \dfrac{Cx^3(2x - 3)}{\sqrt{x + 2}}$ **59.** $y = \frac{1}{2}[3 + C(x - 1)^2]$

61. a. $\log_a x = \dfrac{\log_b x}{\log_b a} = \dfrac{g(x)}{g(a)}$ **b.** $\log_b x = \dfrac{\log_a x}{\log_a b} = \dfrac{f(x)}{f(b)}$ **c.** $\log_a b = \dfrac{1}{\log_b a}$, so $f(b) \cdot g(a) = 1$ **63. a.** 0.7925

   b. -0.7712 **65. a.** 0.1606   **b.** 8.6555   **67. a.** 1.6341   **b.** 0.4033   **69.** $x = \frac{3}{2}$ **71.** $x = 1$

73. $x = 12$ **75.** $\dfrac{1}{\sqrt{x} - \sqrt{x - 1}} = \dfrac{1}{\sqrt{x} - \sqrt{x - 1}} \cdot \dfrac{\sqrt{x} + \sqrt{x - 1}}{\sqrt{x} + \sqrt{x - 1}} = \dfrac{\sqrt{x} + \sqrt{x - 1}}{x - (x - 1)} = \sqrt{x} + \sqrt{x - 1}$, so $\log\dfrac{1}{\sqrt{x} - \sqrt{x - 1}}$
$= \log(\sqrt{x} + \sqrt{x - 1})$ **77.**

$y = -\ln(1 - x)$

79. $x = \ln(2 + \sqrt{5})$ **81.** $x = 2$ or $x = 8$

Review Exercise Set, page 260

1. **a.**

x	0	1	2	3	−1	−2	−3
y	1	$\frac{3}{2}$	$\frac{9}{4}$	$\frac{27}{8}$	$\frac{2}{3}$	$\frac{4}{9}$	$\frac{8}{27}$

b.

x	0	1	2	3	−1	−2	−3
y	0	$\frac{1}{2}$	$\frac{3}{4}$	$\frac{7}{8}$	−1	−3	−7

c.

x	1	2	4	8	$\frac{1}{2}$	$\frac{1}{4}$	$\frac{1}{8}$
y	0	1	2	3	−1	−2	−3

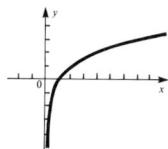

d.

x	0	−1.72	−6.39	−19.09	0.63	0.86	0.95
y	0	1	2		3	−1	−2	−3

3. **a.** $3^2 = 9$ **b.** $10^{-3} = 0.001$ **c.** $2^8 = 256$ **d.** $y = k^v$ **e.** $s = r^z$ **5.** **a.** 16   **b.** $\frac{1}{4}$ **c.** 4

7. **a.** 3   **b.** 2   **c.** −7   **9.** **a.** $\log(x-1) - 3\log(x+2)$ **b.** $\frac{1}{2}[\log(2x-1) - (\log 3 + \log x)]$

11. **a.** $\log \dfrac{Cx\sqrt{2x-3}}{8}$ **b.** $\log \dfrac{x^4}{(x-1)\sqrt{x+2}}$ **13.** **a.** $\log \dfrac{2x^3}{\sqrt[3]{(x-1)(x+2)}}$ **b.** $\log \dfrac{(2x+3)^{3/2}}{2(x+4)^3}$

15. **a.** $\frac{3}{2}$ **b.** −3   **c.** −4   **d.** −5   **17.** $k = -\dfrac{1}{t}\ln\left(1 - \dfrac{y}{C}\right)$ **19.** $x = 3$ **21.** $x = 5$ **23.** $x = \frac{2}{3}$

25. $x = \frac{7}{2}$ **27.** Approximately 15.87 pounds   **29.** Approximately 529,750

31. **a.** Quarterly, \$6,734.28; continuously, \$6,749.29   **b.** Approximately 11.55 years

33. 10.0 pounds per square inch   **35.** Approximately 6.93%   **37.** **a.** 0.5670   **b.** 0.5900

39.

41. 33.22 seconds   **43.** 0.00196

Cumulative Review Exercise Set II (Chapters 4–7), page 263

1. **a.** $(-2, \frac{1}{2}] \cup (2, \infty)$ **b.** $[-\frac{10}{3}, 1] \cup [4, \infty)$

3.

a. 2   **b.** −1   **c.** 1   **d.** 9   **e.** −1

5. \$8,000   **7.** $(f \circ g)(x) = (x-1)^2 + 1$, domain $= \{x: x > 1\}$; $(g \circ f)(x) = 2x$, domain $= R$

9. **a.** $y \geq 0$ on the interval $[-2, 6]$

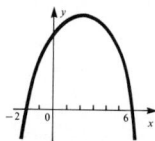

b. $y > 0$ on $[-4, 2) \cup (2, \infty)$

11. $A = \pi \dfrac{r^2}{h^2}(h - x)^2$

13.   Domain $= R$, range $= \{y: \; y \ge 1\}$; f is not 1–1, since, for example, $f(2) = f(0)$

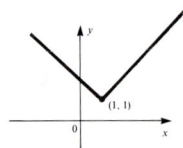

15. $(f \circ g)(t) = \sqrt{t^2 - 4}$, domain $= \{t: \; |t| \ge 2\}$, range $= \{y: \; y \ge 0\}$; $(g \circ f)(t) = t - 4$, domain $= \{t: \; t \ge 1\}$, range $= \{y: \; y \ge -3\}$

17. $\{-1, 2\}$ **19.** $\dfrac{-1}{\sqrt{x}\sqrt{x + h}(\sqrt{x} + \sqrt{x + h})}$ $(h \ne 0)$ **21.**   34.02°C, 1 hour 19.6 minutes

23.   450 units, maximum profit $= \$18,750$ **25.**   10 meters   **27.** $2\frac{1}{2}$ tons; \$400

29.   **a.**

x	0	± 1.31	± 2.53	± 4.37	± 7.32
y	0	1	2	3	4

b.

x	0	± 1	± 2	± 3	± 4
y	0	0.63	0.86	0.95	0.98

c.

x	1	3	5	7	9	-1	-3	-5
y	1	2	4	8	16	$\frac{1}{2}$	$\frac{1}{4}$	$\frac{1}{8}$

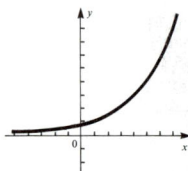

Chapter 8

Exercise Set 2, page 273

1. **a.** $\pi/6$ **b.** $\pi/4$ **3.** **a.** $2\pi/3$ **b.** $3\pi/4$ **5.** **a.** $4\pi/3$ **b.** $3\pi/2$ **7.** **a.** $11\pi/6$ **b.** $\pi/12$
9. **a.** $10\pi/3$ **b.** $-4\pi/5$ **11.** **a.** $135°$ **b.** $300°$ **13.** **a.** $150°$ **b.** $-240°$ **15.** **a.** $100°$
   b. $(360/\pi)° \approx 114.59°$ **17.** **a.** $(540/\pi)° \approx 171.89°$ **b.** $15°$ **19.** **a.** $-(720/\pi)° \approx -229.18°$ **b.** $330°$
21. **a.** $32.85°$ **b.** $102.58°$ **23.** **a.** $27.22°$ **b.** $-56.32°$ **25.** **a.** $-13°03'$ **b.** $153°25'$
27. **a.** $171°53'$ **b.** $406°21'$ **29.** **a.** 0.233 **b.** 5.065 **31.** **a.** $s = 6$ **b.** $r = \frac{4}{3}$
33. **a.** $r = 32/\pi \approx 10.19$ **b.** $\theta = \frac{2}{3}$ **35.** $s = 22\pi$ mi ≈ 69.12 mi   **37.** $s = 5\pi$ in. ≈ 15.7 in.   **39.** 60π rad/sec
41. $\frac{3}{4}$ rad, $(135/\pi)° \approx 43.0°$ **43.** 66,705 mph   **45.** $r_B = 7.78$ in., $r_C = 9.78$ in.

Exercise Set 3, page 278

1. $a = \frac{5}{2}$, $b = 5\sqrt{3}/2$ **3.** $a = 10\sqrt{3}, c = 20$ **5.** $a = 2\sqrt{3}, c = 4\sqrt{3}$ **7.** $a = 4, b = 4$ **9.** $a = 5\sqrt{3}/2, b = \frac{5}{2}$
11. $b = 3, c = 3\sqrt{2}$ **13.** $c = \sqrt{13}$ **15.** $b = 24$ **17.** $b = 48$ **19.** $c = 3$ **21.** $81°09'$ **23.** $23.82°$
25. $5\pi/12$ **29.** **a.** $10\sqrt{6}$ **b.** $\frac{75}{2}(\sqrt{3} + 4)$

31. length $AB = 2a$, length $BD = a$ ∴ $\triangle CBD$ is isosceles. Since $B = 60°$ and $\angle BDC = \angle BCD$, it follows that these two angles are both 60°. So $\triangle CBD$ is equilateral. ∴$CD = a$.

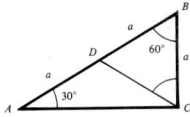

33. $\pi a^2/3$

Exercise Set 4, page 286

1. $B = 32.6°$, $a = 23.8$, $c = 28.2$ **3.** $A = 22.7°$, $a = 5.65$, $c = 14.6$ **5.** $B = 40.3°$, $a = 18.8$, $b = 15.9$
7. $B = 57.5°$, $b = 38.8$, $c = 46.0$ **9.** $A = 25.53°$, $B = 64.47°$, $b = 28.24$ **11.** $A = 67°20'$, $a = 6.13$, $c = 6.64$
13. $B = 54.43°$, $b = 4.841$, $c = 5.952$ **15.** $A = 48.3°$, $B = 41.7°$, $a = 28.5$ **17.** 381 ft **19.** 127 ft
21. 45.1 ft, 49.9 ft **23.** 19.2 mi, 51.3° **25.** 840 meters from B, 926 meters from A **27.** 6.142 mi and 8.331 mi
29. 249°10', 219 mph **31.** 54.3 ft **33.** 51.5 mi **35.** 4.18 km

Exercise Set 5, page 293

1. $|V| = 7.62$, $\alpha = 23.2°$ **3.** $|V| = 4.25$, $\alpha = 240.4°$ **5.** $V_x = 21.2$, $V_y = 13.2$ **7.** $V_x = 1.93$, $V_y = -0.621$
9. $V_x = 3$, $V_y = -3$ **11.** $V_x = -12$, $V_y = -1$
13. **15.** **17.**

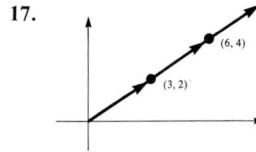

19. 164.7 lb; angle from horizontal $= 24.4°$ **21.** 210°, 138.6 mph **23.** 883N and 469N
25. 192.8°; 2 hr 17 min **27.**

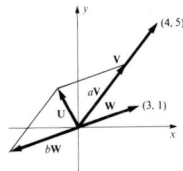

29. $U - V$ can be described as the diagonal from the tip of V to the tip of U.

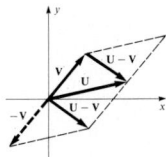

31. Let $R = V + W$ and $R = (R_x, R_y)$. Since the points $(0, 0)$, (V_x, V_y), (R_x, R_y), and (W_x, W_y) are consecutive vertices of a parallelogram, the horizontal and vertical displacements of the vector from (V_x, V_y) to (R_x, R_y) must be equal respectively to those of W. Thus

$$R_x - V_x = W_x \quad \text{and} \quad R_y - V_y = W_y$$

or

$$R_x = V_x + W_x \quad \text{and} \quad R_y = V_y + W_y$$

33. Approx. 634 pounds

Exercise Set 6, page 299

1. $\sin 150° = \frac{1}{2}$, $\cos 150° = -\sqrt{3}/2$, $\tan 150° = -1/\sqrt{3}$, $\cot 150° = -\sqrt{3}$, $\sec 150° = -2/\sqrt{3}$, $\csc 150° = 2$

3. $\sin 330° = -\frac{1}{2}$, $\cos 330° = \sqrt{3}/2$, $\tan 330° = -1/\sqrt{3}$, $\cot 330° = -\sqrt{3}$, $\sec 330° = 2/\sqrt{3}$, $\csc 330° = -2$

5. $\sin 120° = \sqrt{3}/2$, $\cos 120° = -\frac{1}{2}$, $\tan 120° = -\sqrt{3}$, $\cot 120° = -1/\sqrt{3}$, $\sec 120° = -2$, $\csc 120° = 2/\sqrt{3}$

7. $\sin 270° = -1$, $\cos 270° = 0$, $\tan 270°$ undefined, $\cot 270° = 0$, $\sec 270°$ undefined, $\csc 270° = -1$

9. $\sin(7\pi/4) = -1/\sqrt{2}$, $\cos(7\pi/4) = 1/\sqrt{2}$, $\tan(7\pi/4) = -1$, $\cot(7\pi/4) = -1$, $\sec(7\pi/4) = \sqrt{2}$, $\csc(7\pi/4) = -\sqrt{2}$

11. $\sin(-\pi/6) = -\frac{1}{2}$, $\cos(-\pi/6) = \sqrt{3}/2$, $\tan(-\pi/6) = -1/\sqrt{3}$, $\cot(-\pi/6) = -\sqrt{3}$, $\sec(-\pi/6) = 2/\sqrt{3}$, $\csc(-\pi/6) = -2$

13. $\sin 480° = \sqrt{3}/2$, $\cos 480° = -\frac{1}{2}$, $\tan 480° = -\sqrt{3}$, $\cot 480° = -1/\sqrt{3}$, $\sec 480° = -2$, $\csc 480° = 2/\sqrt{3}$

15. $\sin 3\pi = 0$, $\cos 3\pi = -1$, $\tan 3\pi = 0$, $\cot 3\pi$ undefined, $\sec 3\pi = -1$, $\csc 3\pi$ undefined

17. **a.** $-1/\sqrt{2}$ **b.** $-\sqrt{3}$ **c.** 2 **d.** $-1/\sqrt{2}$ **e.** $\sqrt{3}$ 19. **a.** $-\frac{1}{2}$ **b.** $\sqrt{3}/2$ **c.** -1
   d. $-\sqrt{2}$ **e.** -1 21. **a.** $1/\sqrt{3}$ **b.** $\sqrt{2}$ **c.** $1/\sqrt{3}$ **d.** $\frac{1}{2}$ **e.** $2/\sqrt{3}$ 23. **a.** $\cot 32°$
   b. $-\sin 22°$ **c.** $\tan 80°$ **d.** $\cos 70°$ **e.** $-\csc 49°$ 25. **a.** $-\tan(5\pi/12)$ **b.** $-\sec(\pi/8)$
   c. $-\sin(\pi/5)$ **d.** $\csc(\pi/9)$ **e.** $-\cos(\pi/12)$

27. $\sin \theta = -\frac{12}{13}$, $\cos \theta = \frac{5}{13}$, $\tan \theta = -\frac{12}{5}$, $\cot \theta = -\frac{5}{12}$, $\sec \theta = \frac{13}{5}$, $\csc \theta = -\frac{13}{12}$

29. $\sin \theta = -3/\sqrt{13}$, $\cos \theta = 2/\sqrt{13}$, $\tan \theta = -\frac{3}{2}$, $\cot \theta = -\frac{2}{3}$, $\sec \theta = \sqrt{13}/2$, $\csc \theta = -\sqrt{13}/3$

31. $\sin \theta = -\frac{24}{25}$, $\cos \theta = -\frac{7}{25}$, $\tan \theta = \frac{24}{7}$, $\cot \theta = \frac{7}{24}$, $\sec \theta = -\frac{25}{7}$, $\csc \theta = -\frac{25}{24}$ 33. -8

35.
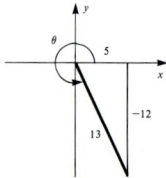
$\sin \theta = -\frac{12}{13}$, $\tan \theta = -\frac{12}{5}$,
$\cot \theta = -\frac{5}{12}$, $\sec \theta = \frac{13}{5}$,
$\csc \theta = -\frac{13}{12}$

37.

$\sin \theta = \frac{1}{3}$, $\cos \theta = -2\sqrt{2}/3$,
$\tan \theta = -1/2\sqrt{2}$, $\cot \theta = -2\sqrt{2}$,
$\sec \theta = -3/2\sqrt{2}$

39.

$\sin \theta = 3/\sqrt{10}$, $\cos \theta = -1/\sqrt{10}$, $\tan \theta = -3$,
$\sec \theta = -\sqrt{10}$, $\csc \theta = \sqrt{10}/3$

41.
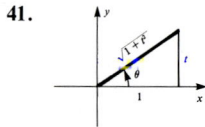
$\sin \theta = t/\sqrt{1 + t^2}$, $\cos \theta = 1/\sqrt{1 + t^2}$,
$\cot \theta = 1/t$, $\sec \theta = \sqrt{1 + t^2}$,
$\csc \theta = \sqrt{1 + t^2}/t$

Solution 1

$\sin \theta = -t/\sqrt{1 + t^2}$, $\cos \theta = -1/\sqrt{1 + t^2}$,
$\cot \theta = 1/t$, $\sec \theta = -\sqrt{1 + t^2}$,
$\csc \theta = -\sqrt{1 + t^2}/t$

Solution 2

43. **a.** $\sin(\pi - \theta) = \sin \theta$, $\cos(\pi - \theta) = -\cos \theta$, $\tan(\pi - \theta) = -\tan \theta$
   $\cot(\pi - \theta) = -\cot \theta$, $\sec(\pi - \theta) = -\sec \theta$, $\csc(\pi - \theta) = \csc \theta$

   b. $\sin(\pi + \theta) = -\sin \theta$, $\cos(\pi + \theta) = -\cos \theta$, $\tan(\pi + \theta) = \tan \theta$,
   $\cot(\pi + \theta) = \cot \theta$, $\sec(\pi + \theta) = -\sec \theta$, $\csc(\pi + \theta) = -\csc \theta$

   c. $\sin(\pi/2 + \theta) = \cos \theta$, $\cos(\pi/2 + \theta) = -\sin \theta$, $\tan(\pi/2 + \theta) = -\cot \theta$,
   $\cot(\pi/2 + \theta) = -\tan \theta$, $\sec(\pi/2 + \theta) = -\csc \theta$, $\csc(\pi/2 + \theta) = \sec \theta$

   d. $\sin(3\pi/2 - \theta) = -\cos \theta$, $\cos(3\pi/2 - \theta) = -\sin \theta$, $\tan(3\pi/2 - \theta) = \cot \theta$,
   $\cot(3\pi/2 - \theta) = \tan \theta$, $\sec(3\pi/2 - \theta) = -\csc \theta$, $\csc(3\pi/2 - \theta) = -\sec \theta$

   e. $\sin(2\pi - \theta) = -\sin \theta$, $\cos(2\pi - \theta) = \cos \theta$, $\tan(2\pi - \theta) = -\tan \theta$,
   $\cot(2\pi - \theta) = -\cot \theta$, $\sec(2\pi - \theta) = \sec \theta$, $\csc(2\pi - \theta) = -\csc \theta$

45. If n is even $(2n + 1)\pi/2$ is coterminal with $\pi/2$, and in this case $(-1)^n = 1$, so formula is correct.
  If n is odd, $(2n + 1)\pi/2$ is coterminal with $3\pi/2$, and in this case $(-1)^n = -1$, so formula is correct.

47. For $k = 0, \pm 4, \pm 8, \ldots, (1 + 2k)\pi/4$ is coterminal with $\pi/4$, and $(-1)^k = 1$, so formula is true.
  For $k = \pm 2, \pm 6, \pm 10, \ldots, (1 + 2k)\pi/4$ is coterminal with $5\pi/4$, and $(-1)^k = 1$, so formula is true.
  For $k = \pm 1, \pm 5, \pm 9, \ldots, (1 + 2k)\pi/4$ is coterminal with $3\pi/4$, and $(-1)^k = -1$, so formula is true.
  For $k = \pm 3, \pm 7, \pm 11, \ldots, (1 + 2k)\pi/4$ is coterminal with $7\pi/4$, and $(-1)^k = -1$, so formula is true.

Exercise Set 7, page 305

1. $C = 120°, b = 2.7, c = 6.7$

3. Solution 1: $A = 82°30', B = 61°00', a = 142$
  Solution 2: $A = 24°30', B = 119°00', a = 59.3$

5. $B = 12.9°, C = 138.6°, c = 30.2$ **7.** $A = 107.0°, a = 16.1, b = 12.4$ **9.** $C = 102°02', a = 9.900, c = 15.93$

11. $A = 113.07°, C = 23.68°, a = 23.52$ **13.** $A = 33°16', C = 38°12', a = 65.14$

15. Solution 1: $A = 39°29', B = 118°01', b = 8.930$
  Solution 2: $A = 140°31', B = 16°59', b = 2.955$

17. $\theta = 68°00', |\mathbf{F}_1| = 156.3$ pounds **19.** $x \approx 1{,}030$ ft. **21.** S $66°20'$ W, 37 minutes

23. 3.51 miles from A, 2.77 miles from B, 1.88 miles from nearest point on shore

Exercise Set 8, page 310

1. $B = 79.1°, C = 40.9°, a = 13.2$ **3.** $A = 23°05', B = 59°35', c = 12.65$

5. $A = 52.8°, B = 32.1°, C = 95.1°$ **7.** $b = 313, A = 46.7°, C = 29.8°$ **9.** $A = 49.8°, B = 93.1°, C = 37.1°$

11. $a = 37.70, B = 54°16', C = 41°21'$ **13.** 13.56 cm **15.** 53.9 pounds, $10.4°$ from 30-pound force

17. 23.4 miles per hour, S $55.7°$ E **19.** 58.27 feet **21.** 477.7 miles **23.** $105°$

25. $|\mathbf{R}| = 84.5$ pounds, $\theta = 61.7°$ **27.** 36.2 miles

Exercise Set 9, page 312

1. 216 **3.** 64.9 **5.** 4.45 **7.** 25.98 **9.** 48.92 **11.** 996 **13.** 0.7784

15. Let A be obtuse as shown. Then, $h = b \sin(180° - A) = b \sin A$.
  Area $= \frac{1}{2}hc = \frac{1}{2}bc \sin A$.

17. 48.7 **19.** 97.6

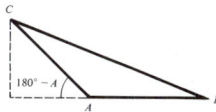

Review Exercise Set, page 313

1. $B = 30°, c = 10, a = 5\sqrt{3}$ **3.** $A = 30°, c = 8, b = 4\sqrt{3}$ **5.** $A = 45°, a = 5\sqrt{2}, b = 5\sqrt{2}$

7. $A = 30°, B = 60°, b = 7\sqrt{3}$ **9.** $B = 57°, a = 7.08, b = 10.90$

11. $a = 111.34, A = 47.51°, B = 42.49°$ **13.** $A = 63.8°, a = 30.06, b = 14.79$

15. a. $4\pi/3$ **b.** $7\pi/4$ **c.** $\pi/12$ **d.** 3π **e.** $8\pi/9$ **17. a.** $4\pi \approx 12.57$ **b.** $(240/\pi)° \approx 76.39°$

19. a. $\frac{1}{2}$ **b.** $-\frac{1}{2}$ **c.** $1/\sqrt{3}$ **d.** 0 **e.** $-\sqrt{2}$ **f.** 2 **g.** 1 **h.** -1 **i.** -2 **j.** $-\sqrt{3}/2$

21. $b = 10.72, c = 20.82, C = 118.9°$

23. Solution 1: $A = 64.49°, B = 83.51°, a = 13.62$; Solution 2: $A = 51.51°, B = 96.49°, a = 11.82$

25. $A = 100.2°, B = 52.2°, C = 27.6°$ **27.** No solution **29.** $A = 37.36°, B = 43.05°, C = 99.59°$

31. Solution 1: $B = 104.21°, C = 50.59°, b = 34.38$; Solution 2: $B = 25.39°, C = 129.41°, b = 15.21$

33. 61.2 feet **35.** 103.12 feet, area $= 4{,}914.91$ square feet **37.** $|\mathbf{V}_2| = 15.0, |\mathbf{V}_1 + \mathbf{V}_2| = 25.0$

39. $|\mathbf{R}| = 80.6$ pounds, $\theta = 53°38'$ **41.** 22.86 feet **43.** 526.46 miles

45. 8.48 miles from first tower, 7.93 miles from second **47.** 646 feet, S $10.6°$ E

Chapter 9

Exercise Set 1, page 322

1. $\sin \theta = -2\sqrt{2}/3, \cos \theta = -\frac{1}{3}, \csc \theta = -3/2\sqrt{2}, \sec \theta = -3, \tan \theta = 2\sqrt{2}, \cot \theta = 1/2\sqrt{2}$

3. $\sin \theta = -\frac{12}{13}, \cos \theta = \frac{5}{13}, \csc \theta = -\frac{13}{12}, \sec \theta = \frac{13}{5}, \tan \theta = -\frac{12}{5}, \cot \theta = -\frac{5}{12}$

5. $\sin \theta = -\sqrt{15}/4, \cos \theta = \frac{1}{4}, \csc \theta = -4/\sqrt{15}, \sec \theta = 4, \tan \theta = -\sqrt{15}, \cot \theta = -1/\sqrt{15}$

7. $\theta = 4\pi/3; \sin \theta = -\sqrt{3}/2, \cos \theta = -\frac{1}{2}, \csc \theta = -2/\sqrt{3}, \sec \theta = -2, \tan \theta = \sqrt{3}, \cot \theta = 1/\sqrt{3}$

9. $\sin \theta = -2\sqrt{2}/3, \cos \theta = \frac{1}{3}, \csc \theta = -3/2\sqrt{2}, \sec \theta = 3, \tan \theta = -2\sqrt{2}, \cot \theta = -1/2\sqrt{2}$

11. a. $(0, 1)$ **b.** $(-1, 0)$ **c.** $(0, -1)$ **d.** $(-\sqrt{3}/2, \frac{1}{2})$ **e.** $(-\frac{1}{2}, -\sqrt{3}/2)$

13. a.   **b.**   **c.**   **d.**

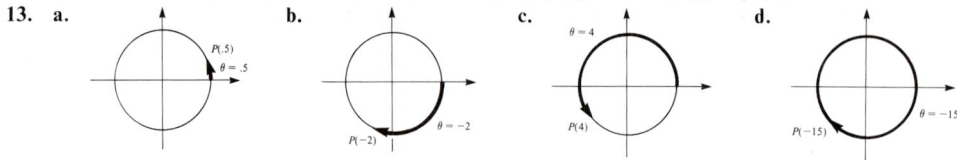

15. a. $\pi/6$ **b.** $\pi/4$ **c.** $\pi/3$ **d.** $\pi/2$ **e.** 0

17. a. $\sin 0.3 = 0.2955$, $\cos 0.3 = 0.9553$, $\tan 0.3 = 0.3093$
  b. $\sin 2.718 = 0.4110$, $\cos 2.718 = -0.9116$, $\tan 2.718 = -0.4509$
  c. $\sin 14.03 = 0.9943$, $\cos 14.03 = 0.1070$, $\tan 14.03 = 9.2955$
  d. $\sin(-3.625) = 0.4648$, $\cos(-3.625) = -0.8854$, $\tan(-3.625) = -0.5249$

19. a. $\pi/2$ **b.** 0   **c.** $\pi/4, 5\pi/4$ **d.** $0, \pi$ **e.** $\pi/2, 3\pi/2$ **f.** $0, \pi$ **g.** $3\pi/2$ **h.** π **i.** $3\pi/4, 7\pi/4$

21. a. $P(\theta)$ is either $(0, 1)$ or $(0, -1)$, so $\tan \theta$ is undefined   **b.** $P(\theta)$ is either $(1, 0)$ or $(-1, 0)$, so $\cot \theta$ is undefined
  c. $P(\theta)$ is either $(0, 1)$ or $(0, -1)$, so $\sec \theta$ is undefined   **d.** $P(\theta)$ is either $(1, 0)$ or $(-1, 0)$, so $\csc \theta$ is undefined

23. If $k \in R$, $\tan \theta = y/x = k$, with (x, y) on the unit circle if $x = 1/\sqrt{1 + k^2}$ and $y = k/\sqrt{1 + k^2}$. So if $P(\theta) = (1/\sqrt{1 + k^2}, k/\sqrt{1 + k^2})$, then $\tan \theta = k$.

Exercise Set 2, page 326

1. $\cos \theta = -\frac{4}{5}$, $\csc \theta = -\frac{5}{3}$, $\sec \theta = -\frac{5}{4}$, $\tan \theta = \frac{3}{4}$, $\cot \theta = \frac{4}{3}$
3. $\sin \theta = \frac{4}{5}$, $\cos \theta = -\frac{3}{5}$, $\csc \theta = \frac{5}{4}$, $\sec \theta = -\frac{5}{3}$, $\cot \theta = -\frac{3}{4}$
5. $\sin \theta = -1/\sqrt{5}$, $\csc \theta = -\sqrt{5}$, $\sec \theta = \sqrt{5}/2$, $\tan \theta = -\frac{1}{2}$, $\cot \theta = -2$
7. $\cos \theta = -2\sqrt{2}/3$, $\csc \theta = 3$, $\sec \theta = -3/2\sqrt{2}$, $\tan \theta = -1/2\sqrt{2}$, $\cot \theta = -2\sqrt{2}$

Exercise Set 4, page 336

1. $(\sqrt{2} + \sqrt{6})/4, (\sqrt{2} - \sqrt{6})/4$ **3. a.** $-(\sqrt{6} + \sqrt{2})/4$ **b.** $-(\sqrt{6} + \sqrt{2})/4$ **5. a.** $(\sqrt{2} - \sqrt{6})/4$
  b. $-(\sqrt{6} + \sqrt{2})/4$ **7. a.** $(\sqrt{6} + \sqrt{2})/4$ **b.** $(\sqrt{6} + \sqrt{2})/4$ **9. a.** $-\frac{56}{65}$ **b.** $-\frac{63}{65}$
11. a. $(2\sqrt{10} - 2)/9$ **b.** $(-\sqrt{5} + 4\sqrt{2})/9$ **13. a.** $31/17\sqrt{5}$ **b.** $38/17\sqrt{5}$ **15. a.** $-\frac{65}{33}$ **b.** $-\frac{65}{16}$
17. a. $\sin(\pi/2 + \theta) = \sin(\pi/2) \cos \theta + \cos(\pi/2) \sin \theta = \cos \theta$
  b. $\cos(\pi/2 + \theta) = \cos(\pi/2) \cos \theta - \sin(\pi/2) \sin \theta = -\sin \theta$
19. a. $\sin(\pi - \theta) = \sin \pi \cos \theta - \cos \pi \sin \theta = \sin \theta$
  b. $\cos(\pi - \theta) = \cos \pi \cos \theta + \sin \pi \sin \theta = -\cos \theta$
31. $0, \pi$
33. a. $\sin \alpha \cos \beta \cos \gamma + \cos \alpha \sin \beta \cos \gamma + \cos \alpha \cos \beta \sin \gamma - \sin \alpha \sin \beta \sin \gamma$
  b. $\cos \alpha \cos \beta \cos \gamma - \sin \alpha \sin \beta \cos \gamma - \sin \alpha \cos \beta \sin \gamma - \cos \alpha \sin \beta \sin \gamma$

Exercise Set 5, page 341

1. $\sin 2\theta = -\frac{24}{25}$, $\cos 2\theta = -\frac{7}{25}$ **3.** $\sin 2\theta = \frac{120}{169}$, $\cos 2\theta = \frac{119}{169}$ **5.** $\sin 2\theta = -\frac{4}{5}$, $\cos 2\theta = \frac{3}{5}$
7. $\sin 2\theta = 2x\sqrt{1 - x^2}$, $\cos 2\theta = 1 - 2x^2$ **9.** $\sin \theta = \sqrt{3}/3$, $\cos \theta = -\sqrt{6}/3$ **11.** $\sin \theta = -\frac{3}{5}$, $\cos \theta = \frac{4}{6}$
13. a. $\sqrt{2 - \sqrt{2}}/2$ **b.** $\sqrt{2 + \sqrt{3}}/2$ **c.** $\sqrt{2 + \sqrt{3}}/2$ **d.** $\sqrt{2 - \sqrt{2}}/2$
15. $\sin(\alpha/2) = 3/\sqrt{13}$, $\cos(\alpha/2) = -2/\sqrt{13}$ **17.** $\sin(\alpha/2) = -\sqrt{3}/3$, $\cos(\alpha/2) = \sqrt{6}/3$ **19.** $P(\theta) = (\frac{3}{5}, \frac{4}{5})$
21. a. $-\sin \theta$ **b.** $-\sin \theta$ **c.** $\cos \theta$ **d.** $-\cos \theta$ **e.** $\cos \theta$
39. $\sin 2\theta = 2x/(1 + x^2)$, $\cos 2\theta = (1 - x^2)/(1 + x^2)$
41. $\sin 3\theta = 3 \sin \theta - 4 \sin^3 \theta$, $\cos 3\theta = 4 \cos^3 \theta - 3 \cos \theta$

Exercise Set 6, page 345

1. a. $2 + \sqrt{3}$ **b.** $2 - \sqrt{3}$ **3.** $\frac{24}{7}$ **5.** $(9 + 5\sqrt{2})/2$
7. $\tan 2\alpha = \frac{120}{119}$, $\tan 2\beta = -\frac{240}{161}$, $\tan(\alpha/2) = -\frac{2}{3}$, $\tan(\beta/2) = 4$ **9.** $\tan 2\theta = -\frac{24}{7}$, $\tan(\theta/2) = 3$ **11. a.** $\sqrt{6}/2$
  b. $-\sqrt{6}/2$ **13. a.** $\sqrt{2}/2$ **b.** $-\sqrt{2}/2$ **15. a.** $2 \sin 4x \cos x$ **b.** $\frac{1}{2}(\sin 8x + \sin 2x)$

Exercise Set 8, page 354

1. $\{\pi/6, 11\pi/6\}$ **3.** $\{\pi/3, 5\pi/3\}$ **5.** $\{\pi/3, \pi/2, 3\pi/2, 5\pi/3\}$ **7.** $\{\pi/3, \pi, 5\pi/3\}$ **9.** $\{\pi/2, 3\pi/2\}$
11. $\{\pi/6, \pi/2, 5\pi/6, 3\pi/2\}$ **13.** $\{\pi/3, 2\pi/3, 4\pi/3, 5\pi/3\}$ **15.** no solution   **17.** $\{\pi/2, 3\pi/2\}$

19. $\{0, 2\pi/9, \pi/3, 4\pi/9, 2\pi/3, 8\pi/9, \pi, 10\pi/9, 4\pi/3, 14\pi/9, 5\pi/3, 16\pi/9\}$ 21. $\{0, \pi/2\}$

23. $\{\pi/24, 11\pi/24, 13\pi/24, 23\pi/24, 25\pi/24, 35\pi/24, 37\pi/24, 47\pi/24\}$ 25. no solution

27. $\{2\pi/9, \pi/4, 5\pi/9, 3\pi/4, 8\pi/9, 11\pi/9, 5\pi/4, 14\pi/9, 7\pi/4, 17\pi/9\}$ 29. no solution

31. $\{0.848, 2.29, 3.87, 5.55\}$ 33. $\{0.464, 1.11, 3.61, 4.25\}$ 35. $\{0.285, 2.86\}$

37. $\{\pi/3, 2\pi/3, 3\pi/4, 4\pi/3, 5\pi/3, 7\pi/4\}$ 39. $\{\pi/6, 5\pi/6, 3\pi/2\}$

Exercise Set 9, page 363

1. Amplitude = 1, period = π

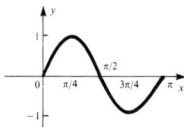

3. Amplitude = 2, period = 2π

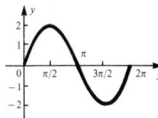

5. Amplitude = 3, period = 4

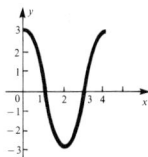

7. Amplitude = 2, period = $2\pi/3$

9. Amplitude = 1, period = 4π

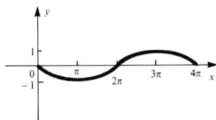

11. Amplitude = 1, period = π

13. Amplitude = 2, period = $2\pi/3$

15. Period = 1

17. Amplitude = 1, period = 2π, phase shift = $\pi/3$

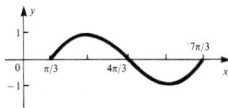

19. Amplitude = 1, period = π, phase shift = $-\pi/4$

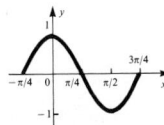

21. Amplitude = 2, period = $2\pi/3$, phase shift = $-\frac{2}{3}$

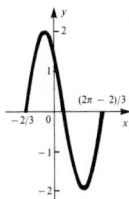

23. Amplitude = 2, period = 2, phase shift = $\frac{1}{4}$

25. Amplitude = 2, period = $2\pi/3$, phase shift = $\pi/6$

27. **a.** $y = \sqrt{2}\sin(x - \pi/4)$; amplitude $= \sqrt{2}$, period $= 2\pi$, phase shift $= \pi/4$

b. $y = 5\sin(x + \theta)$, where $\theta \approx 2.5$ radians as shown; amplitude $= 5$, period $= 2\pi$, phase shift $= -\theta \approx -2.5$

29. Period $= 6\pi$

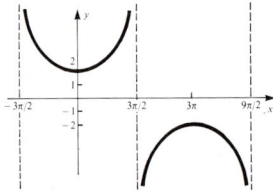

Exercise Set 10, page 368

1. **a.** $-\pi/3$ **b.** $5\pi/6$ **3.** **a.** $3\pi/4$ **b.** $\pi/2$ **5.** **a.** 0 **b.** $-\pi/6$ **7.** **a.** $\pi/2$ **b.** $7\pi/6$
9. **a.** $-2\sqrt{2}/3$ **b.** $\frac{5}{4}$ **11.** **a.** $\frac{4}{3}$ **b.** $\frac{3}{5}$ **13.** **a.** $2\sqrt{2}/3$ **b.** $-\frac{7}{24}$ **15.** $2/\sqrt{5}$ **17.** $-\frac{24}{25}$
19. $-\frac{120}{119}$ **21.** $\frac{4}{3}$ **23.** $\frac{1}{9}$ **25.** $3/\sqrt{10}$ **27.** $\sin\theta = -\frac{3}{5}$, $\cos\theta = \frac{4}{5}$ **29.** $\frac{63}{65}$ **31.** $\frac{11}{10}$

Exercise Set 11, page 374

1. $\theta = 7\pi/4, r = \sqrt{2}; 1 - i = \sqrt{2}[\cos(7\pi/4) + i\sin(7\pi/4)]$ **3.** $\theta = 11\pi/6, r = 2; \sqrt{3} - i = 2[\cos(11\pi/6) + i\sin(11\pi/6)]$

  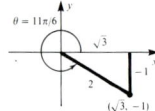

5. $\theta = \pi, r = 4; -4 = 4(\cos\pi + i\sin\pi)$ **7.** $\theta = 4\pi/3, r = 4; -2 - 2i\sqrt{3} = 4[\cos(4\pi/3) + i\sin(4\pi/3)]$

9. $\theta = 0, r = 5; 5 = 5(\cos 0 + i\sin 0)$

11. $-1 - i\sqrt{3}$ **13.** $-5i$ **15.** $3\sqrt{3} - 3i$ **17.** $1 - i$ **19.** $(-3\sqrt{3}/2) + (3i/2)$
21. $z_1 z_2 = 6[\cos(3\pi/2) + i\sin(3\pi/2)] = -6i; z_1/z_2 = \frac{2}{3}[\cos(-\pi) + i\sin(-\pi)] = -\frac{2}{3}$
23. $z_1 z_2 = 8[\cos(5\pi/4) + i\sin(5\pi/4)] = -4\sqrt{2} - 4i\sqrt{2}; z_1/z_2 = 2[\cos(-\pi/4) + i\sin(-\pi/4)] = \sqrt{2} - i\sqrt{2}$
25. $z_1 z_2 = 8[\cos(13\pi/6) + i\sin(13\pi/6)] = 4\sqrt{3} + 4i; z_1/z_2 = \frac{1}{2}[\cos(3\pi/2) + i\sin(3\pi/2)] = -i/2$
27. $z_1 z_2 = 24(\cos 170° + i\sin 170°); z_1/z_2 = \frac{2}{3}(\cos 30° + i\sin 30°) = (\sqrt{3}/3) + (i/3)$
29. $729[\cos(9\pi/2) + i\sin(9\pi/2)] = 729[\cos(\pi/2) + i\sin(\pi/2)] = 729i$
31. $256[\cos(44\pi/2) + i\sin(44\pi/3)] = 256[\cos(2\pi/3) + i\sin(2\pi/3)] = -128 + 128i\sqrt{3}$
33. $256[\cos(20\pi/3) + i\sin(20\pi/3)] = 256[\cos(2\pi/3) + i\sin(2\pi/3)] = -128 + 128i\sqrt{3}$
35. $\zeta_0 = 2[\cos(\pi/6) + i\sin(\pi/6)] = \sqrt{3} + i; \zeta_1 = 2[\cos(5\pi/6) + i\sin(5\pi/6)] = -\sqrt{3} + i; \zeta_2 = 2[\cos(3\pi/2) + i\sin(3\pi/2)] = -2i$
37. $\zeta_0 = 1(\cos 0 + i\sin 0) = 1; \zeta_1 = 1[\cos(\pi/3) + i\sin(\pi/3)] = \frac{1}{2} + i\sqrt{3}/2; \zeta_2 = 1[\cos(2\pi/3) + i\sin(2\pi/3)] = -\frac{1}{2} + i\sqrt{3}/2;$
$\zeta_3 = 1(\cos\pi + i\sin\pi) = -1; \zeta_4 = 1[\cos(4\pi/3) + i\sin(4\pi/3)] = -\frac{1}{2} - i\sqrt{3}/2; \zeta_5 = 1[\cos(5\pi/3) + i\sin(5\pi/3)] = \frac{1}{2} - i\sqrt{3}/2$
39. $\zeta_0 = 4[\cos(3\pi/4) + i\sin(3\pi/4)] = -2\sqrt{2} + 2i\sqrt{2}; \zeta_1 = 4[\cos(7\pi/4) + i\sin(7\pi/4)] = 2\sqrt{2} - 2i\sqrt{2}$
41. $\{\sqrt{3} + i, 2i, -\sqrt{3} + i, -\sqrt{3} - i, -2i, \sqrt{3} - i\}$ **43.** $\{2, 1 + i\sqrt{3}, -1 + i\sqrt{3}, -2, -1 - i\sqrt{3}, 1 - i\sqrt{3}\}$
45. By the hint we have $\rho^n(\cos n\phi + i\sin n\phi) = r[\cos(\theta + 2k\pi) + i\sin(\theta + 2k\pi)]$. So $\rho^n = r, \rho = r^{1/n}$, and $n\phi = \theta + 2k\pi$. Therefore, $\phi = (\theta + 2k\pi)/n$. By taking $k = 0, 1, 2, \ldots, n - 1$, we get all the distinct answers.

Exercise Set 12, page 382

1.

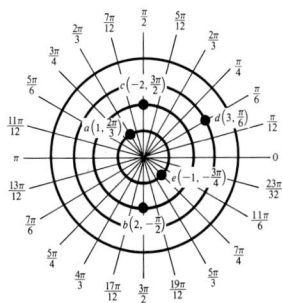

3. $(2, 8\pi/3), (-2, 5\pi/3),$
$(2, -4\pi/3), (-2, -\pi/3),$
$(2, 14\pi/3)$

5. a. $(2, 2)$ **b.** $(3\sqrt{3}, -3)$ **c.** $(-5\sqrt{2}, 5\sqrt{2})$ **d.** $(-4, 0)$ **e.** $-(2, 2)$ **7. a.** $(4\sqrt{2}, 7\pi/4)$
b. $(4, 5\pi/6)$ **c.** $(2, 3\pi/2)$ **d.** $(1, 5\pi/3)$ **e.** $(2\sqrt{6}, 7\pi/6)$ **9.** $\phi = 3\pi/4$ **11.** $r\cos\theta = 3$
13. $r = 4\sin\theta$ **15.** $r^2 = 4/\sin 2\theta$ **17.** $r = -2\cos\theta$ **19.** $x^2 + y^2 = 16$ **21.** $x = 2$
23. $2x - 3y = 5$ **25.** $x = 3$ **27.** $x^2 + y^2 + 2x = 0$ **29.** $y^2 = 1 + 2x$

31.

33.

35.

37. cardioid

39. limaçon

41. lemniscate

43. 3-leaf rose

45. 4-leaf rose

47. limaçon

49. circle

51. cardioid

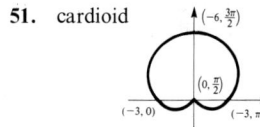

53. a. $r = 16\csc^2 2\theta$, together with $r = 0$ **b.** $r = 4\cos\theta\sec 2\theta$
55. $r = 1 - \cos\theta$
cardioid

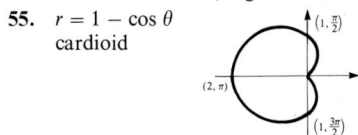

57. $r = \sqrt{2}\cos(\theta - \pi/4)$
circle

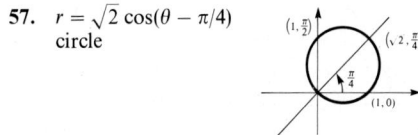

59.

θ	0	$\pi/6$	$\pi/4$	$\pi/3$	$\pi/2$	$2\pi/3$	$3\pi/4$	$5\pi/6$	π	$7\pi/6$	$5\pi/4$	$4\pi/3$	$3\pi/2$	$5\pi/3$	$7\pi/4$	$11\pi/6$
r	2	1.93	1.85	1.73	1.41	1	0.77	0.52	0	-0.52	-0.77	-1	-1.41	-1.73	-1.85	-1.93

Use symmetry

61. 5-leaf rose

63.

65.

67. $(2, \pi/2), (2, 3\pi/2)$

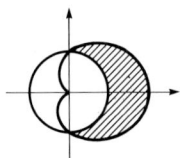

69. $(\frac{3}{2}, \pi/3), (\frac{3}{2}, 5\pi/3)$

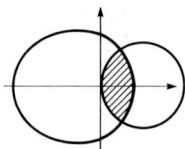

71. $(\frac{5}{2}, \pi/3), (\frac{5}{2}, 5\pi/3)$

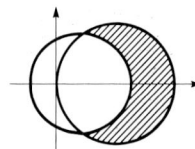

Exercise Set 13, page 386

1.

x	$-\pi/2$	-1	-0.75	-0.5	-0.25	-0.125	0.125	0.25	0.5	0.75	1	$\pi/2$
y	0.637	0.841	0.909	0.959	0.990	0.997	0.997	0.990	0.959	0.909	0.841	0.637

y approaches 1 as x approaches 0

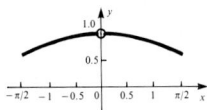

5. 2 **7.** -2 **9.** 1

Review Exercise Set, page 387

1. a. $\dfrac{1+\sqrt{3}}{1-\sqrt{3}}$ **b.** $\dfrac{\sqrt{2}-\sqrt{6}}{4}$ **c.** $\dfrac{\sqrt{2}+\sqrt{2}}{2}$ **d.** $\dfrac{-\sqrt{2}-\sqrt{6}}{4}$

3. a. $2\pi/3$ **b.** $-\pi/3$ **c.** $-\pi/3$ **d.** π **e.** $-\pi/4$ **5. a.** $-\frac{24}{25}$ **b.** $-\frac{7}{25}$ **c.** $2/\sqrt{5}$

7. a. $-\frac{13}{85}$ **b.** $\frac{36}{85}$ **c.** $\frac{13}{84}$ **9.** $\sin(\theta/2) = 5/\sqrt{34}, \cos(\theta/2) = -3/\sqrt{34}, \tan(\theta/2) = -\frac{5}{3}$

11. a. $-\frac{24}{7}$ **b.** $2/\sqrt{7}$ **27.** $\{0, \pi, \pi/6, 5\pi/6, 7\pi/6, 11\pi/6\}$ **29.** $\{3\pi/2, \pi/6, 5\pi/6\}$ **31.** $\{7\pi/6, 11\pi/6, \pi/2\}$

33. a. Period $= 4$ **b.** Amplitude $= 2$, period $= 4$

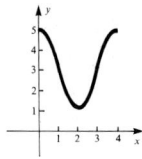

35. $z_1 \cdot z_2 = 6[\cos(13\pi/6) + i\sin(13\pi/6)] = 6[\cos(\pi/6) + i\sin(\pi/6)] = 3\sqrt{3} + 3i; z_1/z_2 = \frac{2}{3}[\cos(-\pi/2) + i\sin(-\pi/2)] = -2i/3$

37. $256[\cos(4\pi/3) + i\sin(4\pi/3)] = -128 - 128i\sqrt{3}$ **39. a.** $5x^2 - 4y^2 + 24x + 16 = 0$ **b.** $x^2 - y^2 = 4$

41. a.

4-leaf rose

b.

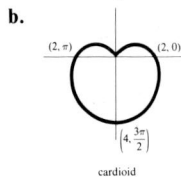

cardioid

43. 1 **51.** $\{\pi/3, 2\pi/3, 4\pi/3, 5\pi/3, \pi/2, 3\pi/2\}$ **53.** $\{\pi/2, 3\pi/2, \pi/6, 5\pi/6\}$

55. a. Amplitude $= 2$, period $= \pi$, phase shift $\pi/6$ **b.** $y = 2\left(\dfrac{\sqrt{3}}{2}\cos x - \tfrac{1}{2}\sin x\right) = 2\sin\left(\dfrac{\pi}{3} - x\right) = -2\sin\left(x - \dfrac{\pi}{3}\right)$;

amplitude $= 2$, period $= 2\pi$, phase shift $= \pi/3$

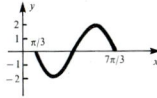

57. $\{4i, -2\sqrt{3} - 2i, 2\sqrt{3} - 2i\}$ **59.** $(3 + 2\sqrt{3}, 5\pi/6)$, $(3 + 2\sqrt{3}, 7\pi/6)$, pole

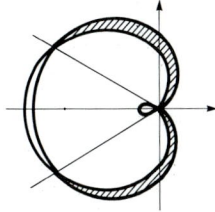

Cumulative Review Exercise Set III (Chapters 8 and 9), page 391

1. a. $B = 60°$, $c = 8\sqrt{3}$, $a = 4\sqrt{3}$ **b.** $A = 30°$, $c = 8$, $b = 4\sqrt{3}$ **c.** $B = 45°$, $a = b = 8\sqrt{2}$
   d. $A = 30°$, $B = 60°$, $b = 10\sqrt{3}$ **e.** $A = B = 45°$, $a = 6\sqrt{2}$ **3. a.** $-\tfrac{24}{25}$ **b.** $\tfrac{33}{65}$ **c.** $-1/\sqrt{5}$
   d. $-\sqrt{5}$ **5. a.** $z_1 z_2 = 8[\cos(3\pi/2) + i\sin(3\pi/2)] = -8i$ **b.** $z_1/z_2 = 2[\cos(7\pi/6) + i\sin(7\pi/6)] = -\sqrt{3} - i$
   c. $z_2^4 = 16[\cos(2\pi/3) + i\sin(2\pi/3)] = -8 + 8i\sqrt{3}$
   d. $\zeta_0 = 2[\cos(2\pi/3) + i\sin(2\pi/3)] = -1 + i\sqrt{3}$; $\zeta_1 = 2[\cos(5\pi/3) + i\sin(5\pi/3)] = 1 - i\sqrt{3}$ **7. a.** $\tfrac{7}{9}$ **b.** $-\tfrac{3}{5}$
   c. $\tfrac{4}{3}$ **d.** $1/\sqrt{5}$ **9. a.** 1.97 radians   **b.** 11.82 inches   **c.** 35.46 square inches
   d. 16.58 square inches   **11. a.** $r = 1.194$ kilometers   **b.** 16.66 miles per hour
15. $\{4i, -2\sqrt{3} - 2i, 2\sqrt{3} - 2i\}$
17. a. Amplitude $= 2$, period $= 4\pi$, phase shift $= 2\pi/3$ **b.** Amplitude $= \tfrac{1}{2}$, period $= 2$, phase shift $= -\tfrac{1}{4}$

21. a. Period $= 2$

b. The given equation is equivalent to $x = \tfrac{1}{2}\sin 2(y - \pi/3)$, with $-\pi/2 \le 2(y - \pi/3) \le \pi/2$, or $\pi/12 \le y \le 7\pi/12$.

23. a. $\{0, 4\pi/3\}$ **b.** $\{\pi/6, 5\pi/6, 7\pi/6, 11\pi/6\}$
25. $\left(\sqrt{3}, \dfrac{\pi}{6}\right), \left(0, \dfrac{\pi}{2}\right)$

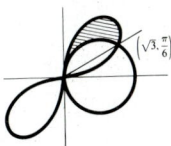

27. $h = 11.76$, $\theta = 35°21'$

Chapter 10

Exercise Set 1, page 403

1. $(4, 2)$ **3.** $(-1, -3)$ **5.** $(4, 3)$ **7.** $\left(\tfrac{17}{11}, \tfrac{2}{11}\right)$ **9.** $(4, -2)$ **11.** $(-5, 6)$ **13.** $(-2, 3, 4)$

15. $(2, -1, 4)$ **17.** $(-6, 2, 5)$ **19.** $(-\frac{11}{14}, -\frac{11}{24})$ **21.** $\left(\dfrac{ac + bd}{a^2 + b^2}, \dfrac{bc - ad}{a^2 + b^2} \right)$

23. If both sides of the second equation are multiplied by $-\frac{1}{2}$ and then 5 is added to both sides, the result is the same as the first equation. So the equations are equivalent. The solution set is $\left\{ \left(c, \dfrac{3c - 5}{4} \right) : \quad c \in R \right\}$.

25. $\begin{aligned} 8x - 6y &= 3 \\ -8x + 6y &= 4 \\ \hline 0 &= 7 \end{aligned}$ This is impossible, so the equations are inconsistent.

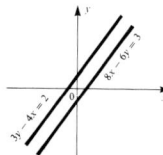

27. The solution of the system consisting of the first two equations is $(-3, 2)$, and this pair also satisfies the third equation.

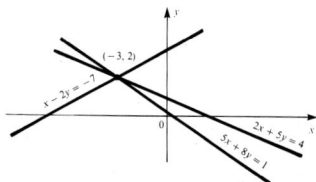

29. 95 and 32   **31.** 4 by 8

33. Airspeed = 525 miles per hour, wind velocity = 75 miles per hour

35. 3 miles per hour walking, 5 miles per hour jogging

37. 86   **39.** 6 hours and 40 minutes   **41.** \$4,000 at 5%, \$7,000 at 7%

43. 14 cubic centimeters of 10% solution, 16 cubic centimeters of 25% solution

45. $10\frac{2}{3}$ pounds Indian tea, $9\frac{1}{3}$ pounds Ceylon tea   **47.** Coffee is \$4.25 per pound, eggs are 90¢ per dozen

49. $(\frac{1}{5}, \frac{1}{10}, -\frac{7}{10})$ **51.** $(\frac{23}{10}, -\frac{8}{5}, -\frac{9}{2}, \frac{29}{5})$

55. Since there are more unknowns than equations, the system is dependent. The solution set is $\{(2c - 2, 5c - 5, 3c - 2, c): \quad c \in R\}$.

57. $a = -1, b = 2, c = 5$ **59.** $\frac{1}{2}$ hour, 15 miles   **61.** 30 hours for A, 24 hours for B, 40 hours for C

Exercise Set 2, page 413

1. $(-4, 3, 1)$ **3.** $(2, -3, 7)$ **5.** $(-3, 4, -2)$ **7.** $\{(2 - c, 1 - c, c): \quad c \in R\}$ **9.** $(2, -1, 0)$ **11.** $(5, 2, -3)$

13. $(2, -1, 4)$ **15.** $(-2, -2, 1)$ **17.** $\{(-3 + 7c, c, 4 - 3c): \quad c \in R\}$ **19.** $\{(10c, 8c, c): \quad c \in R\}$

21. $(\frac{10}{11}, -\frac{3}{11}, \frac{3}{11})$ **23.** Inconsistent   **25.** $(\frac{2}{3}, -\frac{22}{3}, -4)$ **27.** $\{(2, c - 5, 3c - 9, c): \quad c \in R\}$

29. $\{(-5c, -2c, c): \quad c \in R\}$ **31.** $(-\frac{4}{3}, \frac{2}{3}, \frac{7}{3})$ **33.** $(3, -1, 5, 6)$ **35.** $(-19, 16, -22, -9)$ **37.** $(1, -1, 3)$

39. $(2, 3, 0, -1)$ **41.** $(3, 4, -1, 2)$ **43.** Inconsistent   **45.** $\{(c, 2c, -c, 3c): \quad c \in R\}$

47. $(-27, -21, 3, -6, 5)$

Exercise Set 3, page 420

1. a. 11   **b.** -78 **c.** -60 **3. a.** 0   **b.** 5   **c.** 0   **5. a.** -1 **b.** $\begin{vmatrix} 3 & 1 \\ -4 & -3 \end{vmatrix} = -5$

c. 5.   **7. a.** -6 **b.** $\begin{vmatrix} -2 & 1 \\ 5 & -3 \end{vmatrix} = 1$ **c.** 1

9. a. $1 \begin{vmatrix} -4 & 5 \\ -6 & -1 \end{vmatrix} - (-3) \begin{vmatrix} 3 & -2 \\ -6 & -1 \end{vmatrix} + 7 \begin{vmatrix} 3 & -2 \\ -4 & 5 \end{vmatrix} = 34 + 3(-15) + 7(7) = 38$

b. $(-6) \begin{vmatrix} -2 & 1 \\ 5 & -3 \end{vmatrix} - (-1) \begin{vmatrix} 3 & 1 \\ -4 & -3 \end{vmatrix} + 7 \begin{vmatrix} 3 & -2 \\ -4 & 5 \end{vmatrix} = -6(1) + (-5) + 7(7) = 38$

11. 14   **13.** 118   **15.** -14 **17.** 62   **19.** $\{4, -1\}$

21. $\begin{vmatrix} a+kb & b \\ c+kd & d \end{vmatrix} = ad + kbd - bc - kbd = ad - bc = \begin{vmatrix} a & b \\ c & d \end{vmatrix}$

$\begin{vmatrix} a+kc & b+kd \\ c & d \end{vmatrix} = ad + kcd - bc - kcd = ad - bc = \begin{vmatrix} a & b \\ c & d \end{vmatrix}$

23. 44   **25.** 38

29. If x is replaced by x_1 and y is replaced by y_1, the determinant is 0, since two rows are identical (see Problem 28). Similarly, if x is replaced by x_2 and y by y_2, the determinant is 0. Thus, (x_1, y_1) and (x_2, y_2) satisfy the equation. Expanding the determinant shows that the equation is linear, and the conclusion follows.

31. $\{0, 1, -2, -\frac{3}{2}\}$

Exercise Set 4, page 426

1. $(\frac{37}{11}, -\frac{1}{11})$ **3.** $(-\frac{14}{13}, \frac{16}{13})$ **5.** $(\frac{13}{82}, -\frac{25}{41})$ **7.** $(2, \frac{1}{2})$ **9.** $(-\frac{5}{7}, \frac{13}{7})$ **11.** $(14, 8)$ **13.** $(\frac{4}{3}, \frac{22}{9}, \frac{5}{9})$

15. $(3, -2, -3)$ **17.** $(\frac{3}{2}, -\frac{1}{2}, 2)$ **19.** $(\frac{16}{11}, \frac{31}{11}, -\frac{6}{11})$ **21.** $(\frac{21}{17}, -\frac{39}{17}, -\frac{20}{17})$ **23.** $\left(\frac{2a-3}{1-5a}, \frac{a+5}{5a-1}\right)$

25. $\left(\frac{2x^2-1}{2x^2+1}, \frac{2x}{2x^2+1}\right)$ **27.** $\left(\frac{3}{4}, \frac{6-3m}{2}\right)$ **29.** $(\frac{7}{9}, \frac{26}{9}, \frac{19}{9})$ **31.** $(\frac{23}{15}, \frac{2}{5}, -\frac{16}{15}, -\frac{2}{15})$

Exercise Set 5, page 430

1. $\begin{bmatrix} 2 & 6 & 3 \\ 10 & 4 & 16 \end{bmatrix}$ **3.** $\begin{bmatrix} -2 & 2 \\ -6 & 11 \end{bmatrix}$ **5.** $\begin{bmatrix} -2 & 14 \\ 0 & 0 \end{bmatrix}$ **7.** $\begin{bmatrix} -5 & 8 \\ 10 & -1 \\ 27 & 14 \end{bmatrix}$ **9.** $\begin{bmatrix} 21 & 14 \\ 17 & 26 \end{bmatrix}$ **11.** $\begin{bmatrix} 7 & -1 & 10 \\ 13 & 11 & 25 \end{bmatrix}$

13. $\begin{bmatrix} 1 & 9 & -7 & 7 \\ 10 & 6 & -28 & 0 \\ -7 & 15 & 10 & 16 \end{bmatrix}$ **15.** $x = 5, y = -2$ **17.** $\begin{bmatrix} 0 & 0 \\ 0 & 0 \end{bmatrix}$ Neither A nor B need be 0 in order for their product to be 0.

21. $A^2 = \begin{bmatrix} 2 & 2 \\ 2 & 2 \end{bmatrix}$, $A^3 = \begin{bmatrix} 4 & 4 \\ 4 & 4 \end{bmatrix}$, $A^4 = \begin{bmatrix} 8 & 8 \\ 8 & 8 \end{bmatrix}$, $A^n = \begin{bmatrix} 2^{n-1} & 2^{n-1} \\ 2^{n-1} & 2^{n-1} \end{bmatrix}$

23. $(A + B)(A - B) = A^2 - AB + BA - B^2$

25. $A = \begin{bmatrix} a_{11} & a_{12} & a_{13} & \cdots & a_{1n} \\ a_{21} & a_{22} & a_{23} & \cdots & a_{2n} \\ a_{31} & a_{32} & a_{33} & \cdots & a_{3n} \\ \vdots & \vdots & \vdots & \vdots & \vdots \\ a_{n1} & a_{n2} & a_{n3} & \cdots & a_{nn} \end{bmatrix}$, $X = \begin{bmatrix} x_1 \\ x_2 \\ x_3 \\ \vdots \\ x_n \end{bmatrix}$, $B = \begin{bmatrix} b_1 \\ b_2 \\ b_3 \\ \vdots \\ b_n \end{bmatrix}$

Exercise Set 6, page 435

1. $\begin{bmatrix} 2 & -1 \\ 3 & -2 \end{bmatrix}$ **3.** $\begin{bmatrix} -1 & 2 \\ -\frac{3}{2} & \frac{5}{2} \end{bmatrix}$ **5.** $\begin{bmatrix} 1 & 0 & 0 \\ \frac{1}{2} & \frac{1}{2} & 0 \\ -1 & -\frac{2}{3} & \frac{1}{3} \end{bmatrix}$ **7.** $\begin{bmatrix} 0 & 1 & 2 \\ 1 & -2 & -4 \\ 2 & -2 & -5 \end{bmatrix}$ **9.** $\begin{bmatrix} -\frac{1}{2} & \frac{1}{2} & 0 \\ 0 & \frac{1}{2} & \frac{1}{2} \\ \frac{1}{2} & 0 & -\frac{1}{2} \end{bmatrix}$

11. Singular   **13.** $\begin{bmatrix} -80 & 67 & 4 \\ -19 & 16 & 1 \\ -98 & 82 & 5 \end{bmatrix}$ **15.** Singular   **17.** $\begin{bmatrix} 5 & -2 \\ -3 & -1 \end{bmatrix}$ **19.** $\begin{bmatrix} \frac{2}{5} & -\frac{3}{5} \\ \frac{3}{10} & -\frac{1}{5} \end{bmatrix}$ **21.** $\begin{bmatrix} 1 & -2 & 5 \\ 0 & 1 & -4 \\ 0 & 0 & 1 \end{bmatrix}$

23. $\begin{bmatrix} 3 & 3 & -8 \\ 6 & 7 & -18 \\ -1 & -1 & 3 \end{bmatrix}$ **25.** $\begin{bmatrix} 2 & -2 & -3 \\ -2 & 3 & 4 \\ -3 & 4 & 6 \end{bmatrix}$ **27.** $\begin{bmatrix} 23 & -30 & 12 \\ -6 & 8 & -3 \\ 19 & -25 & 10 \end{bmatrix}$ **29.** $\begin{bmatrix} -9 & -3 & -7 \\ -\frac{2}{3} & 0 & -\frac{1}{3} \\ -\frac{17}{3} & -2 & -\frac{13}{3} \end{bmatrix}$

31. $(2, 3, -4)$ **33.** $(\frac{1}{2}, -\frac{3}{2}, 2)$ **35.** $(4, -3, 5)$

39. $|A| = a_{11}a_{22}a_{33} \neq 0$ if, and only if, $a_{11} \neq 0$, $a_{22} \neq 0$, $a_{33} \neq 0$

$A^{-1} = \dfrac{1}{a_{11}a_{22}a_{33}} \begin{bmatrix} a_{22}a_{33} & -a_{12}a_{33} & a_{12}a_{33}-a_{22}a_{13} \\ 0 & a_{11}a_{33} & -a_{11}a_{23} \\ 0 & 0 & a_{11}a_{22} \end{bmatrix}$

41. $\begin{bmatrix} 0 & 0 & -1 & -1 \\ 1 & 4 & 1 & 3 \\ 1 & 2 & 1 & 2 \\ 0 & -1 & 0 & -1 \end{bmatrix}$ **43.** Singular   **49.** $\begin{bmatrix} 1.090 & 0.3789 & -0.4003 \\ 0.8379 & 0.4532 & -0.3122 \\ 0.4750 & 0.2408 & -0.2942 \end{bmatrix}$

Exercise Set 7, page 441

1. $\{(2, 1), (-1, -2)\}$ **3.** $\{(3, 0), (-1, -2)\}$ **5.** $\{(\frac{5}{3}, -\frac{11}{9}), (-1, -3)\}$ **7.** $\{(8, 2), (\frac{17}{4}, -\frac{1}{2})\}$

9. $\{(\frac{3}{4}, \frac{3}{2}), (-\frac{3}{4}, -\frac{3}{2})\}$ **11.** $\{(1, -1), (\frac{25}{4}, \frac{5}{2})\}$ **13.** $\{(-1, -1), (\frac{7}{4}, \frac{4}{7})\}$ **15.** $\{(1, \sqrt{2}), (1, -\sqrt{2})\}$

17. $\{(4, 3), (\frac{8}{3}, \frac{1}{3})\}$ **19.** $\{(9, 6), (9, -6)\}$ **21.** $\{(0, -4), (4, 4)\}$ **23.** $\{(2, 3), (2, -3), (-2, 3), (-2, -3)\}$

25. $\{(5, 0), (-\frac{2}{3}, \frac{17}{6})\}$ **27.** $\{(\frac{3}{2}, \frac{1}{2}), (\frac{3}{2}, -\frac{1}{2}), (-\frac{3}{2}, \frac{1}{2}), (-\frac{3}{2}, -\frac{1}{2})\}$ **29.** $\{(7, 2), (4, -1)\}$ **31.** $\{(2, 1), (\frac{2}{5}, -\frac{11}{5})\}$

33. $\left\{ \left(\dfrac{\sqrt{39}}{3}, \dfrac{1}{3}\right), \left(-\dfrac{\sqrt{39}}{3}, \dfrac{1}{3}\right), (\sqrt{2}, -2), (-\sqrt{2}, -2) \right\}$ **35.** 7 by 18   **37.** 12 and 8   **39.** 12 by 5

41. $2\sqrt{5}$ inches wide by $4\sqrt{5}$ inches high   **43.** \$3,600 at 5%

45. $\left\{ (3, -1), (-4, -8), \left(\dfrac{-1 + \sqrt{17}}{2}, \dfrac{7 + \sqrt{17}}{2}\right), \left(\dfrac{-1 - \sqrt{17}}{2}, \dfrac{7 - \sqrt{17}}{2}\right) \right\}$ **47.** $\{(1, 1), (\frac{1}{2}, 2)\}$

49. $r = 3, h = 8$; or $r = 2\sqrt{2 + \sqrt{13}} \approx 4.74, h = -4 + 2\sqrt{13} \approx 3.21$

51. $x + 2y - 8 = 0$ **53.** 8

Exercise Set 8, page 447

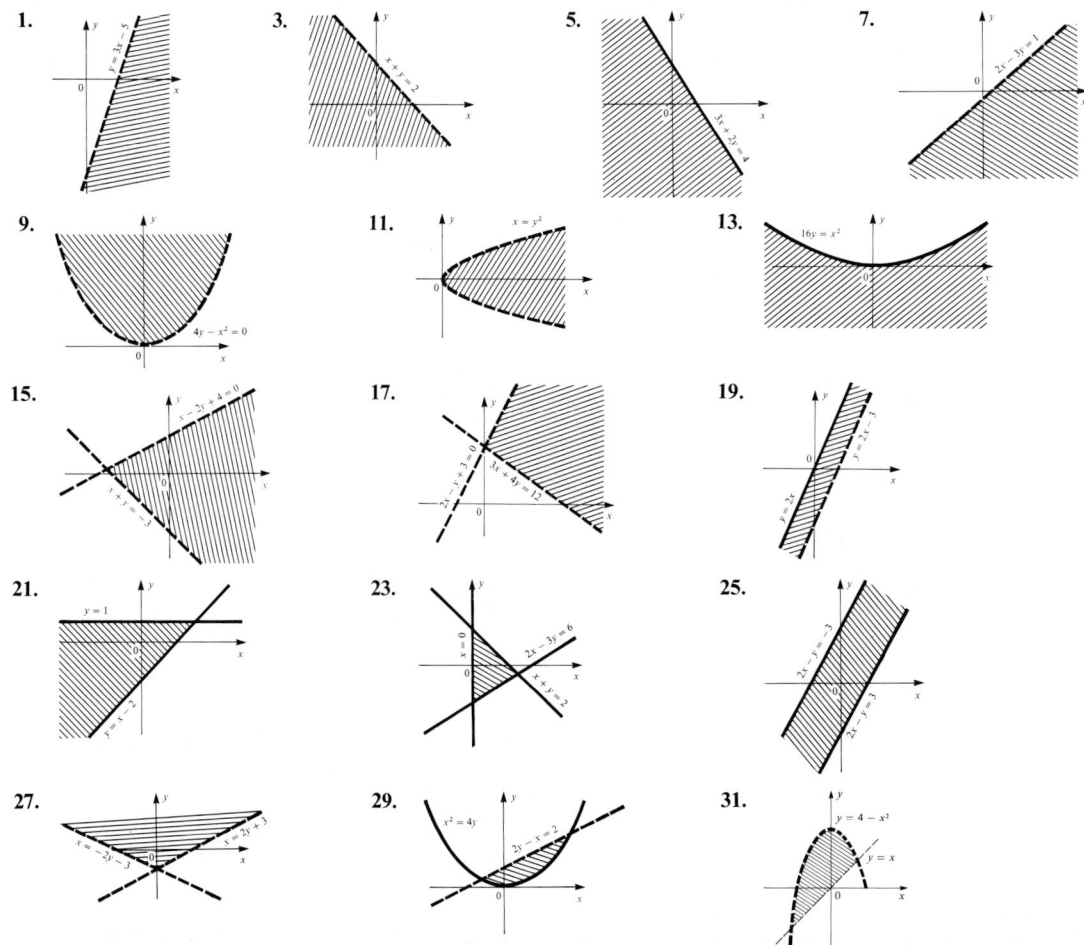

1.   **3.**   **5.**   **7.**

9.   **11.**   **13.**

15.   **17.**   **19.**

21.   **23.**   **25.**

27.   **29.**   **31.**

33.

35.

37.

39.

41.

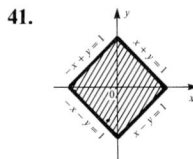

Exercise Set 9, page 451

1. Max $F = 11$ at $(4, 3)$ **3.** Max $G = 24$ at $(0, 4)$ **5.** Min $H = 16$ at $(2, 2)$ **7.** Min $C = 0$ at $(0, 5)$
9. 30 cases of each kind   **11.** 7 hours for A, 5 hours for B **13.** 500 gallons to each owner
15. 8 parts of type A, 10 parts of type B **17.** 20 days for each plant
19. 1 pound of feed number 1, 4 pounds of feed number 2   **21.** 350 gallons from store 2 to A, 400 gallons from store 1 to B

Review Exercise Set, page 454

1. $(3, 2)$ **3.** $(-8, 5)$ **5.** $(9, 5, 3)$ **7.** $(6, 5, -4, 3)$ **9.** $(-6, 8, -5)$ **11.** $(4, -6, -8)$
13. $\left\{ \left(\dfrac{13 - c}{7}, \dfrac{5 + 5c}{7}, c \right) : c \in R \right\}$ **15.** $(10, 6, -4, -3)$ **17.** $\{(-6 - c, 10, 2c + 3, c): c \in R\}$ **19.** Inconsistent
21. a. 1   **b.** 167   **23.** $x = 1$ or $-\frac{4}{5}$ **25. a.** $\left(-\frac{68}{3}, -43 \right)$ **b.** $\left(\frac{19}{44}, \frac{12}{11} \right)$ **27.** $(0, -1, 1)$
29. $\begin{bmatrix} -\frac{7}{5} & 2 & -\frac{8}{5} \\ -\frac{13}{5} & 3 & -\frac{12}{5} \\ 1 & -1 & 1 \end{bmatrix}$ **31.** $(3, 7, 2)$ **33.** $66\frac{2}{3}$ miles, $53\frac{1}{3}$ miles
35. 12 cubic centimeters 40% solution, 18 cubic centimeters 15% solution   **37.** 11 by 5
39. $18\frac{3}{4}$ gallons pure water, $31\frac{1}{4}$ gallons 40% salt solution   **41.** $1,800 at 6% interest
43. $4\frac{1}{2}$ hours for the larger pump, $6\frac{1}{4}$ hours for the smaller one   **45.** $\{(-1, 2), (3, -\frac{2}{3})\}$ **47.** $\{(8, -22), (-2, 8)\}$
49. $\{(2, 0), (-\frac{8}{5}, -\frac{12}{5})\}$ **51.** $\{(\frac{3}{4}, \frac{3}{4}), (\frac{2}{3}, \frac{4}{5})\}$ **53.** 15 and 7 or -7 and -15 **55.** 24 by 7 inches
57. a.

b.

59. a.

b.

61. Max $F = 60$ at $(6, 0)$ **63.** Min $G = 7$ at $(\frac{4}{3}, 4)$ **65.** 250 acres corn, 50 acres oats   **67.** 9 short trips, 1 long trip
69. $\left\{ \left(\dfrac{50 + 13c}{12}, \dfrac{2 - 3c}{4}, \dfrac{2 - 5c}{12}, c \right) : c \in R \right\}$ **71.** $\{(-3c, -4c, c, 2c): c \in R\}$ **73.** $(7, 3, 9, -6, -4)$
75. $(-2, 9, 8, 11)$ **77.** $\left(-\dfrac{6}{a + 2}, -\dfrac{2a + 1}{a + 2} \right), a \neq 2$ **79.** $a = 2, b = -3, c = -5$ **81.** $\{(3, 4), (\frac{21}{34}, \frac{1}{34})\}$
83. $2\frac{2}{3}$ gallons 40% solution, $5\frac{1}{3}$ gallons 25% solution   **85.** $(3, 7)$ and $(-1, -1)$
87. 15 miles per hour riding, 3 miles per hour walking   **89.** 82 pounds lawn fertilizer, 40 pounds garden fertilizer

Chapter 11

Exercise Set 1, page 465

1. $\frac{2}{4}, \frac{4}{7}, \frac{6}{10}, \frac{8}{13}, \frac{10}{16}$ or $\frac{1}{2}, \frac{4}{7}, \frac{3}{5}, \frac{8}{13}, \frac{5}{8}$ 3. $\frac{1}{1\cdot2}, \frac{-1}{2\cdot3}, \frac{1}{3\cdot4}, \frac{-1}{4\cdot5}, \frac{1}{5\cdot6}$ or $\frac{1}{2}, -\frac{1}{6}, \frac{1}{12}, -\frac{1}{20}, \frac{1}{30}$

5. $1, \frac{2}{3}, (\frac{2}{3})^2, (\frac{2}{3})^3, (\frac{2}{3})^4$ or $1, \frac{2}{3}, \frac{4}{9}, \frac{8}{27}, \frac{16}{81}$ 7. $\frac{2}{4}, \frac{4}{10}, \frac{8}{28}, \frac{16}{82}, \frac{32}{244}$ or $\frac{1}{2}, \frac{2}{5}, \frac{2}{7}, \frac{8}{41}, \frac{8}{61}$ 9. $\frac{2}{7}, \frac{2}{10}, \frac{2}{13}, \frac{2}{16}, \frac{2}{19}$ or $\frac{2}{7}, \frac{1}{5}, \frac{2}{13}, \frac{1}{8}, \frac{2}{19}$

11. $\frac{1}{243}, \frac{1}{729}, \frac{1}{2,187}$ 13. $\frac{1}{11}, \frac{1}{13}, \frac{1}{15}$ 15. $\frac{1}{32}, \frac{1}{64}, \frac{1}{128}$ 17. $\frac{12}{37}, \frac{14}{50}, \frac{16}{65}$ 19. $-\frac{6}{15}, \frac{7}{17}, -\frac{8}{19}$ 21. $\dfrac{1}{2n-1}$

23. $\dfrac{1}{3n}$ 25. $\dfrac{2^n-1}{2^n}$ 27. $\dfrac{1}{3n-2}$ 29. $5(0.1)^n$ 31. $2, \frac{4}{3}, \frac{8}{9}, \frac{16}{27}, \frac{32}{81}$ 33. $4, -\frac{4}{3}, \frac{4}{9}, -\frac{4}{27}, \frac{4}{81}$

35. $2, -4, 12, -48, 240$ 37. $\dfrac{n}{2n^2-3}$ 39. $\dfrac{(-1)^{n-1}2^{n-1}}{3^n+1}$ 41. $1, 1, 2, 3, 5$ 43. $1, 2, 2, 1, \frac{1}{2}$

45. For $n = 10, 100$, and $1,000$ the points are

$(\frac{7}{5}, \frac{20}{101}) = (1.4, 0.2)$

$(\frac{26}{25}, \frac{200}{10,001}) = (1.04, 0.02)$

$(\frac{251}{250}, \frac{2,000}{1,000,001}) = (1.004, 0.002)$

The limit point is $(1, 0)$.

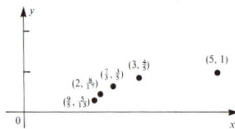

Exercise Set 2, page 470

1. $a_{n+1} - a_n = 3(n+1) - 3n = 3$; so $d = 3$, and the sequence is arithmetic; $15, 18, 21, 24, 27$
3. $a_{n+1} - a_n = [8 - 3(n+1)] - (8 - 3n) = -3$; so $d = -3$, and the sequence is arithmetic; $-7, -10, -13, -16, -19$
5. $a_{n+1} - a_n = \dfrac{13 - 3(n+1)}{2} - \dfrac{13-3n}{2} = -\dfrac{3}{2}$; so $d = -\frac{3}{2}$, and the sequence is arithmetic; $-1, -\frac{5}{2}, -4, -\frac{11}{2}, -7$
7. $\dfrac{a_{n+1}}{a_n} = \dfrac{(-\frac{1}{2})^n}{(-\frac{1}{2})^{n-1}} = -\dfrac{1}{2}$; so $r = -\frac{1}{2}$, and the sequence is geometric; $-\frac{1}{8}, \frac{1}{16}, -\frac{1}{32}, \frac{1}{64}$
9. $\dfrac{a_{n+1}}{a_n} = \dfrac{3^n/9}{3^{n-1}/9} = 3$; so $r = 3$, and the sequence is geometric; $3, 9, 27, 81$

11. Arithmetic, $d = 3$; $a_{16} = 44$ 13. Geometric, $r = -\frac{1}{3}$; $a_{10} = \frac{1}{6,561}$ 15. Arithmetic, $d = 4$; $a_{21} = 70$
17. Geometric, $r = \frac{1}{2}$ 19. Arithmetic, $d = 4$ 21. Neither   23. Neither   25. Neither
27. Geometric, $r = \frac{2}{3}$ 29. Neither   31. $a_1 = -25$ 33. $a_1 = -14, d = 2$ 35. $a_1 = -1, r = -\frac{2}{3}$
37. a. $x = \frac{25}{2}$ b. $x = \pm 10$ 39. $14, 17, 20, 23, 26, 29$
41. $x_{n+1} - x_n = (a_{n+1} + 5) - (a_n + 5) = a_{n+1} - a_n = $ a constant; so $x_1, x_2, x_3, \ldots$ is an arithmetic sequence
43. Arithmetic sequence, $d = \ln 2$
45. Let $r = a_{n+1}/a_n$. Then $\log a_{n+1} - \log a_n = \log(a_{n+1}/a_n) = \log r$, which is a constant. So the sequence $\log a_1, \log a_2, \log a_3, \ldots$ is arithmetic, with common difference $d = \log r$.
47. $1,024$
49. $A = P(1 + r)^n$; the sequence is $P(1 + r), P(1 + r)^2, P(1 + r)^3, \ldots$, which is geometric, with common ratio $1 + r$
51. \$9,830.40

Exercise Set 3, page 476

1. $4 + \frac{7}{3} + \frac{10}{5} + \frac{13}{7}$ 3. $\dfrac{1}{1\cdot2} - \dfrac{1}{2\cdot3} + \dfrac{1}{3\cdot4} - \dfrac{1}{4\cdot5} + \dfrac{1}{5\cdot6} - \dfrac{1}{6\cdot7}$ 5. $\frac{1}{2} - \frac{1}{5} + \frac{1}{10} - \frac{1}{17} + \frac{1}{26} - \frac{1}{37} + \frac{1}{50} - \frac{1}{65}$

7. $2 + 7 + 12 + 17 + 22 + 27 + 32 + 37 + 42 + 47$ 9. $e^{-1} + 2e^{-2} + 3e^{-3} + 4e^{-4} + 5e^{-5} + 6e^{-6}$ 11. $1,010$
13. $9,300$ 15. 0.222222222222 17. 34.5 19. $60,700$ 21. 400 23. $6[1 - (\frac{2}{3})^8] = \frac{12,610}{2,187}$
25. $(\frac{12}{7})[1 - (-\frac{3}{4})^6] = \frac{1,443}{1,024}$ 27. $5,050$ 29. 322 31. 120

33. First job sixth year salary = \$15,500, accumulated earnings = \$82,500; second job sixth year salary = \$14,693.28, accumulated earnings = \$73,359.29; second salary exceeds first in 8 years; accumulated earnings exceed first in 13 years
35. Should take first offer; earnings are \$10,737,418.23 and \$465,000, respectively

Exercise Set 4, page 482

1. Converges to $\frac{3}{2}$ 3. Diverges   5. Converges to $\frac{10}{19}$ 7. Converges to $\frac{30}{11}$ 9. Diverges

11. Converges to 5   13. Converges to 27   15. Diverges   17. Converges to $1/(\sqrt{2}-1)$

19. Converges to $\frac{10}{11}$ 21. $\frac{5}{33}$ 23. $\frac{17}{11}$ 25. $\frac{117}{37}$ 27. $\dfrac{2}{2-x}$, $|x| < 2$

29. $a_1 = 2$, $a_n = \dfrac{-1}{n(n-1)}$ for $n \geq 2$, so series is $2 - \dfrac{1}{2 \cdot 1} - \dfrac{1}{3 \cdot 2} - \dfrac{1}{4 \cdot 3} - \cdots$; $S = \lim_{n \to \infty} S_n = \lim_{n \to \infty} \left[1 + \left(\dfrac{1}{n}\right)\right] = 1$

31. $\dfrac{1}{3 + x^2}$, valid for $\left|-x^2/3\right| < 1$ or $|x| < \sqrt{3}$ 33. $\frac{2}{5}(2 + i)$

35. $1 + 2x + 4x^2 + 8x^3 + \cdots = \displaystyle\sum_{n=0}^{\infty} (2x)^n$, valid for $|x| < \frac{1}{2}$ 37. $\dfrac{1}{2} + \dfrac{x}{4} + \dfrac{x^2}{8} + \cdots = \displaystyle\sum_{n=0}^{\infty} \dfrac{x^n}{2^{n+1}}$ valid for $|x| < 2$

39. The sum is $\lim_{n \to \infty}[4 - (1/3^n)] = 4$; $a_1 = \frac{11}{3}$ and for $n \geq 2$, $a_n = S_n - S_{n-1} = 2/3^n$. So the series is $\frac{11}{3} + \frac{2}{9} + \frac{2}{27} + \frac{2}{81} + \cdots$. Beginning with the second term, this is geometric, with $r = \frac{1}{3}$.

Exercise Set 6, page 491

1. **a.** 3   **b.** 20   **c.** 28   **d.** 120   **e.** 1   **f.** 252   **g.** 435   **h.** 4,368   **i.** 7   **j.** 28

3. **a.** $(k+1)!$ **b.** $k+1$ **c.** $n(n-1)$ 5. $\dbinom{r}{r} = \dfrac{r(r-1)(r-2)\cdots(r-r+1)}{1 \cdot 2 \cdot 3 \cdots r} = \dfrac{r!}{r!} = 1$

7. $\dbinom{n}{n-k} = \dfrac{n!}{(n-k)![n-(n-k)]!} = \dfrac{n!}{(n-k)!k!} = \dbinom{n}{k}$ 9. $(x-y)^5 = x^5 - 5x^4y + 10x^3y^2 - 10x^2y^3 + 5xy^4 - y^5$

11. $a^4 - 12a^3b + 54a^2b^2 - 108ab^3 + 81b^4$ 13. $s^6 - 12s^5t + 60s^4t^2 - 160s^3t^3 + 240s^2t^4 - 192st^5 + 64t^6$

15. $x^{12} - 12x^{10}y + 60x^8y^2 - 160x^6y^3 + 240x^4y^4 - 192x^2y^5 + 64y^6$ 17. $495x^8y^4$ 19. $-2,835a^4b^3$ 21. 1.126

23. $(1+1)^n = \dbinom{n}{0}1^n + \dbinom{n}{1}1^{n-1} \cdot 1 + \dbinom{n}{2}1^{n-2} \cdot 1^2 + \dbinom{n}{3}1^{n-3} \cdot 1^3 + \cdots + \dbinom{n}{n}$

or: $2^n = \dbinom{n}{0} + \dbinom{n}{1} + \dbinom{n}{2} + \cdots + \dbinom{n}{n}$

25. $\dfrac{n-r+1}{r} \cdot \dbinom{n}{r-1} = \dfrac{n-r+1}{r} \cdot \dfrac{n!}{(r-1)!(n-r+1)!} = \dfrac{(n-r+1)n!}{r \cdot (r-1)!(n-r+1)(n-r)!} = \dfrac{n!}{r!(n-r)!} = \dbinom{n}{r}$

27. $\sqrt{1+x} = (1+x)^{1/2} = 1 + \dfrac{x}{2} - \dfrac{x^2}{8} + \dfrac{x^3}{16} - \dfrac{5x^4}{128} + \cdots$ 29. 0.99499

Review Exercise Set, page 493

1. **a.** $\frac{1}{2}, \frac{2}{3}, \frac{3}{4}, \frac{4}{5}$ **b.** 1, 5, 9, 13   3. **a.** $\frac{1}{4}, -\frac{3}{16}, \frac{9}{64}, -\frac{27}{256}$ **b.** $1/\log 2$, $-1/(2\log 3)$, $1/(3\log 4)$, $-1/(4\log 5)$

5. **a.** $\dfrac{1}{n(n+1)}$ **b.** $\dfrac{n}{n+1}$ 7. Arithmetic, $\frac{21}{2}$ 9. Geometric, $-\frac{1}{2,048}$ 11. **a.** 2, 5, 11, 23, 47

b. 1, 2, 6, 24, 120   13. **a.** 9   **b.** $\pm 3\sqrt{5}$ 15. **a.** $\frac{243}{64}$ inches   **b.** $\frac{3,367}{64}$ inches   **c.** 64 inches

17. 1,590   19. $-2,400$ 21. $-1,200$ 23. $\frac{33}{2}$ 25. $\frac{3}{8}$ 27. **a.** $\frac{6}{11}$ **b.** $\frac{4}{27}$ **c.** $\frac{24}{11}$ **d.** $\frac{1,004}{37}$

e. $\frac{101}{99}$ 29. 182   39. **a.** 2,300   **b.** 84   **c.** 4   **d.** 1   **e.** 66

41. **a.** $x^7 - \dfrac{7x^6y}{2} + \dfrac{21x^5y^2}{4} - \dfrac{35x^4y^3}{8} + \dfrac{35x^3y^4}{16} - \dfrac{21x^2y^5}{32} + \dfrac{7xy^6}{64} - \dfrac{y^7}{128}$

b. $1 + 10x^2 + 45x^4 + 120x^6 + 210x^8 + 252x^{10} + 210x^{12} + 120x^{14} + 45x^{16} + 10x^{18} + x^{20}$

43. **a.** $-25,344x^5y^7$ **b.** $-85,995,520x^{11}$ 45. $-\frac{14,581}{729}$ 47. \$66,550

49. $23\frac{1}{4}, 22\frac{1}{2}, 21\frac{3}{4}, 21, 20\frac{1}{4}, 19\frac{1}{2}, 18\frac{3}{4}, 18, 17\frac{1}{4}, 16\frac{1}{2}, 15\frac{3}{4}$

51. $\dbinom{n}{k} - \dbinom{n-1}{k} = \dfrac{n!}{k!(n-k)!} - \dfrac{(n-1)!}{k!(n-1-k)!} = \dfrac{n! - (n-1)!(n-k)}{k!(n-k)!} = \dfrac{(n-1)!(n-n+k)}{k!(n-k)!} = \dfrac{(n-1)!k}{k!(n-k)!}$

$= \dfrac{(n-1)!}{(k-1)![(n-1)-(k-1)]!} = \dbinom{n-1}{k-1}$

53. **a.** $1 - x + x^2 - x^4 + \cdots = \sum_{n=1}^{\infty} (-1)^{n-1} x^{n-1}$, $|x| < 1$ **b.** $\frac{3}{2} + \frac{3x^2}{4} + \frac{3x^4}{8} + \frac{3x^6}{16} + \cdots = \sum_{n=1}^{\infty} \frac{3}{2} \left(\frac{x^2}{2} \right)^{n-1}$, $|x| < \sqrt{2}$

Chapter 12

Exercise Set 2, page 500

1. 16   **3.** $9 \cdot 10^6 = 9{,}000{,}000$ **5.** 12   **7. a.** 75   **b.** 36   **9.** 5^{10} **11.** 216   **13.** 2,688   **15.** 64

Exercise Set 3, page 503

1. a. 12   **b.** 720   **c.** 120   **d.** 336   **e.** 11,880   **3.** 40,320   **5.** 60   **7.** $n = 13$
9. $50 \cdot 49 \cdot 48 \cdot 47 = 5{,}527{,}200$ **11.** 720   **13.** 2,520   **15.** 34,650   **17.** 120   **19.** $n = 6$

Exercise Set 4, page 505

1. a. 28   **b.** 10   **c.** 45   **d.** 6   **e.** 190   **3.** 210   **5.** 45   **7.** 2,970   **9.** 1,200

11. $\binom{52}{13} \approx 6.35 \times 10^{11}$ **13.** 21 lines, 35 triangles   **15.** 5,005   **17.** 3,300   **19.** 4,656

21. $\binom{13}{6}\binom{13}{5}\binom{26}{2} = 717{,}759{,}900$ **23.** $\binom{13}{1}\binom{4}{3}\binom{12}{1}\binom{4}{2} = 3{,}744$; $\binom{13}{1}\binom{4}{3}\binom{39}{2} = 38{,}532$

25. In forming a subset we may select or omit each of the n elements. Thus, for each element we have 2 choices. So there are $2 \cdot 2 \cdot 2 \cdots 2 = 2^n$ different subsets.

Exercise Set 5, page 512

1. $\{H, H, H\}$, $\{H, H, T\}$, $\{H, T, H\}$, $\{H, T, T\}$, $\{T, H, H\}$, $\{T, H, T\}$, $\{T, T, H\}$, $\{T, T, T\}$; $n(S) = 8$
3. $\{R_1, R_2\}$, $\{R_1, R_3\}$, $\{R_2, R_3\}$, $\{R_1, B_1\}$, $\{R_1, B_2\}$, $\{R_2, B_1\}$, $\{R_2, B_2\}$, $\{R_3, B_1\}$, $\{R_3, B_2\}$, $\{B_1, B_2\}$; $n(S) = 10$
5. $n(A) = 6$, $P(A) = \frac{1}{6}$ **7.** $\frac{7}{8}$ **9.** $\frac{3}{10}, \frac{1}{10}$ **11. a.** $\frac{1}{4}$ **b.** $\frac{1}{13}$ **c.** $\frac{1}{52}$ **13.** $\frac{7}{10}$ **15. a.** .7   **b.** .4
c. .2   **17.** $P(A) = \frac{5}{8}$, $P(B) = \frac{11}{24}$ **19.** $\frac{13}{120}$ **21.** $\frac{11}{26}$ **23.** $\frac{1}{1{,}365}$

Exercise Set 6, page 515

1. $\frac{1}{4}$ **3.** $\frac{4}{15}$ **5.** $\frac{1}{32}, \frac{1}{2}$ **7.** $\frac{1}{17}$ **9.** $\frac{4}{663}$ **11.** $\frac{1}{10}$ **13.** $\frac{2}{21}$ **15.** .45   **17.** .000005   **19.** .075
21. a. .49   **b.** .42   **c.** .09
23. $P(A|B) + P(A'|B) = \dfrac{P(A \cap B)}{P(B)} + \dfrac{P(A' \cap B)}{P(B)} = \dfrac{P(A \cap B) + P(A' \cap B)}{P(B)} = \dfrac{P[(A \cap B) \cup (A' \cap B)]}{P(B)} = \dfrac{P[(A \cup A') \cap B]}{P(B)}$

$= \dfrac{P(B)}{P(B)} = 1$

since $A \cap B$ and $A' \cap B$ are disjoint, and $A \cup A'$ is the entire sample space
25. From the hint, the probability that each of the 23 has a birthday different from all the others is
$\frac{364}{365} \cdot \frac{363}{365} \cdot \frac{362}{365} \cdots \frac{343}{365} \approx 0.493$. Therefore, the probability that 2 or more persons have the same birthday is
approximately $1 - 0.493 = 0.507$.
27. 0.962

Review Exercise Set, page 516

1. 64   **3.** $\binom{20}{3} = 1{,}140$ **5.** 2,730   **7.** 45,360   **9.** 210   **11.** 1,800   **13.** 56

15. a. $\frac{1}{4}$ **b.** $\frac{1}{2}$ **c.** $\frac{3}{4}$ **17.** $\dfrac{1}{8!} = \dfrac{1}{40{,}320}$ **19.** $\dfrac{1}{2^{10}} = \dfrac{1}{1{,}024}$

21. a. $\dfrac{1}{\binom{15}{5}} = \dfrac{1}{3{,}003}$ **b.** $\dfrac{3}{\binom{15}{5}} = \dfrac{1}{1{,}001}$ **c.** $\dfrac{3^5}{\binom{15}{5}} = \dfrac{81}{1{,}001}$ **d.** $\dfrac{\binom{5}{3}\binom{5}{2}}{\binom{15}{5}} = \dfrac{100}{3{,}003}$ **23. a.** $\frac{1}{35}$ **b.** $\frac{13}{35}$

25. **a.** $\frac{8}{15}$ **b.** $\frac{1}{15}$ **27.** $P(A|B) = \frac{15}{16}$, $P(B|A) = \frac{5}{6}$ **29.** $\frac{1}{2}$ **31.** $3!(3!4!5!) = 103,680$ **33.** 120

35. $\dbinom{5}{2}\dbinom{9}{3} = 840$ **37.** **a.** $\frac{1}{35}$ **b.** $\frac{1}{5}$ **c.** $\frac{13}{35}$ **39.** $\frac{9}{91}$

Cumulative Review Exercise Set IV (Chapters 10–12), page 519

1. $(\frac{5}{2}, -\frac{3}{4}, \frac{1}{2})$ **3.** **a.** $\begin{bmatrix} -8 & 26 & -6 \\ 20 & -15 & -3 \\ -20 & 0 & 13 \end{bmatrix}$ **b.** $X = \begin{bmatrix} 3 \\ -2 \\ 4 \end{bmatrix}$ **5.** $\{(10c - 1, c, 7c - 2, 0): \quad c \in R\}$

7. 2,250 children; 1,240 adults; 460 senior citizens

9. (b, b, b), (b, b, g), (b, g, b), (g, b, b), (b, g, g), (g, b, g), (g, g, b), (g, g, g) **a.** $\frac{1}{2}$ **b.** $\frac{1}{2}$
   c. No. Let A be the event of at least 2 girls and let B be the event that the first child is a boy. Then $P(A|B) = \frac{1}{4} \neq P(A)$.
   So A and B are not independent.

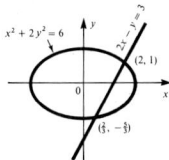

11. $\{(2, 1), (\frac{2}{3}, -\frac{5}{3})\}$ **13.** **a.** $\frac{1}{2}$ **b.** $\frac{7}{9}$ **c.** $\frac{1}{3}$

15. **a.** $-4,032x^8y^5$ **b.** $(1 + x)^{-1} = 1 - x + x^2 - x^3 + \cdots + (-1)^{n-1}x^{n-1} + \cdots$; geometric series with ratio $-x$

$$\sum_{n=1}^{\infty} (-1)^{n-1}x^{n-1} = \frac{1}{1 + x} = (1 + x)^{-1}$$

17. **a.** 504   **b.** 36   **c.** $\frac{5}{84}$ **d.** $\frac{2}{3}$ **e.** $\frac{1}{28}$ **f.** $\frac{3}{14}$

19. **a.** The 1985 dollar will be worth 53¢ compared to the 1980 dollar.   **b.** $A_n = \sqrt{3}(\frac{1}{4})^{n-1}$, $S = \dfrac{4\sqrt{3}}{3}$

21. $\displaystyle\sum_{n=1}^{\infty} \frac{(-1)^{n-1}x^{2n-2}}{4^n}$, $|x| < 2$ **23.** 27 of the first type, 15 of the second

25. Side of square = 20 feet, height of trapezoid = 12 feet, perimeter = 96 feet

Index